ALCOHOL
&DRUG
PROBLEMS

3RD EDITION

ALCOHOL &DRUG PROBLEMS

A PRACTICAL GUIDE FOR COUNSELLORS

EDITED BY SUSAN HARRISON
AND VIRGINIA CARVER
FOREWORD BY JAMES O. PROCHASKA

camh

Centre for Addiction and Mental Health
Centre de toxicomanie et de santé mentale

A Pan American Health Organization /
World Health Organization Collaborating Centre

National Library of Canada Cataloguing in Publication

Alcohol & drug problems: a practical guide for counsellors/editors,
Susan Harrison, Virginia Carver; foreword, James O. Prochaska. — 3rd ed.

Includes bibliographical references and index.
ISBN: 978-0-88868-445-5 (PRINT)
ISBN: 978-0-88868-697-8 (PDF)
ISBN: 978-0-88868-698-5 (HTML)
ISBN: 978-0-88868-885-9 (ePUB)

1. Alcoholism counseling. 2. Drug abuse counseling. 3. Alcoholism
counseling—Canada. 4. Drug abuse counseling—Canada. I. Harrison, Susan, date II. Carver,
Virginia, date III. Centre for Addiction and Mental Health IV. Title: Alcohol and drug problems.

RC564.15.A42 2004   362.29'186   C2004-901496-X

Printed in Canada
© 2004 Centre for Addiction and Mental Health

For information on other CAMH publications or to place an order, please contact:

Sales and Distribution
Tel.: 1 800 661-1111 or 416 595-6059 in Toronto
E-mail: publications@camh.net

Website: www.camh.net

This book was produced by the following:
Development: Michelle Maynes, CAMH
Editorial: Nick Gamble, Sue McCluskey, Michelle Maynes, CAMH; Anna Stancer, Sharon Kirsch,
Martin Ahermaa
Design: Mara Korkola, CAMH
Typesetting: BTT Communications
Print Production: Christine Harris, CAMH
Marketing: Arturo Llerenas, CAMH

P572/ 09-2010 / 2791

Contents

MEETING CLIENTS' NEEDS

Preface

SUSAN HARRISON AND VIRGINIA CARVER

This guide is designed for counsellors who are in a position to help their clients deal with the harmful, sometimes devastating, effects of substance use problems. The book covers core considerations for the counsellor such as theories of addiction, motivational interviewing techniques, assessment and treatment planning, and relapse prevention—and addresses the needs of unique client populations such as youth, women, older adults, and clients living with HIV.

Feedback on the second edition, from both counsellors and those who use the book as a course text, helped guide the changes we have incorporated into this third edition, which we hope will continue to meet the needs of our readers.

We have fully revised and updated the text for this third edition, keeping in mind the feedback we received and the many emerging issues in the addiction field. New or completely revamped chapters have been added on harm reduction; smoking cessation; working with clients who have experienced trauma; working with lesbian, gay, bisexual, transsexual, transgender, two-spirit, intersex and queer (LGBTTTIQ) clients; and working with Aboriginal clients. As well, new research findings, clinical experiences and case studies have enhanced the practical application of this guide.

We wish to thank, first of all, our authors, who have contributed their expertise and many hours of their time to this guide with one goal in mind—to reduce the harm related to alcohol and drug problems. We are again grateful to James O. Prochaska for contributing a provocative Foreword that challenges counsellors to expand the boundaries of our current clinical reach.

Since the second edition was published, many of its authors have retired or moved on to new areas of interest. For some of the chapters, reader feedback prompted us to reconceptualize the content and the approach to the topic, and we sought new authors' perspectives. We are grateful to all our second edition authors for contributing to its success.

We also wish to thank our reviewers who volunteered to review and provide feedback on each of the chapters (in alphabetical order): Ari Blatt, Ana Bodnar, Christine Bois, Bruna Brands, Gloria Chaim, Rebecca Dempster, Luis Fornazzari, Allen W. Heinemann, Marilyn Herie, Eva Ingber, Dennis James, Peggy Kleinplatz, Michael Lester, Robert Mann, Megan McCormick, Cherie Miller, Robert Murray, Alan Ogborne, Michael Piercy, Rupert Raj, Linda Sibley, Ekuwa Smith, Kip Southam, Charmaine Spencer, Glenn Stairs, Mark Tyndall and Lyn Watkin-Merek.

We are also immensely grateful to Michelle Maynes, who co-ordinated the structural editorial work for this third edition, Nick Gamble for his copy editing skills and careful attention to the text and Mara Korkola for her design work. CAMH's library staff helped many of the authors find the information needed to revise their chapters, and we are most grateful to them for helping all of us access the most current research on the topics. Tammy Williams, of the Central East regional office of CAMH, contributed her computer expertise to help us on the administrative side.

We also wish to once again acknowledge Betty-Anne Howard, who provided the initial inspiration for this book.

To these contributors and many others behind the scenes, thank you for your help in bringing this third edition to completion.

To our many readers in addiction and related fields, we hope that this guide continues to be valuable in your professional development and in your day-to-day work with clients.

Foreword

Creating the Future of Addiction Treatment

JAMES O. PROCHASKA

This is a time of great opportunity for the field of behavioural health care generally and for the treatment of substance use problems specifically. Increasingly, society is recognizing that unhealthy behaviours such as problem substance use generate high costs—not only to the people who are affected, but also to their families, employers, communities and health care systems.

Consider a few simple statistics. In the United States, health care costs are $1.5 trillion per year and growing. Of that total, 10 per cent is accounted for by medications, and 50 to 60 per cent is accounted for by behaviour—in other words, people's unhealthy lifestyles.

Typically, less than five per cent of these unhealthy behaviours are treated appropriately and professionally. This means there are large unmet needs and great opportunities—but only if we change the way we do science and the ways in which we apply that science.

Leaders in the National Health Service in Great Britain, for example, have examined these simple statistics and declared that they have an "illness system" and not a health system. It is clear that behaviour change must become their number one order of business.

When such leaders look to science for evidence on how to treat high-risk and high-cost behaviours on a population basis, they can become discouraged. The biggest and best-controlled health behaviour trials ever completed on a population basis have reported in, and the results have been uniformly dismal. These studies have varied in their populations, including prevention and treatment in work sites, schools and communities (Glasgow, 1995; Ennett et al., 1994; COMMIT, 1995; Luepker et al., 1994). They have also varied in their target behaviours, which have included smoking, alcohol and other drug use, unhealthy diet, lack of exercise and the other major killers of our time. But they have not varied in their inability to produce significant effects in the intervention populations.

This inability was not due to a lack of time, talent or resources. The treatment times of these studies ranged from two to five years; their talent included some of the best that our multidisciplinary sciences and professions had to offer; and their budgets ranged from $20 million to $700 million. The problem was probably more basic, concerning their scientific and professional paradigms. Applying an action-oriented paradigm to entire populations led to serious limitations.

In the Minnesota Heart Health Program, for example, action-oriented programs were offered repeatedly for five years. But in the field's most powerful change programs, individualized and interactive clinics and classes, only four per cent of smokers in the treatment communities participated. We simply cannot impact on the health of our communities if we reach only a small percentage of people with high-risk and high-cost behaviours.

Professional and scientific developments are needed to treat entire populations at risk of addiction (Prochaska, in press). A promising approach complements traditional treatment and research paradigms with comprehensive and innovative paradigms. These paradigms are outlined below.

Individual and Population Paradigms

Historically, psychology as a profession and science focused on individual patients and took responsibility only for people in treatment or clinical trials. Research was preoccupied with efficacy as measured, for example, by rates of abstinence in a treatment population. But in the general population, most substance use problems are undiagnosed and untreated. To address these problems, we need to be able to reach out to treat entire populations. In the population paradigm, the focus is on "impact," which takes participation as well as efficacy into account.

PASSIVE REACTIVE AND PROACTIVE PARADIGMS

Health professionals are generally socialized to passively wait for patients and then react. This is appropriate for acute care, where patients are sick, in pain or distressed. But to reach at-risk populations whose behaviours can cause disease or disability, proactive practices must also be put in place. With a health risk assessment, for example, populations can be assessed for behaviours such as smoking, inactivity, substance use and overeating, and for readiness to change these behaviours. This can be done by, for example, reaching out and recruiting people in primary care practices or by phone. Each person can then be proactively prescribed "behaviour medicine" that matches his or her stage of change.

ACTION AND STAGE PARADIGMS

While action-oriented public health campaigns do have impact, they reach only a small percentage of the population. In the United States, for example, action-oriented public health campaigns have targeted smoking for 40 years, yet only 20 per cent of people who smoke (and only eight per cent of those who smoke daily) are in the "action" stage or are prepared to quit. About 40 per cent are in "contemplation," and are intending to quit in the next six months but not in the next month, and the other 40 per cent are in "precontemplation," and are not intending to quit in the next six months (Veilicer et al., 1995). Similarly, in countries such as China and Germany, only five per cent of people who smoke are prepared to quit, and about 70 per cent are in precontemplation (Etter et al., 1997).

To reach a larger percentage of the population, and to impact on the health of nations, action-oriented programs need to be complemented by those that match patients' needs at each stage of change. By matching treatment to stage, people in precontemplation can complete treatment at the same rates as those in preparation.

FROM CLINIC TO HOME-BASED PARADIGMS

Individual and interactive interventions have the greatest efficacy. Historically, such interventions were mainly available from clinic-based therapists. However, stigma and the cost of clinics are barriers for many. For example, obesity has increased at epidemic proportions in the United States in the past 12 years, yet participation in weight management clinics and groups has not increased appreciably. Besides being action-oriented, the clinics and groups themselves are barriers. Marketing research has revealed that five per cent of Americans want weight management programs that are clinic-based, while 50 per cent want programs that are home-based. Obesity is the number-two cause (after smoking) of preventable death in the United States, yet few overweight and obese people are reached by clinic and group programs.

Even when people do attend clinics, most of their time is spent outside of therapy. Only 10 per cent of treatment outcome can be attributed to therapy, and the other 90 per cent to what people do during the rest of the week (Lambert, 2001). Imagine primary care medicine focusing only on the interactions in the physicians' office, without pharmaceuticals to deliver therapy in the home. Home-based behaviour medicine is clearly needed.

CLINICIAN AND COMPUTER PARADIGMS

As a complement to the traditional clinician paradigm, evidence-based treatment can be delivered at home with computers. Computers can provide individualized and interactive interventions with expert systems that model expert clinicians. A growing consensus holds that computer-generated tailored communications are the most promising approach for population-based interventions (Kreuter et al., 1999).

Computer-based tailored communications can provide expert guidance on the principles and processes of change needed to progress through the stages. In one computer-based intervention, people who smoke answer 40 questions and receive reliable and valid feedback about their stage of change, about whether they underestimate the benefits of quitting and overestimate the cons, and about the 10 change processes they are underutilizing, overutilizing or utilizing appropriately compared with peers in the same stage who progressed the most. In follow-up interactions, participants receive normative feedback compared with peers and feedback compared with their own previous assessments. Participants learn what they are doing right, what mistakes they are making and what they can concentrate on to progress the most. (A demonstration program for effective stress management can be sampled at www.prochange.com/stressdemo.) Clinicians can receive similar feedback about their clients and how they can most help particular clients. Such feedback reduced deterioration rates by 50 per cent and doubled positive outcomes (Lambert et al., 2001).

Interactive technologies are likely to be to behaviour treatments what pharmaceuticals are to biological treatments: the most cost-effective means of bringing optimal amounts of science to bear on major health problems in entire populations. For example, a reactive sample of 753 people who smoke was randomly assigned by stage to an intervention that was delivered either by computers alone or by computers plus counsellors. At 12 months, abstinence rates were the same for computers alone as for computers plus counsellors, but at 18 months the abstinence rate for people receiving treatment from computers alone was 24 per cent, while for computers plus counsellors the rate was only 18 per cent. At 18 months, computers alone were more than twice as effective at helping people to quit smoking as one of the best home-based action-oriented treatments (24 per cent versus 11 per cent abstinence; Prochaska et al., 1993).

With computer guides, populations continue to progress to abstinence long after treatment ends, rather than showing declines when treatment terminates. The use of computers may enhance self-efficacy. When intervention ends, people keep progressing from efforts based on self-change or self-reliance. For people who become dependent on therapists, one strategy is to fade out therapists like we fade out nicotine.

FROM SINGLE TO MULTIPLE BEHAVIOUR CHANGE PARADIGMS

Clinical trials have the luxury of treating one problem. In nicotine replacement therapy trials, for example, people with mental health problems were excluded. Yet 45 per cent of cigarettes in the United States are bought by people with mental health problems. In practice, most clients have multiple problems. The highest-risk and highest-cost people are those with multiple behaviour problems. If two behaviour risks are reduced, health care costs can be reduced by $2,000 per year (Edington, 2001).

In our first multiple behaviour trial, we recruited 2,360 parents. Using expert system guides for smoking, diet and sun exposure, we produced significant impacts at

24 months (Prochaska et al., in press). Comparing across treatments for smoking alone and for multiple behaviour treatments that included smoking, the long-term abstinence rates were the same (22 to 25 per cent). This shows that we can increase impacts by treating multiple behaviours without decreasing efficacy for a single addictive behaviour such as smoking.

THE FUTURE FOR THERAPISTS

If health professionals start to proactively intervene with entire populations of people with substance use problems, what might be the consequences for counsellors who specialize in treating these problems? And how can this book help prepare them for such a future?

With proactive outreach practices, clinicians will need to be prepared to match the needs of the important parts of our populations that have traditionally been underserved by our health care systems. Women; ethnic, social and other minorities; and groups with limited resources will need to be appreciated for the special needs they have. The second section of this book addresses the needs of many understudied and underserved populations.

If we are to do justice to entire populations with problems related to alcohol and other drugs, we will need to enhance our knowledge of treating multiple problem behaviours, not just single problems. How do we respond to people with multiple diagnoses or with multiple high-risk behaviours, such as problem alcohol use, sedentary lifestyles, unhealthy diets, high-risk sexual behaviours, anxiety and depression? From an action paradigm, such people, who are quite common, could be overwhelmed by too many demands to take multiple actions and risk multiple failures. From a stage paradigm, we have found that, in populations with four high-risk behaviours, fewer than 10 per cent are in the preparation stage for two or more behaviours. So we can begin to take action on the behaviour that is most prepared, while enhancing motivation or preparation for behaviours in earlier stages. This book includes state-of-the-science information on the multiple behaviours and disorders that most often accompany addictive behaviour.

If we are to create a better future for the treatment of addiction, we must be prepared to complement our current paradigms and practices. As experts and specialists, there will be demands on us to continue to know more than we ever did before. This book can help move us forward into a more demanding but also more rewarding future that we can create together.

References

COMMIT Research Group Intervention Trial for Smoking Cessation (COMMIT): 1. (1995). Cohort results from a four-year community intervention. *American Journal of Public Health, 85*(2), 83–192.

Edington, D.W. (2001). Emerging research: A view from one research center. *American Journal of Health Promotion, 15*(5), 341–349.

Ennett, S.T., Tobler, N.S., Ringwalt, C.L. & Flewelling, R.L. (1994). How effective is drug abuse resistance education? A meta-analysis of Project DARE outcome evaluations. *American Journal of Public Health, 84*(9), 1394–1401.

Etter, J.F., Perneger, T.V. & Ronchi, A. (1997). Distributions of smokers by stage: International comparison and association with smoking prevalence. *Preventive Medicine, 26*(4), 580–585.

Glasgow, R.E., Terborg, J.R., Hollis, J.F., Severson, H.H. & Boles, S.M. (1995). Take heart: Results from the initial phase of a work-site wellness program. *American Journal of Public Health, 85*(2), 209–216.

Kreuter, M.K., Strecher, V.J. & Glassman, B. (1999). One size does not fit all: The case for tailoring cancer prevention materials. *Annals of Behavioral Medicine, 21*(4), 276–283.

Lambert, M.J., Hansen, N.B. & Finch, A.E. (2001). Patient-focused research: Using patient outcome data to enhance treatment effects. *Journal of Consulting and Clinical Psychology, 69*(2), 159–172.

Luepker, R.V., Murray, D.M., Jacobs D.R., Mittelmark, M.B., Bracht, N., Carlaw, R. et al. (1994). Community education for cardio-vascular disease prevention: Risk factor changes in the Minnesota Heart Health Program. *American Journal of Public Health, 84*(9), 1383–1393.

Prochaska, J.O. (In press). Population treatment for addictions. *Current Directions in Psychological Science.*

Prochaska, J.O., DiClemente, C.C., Velicer, W.F. & Rossi, J.S. (1993). Standardized, individualized, interactive and personalized self-help programs for smoking cessation. *Health Psychology, 12*(5), 399–405.

Prochaska, J.O., Velicer, W.F., Rossi, J.S., Redding, C.A., Greene, G.W., Rossi, S.R. et al. (In press). Impact of simultaneous stage-matched expert systems for multiple behaviours in a population of parents. *Health Psychology.*

Velicer, W.F., Fava, J.L., Prochaska, J.O., Abrams, D.B., Emmons, K.M. & Pierce, J.P. (1995). Distribution of smokers by stage in three representative samples. *Preventive Medicine, 24*(4), 401–411.

Core Considerations

Chapter 1

Theories of Addiction and Implications for Counselling

ALAN C. OGBORNE

Many theorists have tried to account for why people use alcohol and other drugs, and especially why they continue or relapse despite negative consequences. Some theories suggest genetic and other biological factors, while others emphasize personality factors or social-environmental factors (Lettieri et al., 1980). While these factors have all been shown to contribute to persistent substance use and to relapse following periods of abstinence, no one set of factors can account for all types of substance use. Rather, substance use appears to result from complex interactions of biological, psychological and social-environmental structures and processes (Arif & Westermeyer, 1988).

This chapter outlines these factors and the ways in which they may interact. Some implications for counselling will also be considered. The focus is on factors that account for why substance use continues once it has started, and why people relapse following periods of abstinence. (Some of these factors also account for why people begin substance use, but that is not the subject of this chapter.)

FOCUS AND TERMINOLOGY

This book is about ways to help people with alcohol and other drug problems. It is not especially about helping "alcoholics" or "drug addicts," although many people who use substances may be given these labels by those who know them and by some clinicians and researchers. This book has a broader focus: it concerns people whose problems with substances vary in kind and severity.

This chapter also has a broad focus: it summarizes theories of substance use, including use that is often labelled "addictive." However, the terms "addictive" and "addiction," and the related term "alcoholism," will generally be avoided, because they have no agreed definitions and have limited value in many counselling settings. These labels are used in this chapter only in a historical context or if they appear in a cited study.

Most experts do agree that the concept of *dependence* is useful. Dependence refers to a cluster of cognitive, behavioural and physiological symptoms of varying severity, consistent with the use of the term by the World Health Organization (1992) and the American Psychiatric Association (2000).

The American Psychiatric Association's (APA) criteria for a diagnosis of substance dependence are met when any three of the following occur at the same time during a 12-month period:
• tolerance as indicated by the need to increase dosage to obtain the desired effect, or reduced effects with continued use of the same dose
• withdrawal symptoms characteristic of a particular substance
• use in larger amounts or over a longer period than the user intended
• persistent desire for the substance, or unsuccessful efforts to cut down
• a great deal of time spent in obtaining or using a substance
• social and other activities given up or reduced due to substance use
• use despite persistent or recurrent problems (e.g., health or social problems).

Although the moralistic implications of the term "substance abuse" concern many experts, the APA uses this term to refer to a condition that is met when one or more of the following symptoms occur within a 12-month period, provided the criteria for substance dependence have not been met during the same period:
• recurrent substance use resulting in a failure to fulfil obligations at work, school or home
• recurrent substance use in physically hazardous situations
• recurrent substance-related legal problems
• continued substance use despite persistent or recurrent social or interpersonal problems caused or exacerbated by the effects of the substance.

We will use the phrase "alcohol or other drug problem" with the understanding that such problems are social constructions. In some cases, such use may be essentially benign, but may be seen as a problem because it contravenes social norms (e.g., occasional use of alcohol by people whose religion forbids it, or the occasional use of cannabis). More serious problems may also be defined differently by each of those involved. Weekend drunkenness may be intolerable to a spouse but just fine to the drinker's companions. An important task for counsellors is to negotiate a common understanding of the problems to be addressed. Relevant issues are discussed in the chapters in this book on assessment and motivational interviewing.

This chapter does not deal with the so-called "disease" concept of alcoholism, which is less a testable theory than an analogy. Nonetheless, it has important implications for the ways in which "alcoholism" is regarded and treated. When viewed as a disease, alcoholism becomes a legitimate condition for treatment by medical and allied professionals, rather than simply a bad habit or a sign of moral weakness. The disease analogy is appropriate if the term is understood to include complex conditions, such as high blood pressure, that are influenced by genetic and lifestyle factors. However, the analogy breaks down when alcoholism is compared with diseases with clear causes, such as tuberculosis or syphilis.

BIOLOGICAL FACTORS

Genetic Inheritance

There is growing evidence that alcohol use is influenced by genetic factors (*Alcohol Health and Research World*, 1995; Shuckit, 1999). The strongest evidence comes from studies of family histories, twins and adopted children, different racial groups, and animals. Genetic factors seem to influence the ways in which humans respond to and metabolize alcohol, and seem to contribute to neurological dysfunctions common in people whose drinking problems begin at an early age (see the discussion of psychological factors, below). Genetic factors also appear to play a role in people's use of tobacco and other drugs (Madden & Heath, 2002).

It is believed that many genes influence people's responses to alcohol, and that their responses reflect a continuum of vulnerability to alcohol problems. This understanding is consistent with behavioural studies that have failed to clearly distinguish between people with drinking problems and others.

The influence of genetic factors is sometimes interpreted as meaning that, in those who are vulnerable, alcoholism is an inevitable, progressive and irreversible condition. This reflects a limited understanding of the role of genetics in determining complex behaviours, and is inconsistent with research. For example:
• There is overwhelming evidence that in both clinical and survey samples many people labelled "alcoholics" have periods of moderate drinking.
• Several early experiments showed that "alcoholics" are able to limit their drinking in laboratory settings when they view the benefits of reduced drinking as worthwhile. These experiments demonstrated the role of environmental factors (such as price) in moderating alcohol consumption, even among "alcoholics" (Mello & Mendelson, 1965; Mello et al., 1968).

Further, there are large differences between otherwise similar societies in consumption levels and rates of alcohol problems. For example, the per capita consumption of alcohol in Norway was only 5.64 litres per year in 1999, and Norway had a low rate of liver cirrhosis. In contrast, in France (where the gene pool is presumably largely the same), the per capita consumption of alcohol was 20.28 liters per year, and France had one of the highest rates of cirrhosis. Such differences also occur within the same society over time. Between 1945 and 1982, the rates of alcohol consumption and alcohol problems increased dramatically in many industrialized countries (Smart & Ogborne, 1996).

If genetics played a determining role in drinking, we would have to conclude that Norwegians have different genes from the French and that the gene pool of the industrialized world has changed dramatically since the end of the Second World War. Neither conclusion could be supported on other grounds, and neither conclusion is necessary because levels of drinking and of drinking problems are clearly influenced by social customs and economic forces. These same forces also influence the drinking behaviour of individuals.

Of course, this does not rule out the influence of genetics on drinking behaviour and alcohol problems. There are wide individual differences in preferences for alcohol and the capacity to drink large amounts, and genetic factors contribute to these differences. However, other factors are clearly important and need to be included in theoretical models.

Equally, the potential influence of genetic factors should be considered when counselling people with alcohol problems. This perspective can contribute to clients' understanding of their problems and to their recovery. However, clinicians should ensure that clients also learn to recognize other factors that influence drinking, especially those factors that are within their own control.

Tolerance and Physical Dependence

The repeated use of alcohol and other drugs can change the body's ability to adapt to the presence of these substances. One result is that people become less sensitive to the substance and so need to increase the dosage to obtain the desired effects. This loss of sensitivity is called *tolerance.*

The body's adjustment to the presence of a drug may also result in withdrawal symptoms when use stops. This condition is called *physical dependence.* In extreme cases, the effect of rapid withdrawal can be life-threatening, because the body has become so dependent on the drug that withdrawal interferes with normal bodily processes.

The adaptive changes that underlie tolerance and physical dependence are not yet fully understood. However, they seem to involve changes to metabolic pathways, cellular adaptation, activation of parallel biochemical systems and changes to the release of neurotransmitters. These changes may help explain why some people who use alcohol and other drugs heavily find it so difficult to stop.

Research on neurobiological aspects of drug use has led to the identification of many relevant structures and processes (e.g., drug-specific receptor sites in the brain and the effects of specific drugs and their metabolites on neurotransmitters). It has been suggested that all addictive behaviours may be the result of common physiological or biochemical actions in the brain, and a good deal of research is currently focused on the neurotransmitter dopamine. Some theorists have suggested that all pleasurable activities, including drug use, result from the release of dopamine in specific areas of the brain. Some animal research supports this view, but it is likely that other mechanisms are also involved.

Some addiction treatment services include education on the biological effects of drugs, in the belief that this will motivate clients to change their behaviour. However, there is little evidence that this type of drug education influences client outcomes (Health Canada, 1999).

PSYCHOLOGICAL FACTORS

Three types of psychological factors will be discussed: (1) personality traits, (2) psycho-dynamic processes and (3) learned cognitions and behaviours.

Personality Traits

Hundreds of studies have searched for differences between people who have substance use problems and other people. In general, these studies do not support the notion that people with substance use problems have different personalities than others and, in the early 1970s, one expert called for an end to this type of research, at least in the alcohol field (Keller, 1972). He also proposed "Keller's Law," which states that whatever trait was considered, the results would show that alcoholics have either more or less of it!

Personality research has, however, continued, and several studies have sought to identify personality characteristics associated with the onset of heavy drinking and other drug use in adolescence. The results suggest that such use is more common among adolescents who show pre–drug use signs of one or more of the following: rebelliousness, other adjustment problems, depression, sensation seeking (Kandel & Yamaguchi, 1985; Stein et al., 1987; Shedler & Block, 1990).

However, no specific pre–drug use traits or clusters of traits have been shown to fully account for the onset or maintenance of drug use in adolescents or others.

There is evidence for common pre-drinking personality traits in one type of problem drinker (Allen, 1996; Molina et al., 2002). These are people who have alcohol problems from an early age (late teens or early 20s) and strong antisocial tendencies. Evidence also suggests that such people have a genetically determined brain disorder involving the prefrontal lobes (Tarter et al., 1988). The relevant neurological disturbances may involve the brain's "executive" functions of planning and goal formulation, persistence, self-monitoring and self-evaluation. These disturbances manifest in:
• attention-deficit disorders
• childhood hyperactivity
• pre-alcoholic essential tremor (a neurological movement disorder that most commonly affects the hands)

- left-handedness
- low academic achievement
- impulsiveness
- lack of inhibition
- emotional instability
- aggressiveness
- antisocial and psychopathic tendencies.

These traits can find expression through heavy drinking and a preference for companions who drink heavily. Although there is less relevant research on people who use drugs other than alcohol, similar neurological disturbances may occur in some people who use heroin and cocaine. Users of alcohol and other drugs with these personality traits may benefit from training in coping skills, self-control and relapse prevention (Ball, 1996).

The relationship between substance use problems and various types of mental illness has been considered in a number of studies (Miller, 1994; Health Canada, 2002). One U.S. study (Reiger et al., 1990) of 20,291 people living in the community found that over 50 per cent of those who qualified for a diagnosis of drug abuse also had one or more mental disorders at some point during their lifetime. Most common were anxiety disorders (28 per cent), depression and other mood disorders (26 per cent), antisocial personality disorder (18 per cent) and schizophrenia (7 per cent). Some had multiple disorders. The prevalence of mental disorders among people with drug use problems varied depending on the drug, from 50 per cent of people who met criteria for a diagnosis of marijuana abuse to 76 per cent of those who met criteria for a diagnosis of cocaine abuse. Almost half the people with such drug use problems also had drinking problems during their lifetime.

However, the relationships between mental health and substance use are complex and difficult to disentangle. Some people with serious mental disturbances (e.g., phobias, rage, anxiety, depression, mania, paranoid delusions) appear to use alcohol and other drugs to self-medicate for mental distress. For others, mental health problems are caused or exacerbated by substance use, and these problems tend to decrease with abstinence. (See Chapter 26 for further discussion of the etiology of concurrent mental health and substance use disorders). While clients with concurrent disorders are generally considered hard to treat, integrated mental health and addiction treatment services seem to be quite successful (Health Canada, 2002).

Psychodynamic Processes

A psychodynamic approach to understanding human behaviour emphasizes psychological forces, structures and functions as they develop and change over time. There is a special interest in childhood experiences and conflicts and their influences in later life. Psychodynamic perspectives on substance use problems focus on unconscious motivation, emotions, self-esteem, self-regulation and interpersonal relationships.

Psychodynamic theories can be traced to the writings of Sigmund Freud and his followers and revisionists. There are perhaps as many variants of a psychodynamic approach to substance use as there are psychodynamic theorists. Freud originally proposed that "alcoholics" were "orally fixated" (i.e., stuck at an early developmental stage) and thus unable to cope with the demands of adult life. Thus they used alcohol to "escape from reality" (a Freudian concept). Later, Freud proposed that "alcoholism" was an expression of repressed homosexuality. He reasoned that male homosexuals turned to drink because they were disappointed with relationships with women and because drinking gave them an excuse to be with other men. Other psychodynamic theorists have proposed that alcoholism is a reflection of unresolved dependency conflicts, a striving for power or a form of self-destruction. "Fixations" at Freud's anal and phallic stages have also been proposed as explanations for alcoholism (Barry, 1988).

Psychodynamic theory does not feature prominently in the mainstream of current substance use research, and it has not been expanded to accommodate recent research on biological factors. Psychodynamic formulations of human behaviour have not led to testable assumptions and, in general, they have little clear empirical support. Purely psychodynamic treatments designed to increase the client's insight have not proven effective (Health Canada, 1999) and have generally been abandoned. However, various forms of non-psychodynamic, client-centred psychotherapy are often used in conjunction with other types of treatment in specialized addiction treatment programs.

The relationship between psychodynamic and learning theories (discussed below) is problematic. Although both theories of substance use emphasize the role of experience (including childhood experiences), learning theorists typically challenge the utility of the concept of "repressed" memories or impulses. Nonetheless, some overviews of the psychodynamic approach (e.g., Khantzian, 1995) seem quite compatible with social learning theory.

Learned Cognitions and Behaviours

Use of alcohol and other drugs activates two basic learning mechanisms. The first, called *classical conditioning*, occurs when an initially neutral stimulus eventually produces the same responses as an existing stimulus with which it has been paired. The best-known example is the experiments of Ivan Pavlov, in which he rang a bell every time he fed his dogs. Initially, the dogs salivated (an *unconditioned response*) only at the sight of food (an *unconditioned stimulus*). However, in time the dogs began to salivate at the sound of the bell. The bell thus became a *conditioned stimulus* and salivation a *conditioned response*.

Another example of a classically conditioned response is the onset of cravings and withdrawal symptoms in response to stimuli associated with substance use. These stimuli, or cues, may be internal to the person (e.g., feelings of depression or anxiety) or may be found in the external environment (e.g., advertisements, social situations or the sight of a syringe). Through classical conditioning, alcohol- or other drug-related stimuli may also invoke mild drug effects that whet the person's appetite for more.

The importance of cues in conditioning craving for a drug is illustrated by the very low rates of heroin use among American veterans who had previously used heroin in Vietnam. This phenomenon may be explained partly by the relative lack of external cues for heroin use in the veterans' home situations (Robins, 1974). For most returning veterans, the main external stimuli for heroin use were not associated with the United States but with Vietnam and the war. In addition, policies were established to reduce the likelihood of internal cues (e.g., coming down from heroin intoxication) occurring in the United States. Thus, no soldier was allowed to board a plane for home without passing a urine screening test.

Classical conditioning has been used to account for increased tolerance of the effects of alcohol and other drugs. Tolerance is typically greater in situations or locations where alcohol or other drugs have previously been used. One theory proposes that these familiar situations become classically conditioned stimuli that evoke unconscious, compensatory physical responses whenever alcohol or other drugs are used. These tolerance responses reflect the body's need to re-establish biological equilibrium disrupted by substance use. By being frequently paired with substance use, the (now conditioned) tolerance responses become stronger, and more of the substance is needed to produce intoxication (Sherman, 1998). This theory has been used to explain why people addicted to heroin sometimes overdose after taking a dose of heroin that is usually well tolerated. It has been found that often, this happens when the person took the dose in an unfamiliar environment, and so the usual conditioned tolerance response did not occur (Siegel et al., 1982).

"Cue exposure" treatments have been used to eliminate classically conditioned substance-related responses through the process of *extinction*. Clients are presented with, or asked to imagine, situations in which they typically used their preferred substance. They are then asked to imagine themselves resisting urges to use the substance. The assumption is that classically conditioned responses to these situations (withdrawal symptoms or drug effects) become "extinguished" through lack of reinforcement. However, studies of this type of intervention have produced mixed results (Health Canada, 1999).

The second learning process activated by drug use is called *operant conditioning*. This occurs when behaviours are shaped by their consequences. Through operant conditioning, positive reinforcements (rewards) are used to increase the frequency of specific behaviours in specific situations, and negative reinforcement (withholding of rewards) or punishments are used to decrease or eliminate behaviours. Behaviours come to be evoked in response to the various stimuli associated with the conditioning process. Depending on the schedules of reinforcement used (e.g., continuous, intermittent, response-dependent or time-dependent), behaviours may be very persistent if the appropriate cues are present.

All drugs used for pleasure can act as positive reinforcers. This is clear from studies showing that animals will learn to perform tasks when drugs are used as rewards. Alcohol and other drugs are, of course, positive reinforcers for drinking and other drug use, and through experience can become associated with a variety of internal and external cues. For many people, these cues may be rather limited (e.g., only at family meal times and never more than once a week). For others, drinking cues can become highly generalized (e.g., when they are happy, sad, alone, with others, and at any time of the day).

One apparent problem with this view of substance use is that many people continue to use alcohol and other drugs despite negative consequences such as hangovers, ill health, and social and legal problems. This appears to be contrary to an operant conditioning analysis. However, this is not the case because these negative consequences do not occur immediately after alcohol or other drug consumption. The immediate effects (the effects of the substance and the relief of withdrawal symptoms) continue to be positive and reinforcing. A person with substance use problems may acknowledge and regret the social and other problems caused by his or her substance use and vow, quite sincerely, to abstain in the future. But without some sort of help, such as relapse prevention treatment, he or she may continue to be overwhelmed by stimuli that evoke substance use (e.g., the sight of old friends, anxiety or arguments with a spouse).

It is widely believed that the use of alcohol and other drugs can relieve stress, which may motivate and sustain a person's consumption. Retrospective and prospective studies with humans lend some support to this stress-reduction theory, but other relationships between stressful events and substance use are not as strong as the theory suggests. A likely explanation is that stress relief from alcohol or other drug use is influenced by expectations that relief will occur (Cohen and Baum, 1995).

Expectations of the effects of alcohol or other drugs are cognitions and, like other cognitions, they both influence and are influenced by classical and operant conditioning. Through conditioning, expectations and other cognitions not only *arise from* stimuli and rewards, but they also influence *reactions* to stimuli, behaviours and consequences. This is a basic premise of social learning theory (Bandura, 1977), which recognizes the behaving and self-aware individual as an active participant in the learning process rather than as a passive victim of circumstances. The theory also emphasizes that learning takes place through modelling, and is shaped by consequences under the control of the individual. Moreover, reactions to stimuli, rewards and punishments are mediated and modified by changes in cognitions. Thus, an "overwhelming desire to drink" can come to be viewed as a passing "crest of a wave" (Marlatt & Gordon, 1985). Similarly, one lapse after treatment can be seen as either a sign that all is lost or as a positive learning experience.

Social learning theory also recognizes the influence on behaviour of self-monitoring and self-evaluation, self-reward and self-punishment, perception of responsibility and control, and expectancy effects. The theory has also given rise to the notions of *learned helplessness* (belief in loss of control) and *abstinence violation effects* ("I have relapsed and so all is lost").

There is strong experimental and clinical support for a social learning analysis of substance use (Wilson, 1988). In addition, alcohol use treatments based on this theory have more support from experimental studies than do other types of treatment for alcohol use (Health Canada, 1999). Treatment methods based directly or indirectly on social learning theory are:
• aversion therapy (including covert sensitization)
• cue-exposure training
• social skills training
• self-control training
• relapse prevention.

Social learning theory, along with theories of client-centred counselling, also influenced the development of motivational interviewing (Miller, 1996). Most of the chapters in this book reflect the influence of both these types of theories.

Social learning theory can explain why other forms of treatment can work for some people. For example, 12-step programs can be seen as creating drug-free environments, providing social reinforcements for abstinence and for related verbal statements, and providing an appealing explanation for problems. Social learning theory does not support the concept of alcoholism as a distinctive entity and regards "loss of control" as a modifiable experience, not as an inevitable, objective consequence of alcohol use. Nonetheless, the theory does not deny that, for some people, acceptance of the label "alcoholic" and the concept of "powerlessness" over alcohol can become the cornerstones of their recovery.

SOCIAL-ENVIRONMENTAL FACTORS

Many social and other environmental factors have been cited as contributing to the onset and maintenance of substance use and to relapse. However, no one factor has been shown to be either necessary or sufficient for use or relapse to occur. Thus, like other factors that influence substance use, social-environmental factors exert their influence in the context of a complex, dynamic multi-factor system.

The availability and cost of alcohol and other drugs clearly influence overall patterns of use (Single, 1988; Godfrey & Maynard, 1988) and can contribute to use and relapse. We have already noted that, at least in the laboratory, price manipulations can influence the drinking behaviour of "alcoholics." There is also evidence that price influences people who drink heavily in the community. Some clinicians have contracted with clients to increase the cost of alcohol and other drugs to deter relapse. Clients agree that if they drink or take other drugs, they will make a donation to a despised cause or forfeit a returnable deposit.

The substance use culture of the dominant society, and especially of clients' peers and family, can contribute to continuing substance use and relapse. This is especially so in cultures that promote heavy or illegal substance use, or substance use to solve problems.

Many other aspects of family life may also contribute to substance use and relapse. Family members may present models of substance use that are emulated by children. Childhood experiences within distressed or dysfunctional families may leave children vulnerable to substance use and a variety of other problems as adults. Family-related factors that can contribute to the onset and maintenance of substance use (and possibly to relapse) include:

- poverty
- membership in a group devalued by the larger society
- alcohol or other drug problems among family members
- parental abuse and neglect
- parental separation
- low cohesion
- low mutual support (Goplerud, 1990).

Systems theory has drawn special attention to the influence of other family processes (Pearlman, 1988). This theory views individuals' behaviour as being determined and sustained by the dynamics and demands of the key people with whom they interact. (This proposition is compatible with social learning theory, described above.) Further, systems theory proposes that behaviours have *functions* within dynamic systems, even when the behaviours and their supporting systems cause problems for those involved. The theory draws attention to ways in which a substance user's family copes with and possibly reinforces substance use, and the implications for the family if the person changes his or her behaviour.

Systems theory proposes that families and other social networks develop "rules" of interaction that can sustain pathological behaviours (e.g., the family implicitly agrees never to plan family events on Friday nights because that is when father goes out to get drunk with his friends). Family members also assume roles, such as "enabler," "martyr" or "sick person," that maintain the homeostasis within the family).

The notion that some family members have "codependency" needs that help maintain a dysfunctional homeostasis has been widely and uncritically embraced by the recovery movement. In addition, popular recovery literature and Web sites often refer to codependency as a disease. However, there is little relevant research on this topic, and the concept of codependency has been challenged by feminist academics (e.g., Babcock & McKay, 1995).

AN INTEGRATED BIOPSYCHOSOCIAL PERSPECTIVE

Figure 1-1 attempts to capture the many factors that influence substance use and to show how they interact. The model was developed for the World Health Organization (WHO, 1981). It identifies biological, personal and social factors and learning experiences, and shows how they may have immediate or more distant influences on a person's disposition to use drugs. It also shows that social and individual factors can be influenced by the *consequences* of drug use. Other feedback mechanisms that can have positive or negative influences on future use, depending on individual users and their circumstances, are also identified.

The model shows that drug actions and their effects may lead to biological responses that account for tolerance and drug-specific withdrawal symptoms. These responses may have either adverse or reinforcing properties. While withdrawal symptoms may initially be aversive, they can be relieved by taking more drugs, and this strengthens the drug-taking response. Repeated experiences of withdrawal can activate a classical conditioning process whereby previously neutral stimuli elicit withdrawal symptoms, or drug-like effects, and lead to further drug use. Over time, through a process of generalization, a variety of internal and external cues (e.g., anxiety, stress or social events) may be associated with withdrawal symptoms and drug effects. This process can lead to an extreme narrowing of a person's repertoire of responses to cues, and a tendency to use drugs whenever these cues are present. The person often increases his or her involvement with other drug users, who facilitate access to drugs and otherwise support drug use. Conversely, involvements with people who might encourage reduced drug use and associated behaviours may become less frequent and significant.

SOME IMPLICATIONS FOR COUNSELLING

The model shown in Figure 1-1 suggests that drug taking can be reduced by making the experience less rewarding and making abstinence or reduced use more rewarding. This could be achieved through a variety of biological, psychological and environmental interventions, some of which have been mentioned in this chapter. A useful summary of the objectives of such interventions was proposed by Daley and Marlatt (1992). These objectives are indicated in Table 1-1 together with the relevant clinical aids or procedures that have the strongest empirical support.

Other chapters in this book describe many of the specific practices identified in Table 1-1. Further evidence for their effectiveness can be found in recent reports from Health Canada (1999, 2000, 2001a, 2001b & 2002), on the Treatment Improvement Protocols (TIPs) Web site (www.treatment.org/Externals/tips.html) maintained by the U.S. Center for Substance Abuse Treatment, and on the Web site of the U.S. National Institute on Drug Abuse (NIDA; www.nida.nih.gov/). However, more research is needed to determine the effectiveness of different treatments for different types of clients, especially for women and youth.

FIGURE 1-1

Factors Affecting Drug Use and Abuse

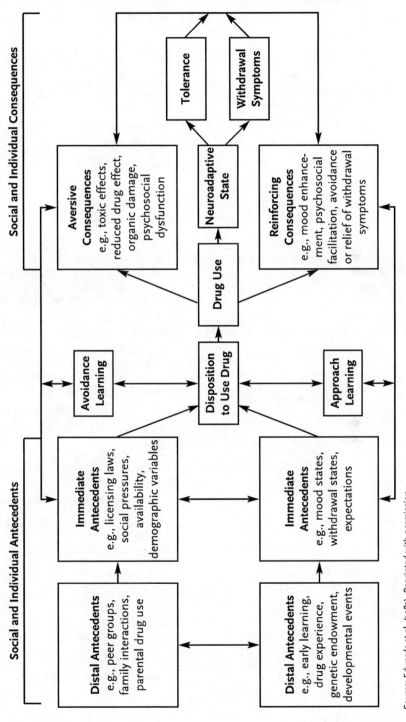

Source: Edwards et al. (1981). Reprinted with permission.

TABLE 1-1

Objectives, Treatment Components and Empirically Supported Clinical Aids

TREATMENT OBJECTIVES	EMPIRICALLY SUPPORTED AIDS/ PROCEDURES
Help client identify high-risk situations and develop strategies to deal with them	Assessments using inventories of risk situations
	Behavioural rehearsal
	Covert modelling
	Assertiveness training
	Coping imagery
	Reframing reactions to relapse
	Meditation and relaxation
	Exercise
Help client understand relapse as a process and as an event	Methods to help client identify factors that contribute to relapse (e.g., functional analysis or instruments such as the Inventory of Drug Taking Situations [IDTS], which help clients identify high-risk situations for relapse)
Help client understand and deal with substance cues and cravings	Monitor cravings
	Behavioural interventions such as avoiding, leaving or changing situations that trigger or worsen cravings; and redirecting activities or getting involved in pleasant activities
	Help and support from others
	Self-help meetings to learn how others have coped
	Medication such as naltrexone (ReVia®) or disulfiram (Antabuse®)
Help client understand and deal with social pressure to use substances	Identify high-risk relationships
	Assess effects of thoughts, feelings and behaviours
	Plan and practise alternative coping skills using role playing
	Evaluate results and modify the coping strategy if required
Help client develop and enhance a supportive social network	Involve family and significant others
	Refer to self-help groups
	Help client decide who should be included in or excluded from social network
	Rehearse asking for help/support
	Develop a written action plan

Based on Daley & Marlatt, 1992.

TABLE 1-1...CONTINUED

TREATMENT OBJECTIVES	EMPIRICALLY SUPPORTED AIDS/ PROCEDURES
Help client develop ways of coping with negative emotional states	Various methods depending on the sources, manifestations and consequences of client's emotional state. May include: • treatment for mental health problems • anger management • leisure planning (for boredom) • counselling on attitudes and beliefs
Assess client for psychiatric disorders and facilitate treatment	Monitor target moods Participate in pleasant activities Develop routines and structures for daily living Identify signs of relapse Psychotherapy Pharmacotherapy
Facilitate transition to follow-up outpatient care or aftercare (for residential programs)	Motivational therapy prior to discharge Telephone or mail reminders for initial appointments Reinforcers for participation in aftercare (e.g., coupons, certificates)
Help client learn to cope with cognitive distortions ("stinking thinking")	Use worksheets to list faulty beliefs such as "awfulizing," over-generalizing, selective abstraction and jumping to conclusions Help show what is wrong with these beliefs Help develop new beliefs
Help client develop a more balanced lifestyle	All of the above Identify sources of stress and pleasure/ self-fulfilment Develop and implement plans to avoid or deal with stress, and to do more fulfilling things
Facilitate pharmacological interventions as an adjunct to psychosocial treatment	Naloxone as an adjunct to psychosocial treatments Medication for psychiatric disorders Methadone for opioid addiction
Help client develop plans to manage a lapse or relapse	Self-talk or behavioural procedures Talk to family Go to self-help group Seek professional help Carry a list of names and phone numbers of people who can help Carry a reminder card about what to do in the case of a lapse Learn from the experience

CONCLUSION

Substance use, and especially continued use despite negative consequences, cannot be explained by any single set of factors. Rather, substance use is determined by several types of factors that interact in complex ways. Clinicians who counsel people with substance use problems need to be aware of these complexities, while giving clients practical advice and help. Despite its overall complexity, however, substance use and relapse can be prevented or reduced if clients acquire appropriate cognitions and skills. Skilled and sensitive counsellors can contribute a great deal to this process, as will be evident from any of the chapters in this book.

REFERENCES

Alcohol Health and Research World, 19. (1995). The genetics of alcoholism (special edition).

Allen, J.P. (1996). Subtypes of alcoholics based on psychometric measures. *Alcohol Health and Research World, 20*(1), 24–29.

American Psychiatric Association. (2000). *Diagnostic and Statistical Manual of Mental Disorders* (4th ed., text rev.). Washington, DC: author.

Arif, A. & Westermeyer, J. (1988). *Manual of Drug and Alcohol Abuse: Guidelines for Teaching in Medical and Health Institutions.* New York: Plenum Medical Book Company.

Babcock, M. & McKay, C. (Eds.). (1995). *Challenging Codependency: Feminist Critiques.* Toronto: University of Toronto Press.

Ball, S.A. (1996). Type A and Type B alcoholism: Applicability across subpopulations and treatment settings. *Alcohol Health and Research World 20*(1), 30–35.

Bandura, A. (1977). *Social Learning Theory.* New Jersey: Prentice Hall.

Barry, H. (1988). Psychoanalytic theory of alcoholism. In C.D. Chaudron & D.A. Wilkinson (Eds.), *Theories on Alcoholism.* Toronto: Addiction Research Foundation.

Cohen, L. & Baum, A. (1995). Stress. In J. Jaffe (Ed.), *Encyclopedia of Drugs and Alcohol.* New York: Macmillan Library Reference.

Daley, D.C. & Marlatt, G.A. (1992). Relapse prevention: Cognitive and behavioral interventions. In J.H. Lowinson, P. Ruiz, R.B. Millman & J.G. Langrod (Eds.), *Substance Abuse: A Comprehensive Textbook* (2nd ed.; pp. 533–542). Baltimore, MD: Williams & Wilkins.

Edwards, G., Arif, A. & Hodgson, R. (1981). Nomenclature and classification of drug- and alcohol-related problems: A WHO memorandum. *Bulletin of the WHO, 59*(2), 225-242.

Godfrey, C. & Maynard, A. (1988). An economic theory of alcohol consumption and abuse. In C.D. Chaudron & D.A. Wilkinson (Eds.), *Theories on Alcoholism*. Toronto: Addiction Research Foundation.

Goplerud, E.N. (1990). *Breaking New Ground for Youth at Risk: Program Summaries* (DHHS Publication No. ADM 89-1658). Washington, DC: Office for Substance Abuse Prevention.

Health Canada. (1999). *Best Practices—Substance Abuse Treatment and Rehabilitation*. Prepared for Office of Alcohol, Drugs and Dependency Issues, Health Canada. Minister of Public Works and Government Services. Cat. No. H39-438/1998E. Ottawa: author.

Health Canada. (2000). *Cocaine Use: Recommendations in Treatment and Rehabilitation*. Minister of Public Works and Government Services. Cat No. H49-155/2001E. Ottawa: author.

Health Canada. (2001a). *Best Practices Treatment and Rehabilitation for Women with Substance Use Problems*. Minister of Public Works and Government Services. Cat. No. H49-153/2001E. Ottawa: author.

Health Canada. (2001b). *Best Practices Treatment and Rehabilitation for Youth with Substance Use Problems*. Minister of Public Works and Government Services. Cat. No. H49-154/2001E. Ottawa: author.

Health Canada. (2002). *Best Practices Concurrent Mental Heath and Substance Use Disorders*. Minister of Public Works and Government Services. Cat. No. H39-599/2001E. Ottawa: author.

Kandel, D.B. & Yamaguchi, K. (1985). Developmental patterns of the use of legal, illegal, and medically prescribed psychotropic drugs from adolescence to young adulthood. In *Etiology of Drug Abuse: Implications for Prevention* (NIDA Research Monograph Series No. 56, DHHS Publication No. ADH 85-1335). Washington, DC: U.S. Government Printing Office.

Keller, M. (1972). The oddities of alcoholics. *Quarterly Journal of Studies on Alcohol, 33*, 1147–1148.

Khantzian, E.J. (1995). Psychological (psychoanalytic) perspective. In J. Jaffe (Ed.), *Encyclopaedia of Drugs and Alcohol* (Vol. 1). New York: Macmillan Library Reference.

Lettieri, D.J., Sayers, M. & Pearson, H.W. (1980). *Theories on Drug Abuse: Selected Contemporary Perspectives* (NIDA Research Monograph 30). Rockville, MD: National Institute on Drug Use.

Madden, P.A.F. & Heath, A.C. (2002). Shared genetic vulnerability in alcohol and cigarette use and dependence. *Alcoholism: Clinical and Experimental Research, 26*, 1919–1921.

Marlatt, G.A. & Gordon, J.R., (Eds.). (1985). *Relapse Prevention*. New York: Guilford Press.

Mello, N.K., McNamee, H.B. & Mendelson, J.H. (1968). *Drinking Patterns of Chronic Alcoholics: Gambling and Motivation* (Psychiatric Research Report No. 24). Washington, DC: American Psychiatric Association.

Mello, N.K. & Mendelson, J.H. (1965). Operant analysis of drinking habits of chronic alcoholics. *Nature, 206*, 43–46.

Miller, N.S. (1994). Prevalence and treatment models for addiction in psychiatric populations. *Psychiatric Annals, 24*(8), 399–406.

Miller, W.R. (1996). Motivational interviewing: Research, practice and puzzles. *Addictive Behaviors, 21*, 838–842.

Molina, B.S.G, Bukstein, O.G. & Lynch, K.G. (2002). Attention-deficit/hyperactivity disorder and conduct disorder symptomatology in adolescents with alcohol use disorder. *Psychology of Addictive Behaviors, 16*(2), 161–164.

Pearlman, S. (1988). Systems theory and alcoholism. In C.D. Chaudron & D.A. Wilkinson (Eds.), *Theories on Alcoholism.* Toronto: Addiction Research Foundation.

Reiger, D.A., Farmer, M.E., Rae, D.S., Locke, B.Z., Keith, S.J., Judd, L.L. et al. (1990). Comorbidity of mental disorders with alcohol and other drug abuse: Results from the epidemiologic catchment area (ECA) study. *Journal of the American Medical Association, 264*, 2511–2518.

Robins, L.N. (1974). *The Vietnam Drug User Returns* (Special Action Office for Drug Abuse Prevention Monograph, Series A, No. 2). Washington, DC: U.S. Government Printing Office.

Shedler, J. & Block, J. (1990). Adolescent drug use and psychological health. *American Psychologist, 45*, 612–630.

Sherman, J.E., Jorenby, D.E. & Baker, T.B. (1988). Classical conditioning with alcohol: Acquired preferences and aversions, tolerance, and urges/craving. In C.D. Chaudron & D.A. Wilkinson (Eds.), *Theories on Alcoholism.* Toronto: Addiction Research Foundation.

Shuckit, Marc A. (1999). New findings on the genetics of alcoholism. *Journal of the American Medical Association, 281*(20), 1875–1876.

Siegel, S., Hinson, R.E., Krank, M.D. & McCully, J. (1982). Heroin "overdose" death: Contribution of drug-associated environmental cues. *Science, 216*, 436–437.

Single, E.W. (1988). The availability theory of alcohol-related problems. In C.D. Chaudron & D.A. Wilkinson (Eds.), *Theories on Alcoholism.* Toronto: Addiction Research Foundation.

Smart, R.G. & Ogborne, A.C. (1996). *Northern Spirits: A Social History of Alcohol in Canada* (2nd ed.). Toronto: Addiction Research Foundation.

Stein, J.A., Newcomb, M.D. & Bentler, P.M. (1987). Personality and drug use: Reciprocal effects across four years. *Personality and Individual Differences, 8*, 419–430.

Tarter, R.E., Alterman, A.I. & Edwards, K.L. (1988). Neurobehavioral theory of alcoholism etiology. In C.D. Chaudron & D.A. Wilkinson (Eds.), *Theories on Alcoholism.* Toronto: Addiction Research Foundation.

Wilson, G.T. (1988). Alcohol use and abuse: A social learning analysis. In C.D. Chaudron & D.A. Wilkinson (Eds.), *Theories on Alcoholism*. Toronto: Addiction Research Foundation.

World Health Organization. (1981). Factors affecting drug use and abuse. *Bulletin of the World Health Organization, 59*(2), 225–242.

World Health Organization. (1992). *The ICD-10—Classification of Mental and Behavioural Disorders, Clinical Descriptions and Diagnostic Guidelines*. Geneva: author.

Chapter 2

Motivational Interviewing

ELSBETH TUPKER AND LORNA SAGORSKY

INTRODUCTION

Motivational interviewing (MI) is one of the most significant innovations of the past 30 years in the way counsellors approach their clients who use substances (Health Canada, 1999; Project MATCH Research Group, 1997; Miller et al., 1998). Instead of struggling with people's resistance and lack of motivation to change their alcohol or other drug use, the MI counsellor expects to encounter ambivalence, sees it as a natural aspect of behaviour change and makes it the focus of counselling. In this approach the counsellor understands that change is a process that goes through stages. The counsellor starts "where the client is at," and explores and builds motivation. The relationship between the counsellor and the client is based on equality: rather than the counsellor telling or teaching the client how to deal with problems, the client is seen as the expert on his or her own situation. In the end, it is the client who talks about changing, not the counsellor.

MI is best defined as "a client centered, directive method for enhancing intrinsic motivation to change by exploring and resolving ambivalence" (Miller & Rollnick, 2002, p. 25). MI is unique in being simultaneously client centred and directive. The interview focuses on the concerns and perspectives of the client, but the counsellor directs the interview by responding selectively and strategically to resolve ambivalence, facilitate talk about change and diminish resistance.

Counsellors intending to use motivational interviewing in their work must not only learn the strategies and techniques, but must also embrace the underlying spirit and principles of MI. This chapter will discuss these issues, as well as the stages of change, how to deal with resistance, the use of MI at assessment, and the adaptation of MI for clients with concurrent addiction and mental health disorders.

THE SPIRIT OF MOTIVATIONAL INTERVIEWING

Motivational interviewing is an interpersonal style, or a "way of being" with the client. It is client centred in that the focus is on the client's concerns, and directive in that the therapist plays an active role in moving the client toward change. The therapeutic relationship is a partnership in which the counsellor takes a supporting rather than an authoritarian role. He or she creates a positive, collaborative inter-personal environment. The counsellor's focus is not on giving information or instilling insight, but rather on eliciting these things from the client. The counsellor respects the client's autonomy and freedom to choose his or her own course of action (Miller & Rollnick, 2002).

Motivation to change is a process that emerges from client-counsellor inter-actions. In the early stages, the counsellor's central task is to structure the sessions so the client talks about his or her concerns and ambivalence about changing. The counsellor encourages the client to explore the pros and cons of changing and of not changing. By asking evocative questions, the counsellor helps the client talk about how drug use fits with his or her life goals and values. This process lets the client see the discrepancy between a life of drug use and what he or she truly values, and leads the client to realize that something needs to change. When the client starts to talk about changing, the counsellor helps increase the client's confidence and commitment to change.

The counselling style of MI is gentle elicitation, rather than teaching or persua-sion. Persuasion tends to put clients in a defensive position, and entrenches resistance as the client tries to convince the counsellor that his or her perspective is right. Resis-tance by the client is a sign that the counsellor is moving too fast, and needs to change his or her motivational strategy. The stages of change model, described below, helps the counsellor choose strategies appropriate to the client's readiness to change (Miller & Rollnick, 2002).

THE STAGES OF CHANGE MODEL

An important theoretical contribution to motivational interviewing is Prochaska and DiClemente's "transtheoretical" or "stages of change" model (DiClemente & Velasquez, 2002). The theory initially explained how people who smoke go about changing their behaviour (Prochaska & DiClemente, 1983). The model has since been generalized to other addictive behaviours. It is usually depicted as a wheel or spiral of different change stages. In each stage, the client needs to focus on specific tasks that will enable movement to the next stage. The stages of change model asserts that a "slip" or relapse is part of the cyclical nature of changing substance use. This model of change has also been successfully applied to various other behaviours, including weight control, high-fat diets, adolescent delinquency, condom use, sunscreen use and mammography screening (Prochaska et al., 1994; Soden & Murray, 1997).

FIGURE 2-1
Stages of Change Model

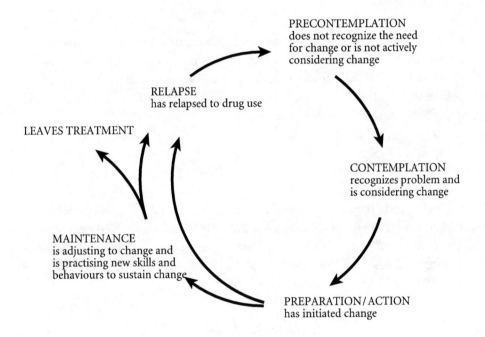

Adapted from Prochaska & Diclemente (1982).

Precontemplation Stage

Clients at the precontemplation stage do not recognize that they have a problem and are not thinking about change. They usually resist treatment; they feel others are pushing them and they do not intend to change. The therapeutic tasks at this stage are to build the client-counsellor relationship, and to let the client know the consequences of his or her behaviour. Strategies include providing clinical feedback that is relevant to clients and that may elicit concern, or asking clients to weigh the good things and less good things about their substance use.

Contemplation Stage

Clients in this stage recognize some of the negative consequences of their substance use, but are ambivalent about changing. They see a need to change but are not ready to do it. This stage may last a long time, so it is important to keep the client engaged. The counsellor's task at this stage is to resolve the client's ambivalence. Strategies include exploring the pros and cons of changing and of not changing, and helping clients to see discrepancies between their drug use and their values.

Preparation Stage

In this stage, clients are thinking about changing in the near future. They may still be ambivalent, so the therapeutic task is to build commitment to change. The counsellor should set goals and make plans for change at a pace that is comfortable for the client. Clinical strategies at this stage focus on eliciting the client's ideas for change, and providing options, advice and direction.

Action Stage

Clients in the action stage are changing; they are giving up old behaviour patterns and replacing them with new ones. There is a lot of activity and energy to try new things. The therapeutic task is to build self-belief and continue with goal setting and implementation. Counsellors can do this by exploring the importance of change and the client's level of confidence about making a change.

Maintenance Stage

In the maintenance stage, clients are making more profound and long-term changes that support the new behaviours of the action stage. The counsellor's task is to generalize new behaviours, focus on preventing relapse, and prepare clients to cope with high-risk situations and to deal constructively with relapse, should this occur.

Relapse

In this model, relapse is considered not as a failure, but as a common and useful aspect of lasting change. Clients in relapse may revert back to an earlier stage, such as precontemplation or contemplation. The therapeutic task in this case is to encourage clients to learn from the relapse and to re-evaluate their goals and strategies.

Practitioners following the stages of change model tailor their counselling to the stage that the client is in. Moving through the stages is not necessarily a fluid process, and most people revert back to an earlier stage in the change process at some point. Therefore counsellors need to identify at assessment which stage the client is in, and to continue to monitor the client's stage of change throughout counselling. Failure to focus on the tasks of the appropriate stage can lead the client to resist treatment, or even to drop out. Motivational interviewing can be employed in all stages of change; the MI strategies appropriate to each stage are discussed further throughout this chapter (DiClemente & Velasquez, 2002).

PRINCIPLES BEHIND MOTIVATIONAL INTERVIEWING

Miller and Rollnick (2002) have identified four broad clinical principles to help counsellors motivate clients:
• Express empathy.
• Support self-efficacy.
• Roll with resistance.
• Develop discrepancy.

Express Empathy

Empathy and its expression were identified in the work of Rogers (1965). He maintained that counsellors who show an understanding of the client's situation from the client's own perspective, without judging, criticizing or blaming, will be the most successful in treating people. The counsellor accepts the client, and listens respectfully with a desire to understand the client's perspective. Paradoxically, this acceptance of people as they are seems to give them freedom to change, whereas insistent non-acceptance ("You're not OK: you have to change") can have the effect of keeping people as they are. This attitude of acceptance and respect also builds a therapeutic alliance and supports the client's self-esteem—an important condition for change (Miller & Rollnick, 2002; Soden & Murray, 1997).

Support Self-Efficacy

Self-efficacy refers to a client's belief that he or she can do something (Bandura, 1977). It is an important motivator for people who are changing their use of alcohol or other drugs. To instil confidence, the counsellor can explore the client's past successes or relate examples of others who have succeeded in the same circumstances.

It is also important to maintain the client's hope for change, even when progress is slow. Counsellors should let the client know there is no single way to achieve success, and that it is often a process of trial and error.

Roll with Resistance

Rather than challenge resistance through persuasion or argument, the counsellor uses the energy of the resistance to further explore the client's views. This approach tends to lower resistance, because the client is not forced to argue for his or her point of view. Specific strategies for dealing with resistance will be discussed later in the chapter.

Develop Discrepancy

"Developing discrepancy," or creating cognitive dissonance, allows the counsellor "to create and amplify, in the client's mind, a discrepancy between present behavior and broader goals" (Miller & Rollnick, 1991, p. 56). Through this process, the client becomes aware of the gap between where he or she is and where he or she would like to be. This occurs when a client realizes that his or her substance use conflicts with personal goals such as good health, vocational or financial success or healthy relationships. Such awareness creates a motivating force that tips the balance of ambivalence in the direction of changing the problem. When successfully done, this process enables the client, not the counsellor, to articulate the reasons for change (Soden & Murray, 1997).

TRAPS TO AVOID

Learning to do motivational interviewing requires *not* doing certain counter productive things, as well as applying the principles and techniques of MI. To build the client's motivation to change, the counsellor must avoid certain traps, discussed below (Miller & Rollnick, 2002).

Question and Answer Trap

A question and answer interview tends to make clients relatively passive, and does not encourage them to explore the deeper levels of their experience and perceptions. It also creates a hierarchy, in which the counsellor alone determines the course and content of the interview. Counsellors should avoid asking more than three questions in a row—rather, the counsellor should be listening and following along with the client.

Confrontation-Denial Trap

The confrontation-denial trap is only one of a number of problematic dynamics that may arise from a counsellor's need to preserve his or her own self-esteem. This situation may arise if, for example, the clinician is so task oriented that he or she gives little consideration to important process issues, such as the client's need to own the therapeutic process. The result is that the counsellor becomes more directive and prescriptive, while the client becomes more entrenched and resistant (Miller & Sovereign, 1989; Soden & Murray, 1997).

Expert Trap

In the expert trap, the clinician solves the client's problems and imposes "corrective" measures to rectify dysfunctional situations. As with the confrontation-denial trap, the client's self-belief and self-esteem are not increased and may even be harmed (Miller & Rollnick, 1991; Soden & Murray, 1997).

Premature Focus Trap

This trap occurs when the counsellor raises the issue of the client's substance use problem before the client is prepared to discuss it. The client may then become defensive, and deny or minimize the issue. To avoid this trap, the counsellor must focus on the client's issues and concerns, rather than his or her own agenda (Miller & Rollnick, 2002; Soden & Murray, 1997).

Labelling Trap

This trap relates to the popular idea that in order to change, a client must first accept that he or she is an "alcoholic" or a "drug addict." Given the stigma usually attached to these labels, it is understandable that people will resist adopting them. People do not need to accept a label or diagnosis in order to change, and so MI avoids the use of labels (Miller & Rollnick, 1991).

Blaming Trap

Clients who blame others for their problems, and counsellors who point out that clients' difficulties are their own fault, are pursuing a course that does not help the client change. It is best to maintain a "no-fault" policy, and focus instead on what is troubling the client and what he or she can do about it (Miller & Rollnick, 1991).

INTERACTIONAL TECHNIQUES

Motivational interviewing relies on four basic techniques that are captured by the acronym OARS (Miller & Rollnick, 2002):
• open-ended questions
• affirmations
• reflective listening
• summaries.

To do MI successfully, a clinician needs to become skilled in these techniques. This involves learning what to say, as well as knowing when to use each technique. A training workshop may help the counsellor learn and practise these ways of working. In addition, demonstration tapes made by Miller and Rollnick (1998) show how many of the techniques are used.

Open-Ended Questions

Open-ended questions are questions that cannot be answered by a simple yes or no or by just a few words. Instead these questions invite the client to talk about his or her life and concerns. Typical opening questions are "What brings you here today?" or "Could you tell me what has happened since we met last week?" Open-ended questions are intended to create momentum, and to help the client explore his or her situation and the possibility of change (Miller & Rollnick, 2002).

Affirmations

These are statements by the counsellor that acknowledge clients' strengths. People with substance use problems often have failures, and may doubt their ability to make things better. Pointing out strengths in a sincere way can instil much-needed hope and confidence (Miller & Rollnick, 2002).

Reflective Listening

Reflective listening is the most central and most challenging skill used in MI. It involves listening attentively and then responding to what the client has said. Reflective responses are a counsellor's best guess at what the client means. The reflection is not intended to question the client's meaning, but to demonstrate understanding and acceptance. Therefore the reflective listener gives this meaning back in the form of a statement, not a question; the intonation of a reflective listening statement goes down at the end, not up as it would in a question (Miller & Rollnick, 2002).

The purpose of reflections is to elicit more exploratory talk from the client, and to move the client toward thinking and talking about change. Merely echoing what the client has said would slow the momentum. Instead the counsellor reflects a part of what was said to explore it more deeply; or the counsellor can touch on what he or she wants the client to talk about next, in order to move the interview forward.

Simple reflections may focus on feelings or on the content of the client's statements, or they may link feelings, thoughts and content. Deeper reflections are about the meaning of the client's experience, or about universal, spiritual or existential issues. Simple reflections are used in the early stages of treatment, while deeper reflections become more appropriate as the relationship develops and the client presents more complex material. Typically the flow of the interview involves an open-ended question followed by two to three reflections (Miller & Rollnick, 2002). Consider the client statement below:

> I came to see you today because my mother passed away this week. You know that she was ill for a long time, and although it's a relief for her, it's very hard for me. I always wanted her to be proud of me, but I know I was always a big disappointment to her, being an alcoholic and never doing what she wanted me to do. I always felt that I never pleased her, and now it's too late to make any changes. And I loved her so much. How can you help me?

Various counsellor reflections are possible. *Echoing* is an exact repetition of the client's words.

> You loved your mother very much and now she has died.

Paraphrasing is repetition with some added content.

> You feel you were always a disappointment to your mother, and now that she has died you can't make it right.

Getting the gist involves repetition and showing understanding by using the client's words.

> Things are very hard for you now. You are mourning your mother's death and on top of that you're very saddened by the fact that you never lived up to her expectations.

Reflecting feelings is talking about the client's affect.

> There are many feelings you're experiencing now. You're very sad that your mother has died, and you're also guilty that you never did what she would have wanted for you. And now there's also a feeling of frustration because whatever you do now, you can't change the past.

Reflecting feelings and content involves linking thought, feelings and events.

> Your mother, whom you loved a great deal, has just died and has left you feeling very upset since you always wanted to do right by her, and because of your drinking you were unable to do this. Now you're in a position where nothing can be changed.

Reflecting meaning involves reflecting the experience as a whole, including personal, human, spiritual, universal or existential elements.

> Living up to your mother's dreams for you was something you always felt you needed to do as a son who loved his mother. But because of your heavy drinking you never felt you achieved this, and you're very sad that now your mother has passed away those ambitions will never be fulfilled.

Summaries

Summaries are a special form of reflective listening in which the counsellor reflects back what the client has been saying over a longer period of the interaction. Summaries communicate the counsellor's interest and build rapport. Summaries can focus on important aspects of the interview, make linkages, as well as change the direction of the interaction. This technique is particularly useful when the counsellor wants to move on from an interaction that is not productive.

Another important approach is eliciting change talk. This is a technique that helps the client resolve ambivalence. Change talk, or self-motivational statements, refers to statements the client makes about the need for change, the benefits of change, his or her hopes for change, or the intention to change. A central goal of motivational interviewing is for clients to make self-motivational statements that articulate concern, recognize that a problem exists, express an intention to change or show optimism about the possibility of change (Miller & Rollnick, 2002). The counsellor may elicit change talk by, for example, asking clients evocative questions, such as an open-ended question about how the client sees things or what his or her concerns are, or asking clients how important something is to them. Once clients begin to talk about change, help them elaborate. The more they hear themselves talking about change, the stronger their commitment to change will become (Miller & Rollnick, 2002).

PRACTICAL STRATEGIES IN MOTIVATIONAL INTERVIEWING

Following are some simple practical strategies to create a motivating and collaborative way of working with a client, while getting the information you need in a short time.

Review of a Typical Day

The client relates what happens in a typical day, including his or her use of substances. This is a good way to build rapport without focusing on the problem. It not only helps the counsellor to know and understand the client better, but also gives a realistic picture of how substance use fits into the client's life. Reflective listening is used to further explore what the client tells you (Mid-Atlantic Addiction Technology Transfer Center, 2003).

Looking Back

This involves the client discussing how things were before his or her substance use began. It gives a good picture of the client's lifestyle, and allows the client to reflect on the changes (usually losses) that have come about since the substance use started. The use of OARS techniques during this process helps the counsellor explore and elaborate on useful material, such as the impact of substance use (Miller & Rollnick, 2002).

Looking Forward

Another technique is to have the client reflect on the impact of continuing his or her current behaviours. The counsellor asks the client what things will be like in the future, given the current state of affairs and assuming things won't change. The client typically considers the impact of substance use over a long period and then examines the anticipated cumulative effects on his or her quality of life. It can also be useful for the client to contemplate the future *without* the problem behaviour. This helps pinpoint the effect of the problem behaviour on the client's lifestyle. Looking back and looking forward may both be used to elicit self-motivational statements, one of the principal goals of motivational interviewing (Miller & Rollnick, 2002).

Looking at the Good Things and the Not-So-Good Things

In this technique, the client is asked to look at both sides of substance use. In MI it is understood that clients use substances because there is a "payoff." The counsellor's acknowledgment of this truth is very powerful for the client. It builds rapport and allows the client to feel understood because, from this point of view, his or her substance use makes sense.

Clients are much more ready to explore the not-so-good things after they have articulated the advantages of their substance use. The phrase "not so good" has been chosen carefully to avoid the implication of a problem (e.g., the "bad things"), which can be a barrier to moving forward.

The counsellor then summarizes the two types of consequences of substance use, and gives the client time to think about this material and reflect back his or her thoughts. This helps the client contrast the positive and negative consequences, which often results in a better understanding of the full impact of the not-so-good things (Mid-Atlantic Addiction Technology Transfer Center, 2003).

Decisional Balance

Once the client has acknowledged that the substance use has both positive and negative consequences, the counsellor can do a cost-benefit analysis. The client looks first at the pros and cons of staying the same and then at the pros and cons of change. This technique gives a good overall view of what change will mean to the client, in both positive and negative terms. It helps the client understand which payoffs of substance use will need to be compensated for, and what benefits can be anticipated. Looking at the entire picture can help the client to see how to create a different lifestyle, and to determine whom he or she can become in the future through the choices made now (Mid-Atlantic Addiction Technology Transfer Center, 2003).

Exploring Values

Focusing on a client's values can stimulate motivation for change and self-motivational statements. Often people have a vision of their "ideal self," which they feel defines them and the things that are important to them. Spending time exploring a client's values, and then examining the effect of substance use on this vision of self, can sometimes move clients quickly and powerfully toward change. As inconsistencies emerge between the person's behaviour and his or her deeper sense of self and values, the person may become increasingly aware that while substance use meets short-term needs, it does not fulfil higher values or lead to long-term satisfaction (Mid-Atlantic Addiction Technology Transfer Center, 2003).

Discussing the Stages of Change Model

It can be useful to explain the stages of change model and to talk with clients about where they are in the change process. This can help them understand some of the stumbling blocks they will encounter, and help them realize that change may take more time and effort than they (and interested others) may expect. In addition, ask clients to look back at previous changes they have made, and to remember how the change process occurred at that time. A new understanding of what moved the client into action in the past may help him or her change now.

Exploring the Importance of Change

In order for clients to make changes, they need to feel that change is important. Ask clients how important a particular change is to them, on a scale of one to 10. If it does not rate very highly, change is less likely. Identifying the person's most important goal may motivate change, by helping the person realize that if the substance use does not change, the person won't reach his or her ultimate goal (Mid-Atlantic Addiction Technology Transfer Center, 2003).

Exploring Confidence

The more confidence a person has in his or her ability to change, the more likely it will happen. Have the client rate his or her confidence on a scale of one to 10, and then help the person find ways to become more confident (Mid-Atlantic Addiction Technology Transfer Center, 2003).

Planning Change

Once it is established that the client wants to change, planning for change needs to be done sensitively and with the client taking the lead. As many options and choices as possible should be presented and considered. The pace of change needs to match what the client can handle. Moving too quickly can set a client back in the stages of change. Initially, work on short-term and simple plans, so it is easier for the client to succeed. Planning for change is a collaborative effort: the client is the expert on himself or herself, and on what he or she wants and can do, while the therapist gives information on possible ways to make changes (Mid-Atlantic Addiction Technology Transfer Center, 2003).

RESISTANCE

In the substance use field it is common to encounter people who are considered resistant. In motivational interviewing, resistance is seen not as a character trait but as a specific behaviour pattern in the interaction between the client and the counsellor. The extent to which clients "resist" is strongly influenced by the therapist's style (Patterson & Forgatch, 1985). MI techniques have been developed to help decrease clients' resistance. Some signs of resistance are arguing, interrupting, negating and ignoring. These behaviours usually signal that the counsellor needs to change the interaction.

If you understand what causes resistance, you can prevent it. Often it occurs when the client and counsellor have different agendas or goals, or when the respective roles are unclear. You can prevent this by agreeing on an agenda before the session and exploring the client's hopes and goals before making any assumptions. To avoid a misunderstanding about the respective roles of the client and therapist, it is best to talk about role expectations early on.

Resistance can also arise when the counsellor uses strategies that are not appropriate for the client's stage of change. Check in regularly with the client to learn where he or she is in the change process, since the client's stage of change may fluctuate over the course of treatment.

Some counsellor behaviours can lead the client to become resistant or to increase resistance. Generally this occurs if the counsellor "takes charge" of the session, and the client-counsellor partnership is broken. It may happen if the counsellor falls into one of the traps discussed earlier, such as confrontation, blaming, labelling or acting as the expert. When a counsellor argues for change or takes up the side of the client's ambivalence that is in favour of change, the client's natural response is to provide counter-arguments. This kind of interaction, in which the therapist does all the work and provides all the change talk while the client argues against it, is unproductive and usually entrenches resistance.

There are certain times when resistance is more common. Resistance is usually a sign of ambivalence. If we think of resistance as a client's attempt to stop hidden, often painful information from becoming visible both to others and to himself or herself, then it is understandable that the client will resist at certain points. For example, a client may resist when considering whether a problem really exists (contemplation stage), when facing the loss of behaviours and lifestyle (action stage), or when facing the risks of new behaviours and lifestyle (action or maintenance stage).

Clients in the precontemplation stage are unaware of a need to change or are simply unwilling to change. These clients, who are in treatment only because they are being "pushed" by others to do something about their substance use, can be particularly challenging. Their resistance may take the form of reluctance, rebellion, resignation or rationalization (DiClemente & Velasquez, 2002).

When a person is *reluctant* to change, it may be due to inertia, lack of knowledge, fear or lack of comfort with the current situation. With these clients it is useful to listen carefully and gently provide feedback and information. It may take considerable time before they move on.

Rebellious clients are usually aware of the need to change their substance use, but are too invested in it to give it up. They can be very argumentative, and so the best approach is to roll with the resistance by letting them express their thoughts and suggesting a range of options to choose from.

Clients who are *resigned* typically feel overwhelmed by the thought of change, and have likely had many failed attempts. They can be low in energy and involvement. With these clients, the focus is on building confidence using reflections and affirmations.

Clients who *rationalize* typically take no ownership of the problem, blame others, have all the answers and get into debates. With these people, the counsellor avoids arguing and acknowledges the positives of the substance use. Reflections can be used to encourage reframing (seeing things in a new perspective).

Dealing with Resistance

Generally it is helpful to join with resistant clients, letting them know that you understand their resistance. Talking about the resistance can help them to move forward. Some effective ways to deal with resistance include exploring ambivalence, identifying achievements and strengths, and offering choices and optimism that things can change.

The following types of reflection illustrate ways of dealing with resistance (Miller & Rollnick, 2002).

SIMPLE REFLECTION
Respond to resistance with nonresistance; your response may include a small shift in emphasis, but should acknowledge the client's perception or disagreement.

Client: "I couldn't change even if I wanted to."

Counsellor: "You can't see any way that you believe would work, and you might fail if you tried."

AMPLIFIED REFLECTION
Reflect what the client has said in an amplified or exaggerated way (while avoiding a sarcastic tone) to elicit the other side of the client's ambivalence.

Client: "I can hold my liquor just fine. I'm still standing when others are under the table."

Counsellor: "So, you really have nothing to worry about—alcohol can't hurt you at all."

DOUBLE-SIDED REFLECTION

Acknowledge what the client has said, and add to it the other side of his or her ambivalence, using material that the client has talked about previously.

> Client: "I don't smoke any more than my friends. What's wrong with a joint now and then?"

> Counsellor: "I can see how this is confusing. On the one hand you've told me you're concerned about how smoking affects you, but on the other hand you're not using more than your friends. Hard to figure out!"

SHIFTING THE FOCUS

Move the client's attention away from a stumbling block that is getting in the way of progress.

> Client: "OK, Maybe I have got some problems with drinking, but I'm not an alcoholic."

> Counsellor: "I don't think whether you are an alcoholic is the issue. What's more important is some of the things happening in your life. Tell me more about…"

REFRAMING

Acknowledge the validity of the client's perspective, and offer a new meaning or interpretation.

> Client: "I can't stand how my parents are always on my case, now that they know I use."

> Counsellor: "Their control is hard to live with, they must care a lot about you and are worried about what could happen."

EMPHASIZING PERSONAL CONTROL

Assure the client that he or she is in control.

> Client: "My wife wants me to talk to you about our marriage, but I don't see the point."

> Counsellor: "She's concerned about the relationship, but you have your own reasons for coming today and that's what is important."

AGREEMENT WITH A TWIST

Offer initial agreement but with a slight twist or change in direction.

> Client: "I just can't see doing anything about my drinking. It's too tough."

> Counsellor: "It's really difficult, and yet it's amazing how much you've been able to accomplish in your life."

ASSESSMENT AND MOTIVATIONAL INTERVIEWING

Although assessment is usually separate from actual therapy, it is an important initial part of the continuum of care. It sets the tone for what clients can expect from the treatment system. Many clients do not return after assessment; there is evidence that a brief MI session at the time of assessment can make follow-through with treatment more likely. It also gives clients who drop out a positive and informative experience to reflect on, and this may lead them to return to treatment at a later date.

Most clients feel anxious and uncomfortable at this first point of contact. Joining with the client by acknowledging these feelings can be effective, and makes clear that you are interested in the client. If you let the client know that he or she has the knowledge and information you are looking for, it sets up a partnership and empowers the client as the expert on his or her own life. The notion that the client is in control and has choices is also an important concept to introduce at this early stage.

Feeding back the results of the client's assessment can enhance the client's motivation. It is most respectful to give the client the feedback material to read and interpret on his or her own, to establish that the client "owns" this information. The assessor should always be willing to answer questions and help interpret the assessment findings. Letting clients compare their assessment results with societal norms is an effective way to bring objectivity into the interpretation. When clients compare themselves to others, it can create discrepancy in their perceptions of what they think is normal or usual (Mid-Atlantic Addiction Technology Transfer Center, 2003).

Most assessments explore the negative consequences of substance use. It is helpful to look at payoffs at the same time, and to talk about the client's ambivalence about change. If you make it clear that ambivalence is normal and acceptable, it can help the client feel understood.

When assessment leads to treatment planning and referral, it is necessary to match the treatment plan to the stage of change the client is in.

MOTIVATIONAL INTERVIEWING AND CONCURRENT DISORDERS

A number of recent studies have illustrated the efficacy of the MI approach with clients who have concurrent addiction and mental health problems (Swanson et al., 1999; Bellock & DiClemente, 1999). People with concurrent disorders may have disabling symptoms and poor functional adjustment, and are frequently demoralized by past failures, which often makes it hard for them to engage in treatment. The relationship-building aspect of MI can help people with concurrent disorders develop a lasting and therapeutic relationship with a counsellor.

In a groundbreaking article, Martino et al. (2002) describe a model called DDMI (Dual Diagnosis Motivational Interviewing). The model includes two types of modifications of MI: (1) the use of MI strategies in an integrated concurrent disorders approach, in which both mental health and substance use are addressed in a co-ordinated way, often simultaneously, and (2) the adaptation of MI techniques for this population.

In the integrated approach, MI is used to target three areas: substance use, medication compliance and attending treatment. All the counsellor's questions, reflections and other MI techniques attempt to integrate and explore the connections between these three areas. For example, the counsellor might ask such questions as: "When you get high, how does it affect your psychiatric symptoms?" This integration can have a positive effect on the final outcome of the treatment.

The adaptation of MI techniques for people with concurrent disorders focuses on the basic principles of MI: expressing empathy, developing discrepancy, rolling with resistance and supporting self-efficacy. All the MI techniques are carried out more simply and concisely, keeping in mind the suggestions listed below:
• Always be clear.
• Always be concise.
• Talk about or reflect one topic at a time.
• Avoid compound questions; address one area at a time.
• Reflect frequently.
• Reflect only on the positive, logical material (not on, for example, disordered thinking or flights of ideas).
• Give enough time for a response.
• Summarize frequently, referring to small pieces of information.
• Summarize concrete verbal or visual material.
• Use appropriate metaphors.
• Use affirmations as much as possible (generally these clients receive very little praise or positive feedback, so this can be a very valuable tool).
• Try to attain some current goals related to the three change areas.
• Have patience.
• Expect relapses and use them as learning experiences.

- When doing a decisional balance, work only on the positives and negatives associated with change.
- Movement from contemplation to action is most likely to occur after a very significant negative experience that the client does not want to repeat in the future (Martino, 2002).

MI's non-confrontational approach and open discussion are a welcome change to the sometimes more traditional didactic and hierarchical methods found in the mental health field. Clients are made to feel that their opinions have some validity, and their points of view are incorporated into decisions. MI can be especially powerful when exploring the good things about substance use and gaining an understanding that use of substances may actually make sense, given the "payoffs" clients experience.

Some of the challenges that need to be addressed when working with the severely mentally ill are decreased cognitive functioning, difficulty reflecting on and acting from the experience of past behaviours, deficits in abstract reasoning, failure (or inability) to follow through on planned intentions, and a general state of anhedonia (inability to experience pleasure), which some escape through the use of substances.

APPLICATIONS OF MOTIVATIONAL INTERVIEWING

Although motivational interviewing was first developed for and applied to alcohol and other drug use, this approach is now increasingly used to counsel people to make health-related changes in other areas, such as diet, exercise and taking medication (Rollnick et al., 1999). The interpersonal style of motivational interviewing can be used by health care professionals in many different settings, and is not necessarily confined to formal counselling.

A number of interventions for substance use problems are derived from MI. The Drinker's Check-up (Miller & Sovereign, 1989) gives meaningful personalized feedback to people with alcohol problems, following a comprehensive assessment. The style in which the feedback is given is non-judgmental, and clients are invited to reflect on the information and come to their own conclusions. A brief motivational intervention at assessment can mobilize the client to contemplate change.

Motivational Enhancement Therapy (MET) is a four-session intervention that applies motivational principles and techniques (Miller et al., 1995), and was developed in Project MATCH, a very large treatment outcome study. (Project MATCH Research Group, 1993). Other brief interventions, such as Structured Relapse Prevention (Annis et al., 1996) and Guided Self Change (Sobell & Sobell, 1993), apply motivational interviewing to the treatment of people with drinking problems, while First Contact (Breslin et al., 1999) applies MI to young people with substance use problems. All these manualized brief treatments are used widely throughout Ontario.

EMPIRICAL SUPPORT FOR MOTIVATIONAL INTERVIEWING

Clinical research on the efficacy of MI is continuously evolving. MI is generally integrated with other treatment techniques and usually serves as a brief preparatory intervention or as the primary treatment. The studies are of applications of MI (AMI) rather than evaluations of pure MI. A recent review of 26 controlled studies of AMI did an analysis using expert ratings of outcomes and methodologies to arrive at a cumulative evidence score (Burke et al., 2002). The results of the 11 AMI studies that focused on alcohol problems compared extremely favourably with the results of other studies of common treatments for alcohol problems. Two of the studies, which used AMI as a first step to prepare the client for further treatment, found positive outcomes regarding drinking levels at three months after treatment. Five of the six studies that examined AMI as a primary treatment showed clear differences in alcohol consumption between those treated with AMI and controls who received no treatment. Generally, compared with other interventions equal in duration and scope, AMI appears to be as good as, but not better than, other treatments for alcohol problems.

As a treatment for other substance use problems, there is evidence from the five studies that were reviewed that AMI is more effective as a first step to more intensive treatment than other credible approaches. As a stand-alone intervention, AMI can be as effective as more extensive group therapy and significantly more effective than no treatment. To date AMI has not been shown to be effective in smoking cessation or reducing HIV risk behaviours. There are some early indications that AMI increases treatment adherence, an important predictor of positive outcome (Zweben & Zuckoff, 2002). In particular, two studies of people with concurrent disorders suggest that AMI, when added to inpatient treatment, improves overall treatment adherence (Martino et al., 2002; Swanson et al., 1999).

While evidence suggests that MI works in the applications noted above, it is less clear how and why it works and with whom. One study found evidence that angry people responded better to MI than less angry people, but clearly more research is needed to help pinpoint when MI is most effective (Miller & Rollnick, 2002).

CONCLUSION

MI's non-confrontational, exploratory approach offers counsellors a more collaborative way of relating to their clients than do most other substance use therapies, and provides a welcome change from more didactic and hierarchal counselling methods. Clients are made to feel that their opinions are valid, and their points of view are incorporated into decision making. Therefore it is a good alternative for counsellors who aim to empower their clients to participate in their own treatment. The practical strategies of MI are designed to reduce the client's resistance and increase motivation for change—both major challenges in the treatment of substance use. The approach can be readily integrated with other treatments, and there are numerous resources available to help counsellors master its techniques.

REFERENCES

Annis, H., Herie, M. & Watkin Merrick, L. (1996). *Structured Relapse Prevention: An Outpatient Counselling Approach.* Toronto: Addiction Research Foundation.

Bandura, A. (1977). Self-efficacy: Toward a unifying theory of behavioral change. *Psychological Review, 84,* 191–215.

Bellock, A. & DiClemente, C. (1999). Treating substance abuse among patients with schizophrenia. *Psychiatric Services, 50*(1), 75–80.

Breslin, C., Sdao-Jarvie, K., Tupker, E. & Pearlman, S. (1999). *First Contact: A Brief Treatment for Young Substance Users.* Toronto: Centre for Addiction and Mental Health.

Burke, L., Arkowitz, H. & Dunn, C. (2002). The efficacy of motivational interviewing and its adaptations: What we know so far. In W.R. Miller & S. Rollnick (Eds.), *Motivational Interviewing: Preparing People for Change.* New York: Guilford Press.

DiClemente, C.C. & Velasquez, M.M. (2002). Motivational interviewing and the stages of change. In W.R. Miller & S. Rollnick (Eds.), *Motivational Interviewing: Preparing People for Change.* New York: Guilford Press.

Health Canada. (1999). Best Practices—Substance Abuse Treatment and Rehabilitation. Cat. No. H39-438/1998E. Ottawa: Minister of Public Works and Government Services.

Martino, S., Carroll, K., Kostas, D., Perkins, J. & Rounsaville, B. (2002). Dual Diagnosis Motivational Interviewing: A modification of Motivational Interviewing for substance-abusing patients with psychotic disorders. *Journal of Substance Abuse Treatment, 23,* 297–308.

Mid-Atlantic Addiction Technology Transfer Center. (2003). *MI Counseling Strategies.* Available: www.motivationalinterviewing.org.

Miller, W.R., Andrews, N.R., Wilbourne, P. & Bennett, M.E. (1998). A wealth of alternatives: Effective treatments for alcohol problems. In W.R. Miller & N. Heather (Eds.), *Treating Addictive Behaviours: Processes of Change* (2nd ed.; pp. 121–132). New York: Plenum Press.

Miller, W.R. & Rollnick, S. (1998). *Motivational Interviewing Video Series.* Albuquerque, NM: Horizon West Productions.

Miller, W.R. & Rollnick, S. (1999). *Teaching Motivational Interviewing: Materials for Trainers.* Albuquerque, NM: MINT-6.

Miller, W.R. & Rollnick, S. (2002). *Motivational Interviewing: Preparing People for Change.* New York: Guilford Press.

Miller, W.R. & Sovereign, R.G. (1989). The check-up: A model for early intervention in addictive behaviors. In T. Loberg, W.R. Miller, P.E. Nathan & G.A. Marlatt (Eds.), *Addictive Behaviors: Prevention and Early Intervention* (pp. 219–231). Amsterdam: Swets and Zeitlinger.

Miller, W.R., Zweben, A., DiClemente, C.C. & Rychtarik, R.G. (1995). *Motivational Enhancement Therapy.* Washington, DC: National Institute of Health.

Patterson, G.A. & Forgatch, M.S. (1985). Therapist behavior as a determinant for client non-compliance: A paradox for the behavior modifier. *Journal of Consulting and Clinical Psychology, 53,* 846–851.

Prochaska, J.O. & DiClemente, C.C. (1982). Transtheoretical therapy: Toward a more integrative model of change. *Psychotherapy: Theory, Research and Practice, 19*(3), 276–288.

Prochaska, J.O. & DiClemente, C.C. (1983). Stages and processes of self-change of smoking: Toward an integrative model of change. *Journal of Consulting and Clinical Psychology, 51,* 390–395.

Prochaska, J.O., DiClemente, C.C. & Norcross, J. (1994). *Changing for Good.* New York: William Morrow.

Project MATCH Research Group (1997). Project MATCH secondary a priori hypotheses. *Addiction, 92,* 1671–1698.

Rogers, C.R. (1965). *Client-Centered Therapy.* Boston: Houghton Mifflin.

Rollnick, S., Mason, P. & Butler, C. (1999). *Health Behavior Change: A Guide for Practitioners.* London: Churchill Livingstone.

Sobell, M. & Sobell, L. (1993). *Problem Drinkers: Guided Self-Change Treatment.* New York: Guilford Press.

Soden, T. & Murray, R. (1997). Motivational interviewing techniques. In S. Harrison & V. Carver (Eds.), *Alcohol and Drug Problems: A Practical Guide for Counsellors* (2nd ed.; pp. 19–59). Toronto: Addiction Research Foundation.

Swanson, A.J., Pantalon, M.V. & Cohen, K.R. (1999). Motivational interviewing and treatment adherence among psychiatric and dually diagnosed patients. *Journal of Nervous and Mental Disease, 187,* 630–635.

Zweben, A. & Zuckoff, A. (2002). Motivational interviewing and treatment adherence. In W.R. Miller & S. Rollnick (Eds.), *Motivational Interviewing: Preparing People for Change* (pp. 299–319). New York: Guilford Press.

Chapter 3

Case Management: Assessment, Treatment Planning and Monitoring

CHRISTINE BOIS AND JACKIE LLOYD-RAI

INTRODUCTION

People presenting with substance use/abuse problems often have a complex array of concerns and may require assistance or support with more than one area of their lives. Clients of addiction services come from all walks of life and all types of social contexts.

The main components of case management are:
• a careful assessment of each client's strengths and problem areas
• treatment planning and referral
• ongoing support.
Case management can ensure that clients are linked with the services needed for long-term recovery.

The addiction field has recognized for many years that, for example, treating drinking-related problems in a variety of life areas can improve outcomes for people with alcohol problems (Institute of Medicine, 1990). Thus the upfront work of assessment is critical to identifying problems and linking clients to a range of health, social and legal services. Even for clients who only have moderate substance use problems and relatively few problems in other life areas, assessors can offer motivational counselling and/or brief interventions, thus providing cost-effective access to the least intrusive treatment necessary (for more on this topic, see Chapter 2 and Chapter 7.

This chapter will discuss six critical functions for engaging and supporting clients through the process of change:

1. screening: to identify if alcohol or other substance use problems exist
2. assessment: to find the person's strengths, problem areas, needs and the impact of his or her substance use
3. treatment planning: to develop a specific service plan for people to gain access to resources effectively
4. linking: to help people get required services
5. advocacy: to intercede on behalf of a person to ensure access to resources
6. monitoring: to evaluate progress, support and other interventions as needed.

These functions may be done by the same counsellor or by different counsellors, depending on their skills, agency mandate and setting. In some agencies or systems, a clinical case manager would carry out many of these functions. Before discussing these functions in more detail, it is helpful to outline some overall principles of treatment.

CASE MANAGEMENT PRINCIPLES: A SYSTEM OF CARE

Over the last 20-plus years, many jurisdictions in Canada have made significant changes in their overall approach to services for clients with substance use problems. The process for getting access to services has become more standardized, with consistent use of specific screening and assessment tools/instruments, implementation of system-wide placement criteria and the recognition that people are clients of the treatment system and not of individual service providers or agencies. (Ontario Substance Abuse Bureau, 1999a; Ontario Ministry of Health, 1999).

The treatment philosophy that underlies assessment and treatment planning is that of a "system of care." In this system, services are integrated and co-ordinated, demonstrate an effective use of resources, eliminate duplication and address shortfalls and gaps.

This system has six principles:

• client-centred service
• the use of best practices
• least intrusive intervention
• individualized assessments
• a stepped approach to care
• integrated treatment.

CLIENT-CENTRED SERVICE

Service delivery that is client-centred challenges counsellors to develop individualized treatment plans that respond to client-identified needs and not to the need of the program to "have" clients. Success is measured by how well a client meets her or his individual goals and how well the plan of care is implemented. Standardized tools/ instruments, repeated at different stages, may be used to measure individual progress.

BEST PRACTICES

"Best practices" are those that are derived from research studies and/or the consensus of expert opinion. Service delivery should reflect best practices in all stages of care, including giving the client a choice of goals, from harm reduction to abstinence (see Chapter 11.

LEAST INTRUSIVE INTERVENTION

"Least intrusive intervention" is the process by which a counsellor uses standardized methods to gather information about clients to help them choose a treatment path that will allow them to meet their treatment goals with the least interruption to their lives. Information gathered at assessment should follow each client across the system, to reduce repetitive information-gathering by each new service provider.

INDIVIDUALIZED ASSESSMENTS

Even though assessment instruments may be standardized, individualized assessments ensure that each assessment captures a client's personal experience and unique circumstances. The assessor takes the time to evaluate change and information accumulated from previous assessments.

A STEPPED APPROACH TO CARE

A "stepped approach" to care provides the least intrusive and least intensive type of treatment that the client requires. In a stepped approach to care, clients move, when ready, through various levels of service, as appropriate. A reassessment with the same standardized instruments can be used to measure a client's progress and correctly identify whether he or she is ready for a less intensive level of service or, alternatively, needs a higher intensity of service to reach his or her treatment goals. A stepped approach means that the treatment plan must be flexible enough to incorporate change if it is needed.

INTEGRATED TREATMENT

Many clients have multiple problems; an integrated treatment plan may need collaboration from a variety of service settings, such as mental health agencies, social services or legal services. If the assessment, or a reassessment, indicates that the client needs a multidisciplinary approach to achieve his or her treatment goals, such an approach is referred to as "integrated treatment." Integrated treatment, which includes co-ordinated service delivery with the allied sectors, is consistent with best practices for some groups, particularly older adults, youth, women and people with co-occurring mental health and substance use disorders.

CASE MANAGEMENT SKILLS AND FUNCTIONS

Though they may not always be carried out by the same person and/or by a designated case manager, the functions of case management are: screening, assessment, treatment planning, linking, advocacy and monitoring. Case managers (which includes anyone performing these functions) need the following skills:

• They need fundamental counselling skills that allow them to listen to clients and build empathic rapport.

• They also need a good working knowledge of the range of services that could most efficiently address the client's needs.

• Because case managers spend considerable time and effort linking with other agencies, they need credibility with these other agencies, as well as the ability to negotiate and communicate with staff of other agencies in a positive and productive way.

• Finally, they need excellent problem-solving skills to identify problems and make efficient use of the system.

Although the functions that are part of clinical case management are described here separately and in sequence, circumstances rarely allow for these functions to be carried out in a simple, orderly way. Following a positive screening result, the process, in theory, begins with an assessment, followed by treatment planning and referral. However, the client's needs affect the order and the type of functions provided. For example, a client who wants help in withdrawing from substances after being put out of the house by his or her spouse might be given an immediate referral to a withdrawal management centre and a legal clinic. In this example, two referrals would have been made to help the client stabilize before an assessment was completed. Thus, the case-management process must be flexible in addressing functions, so clients can be linked to appropriate services at the appropriate time.

Space does not permit discussion of all issues that affect delivery of case management, such as training and education for case managers, the use of professionals versus paraprofessionals to deliver case management, and the role of case managers as change agents in the treatment system. These issues have been discussed in detail elsewhere (Graham & Birchmore Timney, 1990; Willenbring et al., 1991; Substance Abuse and Mental Health Services Administration, 1998).

Screening

Counsellors in human service settings often have concerns that a client's substance use contributes to problems in other life areas or may present a health issue in the client's current situation—for example, a client who is pregnant or who is employed in a safety-sensitive job. Asking some standard questions about use of alcohol and other drugs, or using a brief standardized screening instrument, can help the counsellor and the client identify if alcohol or other drug use is indeed a problem that

needs further assessment and intervention. Routinely screening clients for alcohol and other drug use problems may be particularly important for those groups known to be at particular risk, such as:
• clients with mental health problems
• clients who are victims of violence
• clients involved with the criminal justice system.
A recent Health Canada publication, *Best Practices: Concurrent Mental Health and Substance Use Disorders* (Health Canada, 2001), includes a useful discussion of various levels of screening.

Though screening is generally done by practitioners or services outside the addiction system, it may also be performed by addiction services to screen clients who may be more appropriately referred to other types of specialized services.

The screening process can be conducted in a group format or as part of an individual interview. Screening in a group format allows agencies to manage their waiting lists and offer clients quicker access to initial contact. The screening group can also offer information about assessment and addiction treatment.

STANDARDIZED SCREENING INSTRUMENTS
Commonly used screening instruments include:
• the Michigan Alcoholism Screening Test (MAST)
• the Drug Abuse Screening Test (DAST)
• the Alcohol Dependence Scale (ADS)
• the Alcohol Use Disorders Identification Test (AUDIT)
• the CAGE (the acronym is taken from the key words in the questionnaire—Cut Down, Annoyed, Guilty and Eye-Opener)
• the TWEAK (Tolerance, Worry, Eye-Opener, Amnesia, Cut Down).

When using a standardized screening instrument, counsellors must ensure that the instrument is valid and reliable and has appropriate norms for the client's population group. Some screening instruments may also be used during the assessment process. A recent review by Dawe et al. (2002), and a National Institute of Alcohol and Alcohol Abuse publication, *Alcohol Alert* (NIAAA, 2002), contain more information on screening instruments.

Assessment

Assessment identifies and defines a client's major strengths and needs. Its goal is to get the information necessary to refer a client to the appropriate addiction treatment setting. However, assessment information is also needed to link clients to non-addiction services. Without an accurate assessment, activities could be misdirected and waste both the client's and the counsellor's time and potentially hinder the client's progress.

CLIENT/PATIENT PLACEMENT CRITERIA

Some jurisdictions in Canada and the United States use standardized client or patient placement criteria to assess clients on various dimensions; this allows them to determine "the level and type of service that best suits their current need" (Cross & Sibley-Bowers, 2001, p. 10). The American Society of Addiction Medicine (ASAM) patient placement criteria, now in their second version, are probably the best-known placement criteria in North America (ASAM, 2001).

With system-wide placement criteria, the client is more likely to be appropriately matched to the required level and intensity of service; the result can be greater consistency and accountability, and improved service delivery. Using system-wide criteria can result in easier access, better matches, greater client retention in treatment and the ability to address the current needs of the client. The use of criteria also contributes to improved client outcomes.

In the jurisdiction of Ontario, Canada, all substance use treatment services funded by the Ontario Ministry of Health and Long-Term Care must use standardized admission and discharge criteria, which are linked to a set of standardized assessment instruments. These placement criteria are based on assessing seven areas of client strengths and needs:
• acute intoxication and withdrawal needs
• medical/psychiatric needs
• emotional/behavioural needs
• treatment readiness
• relapse potential
• recovery environment/supports
• barriers and resources (Ontario Ministry of Health, Ontario Substance Abuse Bureau, 2000).

Acute Intoxication and Withdrawal Needs

Acute intoxication and withdrawal needs, as the name implies, refers to assessing whether the client needs withdrawal management services and, if so, the level of this service that is needed. Assessment in this area must determine if the client is stable enough to be supervised in a non-medical withdrawal management service or if the client has acute or potential medical complications that need hospital or other medical care.

Medical/Psychiatric Needs

Assessment should determine if the client has any acute or chronic medical or psychiatric problems that would interfere with his or her ability to participate in addiction treatment. Clients may need to have these problems stabilized and medications reviewed or prescribed before they engage in treatment.

Emotional/Behavioural Needs

Assessing for emotional/behavioural needs determines the client's level of skills and functioning in daily living. It asks whether the client has any problems in activities such as getting up on time in the morning, attending appointments, making meals or maintaining cleanliness. Clients who need support with daily living may need a period of stabilization and/or residential services.

Treatment Readiness

Assessing treatment readiness uses the stages of change model, developed by Prochaska, Norcross and DiClemente. The degree to which the client is ready to make changes will determine the level and intensity of service to which she or he could be referred. For example, a client in the pre-contemplative stage could receive motivational counselling at a community program before considering residential treatment (Prochaska et al., 1994).

Relapse Potential

Relapse potential refers to assessing the likelihood that the client will relapse and assessing the level of treatment support needed to maintain his or her treatment goals (i.e., abstinence or reduced use). For example, a client who is assessed as unlikely to maintain his or her treatment goals without a high level of support may need day treatment or residential treatment, while another client who has been able to maintain abstinence in the past and has good social support may do well with only weekly community treatment.

Recovery Environment/Supports

Another criterion, recovery environment/supports, assesses the client's level of support and safety. For example, a client who lives in a drug-using environment, without friends or family who can support the client's involvement in treatment, may need more intensive or residential treatment.

Barriers and Resources

The final criteria addresses the barriers that prevent a client from participating in treatment, such as lack of transportation, lack of money, or responsibilities such as children or work, and the resources he or she may have or need to have to overcome these barriers. Clients in crisis may need support or resources before they enter treatment or during treatment.

ASSESSMENT INSTRUMENTS

As well as standardized admission and discharge criteria, some jurisdictions, such as Ontario, have also mandated the use of a standardized package of assessment instruments or tools. The use of standardized assessment instruments by all the agencies in a given system provides consistent, credible information and efficient service. There is less duplication, better communication and increased accuracy of information collected. The information is collected to determine the appropriate individualized treatment plan and referral.

With assessment instruments, using a variety of shorter instruments to measure different factors has benefits over using a single, long multidimensional instrument. Using a number of shorter instruments:
• provides better integrity and validity of the data gathered
• allows variation with clients
• generates better outcome measures
• helps to develop policies and best practices.
Another benefit of shorter instruments is that with longer instruments, sections are often left out, compromising the data.

Service providers may be concerned that standardized instruments affect the dynamics of the interview and lose the benefits of the assessor's observations. However, this is not the case. In fact, clients appreciate receiving feedback from assessment instruments that can provide comparisons with standard population scores.

The selection of assessment instruments should go beyond collecting information about alcohol and other drug use. They should also:
• collect information about other life areas
• have psychometric properties (research has been conducted with the instrument, and measures of reliability and validity can be reported for the instrument)
• have clinical relevance (the information collected is useful during treatment for the client and counsellor)
• be appropriate for data collection (Ontario Substance Abuse Bureau, 1999b).

When placement criteria (such as the seven areas of client strengths and needs described earlier) are used, the assessment instruments need to be selected for their ability to measure the dimensions of client functioning relevant to these criteria (Cross & Sibley-Bowers, 2001). Placement criteria provide guidelines to match the client to treatment. These guidelines, along with the client-counsellor interview, results from assessment instruments, and previous treatment experience, combine to give the counsellor a clear information base on which to develop an individual treatment plan.

THE ASSESSMENT PROCESS

Clients arrive at addiction agencies via different pathways. They may be self-referred or referred by their work, the legal system, a family agency, their doctor or some other source. They may be coming to addiction treatment voluntarily or because they are mandated to attend treatment. They come with different life problems and may already be involved with other agencies, have a range of external pressures and supports and have different levels of ambivalence, anxiety and fear (Graham et al., 1995b).

Assessment Methods

Different methods can be used to conduct an assessment. Most current methods include use of a structured but flexible interview format together with standardized assessment instruments. The structured format guarantees that the assessor can both respond to the client's immediate needs and collect all the basic information required to develop a treatment plan. Using only a structured interview guide, without using standardized instruments, does not provide the more objective measures for outcome data, client progress and reference to a population group.

The agency and its staffing structure will determine which person conducts the assessment. In some cases, the person who did the screening may also conduct the assessment. Or, if screening suggests the client has a problem, she or he may be referred to a specialized addiction service for the assessment. In some cases, part of the assessment may be conducted in a group format. The assessment may also require more than one appointment. All information about assessment and its process must be relayed to the client.

When assessment is seen as a process and the beginning of treatment, it then becomes a clinical opportunity to engage the client and to help him or her move toward change (Cross & Sibley-Bowers, 2001).

Initial versus Ongoing Assessment

Initial assessment and ongoing assessment can have different purposes. Initial assessment has been defined as "a process involving mutual investigation or exploration that provides the clinician with detailed information for the purpose of determining with the client, specific needs, goals, characteristics, problems" (Ontario Substance Abuse Bureau, 1999b, Chapter 2). Ongoing assessment gives the client a measure of changes that have happened and determines if the treatment plan needs to be modified.

Beginning the Assessment

The assessment process begins informally when the client and assessor first meet. The formal part of the process begins with the assessor explaining to the client:
• the functions and procedures of assessment
• that the assessment offers the client helpful information for treatment planning, including information about the treatment system
• how long the assessment process usually takes
• that at any time the client may choose not to continue
• the limits to confidentiality (e.g., court subpoenas, medical emergencies, child abuse) and information about consent forms
• any costs associated with the service.

The client also needs to know how, and what kind of, information will be collected, such as information about:
• alcohol and other drug use (including use of prescribed medications)

• functioning in life areas (such as accommodation, marital/family relations, social relations, friends, leisure, education/employment, emotional and physical health, finances)

• previous treatment history (including mental health treatment).

The extent to which these areas are examined will vary with every client; those who have more problems usually need a more extended assessment. The assessor should give the client examples of assessment questions so that he or she can decide whether to participate. The counsellor may need to be aware of different cultural interpretations. See Chapter 19 for more information about cultural diversity as it relates to addiction issues and immigration.

Many clients will decide to proceed with the assessment. However, some clients might need first to explore their fears and expectations about their substance use, particularly their fears about treatment, before they proceed with the assessment. Others may need referrals to other services to stabilize their lives and to start developing a support network before the assessment begins.

Client Sensitivities

Because the assessment process is an important opportunity to engage the client in treatment, the assessor must be attuned to sensitive areas and begin the assessment at a point that is comfortable for the client. For example, female clients, particularly older women, may be sensitive to the stigma associated with heavy drinking and other drug use by women. In such cases, the assessor should begin with questions about less-sensitive life areas; questions related to alcohol and other drug use can be addressed later. Youth, however, may be sensitive about family issues, and the assessor should establish rapport before addressing this area. When considering different sensitivities, the assessor must use a flexible approach, while also collecting the information needed to develop a treatment plan.

Including Family Members

As a support to the client, the assessor may also meet with family members to explain the assessment process and to give them information on how to support the client. It may be appropriate for troubled family members to become clients themselves. In such instances, the family members would independently receive an assessment and case management. When assessing family members, the assessor should fully explore each family member's drug use as well as other problem areas and coping methods.

BENEFITS OF ASSESSMENT

The assessment process allows the client and counsellor to clarify any areas of ambivalence and reduce anxiety and fears. A key function of the assessor is to continually assess the client's readiness for change and offer motivational feedback to encourage the client to set appropriate goals for his or her stage of change.

For many people who have substance use problems, the assessment process is their first opportunity to gain objective feedback and insight about the issues in their lives. Although the main goal of assessment is to refer clients to addiction treatment, some clients will refuse such treatment. They may, however, accept referrals to non-addiction agencies to resolve life problems that have led to, or resulted from, problematic substance use. In some cases, assessment may be the only intervention clients need.

Research has also shown that the assessment process involves more than just matching a client to an appropriate treatment setting (Graham et al., 1995a). To conduct the assessment in a way that is most useful to the client, the assessor should not only collect information about the client's strengths and problem areas, but should also clearly reflect this information back to the client. For example, a client who is feeling devastated because of a drinking and driving offence may be better able to put things into perspective if the counsellor points out the client's strengths and affirms positive accomplishments in other areas, such as having a good employment record or positive family relationships.

Assessment offers clients a chance to learn about the association between their life problems and substance use. For example, sleep disturbances, digestive problems or other physical problems can be linked to substance use. Making these links can reassure clients that they can improve their life situation—they can see their problems with some perspective, which gives them a sense that the problems can be managed. This education not only offers hope, which helps to motivate the client, but it also gives a more objective evaluation of problems and a clear direction for addressing them.

In conclusion, clients who present for assessment have a range of substance-related problems and different attitudes about disclosing problems in various life areas. The assessor needs to know the concerns that are typical of specific groups—including older adults, youth, women, men, family members, members of the Aboriginal community and people with concurrent disorders—to be alert to areas of the assessment that are likely to be problematic, and ensure that the process meets the needs of each client.

Treatment Planning

The treatment planning process helps the client select the appropriate level and intensity of treatment (Ontario Ministry of Health, 2000). When planning treatment, the counsellor can consider the client's preferences and the services available. Although it may change over time, the plan provides a focus for ongoing support by a counsellor or case manager.

Treatment planning comprises two main functions:
• negotiating (between client and assessor) specific interventions to address identified problem areas
• developing a manageable plan.

When negotiating, the clinician must be able to hear what the client wants, is capable of undertaking and agrees to implement. Consequently, like every client, every treatment plan is unique. The client must agree to all aspects of the plan. For example, in a case where the most appropriate service is available in a large urban area, a client from an isolated rural area might find this option frightening and unacceptable.

Within the context of case management, treatment planning does not refer to a clinical treatment plan, which has short-term goals and fits within a particular treatment program or format, such as cognitive behavioural therapy or dialectical behavioural therapy.

Treatment planning involves the following four stages:
• prioritizing problem areas and exploring options with the client
• matching services to the client's specific needs
• identifying potential barriers to using particular services
• preparing the client for treatment.
Treatment planning can be completed in one session or could take several sessions, depending on the client's situation.

PRIORITIZING PROBLEM AREAS AND EXPLORING OPTIONS

The first step in treatment planning is to prioritize the identified problems. This is done by comparing the assessor's and the client's perceptions of the severity of the client's problems and the client's strengths.

Sometimes both parties have similar perceptions of problems and priorities. At other times, discrepancies need to be discussed and negotiated before developing an appropriate and acceptable treatment plan. For example, the assessor and client may have different perceptions of the extent to which alcohol or other drugs are causing problems in the client's life. In this situation, the assessor must determine whether the client is ready to set goals for substance use. If not, the assessor may need to use motivational counselling techniques to help the client set goals.

Each agreed-upon problem area needs to be defined in active terms with clear goals. For example, if the client is having marital problems, the goal could be to improve marital communication. Treatment planning would then focus on specific actions to reach this goal.

MATCHING SERVICES TO THE CLIENT'S SPECIFIC NEEDS

Once problems and goals have been prioritized, the client and assessor begin discussing options for addressing problem areas. The plan must clearly identify the responsibilities of both the client and the counsellor. Each activity must have a clearly defined time frame. For example, if a client decides to seek marital counselling, then a date should be set for the client to have made an appointment with a marital therapist.

At the heart of treatment planning is the concept of matching, which involves selecting treatments or alternatives that:
• are most suited to the client's needs
• will be most likely to result in a positive outcome
• are based on placement criteria.

No single treatment is suitable or effective for all persons with alcohol or other drug problems. Ideally, the specialized addiction treatment system has a selection of referral options, ranging from least intensive to most intensive. Most intensive could be, for example, a hospital-based residential program, and least intensive could be, for example, a community-based program a client may attend once a week or less often. Some clients benefit from mutual aid groups such as Alcoholics Anonymous, while others do not.

Matching is a complex process, because many variables must be considered, including the client's preferences. In fact, client preference is a key factor that determines whether the client will follow through with the plan. However, treatment options also depend on the services available, and the appropriate level and intensity of treatment for the client, based on assessment information and application of placement criteria.

The American Institute of Medicine (1990) concluded that treatment outcomes could be improved significantly by matching on the following variables:
• demographic factors
• psychiatric diagnoses
• personality factors
• severity of alcohol problems
• antecedents to drinking.

All other things being equal, clients with more severe substance use problems (and higher relapse potential) need treatment that is more intensive. For example, clients with moderate levels of dependence may benefit from community-based treatment, while those with severe dependence may require day treatment or a residential program. Some clients, especially those at an early stage of problem substance use, may not need an addiction-specific treatment; the process of clarifying problems through assessment and the support of the assessor/case manager may be enough intervention to resolve the problem.

Matching is also a consideration when referring clients to non-addiction agencies. These referrals must ensure that the client fits with other clients of the agency and the styles of the service providers. The assessor must have detailed knowledge about the other treatment services and community agencies. Assessors should share information about the accessibility of referral agencies, any improvement or deterioration in service, and changes in the existing resources or staff at these agencies.

IDENTIFYING POTENTIAL BARRIERS

The treatment plan must also identify any barriers to implementing the plan. Barriers can include:
• a lack of transportation, money or child care, which could prevent a client from attending certain treatment programs
• the client's beliefs about addiction (e.g., you can't have a drinking problem if you only drink sherry)

• the client's attitudes toward accepting counselling (e.g., men should be able to deal with their own problems)
• the risk that entering treatment may mean giving up a job or an apartment
• for sole-support parents, the risk of losing their children.

Other barriers can originate from the services themselves:

• Non-addiction service providers may have a negative attitude toward people with substance use problems.
• The philosophy and mandate of agencies can be barriers to those with substance use problems; for example, some agencies will not provide services unless the client is willing to make a commitment to abstinence.

In directing clients to agencies, the assessor must know more about the agency than just the nature of services offered. The assessor also needs to know how the client is likely to experience the agency and its services.

All risks and barriers need to be identified, and both the costs and the benefits of potential treatment options considered.

PREPARING THE CLIENT FOR TREATMENT

The final stage of negotiating the treatment plan is to prepare the client for treatment. At this stage:

• The assessor can give the client information and support in maintaining abstinence or reduced use before treatment begins.
• The client can express his or her fears about treatment.
• The assessor can give the client information about what will happen in therapy.

Information about what to expect from therapy is especially helpful for clients who are entering residential treatment. They will need specific information about visiting hours, weekend leaves, contact with family, program guidelines and suggestions about the types of things to take (e.g., postage stamps, writing paper, money).

If the assessor makes an appointment to see the client after treatment begins, it will help reassure the client about the continuity of care.

Linking

Linking is the process of referring or transferring clients to services in the formal and informal caregiving systems. The steps involved in each referral will be determined by the client's need for support and his or her capabilities and resources. For example, for a client who has a strong support system and the knowledge and skills to access resources directly, linking may be as simple as giving the client the name, telephone number and address of an agency. However, for a client in distress, who lives in temporary housing and has limited literacy skills, the assessor/case manager may need to telephone the referral destination directly and arrange transportation for the client.

The referral process is also affected by the characteristics of the referral agency. For example, the assessor needs to know which route (telephone call, letter, referral form) will gain access for the client.

An important counsellor skill is the ability to communicate effectively with referral agencies to ensure successful access for the client. This means being familiar with the information requirements of each referral agency and providing the appropriate client information, especially regarding any sensitivities (e.g., a woman experiencing the social stigma associated with alcohol problems). This process helps to ensure a good match between the client and the service provider.

Following referral or linking to treatment, it is helpful to identify someone as the case manager, if one has not already been identified. The case manager is able to follow the client and the client's plan, to provide advocacy and to monitor the client's progress. The case manager may be the assessor, an addiction counsellor, a mental health counsellor, a probation officer or another provider significant to the client.

Advocacy

Advocacy involves interceding on behalf of a person to help get access to needed resources and support. The counsellor/case manager may need to advocate for a client with treatment agencies and with non-treatment persons, such as family members or employers.

In one study of case management, about half of the assessor/case manager's contacts were with people other than clients (Graham et al., 1995a). Contacts with other agencies happened most often during the assessment phase, while client and family contacts were more common throughout the entire case management process.

Co-ordination, a function that is closely associated with advocacy, brings together support and services to enhance the client's treatment plan. Simply put, when advocating for a client, the assessor/case manager is getting something (a direct service, practical help, information or support) that directly benefits the client. When co-ordinating for a client, the assessor/case manager is doing something (sharing information, negotiating agency roles) that indirectly benefits the client.

Monitoring

Monitoring is the ongoing process of evaluating the treatment plan, adjusting goals/referrals and then taking action as requested or required. It provides the continuity of care that is particularly important if the treatment plan breaks down.

TREATMENT/CLIENT MONITORING
Monitoring helps the client to focus on achieving his or her goals; the treatment plan should be central to this process. That is, the counsellor/case manager must focus on systematic plans for change, rather than on general aspects of the client's life. With the treatment plan as the central core for discussion, the client can remain on track, and there is less risk of discouragement. With the client's permission, feedback concerning progress can also be obtained from other service providers.

Monitoring the treatment and the client can include the following activities:

• Information is collected, which may be used to revise the treatment plan.

• Ongoing assessment helps to determine if the client needs to change his or her current level or intensity of service.

• The counsellor/case manager needs to continually revise the plan with the client— based on new information, as problems arise or as goals are reached (as reported by the client or identified in the latest administration of standardized tools).

• The client and counsellor/case manager monitor the client's use of substances and identify situations in which he or she is at high risk of relapse.

• In the event of a reported or confirmed relapse, the counsellor/case manager may provide relapse prevention counselling, if needed, or refer the client as appropriate.

• The counsellor/case manager encourages the client to keep a realistic perspective and reminds the client of the progress that she or he has made.

• As per release of information documentation, the counsellor/case manager can also enhance the client's support network by telling family members, friends or employers about the client's plan and need for support as appropriate.

• The counsellor/case manager checks whether the client has followed through on referrals and whether the services were appropriate.

• Crises may occur at any time during this monitoring phase. These may include medical emergencies, suicide attempts, drug overdoses, emotional crises, housing needs or financial crises. Monitoring helps to ensure that the counsellor/case manager has up-to-date and accurate information to help the client get the necessary services as soon as possible to prevent serious disruption of the recovery process.

Client monitoring can be done both informally and formally.

Informal Monitoring

Informally, monitoring occurs during every contact with the client. The counsellor/ case manager initially observes the client's condition and notes whether he or she appears healthy, sober, anxious and so on. Every contact with the client should usually include some general monitoring questions (e.g., "How are you? How have things been going?") and more specific questions relating to general problem areas (e.g., "Have things improved with your partner?"). The counsellor/case manager usually follows up on areas where particular actions were planned since the last contact (e.g., "You were planning to attend this or that program since I last saw you. Were you successful with your strategies for avoiding alcohol?").

Formal Monitoring

When the counsellor/case manager or client wants a more objective or quantitative assessment in a life area, more standardized approaches to monitoring can provide a formal case evaluation.

Using the same standardized assessment instruments throughout case management can provide consistent measures of the client's progress and changes. These measures are useful when revising the treatment plan and planning for discharge, as they offer a comparison with the client's status at the initial assessment. When used as part of follow-up, they can help measure the success of case management for that client and give the case manager feedback on long-term outcomes.

INTRODUCING CLOSURE

As part of monitoring, it is appropriate to introduce and maintain, early in treatment, the idea of the eventual ending, or closure, of counselling or case management. It is a good idea to have a contract for the client-counsellor contacts, listing the steps in a phased process of closure. For example, clients may see the counsellor/case manager once a week for four weeks. Then, the subsequent visits could be once a month for three months, with an agreement to make a telephone call once a month for the following three months. Clients can be left with the information that if they need further help in the future, they can contact the counsellor/case manager. For some clients who are living with co-occurring substance use problems and serious mental illness, it may never be appropriate to end the relationship.

CONCLUSION

Case management is a complex process—through screening, assessment, treatment planning and monitoring—that gives clients structured support to address their problems, in a manner that is helpful and timely. While there are standard functions to guide the assessor/case manager, the process is different for every client, because each person is unique.

Case management will be successful if the assessor/counsellor is able to establish good rapport, has knowledge about substance use problems, understands the treatment network, uses current tools or instruments based on best practices and has genuine concern about the client.

REFERENCES

American Society of Addiction Medicine. (2001). *Patient Placement Criteria 2R.* Washington, DC: author. Available: www.asam.org/ppc/ppc2.htm.

Cross, S. & Sibley-Bowers, L. (2001). *The Standardized Tools and Criteria Manual: Helping Clients Navigate the Addiction Treatment in Ontario.* Toronto: Centre for Addiction and Mental Health.

Dawe, S., Natalie, J.L., Hides, L., Kavanagh, D.J. & Mattick, R.P. (2002). *Review of Diagnostic Screening Instruments for Alcohol and Other Drug Use and Other Psychiatric Disorders* (2nd ed.). Monograph #48. Canberra: Commonwealth Department of Health and Aging. Available: www.health.gov.au/pubhlth/publicat/document/mono48.pdf.

Graham, K. & Birchmore Timney, C. (1989). The problem of replicability in program evaluation: The component solution using the example of case management. *Education and Program Planning, 12*(2), 179–187.

Graham, K., Birchmore, C., Bois, C. & Wedgerfield, K. (1995a). Continuity of care in addictions treatment: The role of advocacy and co-ordination in case management. *American Journal of Drug and Alcohol Abuse, 21*, 433–451.

Graham, K., Brett, P. & Bois, C. (1995b). Treatment entry and engagement: A study of process at assessment/referral centres. *Contemporary Drug Problems, 22*, 61–104.

Health Canada. (2001). *Best Practices: Concurrent Mental Health and Substance Use Disorders,* Cat. No. H39-599-2001E. Ottawa: Minister of Public Works and Government Services Canada.

Institute of Medicine. (1990). *Broadening the Base of Treatment for Alcohol Problems.* Washington, DC: National Academy Press.

National Institute on Alcohol Abuse and Alcoholism (NIAAA). (2002). Screening for alcohol problems: An update. *Alcohol Alert, 56* [On-line]. Available: www.niaaa.nih.gov/publications/aa56.htm.

Ontario Ministry of Health. (1999). *Making It Happen: Operational Framework for the Delivery of Mental Health Services and Supports.* Toronto: Queen's Printer for Ontario.

Ontario Substance Abuse Bureau. (1999a). *Setting the Course: A Framework for Integrating Addiction Treatment Services in Ontario.* Toronto: author.

Ontario Substance Abuse Bureau. (1999b). *Assessment Tools for Ontario Addiction Agencies.* Toronto: author.

Ontario Substance Abuse Bureau. (2000). *Admission and Discharge Criteria.* Toronto: author.

Prochaska, J., Norcross, J. & DiClemente, C. (1994). *Changing for Good: A Revolutionary Six-Stage Program for Overcoming Bad Habits and Moving Your Life Positively Forward.* New York: Avon Books.

Diagnostic interviewing. In M. Hersen & S.M. Turner (Eds.), *Diagnostic Interviewing* (2nd ed.). New York: Plenum Press.

Substance Abuse and Mental Health Services Administration. (1998). *Comprehensive Case Management for Substance Abuse Treatment.* Treatment Improvement Protocol Series # 27, U.S. Department of Health and Human Services Substance Abuse and Mental Health Services Administration. Rockville, MD: Centre for Substance Abuse Treatment .

Welsh, Dianne M. (Ed.). (1991). *Alcohol Health and Research World, 15*(3).

Willenbring, M.L., Ridgely, M.S., Stinchfield, R. & Rose, M. (1991). *Application of Case Management in Alcohol and Drug Dependence: Matching Techniques and Populations.* Rockville, MD: U.S. Department of Health and Human Services.

Chapter 3: Appendix
Drug Testing

SHEILA LACROIX

Very little has been written about drug testing that addresses the information needs of drug and alcohol counsellors and other health and social service professionals. One exception is a recent guide published by the Centre for Addiction and Mental Health entitled *Methadone Maintenance: A Counsellor's Guide to Treatment* (Martin et al., 2003).

Drug testing is one of many useful clinical tools used for both diagnostic and therapeutic purposes. However, "drug testing" has also become an issue, as a result of its oversimplification in the public realm and the emphasis on its use for surveillance. The counsellor must not only be familiar with drug testing as a diagnostic tool, but must also be prepared to field general questions about drug testing, from clients and community callers, including concerned parents, schools and people applying for jobs.

SPECIMEN TYPES

Biological specimens that can be tested for the presence of drugs include blood serum, urine, breath, saliva and hair.
• Urine is the most common and preferred specimen collected for routine drug use screening in the outpatient setting. The window for drug detection is longer in urine than in blood serum and the collection procedure is less physically invasive.
• Serum testing is more likely done in the emergency room setting.
• Hair analysis is not considered a standard, routine test. However, it is often ordered in legal cases and used in specialized clinics, such as the Motherisk Program at the Hospital for Sick Children in Toronto, Ontario, that monitor mothers and neonates of high-risk pregnancies.
• Breathalyzers to measure alcohol impairment are used in some outpatient treatment settings, primarily for patient safety. For example, some Ontario methadone clinics use the Breathalyzer if they suspect a client is intoxicated, as an oral methadone dose should not be given to an intoxicated person.

Urine drug screening will be the primary focus of this appendix.

WHY DRUG TESTING?

Urine drug testing is used in the clinical setting for many reasons. Some might question its use in programs that follow a harm reduction as opposed to an abstinence-based approach, but harm reduction and drug testing are not mutually exclusive. Overall, drug testing supplements other assessment measures, such as self-reporting, to:
• confirm drug use or misuse
• track treatment compliance
• help with ongoing treatment planning.
Overall, it can be a useful tool in a treatment process that fosters and maintains trust, good counselling skills and open communication in therapy.

TESTING TO AVOID DRUG INTERACTIONS
Drug testing is very important for client safety in programs involving pharmaco-therapy, such as methadone maintenance treatment or pain management programs for people who are opioid-dependent, to avoid serious drug interactions and dosage problems.

TESTING AS PART OF CLIENT CONTRACTS
Drug testing is also useful in negotiating contracts with patients and maintaining boundaries. For example, as a client in methadone maintenance treatment stabilizes, random testing is done less frequently after a period of negative urine test results, and the client may be awarded privileges such as take-home doses.

THIRD-PARTY PROOF
Drug testing can be a powerful tool for a client to use to prove abstinence to a third party such as an employer, a union or the courts.

MANDATED TESTING
The courts may mandate testing in cases such as drug court treatment programs or child protection cases managed by a child protection agency. In the latter case, once again, safety is the primary issue. For methadone maintenance therapy and other opioid replacement therapies, drug testing is generally mandated by the regulating body, which varies from province to province in Canada. For example, in Ontario, the College of Physician and Surgeons of Ontario (CPSO) both licenses physicians to prescribe methadone and establishes and administers the guidelines.

DETECTION PERIODS

Many publications (Brands & Brands, 1998; Kapur, 1993) include tables of urine-detection periods of commonly used drugs; counsellors may want to keep such a table on hand as a quick reference.

Some tables also include the drug half-life, which is the length of time required for the drug level to fall by 50 per cent. It takes approximately six half-lives to eliminate 99 per cent of a drug. As a general rule, the detection time of most drugs in urine is one to three days. Exceptions include long-acting benzodiazepines such as diazepam, which has a long half-life and may take weeks to eliminate in cases of chronic use. Another exception is marijuana—its active ingredient, tetrahydro-cannabinol (THC), is highly fat-soluble and slowly eliminated from body tissues over a period of a few days to several weeks.

If counsellors do give information to a client, a member of the public or a colleague, they should be sure to indicate that they are providing information from a table, name the source, and clearly indicate that it is an estimate only. They must communicate that detection times differ according to the person's health status, age, gender, use of medications and other factors.

URINE TESTING METHODS

The most common urine testing methods are immunoassay and chromatography. Knowing the testing method, including the limitations and strengths of the method, is crucial to making sense out of drug test results.

IMMUNOASSAY

Immunoassay techniques have the advantage of being fast, extremely sensitive to a class of drugs and relatively inexpensive. They test for a specific class of drugs, so are not appropriate to differentiate drugs with a similar chemical structure. Depending on the manufacturer, immunoassays may vary on the level of sensitivity to specific drugs in a class. Only one drug class can be measured at a time.

CHROMATOGRAPHY

Chromatography techniques are less sensitive but more specific; they are able, for example, to provide results for specific opioids. They enable a better overview of the range of a person's drug intake. These techniques are more expensive, and their results are more likely to be used as evidence in legal cases.

URINE SAMPLE COLLECTION

It is best to collect urine samples randomly for the most accurate picture of the client's recent substance use, because many drugs clear the system rapidly.

Frequency of drug testing depends on the progress of treatment and the client's stability. Early in treatment, it may be weekly; after a period of negative screens, it may be biweekly or even monthly.

Throughout the collection process, professionalism and respect for the client's privacy should prevail. The collection process should be supervised and monitored to avoid any opportunity for tampering with the sample. Supervision allows for the highest level of confidence in the quality of the sample. There are several ways to avoid tampering:

• Clients can be observed through a two-way mirror or with a video camera.
• In the collection area, bluing of the toilet water and providing no access to running water lessen the risk of tampering through sample dilution.
• Taking the temperature of the urine within four minutes of voiding is another way to validate the collection procedure; the temperature should be within the range of 32.5 and 37.7 degrees Celsius (Kapur, 1993).

Once the sample has been collected in a properly labelled container and sealed in the presence of the client, its transportation to the testing laboratory should be monitored through chain-of-custody documentation.

INTERPRETING TEST RESULTS

Drug testing is a medical diagnostic procedure; results are not necessarily yes/no and should be interpreted by a qualified professional, such as a toxicologist or physician who has some medical knowledge of the client. As already discussed, knowing the type of test is essential to the interpretation. Other variables include the following:

• Elimination of a drug and its metabolites can be affected by use of medications and health conditions, in particular those affecting the functioning of the liver and kidney.
• Age and gender differences need to be considered.
• The time of day of the collection can have an effect, as urine concentration varies throughout the day.

While their professional input may be valuable, it is clearly not the responsibility of most counsellors or social workers to interpret test results. An exception to this may be the case of counsellors working in a setting where drug testing is done routinely and, as a result, there is expertise available for consultation— for example, in a methadone maintenance treatment program or a rehabilitation centre for which urine screening is a program component.

POSITIVE RESULTS

A positive drug test result only indicates that a drug was probably used within the detection period. The test result cannot determine:

• when or how much of the drug was ingested
• the level of impairment
• the extent to which the person is dependent on the drug.

Alcohol is the only drug for which there is a direct measurable link between quantities in breath, blood or urine and level of impairment (Kapur, 1993).

FALSE NEGATIVE

A "false negative" means the result is negative for a drug that is present. Basically, a negative result may mean "not detected" as opposed to "not present." Reasons for a false negative include the following, among others:
• The quantity of the drug used is below the detection limit of the test.
• The type of test can be a factor; the more sensitive immunoassay technique may pick up something that some chromatographic techniques may not.
• Synthetic opioids, such as oxycodone, may not be detected by immunoassay techniques.

FALSE POSITIVE

A "false positive" happens when results show that the drug is present when, in fact, it is not. False positive test results are obtained if the urine sample contains an interfering drug or substance that cross-reacts with the reagents. The interfering substance could be from a source other than illegal or misused prescription drugs, such as:
• asthma or allergy medication
• ingested poppy seeds
• prescribed medications, such as those that contain codeine, which metabolizes to morphine (so both codeine and morphine would be detected).

Sometimes clients will offer excuses for positive results, such as exposure to second-hand cannabis smoke or having eaten hemp food products. It is unlikely, except under extreme conditions, that second-hand exposure to marijuana smoke will result in a positive test. Hemp products available in retail stores do not have enough active THC to result in positive test results (Gourlay et al., 2002).

"BEATING" THE DRUG TEST

Tips on beating drug tests abound through word of mouth and the Internet, and counsellors will undoubtedly see and be asked about some of these. There are two basic ways to beat drug tests:
• adulteration or substitution of the sample during or after collection
• ingesting a substance that will mask the drug or alter the result.

One can control for adulteration or substitution by supervising the sample collection. Most "masking" techniques and substances are ineffective. One masking technique is waterloading—drinking copious amounts of water before voiding in hopes that the drug, if present, will be diluted below the detection limit. Another is drinking vinegar, which basically forces one to drink a lot of water (waterloading). However, "in vivo" dilution, through waterloading or the use of diuretics, can be detected by routinely measuring the concentration of creatinine in the urine, which should be within a normal range. Many laboratories include this measure as part of the protocol.

TESTING OF ADOLESCENTS

Because of media coverage and advertising about drug testing, counsellors will likely receive questions from anxious parents, schools and other groups in the community about drug testing to detect drug use or enforce rules. If adolescents are suspected of using drugs, drug testing is not recommended (American Academy of Child and Adolescent Psychiatry, Committee on Substance Abuse, 1996); trust and open communication are essential, and parents should seek professional help if they have concerns about drug misuse.

In schools, where drug testing is used primarily as a means to enforce zero tolerance for drug use, a recent study (Yamaguchi et al., 2003) found a lack of evidence that drug testing deters drug use among students. The practice of drug testing in Canadian schools appears to be rare to non-existent, and is primarily limited to a few private schools.

SUMMARY

These are just a few basic principles, including some pointers, to help counsellors understand both the value and limitations of drug testing in the clinical setting. Urine drug testing should be viewed as an adjunct procedure in the process of assessment and treatment. It is only one of many measures to assess drug use and monitor behaviour change and the process of recovery.

REFERENCES

American Academy of Child and Adolescent Psychiatry, Committee on Substance Abuse. (1996). Testing for drugs of abuse in children and adolescents. *Pediatrics, 98*(2 Part 1), 305–307.

Brands, B. & Brands, J. (Eds.). (1998). *Methadone Maintenance: A Physician's Guide to Treatment.* Toronto: Addiction Research Foundation.

Gourlay, D., Heit, H.A. & Caplan, Y.H. (2002). *Urine Drug Testing in Primary Care: Dispelling the Myths and Designing Strategies.* San Francisco: California Academy of Family Physicians and PharmaCom Group, Inc.

Kapur, B.M. (1993). Drug-testing methods and clinical interpretations of test results. *Bulletin on Narcotics, 45*(2), 115–154.

Martin, G., Brands, B. & Marsh, D.C. (Eds.). (2003). *Methadone Maintenance: A Counsellor's Guide to Treatment.* Toronto: Centre for Addiction and Mental Health.

Yamaguchi, R., Johnson, L.D. & O'Malley, P.M. (2003). Relationship between student illicit drug use and school drug-testing policies. *Journal of School Health, 73*(4), 159–164.

Chapter 4

Ethical and Professional Issues

WAYNE SKINNER AND JANE PATERSON

INTRODUCTION

Historically, there has not been a unified view of key ethical and professional issues in substance use treatment. This is not surprising given that substance use workers have so many different points of origin, both professionally and in life experience. Some of us have professional clinical training, for instance in social work, nursing or psychology. Some of us have come to the helping role through the process of our own recoveries. Some have little professional training, but are rich in practical experience; some are just the opposite—theoretically strong but not well-grounded in clinical practice. Some of us have specific training in substance use treatment; some rely on general knowledge about human biopsychosocial functioning.

In short, substance use counsellors are a diverse group. Our views about the nature of substance use problems and our practices—our methods of intervention—are varied, and at times conflict with each other. These differences need not be seen as problems to be eliminated, of course; they deserve to be appreciated and celebrated. But in establishing consensus and setting up clear-cut and broadly supported ways of acting and conducting ourselves, we do not face an easy task.

This chapter is not a systematic review of ethical and professional issues. Rather than providing firm answers to key questions, we intend to encourage reflection and promote (and provoke) discussion and dialogue about the ethics of substance use treatment.

ETHICAL BEHAVIOUR IN A CHANGING PROFESSIONAL CLIMATE

People who work in social services and health care, whatever their roles, are becoming increasingly professionalized. More and more, helpers are expected, and even regulated through legislation, to be credentialed, to be members in good standing of regulatory colleges, and to engage in ongoing professional development. And more and more, their professional and personal behaviour is governed by increasingly explicit, precise and refined codes of ethics and conduct. Along with this have come increasing expectations of accountability from the public, from funders and from the agencies that employ caregivers.

At the same time, growth of scientifically validated knowledge has led to more evidence-based practice. This has increased the expectation that professionals know and demonstrate standards of practice in their work, and can explain and justify their work within the context of best practices. In recent years, we have also seen an increase in the growth of litigation against professionals by clients and their families when they have been disappointed or injured by the interventions they have received. This has created pressures on workers to be able to justify and defend their professional practices and conduct to their employers, professional associations, the public, courts of law, and of course to their clients. Consequently, the ethical and legal components of clinical practice for substance use workers have a higher profile than ever before.

WHAT DO WE MEAN BY ETHICS?

Broadly, the domain of ethics explores proper conduct from two types of approaches: rule ethics—in which codified rules determine how one should act—and situation ethics—in which circumstantial and situational factors are weighed against general ethical principles. More specifically, in this chapter, we shall explore health care ethics (which include the ethics of substance use treatment)—in which human values of right and wrong are used to make meaningful moral choices in the delivery of care.

At the heart of ethics and the definition of professional roles is conduct: How do I behave? How *should* I behave? While the field may seem quite bare of unifying standards and guidelines, many regulations and rules do in fact guide and shape the conduct of the helper. As much as helpers need to take counsel with themselves about professional conduct, the shape and boundaries of professional roles and behaviour are also increasingly defined by measures constructed by the community, by professions, by employers and by law. Those who belong to a helping profession with a code of ethics have a framework within which their conduct will be evaluated. Agencies also have policies and procedures that guide the actions of their staff. Additionally, legal statutes and regulations govern confidentiality, the reporting of abuse and neglect, and the duty to act if a client threatens self-harm or threatens others.

TOWARD A CONFLICT MODEL OF ETHICS

Many individuals and groups have an interest in the ethics of today's health care environments. Practitioners must follow ethical and professional guidelines, and are responsible to their colleagues. Organizations must protect their interests and maintain their standards. Communities, in turn, have ideas about how service should be delivered and what models of practice should be emphasized. In addition, consumer and family groups have become more active and now collaborate as partners in program planning and service delivery. Generally speaking, accountability is expected by all concerned. It is not surprising, given the various players, that there will be differing, and sometimes opposing, positions on ethical questions, and that even the most conscientious worker will face dilemmas that are not easily remedied.

It is important, then, to create health care environments, and specifically substance use treatment environments, that allow for issues to be resolved through the expression of divergent opinions. "Ethically healthy" environments:
• are co-constructed by practitioners, clients, the organization, the community and professional bodies
• anticipate and acknowledge conflict among the various players in a given situation
• encourage dialogue and attempt to produce consensus and shared understanding
• empower professionals to become aware of the ethical basis that guides their decision making, to reflect on complex clinical issues and ultimately to grow professionally
• provide workers, clients, organizations, communities and professional bodies with both responsibilities and rights
• allow for conflict in the form of differing positions on important issues, and provide means for their expression and resolution.

Our challenge is to see the diversity of people who work in the substance use field as a fundamental reality and one of its special strengths. Between the volunteer and the trained professional is an array of individuals of varied skills and experience, linked by a shared intention to make a positive difference in the lives of people with substance use problems.

This fertile diversity ensures that beliefs and attitudes on even the most basic questions are not shared by everyone in the field, and are often contested and debated. One may ask, "What is addiction?" only to receive a dizzying barrage of answers, many of which contradict each other. Some call addiction a disease. To some, it is genetically based or a learned behaviour. Others will insist that it is a socially constructed concept. Whatever our own answer, it will guide our understanding of the nature of substance use problems and what should be done about them. Similarly, our notions of the helping role and of what constitutes proper, ethical conduct will be shaped by the beliefs and attitudes we hold about human beings and human behaviour. This includes our own socialization to our respective professions.

So, our first point is that professional conduct and ethical standards are themselves formed (though not totally determined) by what we take to be human nature, by how we view substance use problems and by what we think needs to be done about them. It is easy to see why one may wish for a single set of facts, a single set of procedures, a single set of beliefs and a single point of view on ethical questions. It would help quiet the voices of doubt that might otherwise rise within us or be heard in the questions of others. It would eliminate the struggle we must engage in when, in a particular situation, we have to sort out the right thing to do. Yet as appealing as a unified position might be, it does not reflect the current reality of our diverse field.

Perhaps the most ethical position a counsellor can hold today is one that is open to critical self-reflection and self-evaluation. Such a counsellor is prepared to both assess the intention and measure the effectiveness of what he or she is doing. A helper's intentions are often the very best, but intentions alone are a poor measure of ethical appropriateness. The history of clinical practice shows the harm that can be unwittingly inflicted by the well-intentioned helper. Surgery without respect for the need for aseptic procedures, blood transfusions that contain undetected contaminants, use of medication with side-effects that outweigh potential benefits, the requirement that people be drug-free as a condition for receiving help for substance use problems: these are just a few examples. Many methods that were once the standards of care and treatment would be flagrantly unethical today. What will the practitioners of the future have to say about the substance use interventions that we practise today?

Ethics is not an issue for the practitioner alone. It involves a number of views—some converging, some conflicting—about the right action in particular situations. What, for example, is the most ethical position for a substance use agency or employer to take? As we have stated, agencies have interests to protect and standards to maintain. One illustration is the issue of whom to attempt to offer care to. A highly motivated person wanting to stop drinking would be a far lower-risk client than a person who injects drugs, lives on the street and does not want to stop using drugs. By opening its scope of concern and activity to include more difficult and risky—and therefore more needy—clients, an agency might be pursuing its mission, but might also run afoul of the community, clients' families and perhaps even the police. It is easy to see how ethically driven action collides with other pressures in such scenarios.

Just as importantly, how should ethical expectations be extended to clients, families and the community? Clients are in need, but are they absolved of ethical duties? Families and the community have concerns and demands, but do they have responsibilities and obligations? All these elements help to shape the ethical space in which professional practice takes place.

It is in this broader matrix that we locate our discussion of ethics and the professional role: not only to consider the conduct of the individual practitioner, but also to explore the context in which personal conduct takes place. This approach sees ethics as a more complex dynamic with numerous actors, each with obligations and rights. This model of ethics does not presume that an ethical consensus can be reached easily or automatically. Instead, it allows for conflict, and sees ethics as an ongoing conversation that must stay open to discussion, debate and redefinition.

EMPOWERMENT ETHICS

We advocate an empowerment model of ethics, which involves considering professional ethics within the context of ethical organizations. Such a view takes us beyond the notion that ethics is something imposed on the professional by the duties of his or her profession and the policies of the workplace. Rather, behaviour can be fostered or hindered by the dynamic forces that shape particular professional contexts. An ethical organization respects and contributes to a substance use worker's efforts to tailor ethical principles to particular situations.

Members of formal disciplines with their own codes of ethics and professional values may believe they are exempt from the labours of reflection. But the ethical challenge is not simply to follow general rules; it is to locate in a specific situation what is unique to it and what is universal. This exercise determines when general rules should be applied and when the particular circumstances may be considered exceptional. For example, confidentiality is a guiding principle of professional conduct among counsellors, but there are times when other considerations must be given precedence—where the safety of an individual is at stake, for example. The counsellor also has a legal obligation to report cases of suspected child abuse to the appropriate child protection agency. When orienting clients to the rules of the counselling relationship, counsellors must spell out and define the boundaries and limits to the helping process.

The agency's position can be critical in how such situations are addressed and resolved. A workplace preoccupied with liability and litigation might prioritize the documentary record over the process of trying to work out a difficult situation in a way that satisfies a complex set of duties. For example, in the example above, a counsellor legally must inform child welfare authorities of suspected abuse—but his or her duties do not end there. The counsellor also has an ethical duty to let the client know his or her choices in this situation. For example, clients can be given the option of making the report themselves from the counsellor's office, if appropriate. The ethical considerations here extend beyond what must be done to how to do it. If the counsellor has the organization's support in addressing the complexities of such a situation, rather than feeling a heavy-handed pressure to "get on with it," it is more likely that he or she can effectively employ a more rounded response.

One healthy development in recent years has been a significant change in the view organizations and professions take about the errors that professional and other staff make. Such mistakes are inevitable, even with the most careful efforts to avoid them. There has always been a duty to acknowledge procedural risk and, where it occurs, error. However, the evidence has been that, when staff are punished or stigmatized, they are hesitant in this duty. The medical profession has offered leadership in developing an alternative approach to "mistake management," in which education and remediation are preferred to punishment and sanction. This transcends the traditional "behind closed doors" and "public spectacle" approaches to error and allegations of misconduct. The success of this new model will depend on the willingness and ability of organizations to create environments that support openness and disclosure around error. Such a shift must include clear policies and guidelines and demonstrated shifts in practice. It will also require a willingness on the part of professionals and organizations to communicate to the public when errors occur in the helping process. One positive development in this regard has been that a number of professional colleges have established a practice of open consultation about professional dilemmas.

ETHICAL CONFLICT

How can the counsellor evaluate whether aspects of his or her conduct and duty, both to the client and to the community, are ethically defensible and socially acceptable—and, if they are not, what to do about it? Four types of common ethical dilemma can be identified in clinical work:

1. conflict between "want" and "ought"—between what the counsellor *wants* to do and what he or she feels is the *correct* thing to do
2. conflict between two "oughts"—between two competing duties or ethical imperatives
3. conflict between "you" and "me"—between what the client feels is right and what the helper believes
4. conflict between "us" and "them"—between what the helper and client agree on and social standards or rules.

In each of these situations, complex ethical issues are shaped and defined by the counsellor's beliefs about people in general and each client in particular; about substance use problems; about the helping role; and about prospects for treatment. In addition, ethical questions are informed by larger social factors. For example, not so long ago, corporal punishment might have been tolerated or even valued as a sign of parents' dedicated attention to the proper upbringing of children—that is, as a form of ethical behaviour. Now we see in this behaviour a dynamic of victimization with toxic intergenerational aspects. It has become a crime.

Below, we discuss these four types of ethical dilemma in more detail.

1. Conflict between "Want" and "Ought"

Ethical conflict can occur entirely within the counsellor himself or herself. This may happen when the worker feels caught between "want to" and "ought to." Extreme, though not uncommon, examples would be feeling strongly attracted to or repulsed by a client. The counsellor is expected to be especially adept at recognizing the feelings evoked by contact with other people. Being able to work with feelings that usually undo or subvert ordinary relationships is the hallmark of the counselling experience. But when the counsellor feels immobilized by, or pulled towards, behaviour that opposes his or her sense of what he or she should be doing, then an ethical problem has emerged and must be addressed responsibly.

"Responsibly" is a good word to use here, because it encourages us to recognize not only that there is conduct that is proper to being a helper and a counsellor, but also that the counsellor is "response-able": that is, able to make the ethically required response. The appropriate response may take a variety of forms. For instance, in the example given in the previous paragraph, while consultation with colleagues or a supervisor is clearly a proper response, this does not mean that consultation is always required: careful evaluation may be enough to lead the worker to an ethically supportable decision about how to proceed. But consultation should always be an option that the helper is willing to pursue. Not being able to candidly discuss a dilemma with professional colleagues is a sign that factors other than professional conduct are guiding the helper's behaviour. (Such factors may be the result of the organizational climate or ethos. As noted earlier, counsellors may feel that by reporting a concern, they are putting themselves in jeopardy for discipline, rather than opening the door for support and guidance.)

COUNTERTRANSFERENCE AND ETHICAL PRACTICE

One key element of the helping relationship is that it involves taking the client into our care—"our" meaning both the counsellor's and the agency's. The enduring measure of the relationship is that we do not take advantage of the client, especially given the vulnerability and dependence that the helping relationship, to be effective, must sometimes permit. Even when the counsellor believes there is a mutual interest or consent between helper and client, ethical standards regarding relationships must be maintained.

When attraction to or repulsion from a client is so strong as to interfere with the helper's tasks, it is in the best interests of the client (and the counsellor) to transfer the client to another counsellor. This must, of course, be done in a skilled and sensitive way. The counsellor must take care to avoid projecting his or her own conflicted dynamics onto the client; many clients already tend to take on too much responsibility for failed events.

Stereotypically, we think of the counsellor's attraction to a client and the problems it might bring. It is just as important to think of the subtle ways in which the client's behaviour may be objectionable, offensive or a threat. Dealing with violence, aggression or other negative behaviour may offend the helper's beliefs and sensibilities, so that the helper may even resist finding ways of engaging the client, which can be crucial to therapeutic success. Clients with substance use problems may behave in ways that are socially ridiculed or forbidden. They may be stigmatized because of health problems frequently associated with marginalized lifestyles, such as prostitution. Cultural differences can sometimes alienate the helper from the client to the extent that they interfere with the professional obligation to offer care. In all these situations, as in those discussed earlier, an ethical response depends on the counsellor's being able to distinguish between his or her reactions and what he or she understands is required—and being able to act on that understanding.

Again, the ethical climate in the organization can support or inhibit the discussion and resolution of countertransference issues. Such issues should be viewed not as the weakness of individual workers, but as a reality of therapeutic work. If the organization considers professional comportment of primary importance and frowns on the intrusion of thoughts and feelings into the working relationship, counsellors will quickly learn that their concerns are unwelcome and perhaps even risky to reveal. If however the organization understands that the ebb and flow of positive and negative feelings and beliefs is inherent to the client-counsellor interaction, and the organization includes processes for review and reflection that allow disclosure and discussion of countertransference issues, then these issues will be better identified and dealt with by the individual worker and the treatment team as a whole. As we stated earlier, the preferred approach is always for the organization to seek solutions to ethical questions rather than to assign blame.

2. Conflict between Two "Oughts"

In addition to an internal conflict between desire and duty, counsellors may find themselves caught between two duties or ethical imperatives (two "oughts"). The potentially conflicting imperatives of confidentiality and duty to inform have already been mentioned. In addition, the work of exploring painful issues with the client can itself be thought of in such ethical terms. The adage "primum non nolire" (above all, do no harm) is an old motto in medicine. Working closely with a vulnerable person carries with it the challenge of being purposeful and knowing the limits as well as the possibilities of the helping experience. Thus the counsellor should be very clear about his or her reasons for encouraging clients to address—and sometimes confront—painful experiences, feelings and thoughts. What effect, or result, is being sought? In what state does it leave the client? Similarly, counsellors sometimes try to produce a breakthrough by getting a client to give up control over feelings. It is often easy to produce such effects. But again, the helper has to answer why it needed to be done, and how it affected the client.

3. Conflict between "You" and "Me"

A third type of ethical dilemma emerges when there is a conflict between counsellor and client about what should be done. The power in a therapeutic relationship is asymmetrical: the helper has more than the client. This is not to say that the client is totally powerless, but the advantages tend to favour the counsellor. The self-reflective helper should consider the degree to which his or her behaviour is an exercise in power and control, rather than a purposeful attempt to help the client. The ways in which power circulates in the counselling relationship can reinforce the dynamics of dependence and feelings of inadequacy commonly encountered in the treatment of substance use problems, rather than releasing the client from these feelings. The solution is not for the counsellor to deny or to avoid the power of his or her position, but to see how it affects the helping process. The counsellor's goal could be to use the strategic advantages he or she enjoys in the relationship (e.g., the worker knows more about the client than the client knows about the worker; the worker can usually direct what is talked about, when meetings begin and end, etc.) to help empower the client to move toward healthy possibilities.

4. Conflict between "Us" and "Them"

Finally, conflicts that align a client and counsellor (and agency) against a community standard or value can be seen as an ethical issue. An important part of the counsellor's role is to advocate for the needs of the client. These needs may sometimes only be remedied at the societal level, and the remedy may conflict with public values. For example, the formal social rule is that intravenous drug use is illegal and therefore prohibited. Taking that stance alone, the only permissible intervention would be immediately stopping the drug use, followed by abstinence. While counsellors in substance use programs do help clients discontinue drug use, public health concerns have led, in addition, to advocacy of harm reduction measures such as needle exchanges, free condoms and methadone programs. The goal expands beyond stopping unwanted behaviour to avoiding or reducing harmful consequences. While the advancement of harm reduction principles has helped substance use workers extend their services to previously marginalized and excluded populations, it has also created conflict with community perceptions and expectations. In cases where zero tolerance might be the norm for substance use behaviour, such as when working with youth, clinicians within a harm reduction framework may come into conflict with parents who would prefer an abstinence approach. Thus the alliance of client and therapeutic interest opposes public opinion (and, in some cases, established therapeutic philosophies).

The growing willingness of professionals and organizations to draw on evidence-based knowledge has also been a factor in the emergence of harm reduction approaches. Another factor has been the increasing awareness that substance use problems carry with them high rates of co-occurrence of mental and physical health problems, legal problems, poverty and lack of social support. Seeing the complex scope of these human problems is not just the task of the individual helper, but also needs to be asserted by the agency and understood by the community at large.

ETHICS AS A SELF-REFLECTIVE PROFESSIONAL BEHAVIOUR

Ethics and professional roles are not tangential to substance use treatment. Because individual, community, and organizational values and beliefs are so central to the helping project itself, they are at the heart of the routines and assumptions that counsellors take for granted. Extraordinary situations may bring the ethical dimension into particularly sharp relief, but an essential part of the professional role is a commitment to keeping the most commonplace actions and convictions open to scrutiny and challenge.

Consider some very simple questions that any counsellor could ask in trying to see if his or her conduct meets an ethical standard. First, are there aspects of my work with a particular client that I would be embarrassed to see appear on the clinical record? If the details of my work with clients are accurately presented in the file, then I am being open about my work and am prepared to have it evaluated by my peers. If I am holding back information regarding in-session events and my personal conduct, is this something that a detached and objective observer would be able to understand and accept?

Second, are there features of my work that I avoid sharing with my peers and in supervision? The mark of a competent counsellor is not that he or she knows all the answers but that he or she is always open to self-examination and in pursuit of self-improvement. Are there aspects of my work that I withhold because I know or suspect they are wrong, because they would not pass review by my peers or because I fear my work is of poor quality? Being able to seek out consultation, sharing information with colleagues, being open to different ways of doing things—these are signs of a counsellor who seeks most of all to be optimally helpful to clients.

Third, even assuming my intentions are of the highest order, what are the effects of my actions? Ultimately, ethics must concern not only why I do what I do, but also the effects my actions produce. For the ethical counsellor, there are two key measures for this question of effects: the one given by the client and the one that is empirically (or factually) based.

Substance use treatment is a field in which an inventory of specific ethical standards is not likely to be found. It will take some time before the continuing movement toward professionalization in the substance use field will have its full influence. Even when it does, counsellors must practise ongoing critical self-appraisal and be open to the word of the client and the work of the evaluator. Clinical practice that is clearly and honestly documented is the product of a responsible counsellor, as is an attitude of openness that seeks and invites dialogue and consultation about the demanding aspects of working with individuals with substance use problems.

ILLUSTRATIVE EXAMPLES OF ETHICAL/ PROFESSIONAL DILEMMAS

Sometimes an issue has a clear "right and wrong" nature, so that it is not hard to know if behaviour is proper or improper. Sometimes clear legal parameters define a course of action that must be pursued. But even in such cases, the client may still define his or her best self-interest in ways that are not congruent with what is right or necessary. This can add to the dilemma that the counsellor may feel in determining the best course of action for the situation. In addition there are, of course, many situations in which no consensually defined moral standard or legal requirement provides guidance. Here the counsellor is left to resolve perplexing dilemmas on his or her own.

What follow are examples of situations that can challenge counsellors because of the conflicts they may raise within ourselves, between ourselves and others, or between others. The goal here is not to provide the "right" answer, but to draw on real clinical vignettes to raise issues that deserve to be thought about and discussed. Each vignette will be followed by commentary that, rather than resolving the matter, is intended to open discussion.

Situation 1

A client approaches you complaining about the conduct of another worker. In the context of follow-up contact, the worker, an experienced and respected professional, called on the client at her home without having scheduled an appointment. After a brief conversation at the doorway of the client's apartment, the worker, in saying goodbye to the client, gave the client a hug and a kiss on the lips. The client appears to be confused and upset in telling you this information, but is not making a formal complaint about the worker, whom the client feels has been helpful to her.

COMMENTARY

The first response needs to be to the client. If possible, find a place where you can have an undistracted conversation with the client. There are two main reasons: to allow her to tell her story and to determine what type of response and support she needs. In doing that, you will be able to collect the facts that will help you determine your next steps.

Once you have listened to the client and addressed her needs, it is important to document the facts, even in rough note form. If the information suggests that the helper crossed a boundary of proper conduct with the client, you may find yourself wondering whether you should check out the facts by approaching the worker or whether you should involve the worker's supervisor. The argument for talking directly to the worker could include the need to get a full picture of the situation. The problem then becomes your assuming an investigatory role, which might be properly given to someone else with supervisory authority in the agency. On the other hand, you might feel that to report the matter to a supervisor displays a lack of loyalty to a colleague on the basis of a hearsay report. But ultimately the complaint deserves to be drawn to the attention of whoever supervises the helper's work. Whether or not the client's report leads to disciplinary action, the worker's ongoing involvement with the client needs to be ended, and it should be clearly communicated to the worker that he is not to have further contact with the client, including any subsequent discussion of the incident.

Some twists to consider: If the client wanted to share this matter with you alone and have it go no further, should that have a limiting effect on your informing the helper's supervisor? Would it make a difference if the gender of either the client or helper were different (i.e., if the helper were a woman, and/or if the client were a man)?

Situation 2

You are counselling an adult client who is sharing information about childhood sexual abuse and current unusual sexual practices. The client is receiving care in a program where many other staff have access to the chart. You wonder about how much of this information you should include in the record, and whether you should record it at all.

COMMENTARY

Confidentiality is an important principle of client care, but so is having a full and thorough record of the client's course of treatment. Aside from wanting to thoroughly document the clinical record, one could ask why it would be necessary to chart copious detail about events that are likely to be—in the very least—embarrassing to the client. It might be sufficient to thematically identify the issues that are being explored in counselling rather than detailing them. If you have questions about how to work with the client, they could be addressed in individual or peer supervision, rather than making it a matter for general report to the whole team.

In responding to clients—who share many things in the course of substance use treatment—it is important to have a clear sense of which services can be provided by your agency and which can best be provided elsewhere. Sometimes clients open up important issues that cannot be effectively dealt with because of treatment context, lack of expertise or time constraints. In this case, the client appears to be reaching out. It is important to think carefully about what information to put in circulation among staff by detailing it in the chart. Members of a treatment team often need to know background information about the client, but that need not involve complete documentation of the therapeutic exchange between counsellor and client.

Situation 3

You are working with a parent who has custody of a child but who is, in your view, becoming increasingly neglectful. Your attempts to help change the client's behaviour, so it is more positive, have not been fruitful. You mention your concern to your supervisor, who in turn consults the agency's director. The official response is that there is no evidence of abuse or of harmful consequences of neglect, and that reporting the woman would send an ambiguous message to parents seeking treatment for substance use problems. You remain conflicted. You are increasingly concerned about the mother's neglectful behaviour, and yet also worry that reporting the woman will have a negative impact on the therapeutic alliance that you have established with her.

COMMENTARY

Even though the child is not being abused and has not come to harm because of the parent's neglect, you did well to seek consultation and advice. The response leaned in a definite direction, but it is at odds with your own view of the fragility of the child's situation. In most jurisdictions in North America, if a helping professional has reason to suspect child abuse or neglect, he or she is required by law to report the case to the appropriate child welfare agency. The fact that colleagues or supervisors do not agree that there is a need to report does not absolve the helper of the responsibility to decide for himself or herself. Reporting can be anonymous or open. If such a course of action is deemed necessary, it is often valuable to include the client. If the client knows of your intention and the reasons for it, he or she might elect to play an active role in the process, particularly if he or she can accept that the best interests of the child are your motivating force.

Situation 4

You are counselling a couple. One of them tells you that he has been diagnosed with HIV. You ask if he has told his partner of the diagnosis. He responds that he has not and has no intention of doing so. You ask if they are practising safer sex, to which he responds that he is here to deal with his substance use problems, not to talk about their sexual habits. He explicitly states that he does not want any of this brought up in couple counselling sessions. You mention that you are concerned about the risks to the partner. The client repeats that he does not want to discuss it.

COMMENTARY

You are bound to respect client confidentiality, except in certain circumstances where law or the duty to protect life requires disclosure of information. Could this be one of those exceptional circumstances? In all likelihood, it is probably not. But there is much in this case to ensure that the issue is not clear-cut.

First of all, the partner does not have an automatic right to know that the client is HIV-positive. It is, most of us would say, the client's duty to inform, but that is not the same as compelling the client to inform. The client is obligated to not knowingly pass on the infection. But, because the counsellor does not know about the actual risk factors in the couple's relationship, it would not be fair to jump to conclusions.

It would be easy to become alarmed and polarized by the client's position. That could quickly undermine the therapeutic relationship. By respecting the client's desire not to talk about it in the couple's sessions, the counsellor could suggest an alternative approach by meeting individually with the client. The goal would be to acknowledge the client's feelings, to explore his apprehension about sharing the information with his partner and to look at a wide range of life issues—including sexuality—within the context of substance use. By trying to maintain a therapeutic frame, by empathizing with the client's predicament and by offering supportive contact, it might be possible to help both client and partner, without becoming involved in a struggle about what the client should and should not do. For further discussion, consider this unanswered question: What should the counsellor do if it is revealed that the couple does have unprotected sex occasionally and that the client has not informed the partner of his HIV status?

Situation 5

Your substance use client reveals that he is engaged in continuing criminal behaviour related to drug trafficking. Currently unemployed, the client claims the activity allows him to support his family (he has two children) and to make real headway in paying off his considerable debts, especially now that he is drug-free.

COMMENTARY

Congratulations! You have created therapeutic conditions facilitating client self-disclosure. Your reward is to find out something you might have preferred not knowing. Many people with substance use problems engage in illegal acts before, during and after treatment. There is of course strong evidence that treatment reduces rates of illegal activity. The types of illegal activity can vary from driving while impaired to possession of cannabis to trafficking in heroin or cocaine. For illegal substances, the fact of possession is a criminal offence. Some programs would discharge clients for continued criminality while in treatment. If that is an expectation, it should be stated clearly at the beginning of treatment. Such an explicit condition would probably ensure that disclosures of continued criminality would be rare.

Where the client has privileged you with problematic information, the key is to determine whether the situation can be addressed within the counselling relationship or whether you will have to assume another posture. It is also important for the counsellor to reflect on his or her own personal beliefs and values concerning illegal acts such as drug dealing. In law, there is no obligation to act on the basis of the client's self-report of such criminal behaviour. However, if summoned to court, one would be required to give evidence under oath.

It would be easy to react with irritation and intolerance if a client made this kind of disclosure. It could also be an important therapeutic opportunity. The client might have ambivalent feelings about the behaviour, so that discussion could affect his motivation to change and the decisional balance to pursue different options. This situation would also allow for exploration of risk factors related to the behaviour— not just the risk of relapse, but also the risk of violence, and arrest and incarceration. By preserving a therapeutic, client-centred frame, the counsellor can continue to promote positive change with the client.

Situation 6

Your client, an 18-year-old man, recently moved out on his own after years of conflict with his parents and extended family members, who live in the same home. He is using a range of substances, with a number of overdoses and other acts of self-harm in his past. The youngest of four children, none of whom now live at home, he reports that he was the victim of physical abuse by both parents, and of several incidents of sexual abuse by an uncle who lives with them. You inform the client of his rights to make a complaint to the police, who would lay charges against both parents and the uncle. The young man is upset at this proposal, claiming it would be socially embarrassing and would lead to negative consequences in his community. He tells you he would never take action against a family member.

COMMENTARY

If a child (under age 16) is being physically or sexually abused, you, as a professional helper, are obligated to report this information. If the person is over 16 and/or has left the home but there are other children present who are at risk, you also have an obligation to report.

In this case, the victim is of adult age, there are no children at risk in the home and the client does not want to take action. The client's right to decide must be respected. That said, there are services and supports that can assist the client, should he want help. By being respectful and supportive to the client, a helping process can be initiated that may help him improve his feelings about himself and eventually become empowered to take the legal action available to him. Or he may elect to respond to family and social pressures. The choice is his. By sharing his story with the counsellor, he is looking for help with his own circumstances and self-management. This appears to be a formidable project in itself.

Situation 7

Your client is a middle-aged truck driver, who has had a successful career driving transports across the country. He has disclosed that for the past several years, and with increasing intensity, he has been using stimulants, including cocaine, to stay alert for long-distance drives. He admits that it is affecting his behaviour, including his driving, making him a bit more aggressive than he likes to be. When you discuss the situation with your team, several members question you on your obligation to report the client to the Department of Transport.

COMMENTARY

The client is talking about past behaviour, albeit in the recent past. It would be important to know if the client is planning to continue this behaviour, and to consider the risk involved (for example, to know more about the type and amounts of the drug used, and how often he is using it). If a history of drug use and driving were a sufficient condition for reporting clients, most people seeking substance use treatment would need to be reported. The assessment of current and planned behaviour is a better focus for determining reporting duties in such cases. It would be worth exploring the client's self-perceptions of concern and risk, and providing psychoeducational information. This would allow the negotiation, as part of the treatment contract, that the client would not use drugs when driving. Strategies to consider in support of this goal include drug screening.

SUMMARY

There are obligations in law that apply to substance use workers (see Chapter 5). There are also ethical principles to which we, as individuals and as members of helping professions, are committed. Taking a person into our care requires putting the interests of the help-seeker first in ways that do not compromise our duty to enhance the safety and health of the community. The ethics of clinical practice require us to recognize the balance—grounded in both meanings of the phrase "taking care"—that enables the client to heal and grow and the community to be safe and to evolve. The ethical helper is one who continuously and openly struggles with this challenge.

However, ethical behaviour depends not only on the individual clinician's engaging in critical self-reflection and decision making, but also on the organizational, professional and societal forces that affect the ways we act, perceive and value. Organizations that provide treatment services must be willing to acknowledge the complexity of the clinical situations that substance use workers confront, and must create environments that promote ethical behaviour. An ethical environment is one that is continuously shaped by active dialogue among all levels of the community or society. This starts with the client, and extends to the family and beyond to the community. It includes the helping professional, and also the organizations and institutions that sponsor and regulate helping services. Enactment of these individual and organizational principles—with a commitment among all parties to consider the unique ethical aspects of each situation, and with the creation of environments in which counsellors can talk openly about ethical issues with colleagues, supervisors and the clients involved—counsellors can find the guidance they need to respond appropriately to the many difficult issues that predictably emerge in counselling.

SELECTED READINGS

Code of Ethics and Standards of Practice. (2000). Toronto: Ontario College of Social Workers and Social Service Workers.

Gambrill, E. & Prunger, R. (Eds.). (1997). *Controversial Issues in Social Work Ethics, Values and Obligations.* Boston: Allyn & Bacon.

Reamer, F.G. (1998). *Ethical Standards in Social Work.* Washington, DC: NASW Press.

Reamer, F.G. (2001). *The Social Work Ethics Audit: A Risk Management Tool.* Washington, DC: NASW Press.

Chapter 5

Legal Issues

ROBERT M. SOLOMON AND SYDNEY J. USPRICH

INTRODUCTION

Without question, the legal environment has become more challenging for all professionals in the last 30 years. Thus, it is not surprising that professionals are increasingly being sued, and called upon in disciplinary hearings and other legal contexts to explain and justify their conduct. There has been a parallel trend toward recognizing and protecting the legal rights of clients, especially those who are young. Legal issues will continue to play a greater role in the working lives of all health care professionals, including those in the substance use field. This chapter aims to help substance use workers understand the basic legal principles governing assessment and treatment.

In addition to the legal issues inherent in any treatment relationship, several complicating factors can arise in the substance use field. First, some clients only reluctantly enter treatment, in response to a probation order or at the insistence of an employer, spouse, parent or registrar of motor vehicles. What impact do such pressures have on your legal obligations to the client?

Second, some clients may be under the provincial age of majority, yet still have the legal capacity to give a valid consent to treatment. It may sometimes be difficult to determine whether an underage client is competent to consent to the proposed treatment. Assuming that a client is competent to consent, how should you respond to inquiries about the case from parents, school officials, welfare workers or the police? Third, the use of alcohol and other drugs frequently involves conduct that is not only illegal, but which also may endanger the client and others. Do you have any legal obligation to inform the police of a client's criminal activities? Moreover, can you be held civilly liable for failing to warn third parties of the dangers posed by a client?

Such issues arise because substance use treatment often cuts across the criminal justice, health care, child welfare, education and employment systems. Rather than provide an exhaustive legal analysis of these systems and their possible effects on treatment, this chapter focuses on basic legal principles governing treatment relationships and explains their special application to substance use workers.

Equally, we do not have the space to review the relevant statutes and cases in every jurisdiction in Canada. Consequently, the body of this chapter outlines the major principles, while the references point to more specific principles. The exact legal rules vary from jurisdiction to jurisdiction, reflecting differences in provincial case law and statutes.

The first section examines the law governing consent to treatment, while the second section examines confidentiality, disclosure, reporting obligations, and the duty to warn.

CONSENT TO TREATMENT

Introduction to Consent Issues

One hallmark of our legal system is the importance it attaches to the protection of a person's physical integrity. Whether couched in terms of physical inviolability, autonomy, self-determination or privacy, the principle is the same—namely, a person's right to control his or her own body. However, this concept is a double-edged sword, in that the law protects the individual's right to decide, whether the person's decision is wise or foolish.

Virtually any physical interference with another person may result in both criminal liability (*Criminal Code*, s. 265(1)) and civil liability.[1] In the absence of consent, the defendant will be held liable unless he or she can legally justify the interference. In these situations, however, treatment professionals are rarely charged with a criminal offence. Rather, the issue of consent typically arises in determining whether there is a valid defence to a *civil* action for the tort (wrongful act) of battery.

Battery is defined as harmful, or socially offensive, intentional physical contact with another person (see, for example, *Bettel* v. *Yim*, 1978). Merely touching a client may give rise to liability; he or she need not suffer any physical injury. Any surgical procedure, administration of drugs or treatment involving physical contact may constitute battery. Once the client establishes that physical contact occurred, the burden of proof shifts to the professional to establish a valid defence (*Allan* v. *New Mount Sinai Hospital*, 1980; Picard, 1979). If the defendant cannot prove that the client consented or that there is another defence, the defendant will be held liable for all the consequences of the battery. In most cases, the key issue is not whether physical contact occurred, but whether the clinician can establish the defence of consent.

The legal principles governing the defence of consent have developed almost exclusively from cases involving surgery and other physical interventions. However, the tort of battery is also relevant to substance use treatment programs that include physical examinations, taking blood samples, administering drugs or other physical contact. Treatment that involves only the taking of a history, questionnaires, counselling or similar non-physical interactions cannot give rise to a battery claim. Nonetheless, the issue of consent and the principles governing it are still relevant in these situations.

General Principles of Consent

As a general rule, a treatment professional must obtain consent for any test, procedure, surgery, counselling or physical examination. Consent should be obtained in advance, and should cover the intervention as well as any related issues regarding record-keeping, confidentiality, reporting obligations and other disclosures of information. The consent must relate to the specific treatment or counselling undertaken (*Parmley* v. *Parmley and Yule*, 1945; *Schweizer* v. *Central Hospital*, 1974). If the client is competent to give a valid consent, then his or her consent alone is required (*Johnston* v. *Wellesley Hospital*, 1971; *Gillick* v. *West Norfolk*, 1985; *C.* v. *Wren*, 1986). The consent of the next-of-kin is relevant only if the client is not competent to give consent. Even then, the validity of a substitute consent is limited (*In Re B [A Minor]*, 1981; *Re Superintendent of Family & Child Services and Dawson*, 1983; *"Eve"* v. *"Mrs. E.,"* 1986).

To be valid, consent must be given voluntarily. However, the concept of volition is defined broadly, and rests on whether the client's decision was the product of his or her conscious mind (*Smith* v. *Stone*, 1647; *Gilbert* v. *Stone*, 1648). For example, clients who reluctantly consent to drug treatment because it is a term of probation, or because they have been threatened with being fired from a job or expelled from school, will still be held to have consented "voluntarily."

A client may consent implicitly or explicitly (*O'Brien* v. *Cunard*, 1891; *Reynen* v. *Antonenko*, 1975; *Strachan* v. *Simpson*, 1979). The fact that a client comes for treatment provides a broad measure of implicit consent. Clients may seek treatment for alcohol or other drug problems, and yet expressly limit the scope of their consent. A substance use worker may refuse to treat the client if these limitations are unreasonable. However, the worker cannot ignore or override the client's stated prohibitions (*Mulloy* v. *Hop Sang*, 1935; *Allan* v. *New Mount Sinai Hospital*, 1980).

Informed Consent

To be valid, a client's consent must be based on a full and frank disclosure of the nature of the treatment and its risks. In keeping with the rise of client rights, the courts require that clients be given enough information to make an informed decision about the proposed treatment and its alternatives. This does not mean that clients must be told of all the possible risks (*Reibl* v. *Hughes*, 1980; *Hopp* v. *Lepp*, 1980; *Haughian* v. *Paine*, 1987). The legal principles governing informed consent are summarized below.

- A practitioner's failure to disclose the risks of a procedure or treatment may give rise to a civil suit in negligence.
- Practitioners have a legal duty to disclose to their patients or clients all the material risks associated with a proposed procedure. The term "material risk" includes:
  (a) a low-percentage risk of a serious consequence. In the founding case, a 4 per cent chance of death and a 10 per cent chance of paralysis were held to constitute material risks (*Reibl* v. *Hughes*, 1980). The courts have increasingly held that very small and even remote risks of death or serious injury are material. Examples include:
    — a very small risk of stroke during a neck manipulation by a chiropractor (*Leung* v. *Campbell*, 1995).
    — an extremely small chance of stroke from taking oral contraceptives (*Buchan* v. *Ortho*, 1986).
    — a 1/40,000 to 1/100,000 chance of death as a result of a severe reaction to a diagnostic dye (*Meyer Estate* v. *Rogers*, 1991).
  (b) a substantial probability of a relatively minor consequence, such as a 35 per cent risk of a minor infection.
- In addition to informing the patient of the physical nature of the risk (e.g., cutting a nerve), the practitioner must explain the impact of such an eventuality on the patient's life (*Tremblay* v. *McLauchlan*, 2001).
- Practitioners must also disclose non-material risks that they know, or ought to know, would be of particular concern to the patient.
- Practitioners should discuss with the patient the consequences of leaving the problem untreated.
- The courts have increasingly required full disclosure of the alternatives to the proposed treatment, particularly if the proposed treatment involves significant risks (*Haughian* v. *Paine*, 1987; *Van Mol* v. *Ashmore*, 1999).
- Practitioners must answer all questions openly and honestly, even if the answers would discourage the patient or client from consenting.
- Responsibility for obtaining an informed consent rests with the person performing the service. While practitioners may delegate this task to a subordinate, they are ultimately accountable for ensuring that an informed consent was obtained (*Semeniuk* v. *Cox*, 1999).
- Practitioners do not have any clear therapeutic privilege to withhold information because they feel that a patient or client is unable to cope with the information. They do, however, have the freedom to decide how they will present the information and what they will emphasize.
- Practitioners do not have to disclose information to patients or clients who have expressly stated that they do not want to be informed of the risks, benefits and alternatives.

• Practitioners who do not meet these standards of disclosure are in breach of their duty of care. However, the patient or client must also establish that the failure to be informed caused or contributed to his or her injuries. In effect, the failure to inform must have induced the plaintiff to consent to treatment that he or she would not otherwise have had, and that treatment must have caused the plaintiff's loss (*Arndt* v. *Smith*, 1997; *Lacroix* v. *Dominique*, 2001).

Exceptions to the General Principles of Consent

The courts have relaxed the strict requirements of consent in three situations. First, in an unforeseen medical emergency where it is impossible to obtain the patient's consent, a health professional is allowed to operate without consent to preserve the patient's health or life (*Marshall* v. *Curry*, 1933; *Murray* v. *McMurchy*, 1949). This right is granted to health care professionals in order to save lives. This is the basis upon which emergency room staff are permitted to operate on unconscious accident victims.

The second exception involves clients who have given a general consent to a course of therapy, treatment program or operation. In such situations, a client will be viewed as implicitly consenting to any subordinate tests, procedures or interventions that are necessarily incidental to the broader course of treatment (*Male* v. *Hopmans*, 1967; *Villeneuve* v. *Sisters of St. Joseph*, 1971). However, this implied consent will be negated if the client objects. While it may not be legally necessary, it is wise to obtain a specific consent for any subordinate procedures that pose significant risks or involve sexually, legally or emotionally sensitive issues.

Third, the courts at one time permitted health care professionals to withhold information from a client if the disclosure would undermine the client's morale or discourage him or her from having needed treatment (*Kenny* v. *Lockwood*, 1932; *Male* v. *Hopmans*, 1967). However, recent cases have rejected or narrowed the therapeutic privilege doctrine. For example, the judge in *Meyer Estate* v. *Rogers* (1991) stated that the doctrine is no longer part of Ontario law. In *Pittman Estate* v. *Bain* (1994), the court acknowledged the therapeutic privilege to withhold information, but defined it very narrowly. Health care professionals do have some discretion, but it is best viewed as being limited to:
• how they inform clients
• the technical matters they discuss
• the emphasis they place on the relative risks of undergoing versus foregoing treatment.

Consent Forms and the Burden of Proof

Unless a statute states otherwise, a client may give consent orally or in writing. Since the client's presence provides some measure of implied consent, it is not legally necessary to obtain written consent for routine treatment sessions. However, it is wise to obtain written consent for treatment that involves significant risks, is complex or innovative, or entails potentially sensitive legal, sexual or emotional issues. Similarly, written consent is recommended if the client is immature, unstable or lacks good judgment. Based on these criteria, it would be prudent for substance use workers to obtain written consent at the outset of the treatment relationship. Moreover, if agency policy required signed consents, then counsellors would be required to comply.

A signed consent form provides only some evidence of consent, not conclusive proof. The key legal issue is not whether a client signed a consent form, but whether he or she understood the nature of the proposed treatment and its risks and benefits, was given sufficient information to make an informed decision, and consented to the treatment. A signed consent form is only as good as the information it contains and the circumstances in which it is presented to the client. A signed consent form would be of little value if:
- it was written in technical language that the client could not understand
- it was presented as a mere technicality, or there was no opportunity to read it
- it was written in general language that did not identify the specific treatment and its risks
- the client's questions were not adequately answered
- the client was in severe pain, intoxicated or drugged when signing it.

Competence to Consent

To be valid, a consent must be given by a client who is legally competent. The general test of competence is whether the client can understand the information relevant to making an informed decision and appreciate the reasonably foreseeable consequences of that decision. This very low threshold test is applied on a case-by-case basis. As stated earlier, if the client is competent to consent, then his or her consent alone is relevant. Indeed, it would be inappropriate even to discuss a client's treatment with the next-of-kin without the client's consent, because this would involve a breach of confidence. Consequently, the assessment of a client's competence to consent is a critically important preliminary issue.

MINORS
General Principles
The age of majority varies across Canada. Moreover, this legislation typically does not govern the age of consent to treatment. In the absence of a statute to the contrary, the test of competence is the same whether the client is a minor or an adult. Generally,

the court will assess whether the client understands the proposed treatment and its risks, benefits and alternatives, and appreciates the consequences of having or foregoing it. If a minor meets this test, then his or her consent is valid and parental consent is unnecessary. In some cases, the courts have relied on indications of independence as a guide to a minor's competence. As the following case illustrates, Canadian courts increasingly recognize the right of young people to make their own treatment decisions.

In *C. v. Wren* (1986), the plaintiffs sought an injunction to prevent a doctor from performing an abortion on their 16-year-old daughter. As was then required by the *Criminal Code*, the daughter had obtained approval from a therapeutic abortion committee. The court sympathized with both the parents and their daughter in this "painful dispute" over the ethics of the proposed abortion. However, the legal issue was clear—could this 16-year-old girl give a valid consent to a therapeutic abortion? The court concluded that the daughter understood the nature of the procedure and its risks, and therefore was competent to give a valid consent. Consequently, the parents' application for an injunction was dismissed.

Statutory Age-of-Consent Provisions

The general test of competence applies unless a statute states otherwise. In any one jurisdiction, several statutes may impose age-of-consent requirements for specific types of treatment. For Ontario examples, see the *Human Tissues Gift Act*, s. 3 and *Child and Family Services Act* (CFSA), ss. 27, 28 & 132. Since this chapter cannot review all the relevant legislation in each province, the Ontario *CFSA* is used to illustrate the operation of the statutory provisions.

The *CFSA* applies only to specified service providers, which include the Minister of Community and Social Services, approved agencies, children's aid societies and licensees (s. 3(1)). The Act is also limited to stipulated services, including child development, child treatment, child welfare, community support and young offender services (ss. 3(1) & 88). Thus, the *CFSA*'s age-of-consent provisions do not apply to treatment provided under the *Health Care Consent Act,* such as substance use counselling provided by a psychologist in the outpatient clinic of a public hospital. In contrast, a social worker providing identical counselling in an approved agency would be subject to the *CFSA*'s provisions.

The *CFSA* establishes different age requirements for consent, depending on the type of treatment:

• A person 16 years or older may consent, without parental knowledge or approval, to any services or care (s. 27(1)).
• A person under 16 needs parental consent for residential care services or the administration of psychotropic drugs (ss. 27(2) & 132).
• A child 12 years or older may consent to counselling services without parental knowledge or consent. However, if the person is younger than 16, the counsellor must advise the person that it is desirable to involve his or her parents (s. 28).

Summary

Unless a statute states otherwise, minors can give a valid consent to alcohol and other drug treatment. The key issue is whether the minor is capable of understanding the proposed treatment and its risks. If the minor meets this test of competency, the consent of the parent or guardian is not required. As in Ontario, several provincial statutes may impose age-of-consent requirements for certain types of treatment. The end result is that the age of consent to substance use treatment is governed by a complex tangle of common law and statutory provisions that vary from province to province.

ADULTS

The general test of competence is the same whether the client is a minor or an adult. The principles apply equally to those in custody or under other legal restraints, unless there is express statutory authority to the contrary (*Attorney General of British Columbia* v. *Astaforoff*, 1984; *Attorney-General of Canada* v. *Notre Dame Hospital*, 1984). If the person is competent, his or her consent to treatment must be obtained. Although a client's refusal to consent to treatment may constitute a breach of probation or a violation of parole, that does not alter the treatment worker's obligation to abide by the client's decision.

The issue of an adult's competency may also arise in cases involving mental illness or dementia. However, the mere fact that a client is, for example, mentally ill does not mean he or she is incapable of giving a valid consent. Rather, clinicians must assess each client's ability to understand the proposed treatment and its risks. Although this principle is easy to state, it may be difficult to apply in many situations, such as that of an occasionally disoriented person with a severe alcohol problem (*Kelly* v. *Hazlett*, 1976; *MacKinnon* v. *Ignacio et al.*, (1978); *Re T*, 1992).

One area that has caused confusion is the role of health care professionals in treating people suspected of impaired driving. Although this issue is more relevant to hospital emergency staff than to substance use workers, a brief summary of the current law follows. Health care professionals must refuse police requests to take blood samples or conduct other tests on unwilling or unconscious suspects for enforcement purposes. These situations must be distinguished from medical emergencies in which it is impossible to obtain the suspect's consent. In such cases, the staff may perform any medical procedures needed to save the life or preserve the health of the suspect. Even in these situations, the blood samples or test results should not simply be given to the police. Rather, the police must obtain a search warrant authorizing them to seize the evidence (*Pohoretsky* v. *The Queen*, 1987; *R.* v. *Dyment*, 1988; *R.* v. *Greffe*, 1990).

In 1985, Parliament introduced a special warrant that authorizes blood samples to be taken from unconscious impaired driving suspects in limited circumstances. A health care professional acting under this warrant is protected from both civil and criminal liability. Nonetheless, the legislation permits health care professionals to refuse to participate in the procedure (*Criminal Code*, ss. 256 & 257).

Substitute Consent

The issue of substitute or next-of-kin consent arises only if the client is not competent to give or withhold consent. In such circumstances, the law permits the client's substitute decision maker to give or refuse consent on the incompetent client's behalf. In Ontario, the *Health Care Consent Act* (*HCCA*) sets out a ranked list of those who may give substitute consent for treatment (s. 20). However, it can be hard to find a substitute decision maker in some cases, such as those involving people living on the street. The *HCCA* states that if no one else higher in the list is readily available or willing to serve as a substitute decision maker, then the Public Guardian and Trustee (PGT) has authority to make the decision (s. 20(5)). Similarly, the PGT can give substitute consent if two substitute decision makers at the same rank disagree on whether to give or refuse consent (s. 20(6)).

The power to exercise substitute consent is not absolute. The decision to give or withhold consent must accord with any known prior expressed wish of the individual (*Malette* v. *Shulman*, 1990). If there is no such wish, the substitute decision maker must make the decision in the incompetent patient's best interest. Thus, a court could invalidate a parental decision to refuse drug treatment for their incompetent child, if the parents' refusal was not in the child's best interest ("*Eve*" v. "*Mrs E.,*" 1986). The court could order that the child be given treatment or be made a ward of the provincial child welfare agency. The agency would then give the necessary consent for the child to receive the needed treatment.

Factors That Invalidate Consent

Once it is established that a client consented, it must be determined whether any factors negate consent. If the consent is negated, the treatment worker's legal position is the same as if there had been no consent. Three factors negate consent: mistake, duress (coercion) and deceit (fraud).

If a client consented to treatment under a mistaken belief created by the treatment professional, the client's consent would be negated (*Boase* v. *Paul*, 1931; *Parmley* v. *Parmley and Yule*, 1945; *Guimond* v. *Laberge*, 1956). This issue would arise if a clinician inadvertently overstated the benefits of the treatment or failed to adequately answer the client's concerns about the risks, and the client consented based on these misapprehensions. While it is important to encourage clients to have beneficial treatment, care must be taken not to overstate the benefits or understate the risks.

Consent is invalid if it was obtained under duress, which the courts have defined narrowly as an immediate threat of physical force (*Latter* v. *Braddell*, 1880; *Re Riverdale Hospital and C.U.P.E.*, 1985). As long as the courts continue to use this restrictive definition, the issue is unlikely to arise in a typical drug treatment situation. The fact that a client consented only reluctantly—e.g., to avoid being thrown out of the house, expelled from school or charged with breach of probation—does not constitute duress. However, the issue of duress would arise if a client consented because of an unlawful threat of being physically restrained or drugged.

A client's consent is also invalid if it was obtained through deceit, which the courts have limited to a person's lying or acting in total disregard for the truth. Deceit will negate consent only if it relates to the nature of the proposed treatment or its potentially harmful consequences, as opposed to any other matter (*Bolduc* v. *R.*, 1967; *R.* v. *Cuerrier*, 1998). The issue of deceit would arise if, for example, a counsellor knowingly misled research subjects into believing they were receiving an active drug, when they were being given a placebo.

Conclusion

With limited exceptions, treatment relationships in our legal system are based on consent. Although consent issues usually relate to medical procedures, they apply equally to psychological assessment, treatment and counselling. Therefore, before beginning counselling or treatment, substance use workers should ensure they have obtained a valid consent. The following checklist will help with this task.

CONSENT CHECKLIST
• Is the client capable of giving or refusing consent? (Can the client understand the procedure and its risks, and appreciate the likely consequences of having or failing to have the proposed treatment?)
• If the client is capable of giving consent, has he or she explicitly consented to the proposed treatment?
• If not, has the client implicitly consented and how was that implicit consent demonstrated?
• Is the consent valid in that the client consented voluntarily?
• Is the consent valid in that it is an informed consent? (Have the risks and benefits of the proposed treatment and its alternatives been explained? Have the material risks been disclosed? Have the client's questions been fully and frankly answered?)
• Is there adequate proof of consent? Is this a situation in which the consent should be in writing?
• If the client is not capable, is this an emergency in which the health practitioner is authorized to intervene without consent?
• If this is not an emergency, has a valid substitute consent been given?
• Do any factors—mistake, duress or deceit—invalidate the consent or substitute consent?

CONFIDENTIALITY AND DISCLOSURE OF CLIENT INFORMATION

Confidentiality

The term "confidentiality" has several meanings in common usage. However, when used in a legal context, confidentiality refers to the legal obligation not to disclose *willingly*, without the client's consent, information that has been received in confidence (*Halls* v. *Mitchell*, 1928; *Cronkwright* v. *Cronkwright*, 1971; *R.* v. *Dersch*, 1993). Consequently, a substance use worker who disclosed information without a client's consent would not be in breach of confidentiality if he or she was *required* to do so by a search warrant, subpoena or other court order. Nor would a counsellor breach confidentiality if he or she complied with the province's mandatory child abuse reporting provisions or disclosed information as required by other statutes.

The public tends to view confidentiality as an absolute guarantee of silence. Many people believe that information given in confidence to health care professionals will never be disclosed without explicit consent. As a result, counsellors may find themselves caught between their legal obligation to comply with court orders or mandatory reporting provisions, and their clients' reasonable, but mistaken, understanding of confidentiality. To avoid being seen as betraying a client's trust, counsellors should explain the meaning and limits of confidentiality at the outset of the relationship.

An obligation of confidentiality will not usually arise until a health care professional has entered a counselling or other treatment relationship with a client. The courts will likely hold that a confidentiality obligation begins when it would be reasonable for the client to expect privacy. Although not all telephone requests for appointments or information would give rise to such an obligation, some might. For example, a reminder for an eye appointment left with a client's secretary is likely to be treated differently from a reminder for an appointment with a substance use counsellor. Obviously, the more serious the matter and the more emotionally, sexually or legally sensitive the issue, the greater the expectation of privacy.

An obligation of confidentiality applies to all information that a client gives in confidence, whether it relates to the client or to other people. However, the confidentiality requirement is generally limited to statements and observations made within the professional relationship. Thus, no confidentiality obligation would apply to a substance use counsellor who happens to see an intoxicated client stagger to his car at a shopping mall. Like any other member of the public, the counsellor could choose to call the police. However, the counsellor would have to limit his or her statements to what was seen at the mall, and would breach confidentiality if he or she disclosed any information from the treatment relationship, including that the person was a client. Treatment workers may be under several different sets of confidentiality obligations at any one time. First, a number of provincial statutes impose confidentiality obligations on health care professionals in specific situations. Second, counsellors may be subject to ethical and professional codes of confidentiality. Third, a clinician who promises, either implicitly or explicitly, to maintain confidentiality will have a common law duty to honour that obligation. Fourth, the courts are likely to assume that confidentiality is an inherent element of all therapeutic relationships. Thus, even in the absence of a statute, professional code, or promise of confidentiality, those who present themselves to the public as counsellors may be expected to treat client information as confidential.

Depending on the source of the obligation, a breach of confidentiality can lead to penal, professional and civil liability. A person who breaches a statutory confidentiality obligation may be prosecuted. For example, a substance use worker in Ontario who wrongfully discloses information from the clinical record of a psychiatric patient may be prosecuted under the *Mental Health Act* and fined up to $25,000 (ss. 35 & 80). If a clinician is a member of a regulated profession, such as psychology, breaching confidentiality may be grounds for a finding of professional misconduct and may lead to a fine, reprimand or licence suspension. A breach of confidentiality may also result in civil liability in negligence or in the emerging tort action for intentional breach of confidence.

Privilege

The legal term "privilege" refers to the right to refuse to disclose confidential information when testifying, when faced with a subpoena for client records, or when subject to a mandatory reporting obligation (Sim, 1984; Sopinka et al., 1999, ch. 14). As a general rule, people called as witnesses in court or before other legal tribunals must answer all relevant questions put to them (see, for example, *Canada Evidence Act*, s. 46). Similarly, those served with subpoenas or other court orders must provide the records or files that are sought. Privilege is an exception to these general rules. In the absence of privilege, a person who defies a court order or refuses to answer questions when testifying may be found in contempt of court.

Traditionally, the only professional relationship to which privilege applied was that between solicitors and their clients. Solicitor-client privilege is based on the view that our legal system requires clients to speak freely with their lawyers. This will only occur if such communications remain confidential. However, even solicitor-client privilege is limited. It applies only to statements about past criminal offences, and not to statements about ongoing or future crimes. Nor does it apply to physical evidence. Although other professionals, such as priests, police, psychologists, journalists and social workers, have claimed a comparable need for privilege, common law has not granted such automatic protection to these relationships.

Courts have discretion to grant privilege on a case-by-case basis to confidential communications other than solicitor-client relationships (*Slavutych* v. *Baker*, 1976).

The party seeking privilege must meet the following four requirements:

1. The communication must have originated in confidence.
2. Confidentiality must be essential to maintaining the relationship.
3. The relationship must be one that society values and wishes to foster.
4. The injury to the relationship from disclosure of the information must outweigh the benefit of having the relevant evidence available to resolve the case.

Communications made in the course of most care relationships would likely satisfy the first three requirements. First, clients expect that the information they give to counsellors or other health care professionals will be kept confidential. Indeed, most professionals explicitly state that all information their clients provide will be kept confidential. Second, successful treatment relationships are largely built on trust. Most clients would not disclose intimate details about their lives unless they were assured of confidentiality. Without such information, a substance use worker would be unable to accurately assess the client's problems and provide proper care. Third, society has an interest in promoting successful treatment relationships.

The fourth requirement has been the most difficult to satisfy. If the confidential information is relevant to the case, the courts have tended to deny privilege and order disclosure. Not surprisingly, some judges may rule that the interests of justice in resolving cases outweigh the importance of granting privilege and maintaining confidentiality. As the following case illustrates, this is particularly true in criminal, child abuse and child custody cases. The courts also appear more reluctant to grant privilege when it is sought by an accused, as opposed to a victim (*R.* v. *R.S.*, 1985; *R.* v. *Gruenke*, 1991).

In *Gibbs* v. *Gibbs* (1985), an estranged husband and wife were involved in custody proceedings. The wife had a long history of mental illness that required hospitalization on several occasions, and was reportedly displaying those symptoms again. The husband argued that his wife could not be relied upon to care for their two children and that he should be granted custody. In order to support his claim, the husband requested that his wife's psychiatric records be disclosed. The Court ordered disclosure of the records despite the doctor's conclusion that this would likely have an adverse effect on the wife's treatment. The judge stated that the potential harm to the children far outweighed any risks to the wife.

Despite frequent recommendations that privilege be extended, legislatures have been reluctant to grant immunity from disclosure. Even where legislation purports to provide privilege, the courts have tended to interpret privilege narrowly, on the basis that the interests of justice require disclosure of all relevant information. Furthermore, a provincial statute that privileges specific communication may be challenged if it conflicts with federal legislation that authorizes disclosure of that same communication (see, for example, *R.* v. *B.*, 1979). However, note that Parliament has enacted special statutory privileging provisions to provide greater protection from disclosure to the records of sexual assault victims (*Criminal Code*, ss. 278.1–278.91).

In summary, while almost all information that treatment workers obtain in providing treatment is confidential, little, if any, is privileged. Perhaps more importantly, privilege is granted on a case-by-case basis and a treatment worker can never know at the time of making a record whether it will be privileged. Consequently, treatment workers should assume that some day they will have to testify and that their records may be examined in court. This realization should encourage treatment workers to take their record-keeping obligations seriously and to adopt a professional and objective tone in preparing client records.

Disclosure of Client Information

CLIENTS' ACCESS TO THEIR RECORDS

Treatment and care records do not belong to clients. Rather, they are the property of the agency and the people providing the service. Nonetheless, in the absence of a statute to the contrary, the client has a right of reasonable access to this information (*McInerney* v. *MacDonald*, 1992). The professional does not have to produce the records immediately or turn over original documents. He or she may offer to provide a summary of the records or to review the file with the client. However, if the client demands access to, or a copy of, the complete treatment record, the court will uphold the client's right. Agencies can charge clients for the administrative and duplicating costs of copying the record for the client.

If the treatment professional believes that allowing the client access would harm or endanger the client or a third party, the professional can refuse the request and apply to the court. The burden of proof is on the treatment professional to justify denying a client access. This has two important implications. First, substance use workers should assume that their clients may read the entire file some day. Second, professionals should not promise colleagues or other third parties that their comments about the client will remain confidential, because they may not be able to keep such a promise.

DISCLOSURE WITH A CLIENT'S EXPRESS OR IMPLIED CONSENT

In the absence of a statute to the contrary, a substance use worker ordinarily cannot disclose client information without that client's consent—not even to employers, family members, probation officers or the police. Even simple inquiries, such as whether a person is a client, are best left unanswered with an explanation that all client information is confidential. Even if the client was referred by an employer, probation officer or other third party, the treatment worker must generally obtain the client's consent before disclosing information to that other party.

Although the client's express consent is usually required, implied consent may be assumed in some situations. First, treatment professionals may share confidential client information without express consent for the purposes of providing proper care.[2] For example, a counsellor who suspects that his or her client is suicidal may consult a colleague who is an expert in that area to determine how best to proceed. In such a case, the colleague is subject to the same confidentiality obligations. Second, professionals may be permitted to disclose patient information without consent in compassionate circumstances. For example, hospitals treating unconscious accident victims routinely notify the next-of-kin. Third, there appears to be a right to share confidential information for internal administrative purposes, such as audits and quality assurance reviews.

Depending on the circumstances, there may also be an implicit right to share confidential information with a client's parents, spouse, employer or other referring agency. For example, if the client's parents attended the initial session, the substance use worker may discuss with them, at a later date, information from that session. Clients often approach treatment professionals to document their claim for an employment, insurance or government benefit. In many such cases, it is obvious that there is implied consent to disclose client information to the party providing the benefit. It has been suggested that client information may also be used without consent for research or teaching purposes, provided the client cannot be identified. Although some statutes authorize such disclosures in limited circumstances, there does not appear to be any common law authority for this proposition. Given the increasing concern about privacy, clinicians are advised to obtain express consent in all of these situations.

Reporting Obligations

REPORTING CRIMINAL OFFENCES

In addition to disclosing information when faced with a court order or search warrant, treatment professionals may be required by statutes to report certain information to appropriate authorities. However, contrary to what many people believe, there is no general obligation to report federal or provincial offences, to assist the police or to answer police questions (see, for example, *Koechlin* v. *Waugh*, 1957; *R.* v. *Carroll*, 1959; *Rice* v. *Connolly*, 1966; *Kenlin* v. *Gardiner*, 1967; *Colet* v. *The Queen*, 1981). With the exception of treason (*Criminal Code*, s. 50(1)(b)), it is not a criminal offence to fail to report to police any crimes that have been or may be committed.

Consequently, substance use workers are not required by federal law to report a client's illicit drug use to the police, nor even acknowledge that a client is in treatment. Professionals can refuse to respond to a police officer's or probation officer's request for client information, but they cannot lie or deliberately mislead officers. Staff who do so may be charged with obstructing justice or similar offences (*Criminal Code*, ss. 129 & 139).

PROVINCIAL REPORTING OBLIGATIONS

Provincial statutes impose a number of mandatory reporting obligations on health care professionals and others. These obligations vary from province to province. Moreover, they tend to be defined precisely, applying to named categories of professionals in very specific circumstances. The major reporting obligations are designed to help control communicable diseases, hazardous driving and child abuse. In these situations, the perceived threat to the public is viewed as outweighing the client's right to confidentiality, thus justifying the reporting obligation.

Most provinces have legislation that requires medical professionals to report to public health officials patients who have specified communicable diseases. Physicians providing services to patients who are not hospitalized may be required to report any patient who they believe has a communicable disease. Hospital administrators have a similar reporting obligation with respect to patients (see, for example, the Ontario *Health Protection and Promotion Act*, ss. 25–26).

Educators may also be required to report any student who they suspect has a communicable disease (see, for example, the Ontario *Education Act*, s. 265(k) & (l)). The list of diseases is extensive and typically includes HIV/AIDS , hepatitis, tuberculosis, venereal diseases and various types of influenza. Failure to report is an offence in some provinces and can result in fines. Generally, no action or other proceeding may be brought against a person who makes the required report in good faith.

Most provinces require physicians to report the name, address and clinical condition of any patient of driving age who has or may have a condition that may make driving hazardous. Although these provisions were probably intended to deal with medical conditions, such as failing eyesight, heart disease and epilepsy, they are broad enough to encompass substance use problems. However, the legislation is usually limited to medical practitioners and optometrists.[3] Consequently, substance use workers would have no statutory obligation to report a client who admits to alcohol- or drug-induced blackouts while driving. Indeed, if they were to report such clients, they might be in breach of their confidentiality obligations. Such dilemmas can occur in various circumstances, and approaches to handling these problems are covered later in this chapter.

Several jurisdictions require health care professionals to report to the relevant governing body any reasonable suspicion that any other health care professional has engaged in sexually inappropriate conduct with a patient (see, for example, Ontario's *Regulated Health Professions Act, 1991* (RHPA), s. 4, and the RHPA's *Schedule 2, Health Professions Procedural Code*, ss. 85.1–85.7). Thus, for example, a nurse or occupational therapist who was informed by a female patient that the patient's family doctor had made sexual advances would be required to report this information to the College of Physicians. Similar legislation has been introduced for social workers, but it requires reporting only sexual improprieties committed by other social workers and social service workers (see, for example, the Ontario *Social Work and Social Service Work Act*, ss. 43–45).

The most comprehensive reporting obligations are contained in provincial child protection legislation. Two sets of reporting obligations may apply—one that applies to everyone and a broader set that applies to those who have contact with children in a professional capacity, such as educators, child care workers and the police. The obligation to report is defined broadly, usually in terms of having a reasonable suspicion that a child has been, or may be, abused. Child abuse is also defined broadly to include physical and sexual mistreatment, as well as the failure to provide proper medical and psychological treatment. This broad definition would include children who are not receiving treatment for alcohol or other drug problems, and children who are endangered by their parents' substance use problems. Thus, a substance use worker may be required to report to provincial child welfare officials a parent who drives with his or her children while high or intoxicated.

The failure to report child abuse may be a provincial offence that is subject to a substantial fine. The legislation usually states that no civil action can be brought against a person who has reported as required, even if it turns out that there was no abuse. Child protection legislation takes precedence over any conflicting provisions of other provincial statutes—and over professional confidentiality obligations, except for solicitor-client privilege (see, for example, Manitoba's *Child and Family Services Act*, ss. 9(4), 17 & 18).

The following summary of Ontario's legislation illustrates a number of common features of various child abuse reporting provisions.

Reporting Obligations: Ontario's *Child and Family Services Act*

Despite the provisions of any other Act, anyone who has reasonable grounds to suspect any of the following circumstances must immediately report the suspicion and the grounds upon which it is based to a Children's Aid Society (s. 72(1)):
• A child has suffered or is at risk of suffering physical harm that:
   (i) is inflicted by the parent or person in charge of the child;
  (ii) resulted from that person's failure to adequately care or provide for, supervise or
       protect the child; or
 (iii) resulted from that person's pattern of neglect.
• A child has suffered or is at risk of suffering emotional harm, as demonstrated by serious anxiety, depression, withdrawal, self-destructive or aggressive behaviour, or delayed development, which is caused or contributed to, as described above, by the parent or person in charge of the child.
• A child has suffered or is at risk of suffering sexual molestation or exploitation inflicted by the parent or person in charge of the child, or caused by that person's fail-ure to protect the child when that person knows or ought to know of the possibility.
• A child requires medical treatment, treatment for emotional harm, or treatment for a mental, emotional or developmental condition that could seriously impair the child's development, and the parent or person in charge of the child fails or refuses to provide the treatment, or is unavailable or unable to consent.
• A child has been abandoned, the child's parent has died or is unavailable to exercise custodial rights and has not made adequate arrangements for the child's care, or the parent is unable or unwilling to resume responsibility for his or her child in residential care.

• A child under 12 has killed or seriously injured another person or caused serious property damage and needs treatment to prevent a recurrence, but the parent or person in charge of the child fails or refuses to provide it, or is unavailable or unable to consent.
• A child under 12 has, on more than one occasion, injured another person or damaged another's property with the encouragement of the person in charge of the child or because of that person's failure or inability to adequately supervise the child.

Under section 72(1), the duty to report applies to those who perform professional or official duties with regard to children, including health care professionals, teachers, counsellors, clergy, youth and recreation workers, service providers, peace officers, coroners and solicitors. It is an offence for these people to fail to report as required and, upon conviction, they may be fined up to $1,000 (s. 72(4) and (6.2)). The reporting obligation is ongoing. Any person who has additional grounds to suspect one of the above circumstances must promptly report these grounds to a Children's Aid Society, even if he or she has made previous reports regarding the child (s. 72(2)). Reports must be made directly to a Children's Aid Society. A person must not rely on a third person to report on his or her behalf (s. 72(3)). The term "child" is defined, for the purposes of reporting, as a person under 16 years of age. These duties to report apply even if the information is confidential or privileged (s. 72(7)). However, nothing in this section overrides the privilege that may exist between a solicitor and his or her client (s. 72(8)).

No action can be brought against a person for complying with these reporting obligations, unless he or she acted unreasonably or in bad faith (s. 72(7)).

Civil Liability for Failing to Control or Warn

Traditionally, the law did not require an individual to control the conduct of another person, whether to protect that person or others whom he or she might foreseeably endanger. Although the courts continue to pay lip service to the concept that "you are not your brother's keeper," they have recognized a growing number of special relationships in which one party will be held civilly liable for negligently failing to control the conduct of another. It is now well established that such a relationship exists between:
• children and their parents and teachers (*Myers* v. *Peel County Board of Education*, 1981; *Bain* v. *Calgary Board of Education*, 1993; *La Plante* v. *La Plante*, 1995)
• police and prisoners (*Williams* v. *New Brunswick*, 1985; *Reeves* v. *Commissioner of Police*, 1999)
• employers and employees (*Jacobsen* v. *Nike Canada Ltd.*, 1996; *Barrett* v. *Ministry of Defence*, 1995).

The courts have consistently held that a similar relationship exists between health care professionals and their clients (Mustafic v. Smith (G.), 1988; Molnar v. Coates, 1991; Monteith v. Hunter, 2001).

Several challenging issues may arise in applying these principles to substance use workers. Consider a situation in which an intoxicated client attends a counselling session and causes a car accident while driving home. The counsellor may be sued for negligently allowing the client to leave in a condition that posed a foreseeable risk of injury to the client and others. Such a case might succeed if the counsellor had been negligent in failing to recognize the client's intoxication, or had realized that the client was impaired but did not make a reasonable effort to stop him or her (see *Monteith* v. *Hunter*, 2001).

A health care professional who learns of a client's plan to commit a serious crime may be held accountable for failing to warn or otherwise protect the intended victim. Although Canadian courts have not yet addressed this issue, some American courts have made health care professionals liable in these situations. In the leading case of *Tarasoff* v. *Regents of the University of California* (1976), the court held that a psychologist owed a duty of care to warn the intended victim of one of his patients. The patient, who was being treated at the University Hospital, told his psychologist that he would kill his former girlfriend when she returned from her vacation. The psychologist concluded that the patient was dangerous, and contacted campus police. The patient was picked up, briefly detained, then released. Neither the former girlfriend nor her family were warned. When the former girlfriend returned from vacation, the patient killed her. In imposing a "duty to warn" on the psychologist and the university, the court emphasized that the psychologist's confidentiality obligation to his patient ended when the public peril began.

A treatment professional may realize during treatment that a young client is endangered by his or her substance use problems, physical condition or home situation. If the client is within the age limit of the provincial child protection legislation, then the matter must be reported. In this case, there is no breach of confidentiality because the disclosure is mandated by law.

A more difficult situation arises if the client is older and no mandatory reporting obligation exists. If the counsellor breaches the client's confidence, it is possible that he or she may be sued or prosecuted. However, this is unlikely if the counsellor breached confidence in a reasonable effort to protect the client from serious harm. If the counsellor maintains confidentiality and the client is injured, then the counsellor may be sued for failing to protect the client.

As in *Tarasoff*, the situation becomes more complex when the choice is between maintaining the client's confidentiality and protecting an innocent third party. There have been several successful suits against American health care professionals for failing to act in these circumstances, but no comparable Canadian cases. Although the following Supreme Court of Canada case did not specifically address a treatment professional's civil liability for failure to warn, it strongly suggests that the public interest (in averting risk of death and injury) should prevail over doctor-patient confidentiality.

In *Smith* v. *Jones* (1999), a psychiatrist interviewed the accused at the request of his lawyer. The accused, who was charged with the aggravated sexual assault of a prostitute, told the psychiatrist that he planned to kill prostitutes. The psychiatrist told the lawyer that the accused was dangerous and would likely commit future crimes. The accused pleaded guilty, but the psychiatrist's concerns were not addressed at the sentencing hearing. The psychiatrist sought a declaration allowing him to disclose the privileged information in the interest of public safety. The Supreme Court of Canada stated that danger to public safety may, in appropriate circumstances, justify setting aside solicitor-client privilege. The Court stated that there must be a clear risk of imminent serious bodily harm or death to an identifiable person or group. The Supreme Court upheld the psychiatrist's request for a declaration authorizing disclosure of the privileged information.

Conclusion

Treatment professionals should assume that all client information is confidential, but that nothing will be privileged. As a working guideline, information should not be disclosed without the client's consent, unless the professional is compelled by law to do so.

The statutory requirements governing disclosure and reporting are complex and varied. They may be supplemented by the rules that agencies or institutions adopt. Moreover, additional requirements may be imposed by the governing bodies of particular professions. This chapter covered the general principles and specific examples of common situations, but it is up to each substance use worker to determine the requirements that pertain to his or her specific situation.

ENDNOTES

1. Depending on the facts, a physical interference can give rise to one or more civil actions in tort: battery (physical contact); assault (threat of immediate physical contact); and false imprisonment (imposition of a total restraint of movement).
2. However, some discretion must be exercised in disclosing confidential information even to colleagues; see *Re: Lavasseur and College of Nurses of Ontario* (1983), 18 A.C.W.S. (2d) 126 (Ont. H.C.).
3. See, for example, Manitoba *The Highway Traffic Act*, S.M. 1985–86, c. 3, s. 157(1); British Columbia *Motor Vehicle Act*, R.S.B.C. 1996, c. 318, s. 230; Ontario *Highway Traffic Act*, R.S.O. 1990, c. H.8, ss. 203(1) and 204(1). See also Nova Scotia *Motor Vehicle Act*, R.S.N.S. 1989, c. 293, s. 279(7), which authorizes, but does not require, medical practitioners to report patients who may be unfit to drive.

REFERENCES

Picard, E. (1979). Onus of proving consent to trespass to the person: On whom does it rest? *Alberta Law Review, 17,* 322.

Sim, P. (1984). Privilege and confidentiality: The impact of *Slavutych* v. *Baker* on the Canadian law of evidence. *Advocates' Quarterly, 5,* 357.

Sopinka, J., Lederman, S. & Bryant, A. (1999). *The Law of Evidence in Canada* (2nd ed.). Markham, ON: Butterworths.

Statutes

Canada Evidence Act, R.S.C. 1985, c. C-5.
Child and Family Services Act, R.S.O. 1990, c. C.11.
Child and Family Services Act, S.M. 1985–86, c. C.80.
Criminal Code, R.S.C. 1985, c. C-46.
Education Act, R.S.O 1990, c. E.2.
Health Care Consent Act, S.O. 1996, c. 2.
Health Protection and Promotion Act, R.S.O. 1990, c. H.7.
Human Tissues Gift Act, R.S.O. 1990, c. H.20.
Mental Health Act, R.S.O. 1990, c. M.7.
Regulated Health Professions Act, 1991, S.O. 1991, c. 18.
Social Work and Social Service Work Act, 1998, S.O. 1998, c. 31.

Cases

Allan v. *New Mount Sinai Hospital* (1980), 28 O.R. (2d) 356 (H.C.), reversed on other grounds
    (1981), 33 O.R. (2d) 603 (C.A.).
Arndt v. *Smith* (1997), 35 C.C.L.T. (2d) 233 (S.C.C.).
Attorney General of British Columbia v. *Astaforoff,* [1984] 4 W.W.R. 385 (B.C. C.A.).
Attorney-General of Canada v. *Notre Dame Hospital* (1984), 8 C.R.R. 382 (Que. S.C.).
Bain v. *Calgary Board of Education* (1993), 18 C.C.L.T. (2d) 249 (Alta. Q.B.).
Barrett v. *Ministry of Defence,* [1995] 3 All E.R. 87 (C.A.).
Bettel v. *Yim* (1978), 20 O.R. (2d) 617 (Co. Ct.).
Boase v. *Paul,* [1931] 4 D.L.R. 435 (Ont. S.C.).
Bolduc v. *R.* (1967), 63 D.L.R. (2d) 82 (S.C.C.).
Buchan v. *Ortho Pharmaceutical (Can.) Ltd.* (1986), 25 D.L.R. (4th) 658 (Ont. C.A.).
Colet v. *The Queen,* [1981] 1 S.C.R. 2.
Cronkwright v. *Cronkwright* (1971), 14 D.L.R. (3d) 168 (Ont. H.C.).
C. v. *Wren* (1986), 35 D.L.R. (4th) 419 (Alta. C.A.).
"Eve" v. *"Mrs. E.",* [1986] 2 S.C.R. 388.
Gibbs v. *Gibbs* (1985), 1 W.D.C.P. 6 (Ont. S.C.).
Gilbert v. *Stone* (1648), 82 E.R. 539 (K.B.).
Gillick v. *West Norfolk and Wisbech Area Health Authority,* [1985] 3 All E.R. 402 (H.L.).

Guimond v. *Laberge* (1956), 4 D.L.R. (2d) 559 (Ont. C.A.).

Halls v. *Mitchell*, [1928] 2 D.L.R. 97 (S.C.C.).

Haughian v. *Paine* (1987), 40 C.C.L.T. 13 (Sask. C.A.).

Hopp v. *Lepp* (1980), 112 D.L.R. (3d) 67 (S.C.C.).

In Re B (A Minor), [1981] 1 W.L.R. 1421 (C.A.).

Jacobsen v. *Nike Canada Ltd.* (1996), 133 D.L.R. (4th) 377 (B.C. S.C.).

Johnston v. *Wellesley Hospital*, [1971] 2 O.R. 103 (H.C.).

Kelly v. *Hazlett* (1976), 1 C.C.L.T. 1 (Ont. H.C.).

Kenlin v. *Gardiner*, [1967] 2 Q.B. 510 (Q.B.).

Kenny v. *Lockwood*, [1932] 1 D.L.R. 507 (Ont. C.A.).

Koechlin v. *Waugh* (1957), 11 D.L.R. (2d) 447 (Ont. C.A.).

Lacroix (Litigation Guardian of) v. *Dominique* (2001), 6 C.C.L.T. (3d) 212 (Man. C.A.).

La Plante v. *La Plante* (1995), 125 D.L.R. (4th) 596 (B.C. C.A.).

Latter v. *Braddell* (1880), 50 L.J.Q.B. 166 (C.P.).

Leung v. *Campbell* (1995), 24 C.C.L.T. (2d) 63 (Ont. Gen. Div.).

MacKinnon v. *Ignacio, Lamond and MacKeough* (1978), 29 N.S.R. (2d) 656 (S.C.).

Male v. *Hopmans* (1967), 64 D.L.R. (2d) 105 (Ont. C.A.).

Malette v. *Shulman* (1990), 67 D.L.R. (4th) 321 (Ont. C.A.).

Marshall v. *Curry*, [1933] 3 D.L.R. 260 (N.S. S.C.).

McInerney v. *MacDonald* (1992), 93 D.L.R. (4th) 415 (S.C.C.).

Meyer Estate v. *Rogers* (1991), 6 C.C.L.T. (2d) 102 (Ont. Gen. Div.)

Molnar v. *Coates* (1991), 5 C.C.L.T. (2d) 236 (B.C. C.A.).

Monteith v. *Hunter* (2001), 8 C.C.L.T. (3d) 268 (Ont. S.C.J.).

Mulloy v. *Hop Sang*, [1935] 1 W.W.R. 714 (Alta. S.C.).

Murray v. *McMurchy*, [1949] 2 D.L.R. 442 (B.C. S.C.).

Mustafic v. *Smith (G.)* (1988), 55 Man. R. (2d) 188 (C.A.).

Myers v. *Peel County Board of Education* (1981), 123 D.L.R. (3d) 1 (S.C.C.).

O'Brien v. *Cunard S.S. Co. Ltd.* (1891), 28 N.E. 266 (S.J.C. Mass.).

Parmley v. *Parmley and Yule*, [1945] 4 D.L.R. 81 (S.C.C.).

Pittman Estate v. *Bain* (1994), 112 D.L.R. (4th) 257 (Ont. Gen. Div.)

Pohoretsky v. *The Queen* (1987), 33 C.C.C. (3d) 398 (S.C.C.).

Reeves v. *Commissioner of Police of the Metropolis*, [1999] 3 All E.R. 897 (H.L.).

Reibl v. *Hughes* (1980), 114 D.L.R. (3d) 1 (S.C.C.).

Re Lavasseur and College of Nurses of Ontario (1983), 18 A.C.W.S. (2d) 126 (Ont. H.C.).

Re Riverdale Hospital and C.U.P.E. (1985), 19 L.A.C. (3d) 396.

Re Superintendent of Family & Child Services and Dawson (1983), 145 D.L.R. (3d) 610 (B.C. S.C.).

Re T, [1992] 4 All E.R. 649 (C.A.).

Reynen v. *Antonenko* (1975), 30 C.R.N.S. 135 (Alta. S.C.).

Rice v. *Connolly* (1966), 2 Q.B. 414 (Q.B.).

R. v. *B.* (1979), 2 Fam. L. Rev. 213 (Ont. Prov. Ct.).

R. v. *Carroll* (1959), 23 D.L.R. (2d) 271 (Ont. C.A.).

R. v. *Cuerrier* (1998), 162 D.L.R. (4th) 513 (S.C.C.).

R. v. *Dersch*, [1993] 3 S.C.R. 768.

R. v. *Dyment* (1988), 45 C.C.C. (3d) 244 (S.C.C.).

R. v. *Greffe*, [1990] 1 S.C.R. 755.

R. v. *Gruenke*, [1991] 3 S.C.R. 263.

R. v. *R.S.* (1985), 19 C.C.C. (3d) 115 (Ont. C.A.).

Schweizer v. *Central Hospital* (1974), 6 O.R. (2d) 606 (H.C.).

Semeniuk v. *Cox* (1999), 48 C.C.L.T. (2d) 286 (Alta. Q.B.).

Slavutych v. *Baker*, [1976] 1 S.C.R. 254.

Smith v. *Jones*, [1999] 1 S.C.R. 455.

Smith v. *Stone* (1647), 82 E.R. 533 (K.B.).

Strachan v. *Simpson*, [1979] 5 W.W.R. 315 (B.C. S.C.).

Tarasoff v. *Regents of the University of California*, 17 Cal. Rptr. 3d 425 (U.S. 1976).

Tremblay v. *McLauchlan* (2001), 6 C.C.L.T. (3d) 238 (B.C. C.A.).

Van Mol (Guardian ad litem of) v. *Ashmore* (1999), B.C.J. No. 31 (C.A.).

Villeneuve v. *Sisters of St. Joseph of Diocese of Sault Ste. Marie* (1971), 18 D.L.R. (3d) 537 (Ont. H.C.).

Williams v. *New Brunswick* (1985), 34 C.C.L.T. 299 (N.B. C.A.).

Chapter 6

Tips for Testifying in Court

SYDNEY J. USPRICH, ROBERT M. SOLOMON AND CATE SUTHERLAND

WHY ME?

Substance use workers who deal with clients involved in the criminal justice system may, at some point, have to appear in criminal court. The most common reasons are (1) to provide evidence about a client's attendance (or non-attendance) or participation in a treatment program, and (2) to explain substance use assessment findings or treatment recommendations relating to a client. Substance use workers may also have to appear in family court to testify in child welfare matters. Some children in our society are, unfortunately, affected by the substance use problems of adults. When such a situation comes to the attention of an authority, it is often referred to court for resolution. Situations that may require a counsellor's testimony include disagreements regarding custody of, or access to, children, and court cases in which the Children's Aid Society (CAS) is following a complaint that a child needs protection. Family court also handles criminal matters involving young offenders (ages 12 to 17).

Testifying in court does not rank high on anyone's list of enjoyable activities, but if you are subpoenaed as a witness in a trial or other hearing, you must attend and give evidence. Remember that you are not on trial. You are simply doing your duty by telling the court what you know, in order to help the court arrive at a fair decision.

For the layperson, the courtroom can be an intimidating place, and appearing there can be stressful. But the experience need not be as unpleasant as some people fear. The more you understand about the process of testifying, and the better prepared you are, the less uncomfortable the experience will be.

Providing testimony in an efficient, professional manner is an easily learned skill. This chapter outlines a number of steps you can take to reduce your stress and to ensure that the image you present in court reflects the credibility and quality of your program. It offers advice on preparing for court appearances and testifying, and provides tips on courtroom etiquette.

PREPARATION

Learn about Courts

Preparation should start long before you appear in court. If you have never been to criminal court before, sit through some criminal proceedings to familiarize yourself with the procedures. Pay close attention to how things are done so you will know what to expect. This will help eliminate the fear of the unknown.

If you want to observe the proceedings in family court, prior arrangements may be required. Since matters handled by family court involve children, the proceedings are closed to the public for the obvious reason of preserving the child's privacy. However, you can usually arrange to observe family court by calling the court office to explain your purpose.

After you have observed some court proceedings, envision yourself on the stand, calmly responding to questions. Before your first court appearance, it may help to have someone rehearse, or role-play, with you.

Talk to the Lawyers

Once you learn that you may be called as a witness, find out whether you will appear for the Crown or for the defence counsel (the client's lawyer). You will probably have been contacted by a lawyer for the side planning to call you as a witness. Tell the lawyer as early as possible about any dates on which it would be difficult to attend court. For example, you may have vacation travel plans that would make it extremely disruptive and expensive to attend court on certain dates. The earlier the lawyer knows this, the easier it will be to arrange a more convenient date.

As part of their preparation, most lawyers try to meet their prospective witnesses to review the witnesses' evidence. Accordingly, you may be contacted long before the trial by the lawyer or someone else from his or her law firm to discuss your testimony.

There is no legal requirement for you to participate in this sort of discussion. In a strict legal sense, a subpoena obligates you only to appear in court and give evidence. However, as well as helping the lawyer, the pretrial discussion can help you as a witness. You will learn in advance the type of questions you will be asked when you testify.

The lawyer for the other side may also contact you to discuss the case and the evidence you will be giving. You do not have to participate in such a discussion, but there is nothing improper about doing so. The side calling a witness does not "own" that witness; any witness is free to talk to the other side to the extent that he or she wishes. You may wish to seek guidance from your employer or from the lawyer for whom you will be testifying as to whether, and to what extent, you should co-operate with the counsel for the other side.

After reviewing your records and speaking to the lawyer(s), you will have some idea of what you plan to say in court. But sometimes questioning takes unexpected turns. For example, the Crown attorney may tell you that you will be asked to testify on the client's poor attendance in the program, but on cross-examination the defence lawyer may focus on the subject matter of the client's sessions.

Review Your Client's Records

Preparation for testifying also involves reviewing your client's records. Thorough and accurate records are indispensable to witnesses. Records help reconstruct the facts of a case. A trial often takes place several years and hundreds of clients after an event occurred, and the records may be the only way a substance use worker can recall the details of the case.

In addition, the records themselves can be invaluable during the trial or hearing. A record that the witness made or approved close to the time of the event can be used by the witness while testifying (see Sopinka et al., 1999, ss. 16.77–16.98). Furthermore, the actual record may be admissible as documentary evidence, even if the witness does not testify (see *Ares* v. *Venner*, 1970; for an example of a statutory provision, see the Ontario *Evidence Act*, ss. 35 & 52). At times this use of the record is vital. For example, if the potential witness has died or is otherwise unavailable, the record may become the sole source of information and evidence.

The state of the records can influence a witness's credibility in court. A witness who faces the court armed with a complete record of facts and observations is in a strong position. If the record is accurate, objective and complete, the witness will be perceived as organized, methodical and conscientious.

But be forewarned that if you use a file on the witness stand, it can be taken from you to be entered as an exhibit. When you take a file to court, always photocopy the contents beforehand and leave the copies in your office.

Make Notes

As well as reviewing official records, it is often useful to make additional notes as soon as you learn that you will be a witness. Litigation is a slow process, and considerable time may elapse before the trial takes place. As soon as you know that you may be a witness, make notes of everything you remember about relevant matters to help pre-serve your memory of those events. Since these notes are made after the events in question, you cannot use them when testifying. Nonetheless, the notes can be useful to refresh your memory prior to testifying.

DAY OF THE TRIAL

When the day comes, remember to bring any relevant records or documents, as instructed by the lawyer who requested your testimony, and any personal notes you have made. Arrive at the courthouse a few minutes early. Let the lawyer for whom you are appearing know that you are there, ask if there are any last-minute changes, and briefly review your testimony.

If the trial is in progress, check with the court usher to see whether there has been an order excluding witnesses. At some trials, the judge may make such an order at a lawyer's request. In such cases, witnesses are not allowed in court to hear other wit-nesses prior to giving their own testimony. In that event, it would be improper for you as a witness to enter the courtroom, so you could simply wait, or ask the usher to take a note to the lawyer.

When you are called to the witness stand, you will be "sworn in" before giving evidence. The usual procedure is to be sworn in by taking an oath on the Bible. Since the Christian Bible contains the Old Testament, many members of the Jewish faith are content to swear on the standard Bible. If your religious beliefs require that the oath be taken in a different way, this is permissible, but you should inform the lawyer in advance so that arrangements can be made. For example, a Muslim may wish to take the oath on the Koran, which may not be routinely available. As well as informing the lawyer in advance of any special requirements, it may be simplest for the witness to bring along the appropriate holy book or other objects needed.

Witnesses who object to swearing a religious oath have the option of "affirming" the truth (see, for example, *Canada Evidence Act*, s. 14). This is simply a solemn promise, without any religious connotations, to tell the truth. It is best if you advise the lawyer in advance that you intend to affirm, rather than take an oath.

GIVING EVIDENCE

After the oath or affirmation formalities, you are ready to give your evidence. The lawyer calling a witness begins with what is known as "examination-in-chief" or "direct examination." Once the lawyer who called you as a witness finishes asking questions, it becomes the turn of the lawyer for the other side. This latter questioning is called "cross-examination." At the conclusion of the cross-examination, the witness's testimony has usually ended, but sometimes the original lawyer may ask further questions in "re-examination."

The judge, who may also ask questions at any stage, usually tells you when you are finished as a witness and may leave the witness stand. Unless you have been told that you are subject to recall as a witness, which rarely occurs, you may either leave the court or take a seat in the courtroom audience. Even if there has been an order excluding witnesses, it no longer applies to you after you have finished giving evidence.

Be Clear and Concise

When giving evidence, as a rule, give brief, direct answers to direct questions. Do not elaborate unless specifically requested to do so and, even then, be concise.

Answer only what is asked of you. Do not offer information that is not requested, even if you think it is important. Remember, you are not in court to tell a story, but merely to provide evidence. In addition, do not let yourself get caught up in explaining the rationales of your field. Speak only about the particular client in his or her particular situation.

Give your testimony in a clear, well-modulated voice, loud enough to be heard by all. Speaking inaudibly implies that you lack confidence in the information you are giving, and makes it hard for others to understand you.

Take your time. Hurried answers are sometimes incorrect answers. Give your answers in words so a proper record can be made. For example, answer "Yes," rather than nodding your head. If you happen to respond with physical motions or gestures, the lawyer questioning you may describe your response to "talk it onto the record." For example:

LAWYER: How big was the knife?

WITNESS: About this long.

LAWYER: The witness is indicating with her hands a length of about six inches.

In assessing a witness's evidence, the court often considers not only what you say, but also how you say it. Your credibility can be affected by both your verbal and non-verbal presentation on the stand. You should answer in a clear, straightforward manner and avoid being either hesitant or arrogant. However, if you are unsure about something, it is not fair to anybody to answer with a confidence you do not feel.

Court Decorum

Stand (or sit, if invited) in the witness box as calmly as you can, without giving the impression that you are a mannequin. There is a fine line here. You do not want to appear so relaxed that you seem indifferent to the proceedings. On the other hand, you do not want a ramrod posture to project an air of nervousness and rigidity. If you are standing, keep your hands out of your pockets.

Wear your "poker face" to court. Do not react visibly to what you hear. You should appear totally objective at all times.

Courts generally have rather specific, though unwritten, rules on what is considered proper attire—conservatism is the name of the game. This usually means suits, or at least a shirt and tie for men, and suits or dresses for women. Generally, hats are not permitted in court.

When sitting in court before or after giving evidence, do not talk during the proceedings. If you find it necessary to communicate with someone, speak in the most discreet whisper. Better yet, pass a note.

Addressing Members of the Court

When giving evidence, speak directly to the person asking the question, and make eye contact. Never address the defendant directly while you are on the stand. Do not refer to an adult client by his or her first name; use "Mr." or "Ms."

Lawyers are also addressed as "Mr." or "Ms.," or simply "Sir" or "Ma'am" (Madam). Although it will rarely arise, you may wish to refer to a trial lawyer other than the one who is currently questioning you. Aside from referring to the lawyer by name ("Mr./Ms. Smith"), you may—especially if you don't know the lawyer's name— refer to him or her simply as "counsel" (where the context makes clear to which lawyer you are referring) or "counsel for Mr. Jones," "counsel for the hospital," etc. In most jurisdictions, you should address the judge as "Your Honour." The correct terminology will depend on the level of court and the province in which the trial takes place. You can ask the lawyer beforehand, or simply copy the terminology the lawyers use in addressing the judge. As an easy alternative, simply address the judge as "Sir" or "Ma'am." If you need to refer to the judge in the third person, the correct form is "His/Her Honour."

Do not address the judge directly unless he or she has spoken to you first. The only exception to this rule is when you need to refer to the file or your notes. Generally, you are expected to provide your testimony without looking in the file while you are on the stand. If you need to do so, turn to the judge and ask, "May I refer to my notes, Your Honour?" The judge will probably give permission. But, if the witness must rely on notes rather than his or her recollection, lawyers have the right to determine whether the notes are reliable. This typically consists of questions about when the notes were made.

Direct Examination

Direct examination typically begins with mundane matters such as the witness's name and relevant qualifications. The lawyer will often recite this information and simply expect the witness to agree:

> LAWYER: You are Mary Smith and are employed as a counsellor at the Central Addictions Centre?
>
> WITNESS: Yes, sir.
>
> LAWYER: The Central Addictions Centre is located at 123 Main Street in downtown Blankville?
>
> WITNESS: That's right.
>
> LAWYER: I understand that in your professional capacity you were providing counselling to John Doe in May of 2002?
>
> WITNESS: Yes, he had been seeing me professionally from March through June of that year.

Particularly if you are being called as an "expert" witness, the lawyer may wish to bring out extensive details of your professional qualifications, such as education, experience and membership in professional bodies. Such issues should be discussed well before the trial, so the witness can be properly prepared with the appropriate information. Indeed, the lawyer may have requested a curriculum vitae or résumé for this purpose.

Cross-Examination

The opposing lawyer (i.e., a lawyer who did not call the witness to testify) may try to achieve several goals through cross-examination. The lawyer may try to get more information from the witness that will help the other side, or new facts that may weaken evidence already given. The lawyer may try to get the witness to qualify an earlier answer, concede that there is some doubt on a particular point, or admit that an alternative explanation is possible.

Sometimes, the lawyer may attempt to weaken evidence by discrediting a witness. There may be an effort to suggest that the witness is mistaken, biased, forgetful, or not credible for a variety of other reasons.

Some lawyers will ask convoluted or awkward questions, and it can be hard to understand just what they want to know. Listen carefully to the question and make sure you understand before you reply. Do not hesitate to admit your confusion. Simply say, "I'm sorry, I don't understand the question. Could you please repeat it?"

This forces the lawyer to rephrase the question in a clearer form, and also gives you a few extra seconds to form an answer.

Although lawyers should not do so, they sometimes ask "double-barrelled" questions. This is especially likely in cross-examination, where the lawyer can ask leading questions that require only a "yes" or "no" answer. If you simply answer yes or no, it may be unclear whether your answer is in response to both halves of the question or only the last part. It is best to respond to such double questions by explicitly answering both halves. For example, a witness might be asked, "Was the client intoxicated and attempting to attack you?" Rather than answering "Yes," it is clearer if the witness were to say, "Yes, he appeared drunk and attempted to attack me."

Another awkward type of question is one framed in the negative. For example: "You didn't see him do it, did you?" A simple reply of "No" could mean either "No, I didn't see" or "No, I disagree with you. I did see." Make sure that your answer is properly understood by responding fully: "No, I didn't see."

A device that lawyers commonly use in cross-examination is to cut a witness off before he or she can give a full answer or a qualification to an answer. The result may be that your answer is misleading because it is incomplete. If that should happen, ask the lawyer, firmly and courteously, to let you complete your answer. Often, however, the judge or the other lawyer will intercede on your behalf, asking that you be allowed to finish.

Sometimes, cross-examination gets rough. While it may feel like a personal attack, it is not. Remember, a lawyer's first obligation is to his or her client, and it is the lawyer's duty to test all evidence vigorously. While the lawyer may be aggressive toward you on the stand, you will probably find that this ends at the courtroom door.

Must I Answer?

Generally, witnesses must answer all relevant questions put to them. Privilege is one of the few exceptions to that general rule. The legal term "privilege" means the right to refuse to disclose confidential information when giving testimony. (Privilege is discussed in more detail in Chapter 5. For a comprehensive review of privilege, see Sopinka et al., 1999, Chapter 14.) Traditionally, the only professional relationship to which privilege applied was that between solicitors and their clients. In the absence of privilege, a person who refuses to answer a question when required to do so may be jailed for contempt of court.

Canadian law has no equivalent to the American device of "taking the Fifth." Under the Fifth Amendment to the U.S. Bill of Rights, a witness may refuse to answer a question that tends to incriminate him or her. In Canada, a witness would have to answer such a question. However, the *Canadian Charter of Rights and Freedoms* protects a witness from having any incriminating answer used against him or her in any other proceedings (except a prosecution for testifying falsely; *Charter*, s. 13.). This protection automatically applies to all the witness's answers without the witness having to ask for it.

Limits on Testimony

Generally, a witness's testimony is confined to information within his or her personal knowledge—that is, evidence based on his or her own observations rather than on what other people may have told the witness. As a result, a witness is not usually allowed to give what lawyers call "hearsay" evidence.

The rule against hearsay means you will often not be allowed to repeat what other people have told you. The hearsay rule is complex and not always easy to apply. First, the rule has many exceptions that permit hearsay evidence to be given. Second, hearsay evidence will not always be in the obvious form ("Charlie told me . . . "). For example, information that the witness obtained from someone else's notes may be considered hearsay.

As a witness, you are not expected to be a lawyer with expert knowledge of the hearsay rule. When you discuss your evidence with the lawyer before the trial, he or she can advise you as to what conversations you may or may not be allowed to repeat because of the hearsay rule. If the issue arises while you are giving evidence, it is always appropriate to ask the trial judge whether you may say what someone has told you.

In situations where you are allowed to repeat statements that other people have made, these statements may sometimes include offensive language. There is no need to be embarrassed by this. The judge and the lawyers have undoubtedly heard such language before. Bear in mind that it is not you who used that language; you are merely quoting what someone else has said. The importance of the evidence might depend on the fact that the speaker used that language. While it is best to quote the speaker's words as accurately as possible, you can paraphrase the words if you are truly uncomfortable repeating them. In that case, you should make clear that you are doing so.

Another area with restrictions on testimony involves the giving of opinions or conclusions by a witness. Only an expert witness testifying specifically on a matter within his or her area of expertise may give an opinion. An ordinary witness must give only his or her observations, not the opinions or conclusions that the witness may have drawn from those observations. However, a witness may give opinions about common matters on which, in a sense, everybody is an "expert." For example, a witness could testify that someone appeared drunk, was happy or sad, and so forth. Again, you are not expected to be a lawyer and to know all the fine distinctions. The lawyers and the judge will provide guidance on what you may or may not say.

The lawyers and the judge have a shared responsibility to keep inadmissible evidence out of the trial. If some evidence that you are about to give is inadmissible because of the hearsay rule, the opinion rule or some other reason, you may be interrupted and told not to give that evidence. Sometimes this interruption will take the form of an objection by the lawyer who is not currently questioning you. He or she will interrupt by saying "Objection" or "I object." If that happens, stop what you are saying. The judge, after listening to both lawyers' arguments, will decide whether the evidence is admissible and will advise you whether you can continue.

Family Court

Many of the procedures related to testifying in criminal court also apply to family court. However, a few differences between these courts are noted in this section. For example, as a witness in family court, you are less likely to be permitted in the courtroom during other testimony in the case. Instead, you will have to wait in the outer area until called to give your testimony.

Another minor difference involves the number of lawyers that participate in the proceedings. In provincial criminal matters, there are typically two lawyers—the Crown and the defence. Child welfare cases, however, often have more than two lawyers, because anyone who is a party in the case could be represented. A child could have a separate lawyer, as could the Children's Aid Society, if involved, and other parties such as the parents (separately or together) or a third party seeking custody or access. This does not necessarily mean that each lawyer will have many questions or that you will be on the stand for longer, although both are possible. Typically, one or two lawyers will elicit the main parts of your testimony. The others may ask a few more questions to clarify or obtain slightly different types of information.

This leads to the most important differences between family and criminal court—the nature of testimony and witness status. In child welfare matters, there can be a wider interpretation of the relevance of evidence, giving lawyers more latitude in the questions asked or the avenues explored with witnesses. Decisions made in family court profoundly affect the lives of children, so it is understandable that the court would wish to hear any pertinent information.

So, as you prepare for court by determining the expected direction of your testimony and carefully reviewing your client files, realize too that questions may arise that do not seem directly related to the client's treatment or your involvement with the client. In such situations, you must carefully decide whether you know the answer. Remember, witnesses can only testify about what they know.

Consider the following illustration. Let's suppose that, during treatment, Mr. Smith, a single father, reports that his drinking has been a problem for about 10 years. Among other things, he tells you that he is often hung over and that he often slips some whisky in his morning coffee, while his 12-year-old son, Junior, is eating breakfast. Mr. Smith says his son is often with a babysitter while he is at a bar, and when he drinks at home, his son stays in his room. He also admits that he has missed a couple of Junior's school functions because he was drinking, which made his son angry. Mr. Smith says he feels bad about all this, and intends to make it up to Junior. Later, in court, you are asked about Mr. Smith.

> LAWYER: How has Mr. Smith's drinking problem interfered with his ability to be a good father to Junior?
>
> WITNESS: I'm sorry. I can't answer that question. As Mr. Smith's substance use worker, I'm not qualified to comment on his abilities as a father.

The point is that you must consider the whole question and its implications, then decide whether you can answer it as asked. Mr. Smith provided plenty of information about his drinking and his son, but the question was about his "ability to be a good father." Carefully heed previous advice in the chapter about answering questions, and do not extrapolate pieces of information. For instance, the information in Mr. Smith's scenario speaks volumes about his alcohol problem, but really says nothing concrete about his ability to care for the child.

Another aspect of the special nature of testimony in family court involves the witness's status. The limits on testimony by a witness or expert witness are described elsewhere in the chapter. For substance use workers and other professionals, questions in family court often fall in a grey area, eliciting testimony that falls somewhere between personal and expert knowledge. In this grey area, it is assumed that the witness has a certain amount of knowledge, based on overall experience and observations, as a result of employment in the profession. Questions and answers in this area need the assent of the court. The seeking of assent is often prompted by an objection from one lawyer to another lawyer's question, usually on the basis that it calls for an opinion or is not specific to the client.

If allowed, such questions are typically very general in nature. Unless the worker has a head full of statistics, they tend to result in the witness giving a sort of personal "semi-opinion" or conclusion. Examples of these types of questions are:

> Based on your experience, is it common for a person's drinking problem to affect other family members?
>
> In the five years you have been employed as a substance use worker, what have you observed about . . . ?

Again, think before answering, and try to avoid bias. Also avoid the use of absolute terms like "never" or "always." Begin your answers with phrases such as "It is my experience that . . . " or "I have observed that . . . " Also, if needed, insert qualifiers such as "It is my experience that it is common for . . . , but that it does not occur in every case."

Finally, a caution about expert witness status. It is typically reserved for people with significant experience, who have been advised prior to the case that they will testify as an expert. In such cases, the witness's status is established at the beginning of his or her testimony. However, be aware that a lawyer can also seek expert status for a witness, without prior warning, during the witness's testimony.

The testimony of substance use workers is often very important to judgments made in family court. Be prepared and take the responsibility seriously. Your expertise can be a considerable help to the court.

Conclusion

Although testifying in court will never be a delight, it need not be a dreaded, anxiety-filled experience. Understanding what is expected of you as a witness will make testifying less intimidating. Good preparation is even more important. While this may seem like a lot of work for a few minutes on the stand, the effort will be worthwhile. If you are prepared, you will feel more comfortable and be able to give your evidence in a relaxed, straightforward manner. This will enable you to make a better impression as a witness and to leave court feeling that you made a significant contribution to the administration of justice.

REFERENCES

Ares v. *Venner*, [1970] S.C.R. 608.

Canada Evidence Act, R.S.C. 1985, c. C-5.

Canadian Charter of Rights and Freedoms.

Evidence Act, R.S.O. 1990, c. E.22.

Sopinka, J., Lederman, S. & Bryant, A. (1999). *The Law of Evidence in Canada* (2nd ed.). Markham, ON: Butterworths.

Chapter 7

Guidelines for Advising on Alcohol Treatment Goals

MARTHA SANCHEZ-CRAIG, D. ADRIAN WILKINSON AND TONY TONEATTO

INTRODUCTION

When treating clients for alcohol problems, the therapist has to decide whether to discuss a choice of goals with the client. Allowing clients to choose between abstinence and moderation is still anathema to many in the field of treatment. Others, with equal passion, see the denial of choice as a denial of the dignity and respect that they are ethically bound to accord their clients. This furious controversy has been portrayed alternately as a clash of ideologies and as a straightforward disagreement about the interpretation of scientific facts. Some have argued that, since this question is a controversy only in certain cultural contexts, it must be largely sociocultural in origin. (Readers can review Duckert et al., 1989; Fingarette, 1988; Heather, 1989; Heather & Robertson, 1983; Kissin, 1983; MacAndrew & Edgerton, 1969; Peele, 1984, 1987; Sobell & Sobell, 1986/87; and Wallace, 1987a, 1987b for varied treatments of these issues.)

We believe that all the above interpretations of the controversy are valid:

1. There are differing conceptions of alcohol dependence, some consistent with choice of goal, others not (Chaudron & Wilkinson, 1988; Sobell & Sobell, 1986/87). These various conceptions often lead to irresolvable definitional problems. These are ideological differences and those who hold a particular position may be unwilling to modify their stance, regardless of the persuasiveness of alternative arguments.

2. Interpretations of the scientific data vary. Scientists have failed to reach consensus about valid empirical tests of the advisability of offering choice to clients, so there are varying interpretations of these data (Ambrogne, 2002; Adamson & Sellman,

2001; Booth et al., 1992; Hodgins et al., 1997; Heather, 1989; Heather & Robertson, 1983; Sobell & Sobell, 1986/87).

3. There is considerable cultural variation in the perceived importance of the issue, so the importance of cultural context is clear (Ambrogne, 2002; Dawe & Richmond, 1997; Rosenberg et al., 1996; Miller, 1986; Peele, 1984, 1987). Traditionally, controlled drinking goals have been more acceptable in Europe and Canada than in the United States.

This chapter makes no attempt to resolve any of these issues. It is a practical guide for practitioners who already believe that most clients with alcohol-related problems should be encouraged to choose whether to aim for abstinence or moderation. People who doubt the wisdom of offering such choice are referred to the extensive literature aimed at resolving this question. Those convinced that encouraging choice is rash must only deplore the inclusion of this chapter in a book such as this. The rest of this chapter will explore goal choice in more depth, including a discussion of types of clients for whom a choice of abstinence is the only practical option.

AIMS OF CHAPTER

Our aim is to review empirical and conceptual factors that have a direct bearing on the advice that should be given to clients who are in the process of choosing their goal. We attempt to identify the information that should be brought to the client's attention, in the hopes of influencing the decision process. We also offer guidelines to identify the minority of clients who, in our opinion, should not be offered choice. In addition, we suggest a sequence that permits the most effective provision of advice to clients selecting their goals. Thus, most of the chapter is very practically oriented.

Clients Who Should Not Be Encouraged to Choose Their Goal

Broadly speaking, two groups of clients should not be offered the choice between abstaining or moderating their use of alcohol:

1. clients for whom it is illegal to use alcohol. The legal prohibition might relate to the age of the client or to a court order, such as conditions of probation.

2. clients who are judged mentally or developmentally incompetent to exercise responsible choice. Under this circumstance, it is a clear professional responsibility not to offer choice. In some jurisdictions, alcohol use might not be illegal for young people, but their lack of maturity could nonetheless rule out discussion of alcohol use as an option. In addition, since alcohol use can result in serious cognitive impairment (Parsons et al., 1987), some people who are dependent on alcohol may not be mentally fit to choose their goal responsibly. This state may be transitory for some clients, such as those who come to treatment sessions intoxicated, when the issue of goal choice would not be fruitfully addressed.

With these general exceptions, we believe clients should be encouraged to choose their goals. This does not, of course, mean the therapist will not try to influence the choice. The therapist should have significant input into the decision process, sometimes actively recommending one option on the basis of the considerations set out in the following sections.

INFORMATION TO BE REVIEWED AS A PRECURSOR OF CLIENT CHOICE

Client's Medical Status

With certain medical conditions, any alcohol use is inappropriate. Examples are active liver disease or cirrhosis, pancreatitis, bleeding ulcers or esophageal varices. Clients should ask their physician whether they have any physical condition that would make any use of alcohol inadvisable. The physician's opinion should be reviewed with the therapist in considering the goal. Therapists should strongly recommend abstinence for clients whose physicians advise them not to drink. If the client insists that he or she will continue to drink, the therapist should urge minimal use, such as purely ceremonial use.

Risks of Alcohol Consumption

Clients should know the risks of alcohol consumption, both acute and chronic. In our program at the Centre for Addiction and Mental Health, we attempt to ensure that clients know the risks of intoxication, the effects of varying doses of alcohol, and the long-term health risks of different levels of use. We also emphasize the relevance of individual differences (e.g., gender, physique) to the risks of drinking. Our program stresses: "All drinking has risks. If you want to avoid the risks, don't drink." This warning applies both to the risks of intoxication and to chronic effects.

Family History and the Choice of Goal

About 40 per cent of the clients in our program report a history of alcohol dependence among first-degree relatives (a "positive family history"). We have found that clients with a positive family history have rates of successful outcome very similar to those of clients with a negative family history (Sanchez-Craig et al., 1987). Clients in our program with a positive family history are not more likely to choose abstinence rather than moderation as their goal. However, among clients who successfully choose to reduce their drinking, those with a positive family history tend to use alcohol much less frequently than their counterparts with a negative family history. We review this finding with our clients as something to consider when setting their own goal. We also inform them that another investigator has reported that clients with a positive family history were more likely to choose abstinence than moderation in a program offering choice of goals (Miller & Joyce, 1979).

Drinking History and the Choice of Goal

When considering the choice of goal in treatment sessions, we discuss the client's lifetime history of drinking. If the client has an extensive history of problem-free drinking, or of problem-free drinking in particular circumstances (e.g., when drinking at home with the family), then the therapist is more likely to support a goal of moderation. When the client's problems began at the outset of drinking, and the client almost always drinks heavily, then abstinence is more strongly recommended. This is because clients will probably be more successful in reacquiring old habits of moderation, or maintaining the habit of situationally specific moderation, than in acquiring a brand-new pattern of alcohol use.

In addition, if the client becomes intoxicated almost every time he or she drinks, it suggests that intoxication has been the sole purpose of the person's alcohol use. This may be because the client has difficulty controlling drinking once he or she begins, or may point to the presence of concurrent mental health problems that the client is "self-medicating" through the use of alcohol. Clients aiming for moderation should do so to enjoy alcohol for refreshment, to enhance meals and to participate in ceremonial and social functions, but not explicitly to become intoxicated. Hence, if the sole attraction of alcohol has been intoxication, moderation is likely to be an unattractive goal and is discouraged by the therapist. The client's cultural milieu is likely to be particularly relevant here. In certain cultures, such as Scandinavian cultures, intoxication is a fairly common goal of drinking, whereas other cultures, such as Italian and Spanish, strongly disapprove of intoxication. Canada, being multicultural, contains considerable local cultural variations in attitudes to alcohol use and intoxication. These variations should be borne in mind in working with clients.

Another important consideration when reviewing the client's history is how the client has acted in the past when intoxicated. If intoxication has caused marked changes in behaviour, particularly antisocial or reckless behaviour, then the risks associated with any drinking are increased. Hence, if a client has a history of such behaviour changes when intoxicated, the therapist is likely to more strongly recommend a goal of abstinence.

History of Treatment and the Choice of Goal

Many clients tell us they have avoided seeking treatment because they were afraid that a goal of lifelong abstinence would be imposed upon them, and that treatment workers would not consider them serious about change unless they accepted the imposed goal. With such clients, we stress that flexibility of goal choice is a feature of our approach.

Other clients tell us they have experience with abstinence-based approaches, and that abstinence is their preferred route. We also see clients who have sampled 12-step approaches and other programs that insist on abstinence as the only appropriate goal, but who felt those concepts were not suited to them. Hodgins et al. (1997), in a study of outpatient clients, found that choosing abstinence was related to a history of AA attendance. In each of these types of case, the client's past history of treatment (or avoidance of treatment) quickly focuses the therapist on important aspects of the person's self-concept and probable goal preference.

In addition to considering the client's attitudes to previous treatment efforts, it is important to review the outcomes of earlier treatment. In our experience, clients who have had lengthy periods of successful abstinence often want to return to that path, though they may prefer a new treatment approach with a different philosophical or theoretical basis. We have also seen some clients who have determined to switch from successful abstinence to moderate drinking, and are looking for guidance on how to minimize the risks of the transition. We do not counsel clients to switch from long abstinence to moderation, but will assist those who have decided on their own to make the change and who ask for help. Recent long-term follow-up studies in Sweden show that many former treatment clients successfully take this route without any therapeutic assistance (Nordström & Berglund, 1987). A third type of outcome is reported by clients who have received traditional abstinence-focused treatment, but have rejected the idea of "loss of control over drinking." After participating in the previous program, these clients unsuccessfully attempted moderate drinking. They come to us seeking advice on how they can more effectively attempt moderation of alcohol use.

Alcohol Dependence and the Choice of Goal

One of the principal objectives of many programs incorporating flexible goals has been to encourage people who are not severely dependent on alcohol to enter treatment. The rationale has been that these people are often deterred from seeking treatment by fear that abstinence will be the only legitimate goal of treatment (see e.g. Sanchez-Craig et al., 1987; Sanchez-Craig & Wilkinson, 1986/87). Interviews with clients about why they have avoided treatment for years (despite recognizing the problems caused by their alcohol use) confirm the validity of this assumption in many cases. Thus, programs offering moderation are frequently targeted to clients who are not severely dependent on alcohol.

Another reason to target such clients has been the controversial nature of the goal of moderation. It is less contentious to offer choice to these clients than to clients with severe alcohol dependence, who as a group have a high incidence of illnesses (e.g., cirrhosis, esophageal varices) that make any drinking inadvisable. As a result, flexibility of goal choice is seen as less desirable for this group. Furthermore, many severely dependent drinkers have had numerous contacts with treatment agencies and self-help groups, and already believe that choice of goals is not a realistic option. Early studies also suggest that clients with relatively low levels of alcohol dependence were more likely to successfully moderate drinking, whereas abstinence was more often achieved by those more severely dependent on alcohol (Adamson & Sellman, 2001; Hodgins et al., 1997; Orford et al., 1976; for a review see Sobell & Sobell, 1986/87).

Gender and the Choice of Goal

A number of studies have found that women are more likely than men to successfully moderate drinking after treatment (Miller & Caddy, 1977; Sanchez-Craig et al., 1989, 1991). This finding applies when the outcome criterion is an arbitrary definition of moderate drinking selected by the investigators; when the outcome measure is reports of alcohol-related problems, the gender difference is less likely to be observed. In addition, there appears to be a gender difference in the type of intervention to which men and women respond best (Sanchez-Craig et al., 1989, 1991). Hence, though there is some evidence that women are more likely to attain moderate drinking, we do not believe that current data warrant different advice to women and men about abstinence or moderation as their goal.

The Role of Client Preferences and Beliefs

It derives directly from the philosophical grounding of our approach (Sanchez-Craig, 1990) that client preferences and beliefs are among the most crucial data we consider when working with clients on goal selection. However, this is not merely an ideological preference. There are data that support this position, and we review them briefly here.

Among traditionalists, client preference for flexibility in treatment goals tends to be seen as evidence of "denial." This presumed symptom of the "disease" of alcoholism is considered part of the innate personality of the "alcoholic" (Miller & Sovereign, 1989), which must be challenged and overcome before treatment can succeed. It is certainly true that many people with alcohol dependence minimize, trivialize and rationalize their dependence, but it does not necessarily follow that this is a symptom of disease. Rather, denial may be viewed as a natural psychological reaction to the judgments of others about one's behaviour and abilities. This view is supported by the evidence that directive or confrontational therapists tend to engender resistance in their clients (Patterson & Forgatch, 1984). Thus, the denial by traditionalist therapists of autonomy for their clients can provoke a reactive denial of problems by the clients. This is not to say that people who drink excessively do not falsely deny that their drinking causes problems. The issue is how best to undercut their denial. In many cases, confrontation seems merely to strengthen it.

Miller (1983, 1985, 1987) has reviewed the literature on clients' motivation for treatment and its relation to their goals, and concluded that:

> Personal goals are an important aspect of motivation for change. The pro-
> vision of negotiable and alternative treatment goals can encourage early
> intervention, compliance with recovery related programs, and favorable
> treatment outcome (1987, p. 133).

As a direct test of this conclusion, Miller & Sovereign (1989) varied the directive-ness of feedback to clients who received their "Drinker's Check-up," an assessment aimed at motivating people who drink heavily to change their drinking patterns. Clients who received directive feedback showed significantly greater resistance (argu-ing, interrupting and changing the subject) and denial (minimizing the problem) than those who were given the same feedback in a non-confrontational, non-directive manner. The resistant clients also had poorer outcomes. Thus, the therapists' behaviour engendered resistance and contributed to poorer outcome.

Orford & Keddie (1986) examined the relative importance of clients' preferences and beliefs versus their level of alcohol dependence as predictors of outcome among clients offered a choice of goals. They found that clients' preferences and beliefs appear to be more strongly related to outcome than is their level of dependence.

Sanchez-Craig et al. (1984) randomly assigned people with drinking problems to the goal of abstinence or to a condition allowing clients to choose their own goals. Clients who were offered choice were more accepting of the assigned condition, were more successful in the initial phases of treatment, and required fewer elective coun-selling sessions during the aftercare phase of the program. Of particular importance was the subsequent discovery that the benefits of choice were most apparent among those clients who drank most heavily before treatment (Sanchez-Craig & Lei, 1987), and who had higher levels of alcohol dependence. In short, clients given choice were less resistant and more successful, particularly those with evidence of a more severe problem. Thus it appears that respecting the judgment of clients is more than just a philosophically based value held by certain therapists. It has beneficial effects on the outcome of treatment.

Many therapists sincerely believe that giving any credence and respect to the opinions of "alcoholics" about their ability to moderate their drinking successfully is either naive or professionally irresponsible. Failure to confront alcoholic denial is con-sidered by such clinicians to be "enabling the alcoholic's addiction." Our problem with this position is precisely that it represents a statement of belief by certain thera-pists. The assertion has not been scientifically or clinically tested. In our view, the "denial" of greatest concern here is the denial of appropriate services to people with alcohol-related problems because of the untested beliefs of many treatment workers. There is nothing wrong with having a diversity of treatment approaches for alcohol dependence, since we do not definitively know of an effective treatment, and there are strong theoretical and empirical reasons for expecting that there is no uniquely good approach (Cox, 1987; Miller & Heather, 1986). If one view of appropriate treatment prevails, and its disciples are able to suppress the offering of alternative approaches without scientific justification, then our clients and the public will be very poorly served. In the absence of evidence to the contrary, we urge that clients be given the dignity of being treated as if they are not self-deluded, which is the basic assertion of the construct of denial.

Environmental Constraints on the Choice of Goal

In some cases, environmental factors may argue against advising moderation as the goal of treatment. We review those most frequently encountered below.

FAMILY AND SOCIAL NETWORK

If trying to moderate drinking is likely to cause serious tensions in the client's family or with other close associates, we tend to urge the client to consider abstaining, at least in the medium term. Sometimes such tensions arise because other family members have successfully completed programs that stress the disease concept of alcoholism, and the imperative for abstinence. In other cases, family members may have been frequently wounded (emotionally or physically) by the client's intoxicated behaviour so that the prospect of any drinking is stressful enough to jeopardize the relationship.

LEGAL STATUS

If a client has been referred because of a legal problem caused by alcohol use or involving intoxicated behavior, it may be unwise to recommend a goal of moderation. This is clearly the case when drinking is precluded by the terms of probation. Sometimes the client's legal counsel strongly recommends abstinence, and this opinion too should weigh heavily. In general, if drinking has caused legal problems that are unresolved at the time of the client's treatment, abstinence is likely to be a prudent goal.

OCCUPATIONAL FACTORS

Certain work environments promote drinking. Working in bars and restaurants, in either a service or entertainment capacity, often involves high availability of alcohol and considerable social pressure to drink. Because of these conditions, some of our clients who work in such establishments have opted for abstinence. Members of the armed forces often have access to alcohol at low prices through the various social clubs for military personnel. In such settings, social pressures to drink are often strong. Because of the combination of high availability and social pressure, this occupational group may also prefer to abstain.

CULTURAL FACTORS

As we have previously discussed, in certain cultures moderate alcohol use in social gatherings is very much the norm, whereas in others occasional heavier use is more common (MacAndrew & Edgerton, 1969). When discussing treatment goals with clients, it is important to consider such variation in cultural background, and the influence it can have on the meaning of alcohol use.

Another cultural factor that can influence the client's preparedness for moderate drinking is the culture of youth. In Canada, in our experience, many young people have most of their early drinking experiences outside the family, for example with peers at parties, where the goal of drinking is frequently intoxication. Consequently, many young people develop drinking problems with almost no experience of using alcohol in moderation. This history suggests a longer period of abstinence before a goal of moderation is attempted, and a thorough examination by therapist and client of the personal meaning of alcohol use to the client.

Clearly, several factors can be considered in recommending controlled drinking versus abstinence. While no single factor has been shown to consistently predict success in controlling drinking, Rosenberg (1993) found in his review of the literature that factors associated with successful controlled drinking included less severe alcohol dependence, being employed, being younger, being female and being psychosocially stable.

MODERATE DRINKING: HOW MUCH IS TOO MUCH?

By moderate drinking we mean drinking at a level that does not jeopardize one's health, one's ability to carry out day-to-day responsibilities (at home, at work or in the community) or one's safety or the safety of others. This definition implies that moderate drinking involves abstaining in a number of circumstances, such as before or during driving or conducting hazardous tasks (at work or play) and when pregnant or breastfeeding.

Note that this is not a prescription for "safe" or risk-free drinking. The only incontrovertibly safe level of drinking is abstinence. Many of our clients acknowledge this fact but still wish to attempt "low-risk" drinking. Then they ask what guidelines we can give them. We tell them what drinking levels our clients have reported when they claim to suffer no adverse effects of their drinking (Sanchez-Craig, 1986; Sanchez-Craig & Israel, 1985). In a number of studies, we have found that very few clients who stay within these guidelines report adverse effects of their drinking. Some who drink over the guidelines also report no adverse effects, but the risk increases as the level of drinking increases.

Those who become moderate drinkers after attending our clinic:*

- have two or more abstinent days each week
- do not consume more than four standard drinks (if male) or three standard drinks (if female) on any day
- do not consume more than 12 standard drinks (if male) or nine standard drinks (if female) in any week
- avoid drinking to cope with problems of daily life (e.g., drinking to blunt emotions or facilitate some action such as asserting oneself)
- do not use alcohol frequently in association with recreational activities and free-time activities.

We stress to clients that the pattern of drinking they establish should fit with their lifestyle, while avoiding adverse consequences. We also stress that the limits clients set should be what they judge to be their upper limit of sensible drinking. The goal is not a target that the clients are aiming to achieve each day or each week, but is the upper limit of what they consider prudent for themselves.

Setting the Goal

THE INITIAL GOAL

In discussing with clients their approach to their longer-term goal (whether abstinence or moderation), we present three possible routes:

1. to taper down from the present high level of alcohol use until the level of the longer-term goal is reached (whether it is abstinence or a specified level of moderate use). Few clients choose this route; those who select it usually drink quite heavily (usually 10 or more drinks a day) and fear the effects of abrupt withdrawal of alcohol.
2. to abstain or start drinking at a moderate level immediately, and continue with this pattern
3. to start with an initial period of abstinence before deciding on the longer-term goal. This approach allows more time to carefully weigh the pros and cons of each option. It is the route we generally recommend to clients.

Our program thus distinguishes between the initial goal of treatment and the longer-term goal. If the client believes that he or she can accomplish it, we recommend an initial goal of a short period of abstinence—usually two or three weeks. (The research that supports this recommendation is presented and reviewed

---

*Editors' note: These authors' guidelines are based on a clinical population (people who have had problems with alcohol and who are reducing their consumption). Guidelines developed for the general population often differ. For example, the Centre for Addiction and Mental Health recommends no more than two drinks on any day for the general population, while the National Institute of Alcohol Abuse and Alcoholism (1995) suggests a maximum of one drink a day for women and two drinks a day for men.

in Sanchez-Craig & Lei, 1987, and Sanchez-Craig et al., 1987.) We give the client the following rationale for an initial period of abstinence:

- We have found that clients who manage to abstain for the first three weeks of the program are more successful at achieving long-term moderation.
- An initial period of abstinence significantly reduces the person's tolerance for alcohol, so that returning to previous drinking levels would cause unpleasant effects of intoxication. In addition, marked loss of tolerance clearly shows the client the physical benefits of the change in his or her drinking.
- Cognitive abilities dulled by long-term heavy use of alcohol are likely to improve significantly in two to three weeks of abstinence, but not if the client merely reduces use, even if the reduction is quite substantial.
- Clients will discover how they cope spontaneously with temptations to drink and with social pressures to drink. Discovering such existing coping skills can help the client achieve his or her longer-term goal, whatever that goal might be.

SPECIFYING THE GOAL

If a client chooses a goal of abstinence, he or she is choosing, simply, to not drink alcohol under any circumstances. The therapist and client usually agree on a date to review the suitability of the abstinence goal.

Moderate use can range from rare ritual or ceremonial use to specified levels of regular drinking. When clients specify their goal we ask them to specify seven conditions of moderation:

- **maximum daily quantity**: the maximum number of drinks the client will consume in any day
- **maximum frequency**: the maximum number of drinking days in any week
- **maximum weekly quantity**: the maximum number of drinks the client will consume in any week (this is often less than maximum daily quantity multiplied by maximum frequency)
- **types of beverage**: the types of alcoholic drink that the client plans to avoid completely. Most frequently mentioned are more concentrated drinks such as straight liquor or cocktails, which can more readily lead to intoxication.
- **contexts for abstinence**: situations of high risk for drinking excessively, in which the client resolves not to drink at all
- **contexts for drinking**: environmental, social, cognitive or emotional contexts in which the client has identified low risk of excessive drinking and good coping skills, and in which he or she may drink moderately
- **assessment period**: the number of weeks or months over which the client will assess the goal's suitability.

Additional guidelines summarized by Ambrogne (2002) advise that clients should not consume more than one drink per hour, and that they should never drink when operating hazardous machinery or doing any activity that could be harmful if performed under the influence of alcohol, or if they are pregnant or breastfeeding.

Clients are always urged to attempt realistic goals. By this we mean goals that may initially be challenging, but which the client believes he or she can attain. We encourage clients not to set goals that they are unlikely to achieve. It is better for the person to approach the ultimate goal gradually than to set himself or herself up for disappointment by choosing unrealistic goals.

We also review with clients the most constructive way of interpreting failure to achieve their goal. Initial failure is an opportunity for the person to learn how to be more successful in the future, rather than an indication of personal inadequacy.

We tell clients that the goal is not "carved in stone." It can be adjusted from time to time until it suits the client's lifestyle, while causing no alcohol-related problems. From time to time (e.g., holidays), clients may relax the criteria for a brief period. However, we stress that changes to the goal should be very deliberate, and should not be undertaken while the client is under the influence. Changing the goal on such occasions can serve as a rationalization for drinking too much.

As part of the treatment plan we structure a set of follow-up appointments to review the client's success in achieving his or her goals. At these sessions the client can make further adjustments to the specified goal. Structuring the follow-up emphasizes that the client should continue to abide by the treatment plan in order to succeed over the long term.

A FINAL WORD

Whether the therapist likes it or not, the client ultimately chooses his or her goal. The approach and considerations laid out in this chapter can serve as the basis for making that choice rational and collaborative. In our experience, dogmatic assertions by therapists about what clients can and cannot do tend to undermine the establishment of a collaborative therapeutic relationship.

REFERENCES

Adamson, S.J. & Sellman, J.D. (2001). Drinking goal selection and treatment outcome in out-patients with mild–moderate alcohol dependence. *Drug and Alcohol Review, 20*, 351–359.

Ambrogne, J.A. (2002). Reduced-risk drinking as a treatment goal: What clinicians need to know. *Journal of Substance Abuse Treatment, 22*, 45–53.

Booth, P.G., Dale, B., Slade, P.D. & Dewey, M.E. (1992). A follow-up study of problem drinkers offered a goal choice option. *Journal of Studies on Alcohol, 53*, 594–600.

Chaudron, C.D. & Wilkinson, D.A. (Eds.). (1988). *Theories on Alcoholism*. Toronto: Addiction Research Foundation.

Cox, W.M. (Ed.). (1987). *Treatment and Prevention of Alcohol Problems: A Resource Manual*. Orlando, FL: Academic Press.

Dawe, S. & Richmond, R. (1997). Controlled drinking as a treatment goal in Australian alcohol treatment agencies. *Journal of Substance Abuse Treatment, 14*, 81–86.

Duckert, F., Koski-Jannes, A. & Ronnberg, S. (Eds.). (1989). *Perspectives on Controlled Drinking*. Helsinki, Finland: Hakapaino Oy.

Fingarette, H. (1988). *Heavy Drinking: The Myth of Alcoholism as a Disease*. Berkeley: University of California Press.

Heather, N. (1989). Controlled drinking treatment: Where do we stand today? In T. Loberg, W.R. Miller, P.E. Nathan & G.A. Marlatt (Eds.), *Addictive Behaviors: Prevention and Early Intervention* (pp. 31–50). Amsterdam: Swets and Zeitlinger.

Heather, N. & Robertson, I. (1983). *Controlled Drinking* (Rev. ed.). London: Methuen.

Hodgins, D.C., Leigh, G., Milne, R. & Gerrish, R. (1997). Drinking goal selection in behavioral self-management treatment of chronic alcoholics. *Addictive Behaviors, 22*, 247–255.

Kissin, B. (1983). The disease concept of alcoholism. In R.G. Smart, F.B. Glaser, Y. Israel, H. Kalant, R.E. Popham & W. Schmidt (Eds.), *Research Advances in Alcohol and Drug Problems* (Vol. 7; pp. 93–126). New York: Plenum.

MacAndrew, C. & Edgerton, R.B. (1969). *Drunken Comportment: A Social Explanation*. Chicago: Aldine.

Miller, W.R. (1983). Motivational interviewing with problem drinkers. *Behavioral Psychotherapy, 11*, 147–172.

Miller, W.R. (1985). Motivation for treatment: A review with special emphasis on alcoholism. *Psychological Bulletin, 98*, 84–107.

Miller, W.R. (1986). Haunted by the Zeitgeist: Reflections on contrasting treatment goals in Europe and the United States. In T. Babor (Ed.), *Alcohol and Culture: Comparative Perspectives from Europe and America* (pp. 110–129). New York: Annals of the New York Academy of Sciences.

Miller, W.R. (1987). Motivation and treatment goals. *Drugs and Society, 1*, 133–151.

Miller, W.R. & Caddy, G.R. (1977). Abstinence and controlled drinking in the treatment of problem drinkers. *Journal of Studies on Alcohol, 38*, 986–1003.

Miller, W.R. & Heather, N. (Eds.). (1986). *Treating Addictive Behaviors: Processes of Change.* New York: Plenum.

Miller, W.R. & Joyce, M.A. (1979). Prediction of abstinence, controlled drinking and heavy drinking outcomes following behavioral self-control training. *Journal of Clinical and Consulting Psychology, 47*, 773–775.

Miller, W.R. & Sovereign, R.G. (1989). The check-up: A model for early intervention in addictive behaviors. In T. Loberg, W.R. Miller, P.E. Nathan & G.A. Marlatt (Eds.), *Addictive Behaviors: Prevention and Early Intervention* (pp. 219–231). Amsterdam: Swets and Zeitlinger.

National Institute on Alcohol Abuse and Alcoholism (1995). *The Physician's Guide to Helping Patients with Alcohol Problems.* Publication No. 95-3769. Rockville, MD: National Institutes of Health.

Nordström, G. & Berglund, M. (1987). Aging and recovery from alcoholism. *British Journal of Psychiatry, 151*, 389–392.

Orford, J. & Keddie, A. (1986). Abstinence or controlled drinking in clinical practice: A test of the dependence and persuasion hypotheses. *British Journal of Addiction, 81*, 495–504.

Orford, J., Oppenheimer, E. & Edwards, G. (1976). Abstinence or control: The outcome of excessive drinking two years after consultation. *Behavior Research and Therapy, 14*, 409–418.

Parsons, O.A., Butters, N. & Nathan, P.E. (Eds.). (1987). Neuropsychology of Alcoholism: Implications for Diagnosis and Treatment. New York: Guilford Press.

Patterson, G.R. & Forgatch, M.S. (1984). Therapist behavior as a determinant for client noncompliance: A paradox for the behavior modifier. *Journal of Consulting and Clinical Psychology, 53*, 846–851.

Peele, S. (1984). The cultural context of psychological approaches to alcoholism. *American Psychologist, 39*, 1337–1351.

Peele, S. (1987). Why do controlled drinking outcomes vary by investigator, by country and by era? *Drug and Alcohol Dependence, 20*, 173–201.

Rosenberg, H. (1993). Prediction of controlled drinking by alcoholics and problem drinkers. *Psychological Bulletin, 113*, 129–139.

Rosenberg, H., Devine, E.G. & Rothrock, N. (1996). Acceptance of moderate drinking by alcoholism treatment services in Canada. *Journal of Studies on Alcohol, 57*, 559–562.

Sanchez-Craig, M. (1986). How much is too much? Estimates of hazardous drinking based on clients' self-reports. *British Journal of Addiction, 81*, 251–256.

Sanchez-Craig, M. (1990). Brief didactic treatment for alcohol and drug-related problems: An approach based on client choice. *British Journal of Addiction, 85*, 169–177.

Sanchez-Craig, M., Annis, H.M., Bornet, A.R. & MacDonald, K.R. (1984). Random assignment to abstinence and controlled drinking: Evaluation of a cognitive-behavioral program for problem drinkers. *Journal of Consulting and Clinical Psychology, 52*, 390–403.

Sanchez-Craig, M. & Israel, Y. (1985). Pattern of alcohol use associated with self-identified problem drinking. *American Journal of Public Health, 75*, 178–180.

Sanchez-Craig, M. & Lei, H. (1987). Disadvantages to imposing the goal of abstinence on problem drinkers: An empirical study. *British Journal of Addiction, 81*, 505–512.

Sanchez-Craig, M., Leigh, G., Spivak, K. & Lei, H. (1989). Superior outcome of females over males after brief treatment for the reduction of heavy drinking. *British Journal of Addiction, 84*, 395–404.

Sanchez-Craig, M., Spivak, K. & Davila, R. (1991). Superior outcome of females over males after brief treatment for the reduction of heavy drinking: Replication and report of therapist effects. *British Journal of Addiction, 86*, 867–876.

Sanchez-Craig, M. & Wilkinson, D.A. (1986/87). Treating problem drinkers who are not severely dependent on alcohol. *Drugs and Society, 1*, 39–67.

Sanchez-Craig, M., Wilkinson, D.A. & Walker, K. (1987). Theory and methods for secondary prevention of alcohol problems: A cognitively based approach. In W.M. Cox (Ed.), *Treatment and Prevention of Alcohol Problems: A Resource Manual* (pp. 287–331). New York: Academic Press.

Sobell, M.B. & Sobell, L. (Eds.). (1986/87). Moderation as a goal or outcome of treatment for alcohol problems: A dialogue. *Drugs and Society, 1*, 1–171.

Wallace, J. (1987a). Waging the war for wellness. Part I: The attack of the "antitraditionalist lobby." *Professional Counsellor* (January/February), 21–39.

Wallace, J. (1987b). Waging the war for wellness. Part II: The attack upon the disease model. *Professional Counsellor* (March/April), 21–27.

Chapter 8

Relapse Prevention

MARILYN A. HERIE AND LYN WATKIN-MEREK

INTRODUCTION

The chronic, relapsing nature of alcohol and other drug problems has been recognized since the early 1970s (Hunt et al., 1971). In the late 1970s and early 1980s, researchers began to focus on the factors that affect the process of relapse (Litman et al., 1979, 1984; Wilson, 1980) and on the development of "relapse prevention" treatment strategies (Marlatt & Gordon, 1985; Annis, 1986). Despite advances in substance use treatment, relapse prevention continues to be a major issue. For this reason, many researchers have come to regard addiction as a "chronic relapsing disorder" (Dimeff & Marlatt, 1998). In other words, relapse prevention should be regarded as a series of small steps towards change rather than as a wholesale solution to the problem of relapse.

Relapse is defined as a failure to maintain behavioural change, rather than a failure to initiate it. Treatment approaches based on social learning theory, specifically Bandura's theory of self-efficacy, hold that the strategies that are effective in initiating a change in drinking or drug use behaviour may be ineffective at maintaining that change over time and avoiding relapse (Bandura, 1977, 1978, 1986). Definitions of relapse have evolved over time from "all or nothing" (relapse occurs at the time of first drink or drug use) to consider the nuances of quantity/frequency measures, lifestyle changes and progress in the direction of change (Dimeff & Marlatt, 1998).

This chapter examines the nature of relapse, along with some key questions: What is it? How do we define it? Are there problems with the term "relapse" itself? We then briefly review the major relapse prevention models developed by Terrence

Gorski (1989) and Alan Marlatt (1985, 1996) and the Structured Relapse Prevention manual-based approach developed by Helen Annis and colleagues (1996). This review is followed by a discussion of research and practice implications of relapse prevention with diverse client populations. The chapter concludes with a brief discussion of empirical support for relapse prevention approaches.

TOWARD A DEFINITION OF RELAPSE

Addiction research and treatment has often been guided by binary thinking, where "alcoholism" can be compared to pregnancy: "either you have it or you don't, and there is nothing in between." (Miller, 1996, p. S15). This overly simplistic concep-tual-ization of a complex problem has also been applied to treatment outcomes, judging them as either successful (abstinent) or relapsed (non-abstinent). But if treat-ment success were always judged solely on abstinence alone, almost all who complete treatment would be considered to have relapsed.

As Miller (1996) puts it:

> Treating addictive behaviors seems not so much like turning off a water faucet, but more like diminishing and altering the flow of . . . water. At a societal level, it is like trying to change the flowing course of a stream. Sometimes the change is slight, and sometimes it is dramatic. Sometimes it is long lasting, and sometimes the stream quickly flows back into its original course (p. S16).

Categorizing substance use treatment outcomes as either abstinent or non-abstinent ignores the behavioural changes that may occur post-treatment. For example, there may be changes in the number of drinks consumed, the number of drinking days and the frequency of binge use. There may also be changes in the use of other drugs, including prescription, over-the-counter and nicotine.

Defining and categorizing types of relapse is also problematic. Asking a client whether he or she had a relapse can be interpreted in a number of ways: Did you drink (at all)? Did you drink above a certain threshold? Or, did you drink more than the limit you had set for yourself?

Miller (1996) suggests that the term "relapse" itself imposes "binary decision" or "either/or" rules on a person's behaviour. Such rules, used to determine whether or not a person has relapsed, are based on a number of often arbitrarily applied criteria, such as:

- threshold (the amount of substance use)
- window (the period of time judged)
- reset (the period of abstinence required before a person can be considered to have relapsed)
- polydrugs (the types of substance use that constitute a relapse)

• consequences (behaviours/consequences associated with substance use required before a person can be considered to have relapsed)
• verification (self-report or collateral reports).

That there is no single empirically or theoretically ideal combination of these factors highlights the inherent ambiguity in the term "relapse."

Miller (1996) further points out that the concept of relapse can, in itself, be harmful in its implicit imposition of a value judgment:

> Backsliding is an old synonym for sin, and few would fail to grasp which side of the relapse dichotomy is judged the more desirable. "Relapsed" has a connotation of failure, weakness and shame, of having fallen from a state of grace. Such overtones are likely to compromise self-regard and add needless affective meaning to what is a rather common behavioral event (p. S25).

Defining relapse—once thought to be straightforward—has proven to be more complex. Current definitions tend to be critical of the concept, and to take the person's movement in the direction of change into account.

PERSPECTIVES ON RELAPSE PREVENTION

The theory and practice of the major perspectives in relapse prevention are summarized here, followed by an overview of a manual-based approach, Structured Relapse Prevention (Annis et al., 1996), which was developed from Marlatt's (1985) model.

The Gorski Relapse Prevention Model

Terrence Gorski's model focuses on relapse prevention in the context of an abstinence-based, 12-step approach. In Gorski's view, chemical dependence is a disease that can be remitted only through total abstinence from all substances. Abstinence, however, is only the first step towards sobriety, which is defined as "a lifestyle that promotes continued physical, psychological, social and spiritual health" (Gorski, 1989, p. 3).

Gorski divides recovery into a series of stages through which the "addicted" person must progress to achieve sobriety: (1) transition; (2) stabilization; (3) early recovery; (4) middle recovery; (5) late recovery; and (6) maintenance. Progression through these stages can take 18 months or longer. Gorski provides a framework of self-reflective and interpersonal exercises that are tailored to each of these recovery stages and complement the approach and teachings of the 12 steps of Alcoholics Anonymous (AA). These tasks are intended to be completed in parallel with attendance at AA meetings.

Many of the relapse prevention exercises introduced by Gorski reflect cognitive-behavioural principles and methods. For example, in the stage of "early recovery," Gorski encourages individuals to reflect on both the "drinking problem and the thinking problem" (as it is called in AA). The latter refers to the irrational thoughts, unmanageable feelings and self-defeating behaviours that can often lead to a relapse. Gorski asks individuals to write down what they think of their "addicted self" versus their "sober self," and to note the feelings they have about each "self." The object of the exercise is to challenge the belief and experience of alcohol or other drug use as positive or enjoyable.

Gorski's model is far-reaching and comprehensive in that it addresses physical and mental health, social support, family of origin issues and self-esteem. Although the model has not been well-researched, increasing attention is being given to the efficacy of AA approaches to addiction treatment (see www.niaaa.nih.gov/publications/aa49.htm for a summary of recent research findings).

Although Gorski's model has helped many people to recover from their addictions, his approach, which relies on 12-step principles and teachings, may alienate clients who do not find that approach congenial to their belief systems or preferences. For example, the self-help group Women for Sobriety was founded in response to the AA emphasis on powerlessness over alcohol or other drugs (step one of the 12 steps). These women believed that they had already surrendered their power to a great extent through their own past experiences of abuse and oppression and that they needed to focus on reclamation of their personal power. Not all clients want to address (or find relevant) the spiritual component in AA teachings, and the emphasis on total abstinence from all substances may not be suitable for some clients. Gorski's recent work, however, is less explicitly reliant on the spiritual components of AA. See his chapter on relapse prevention with adolescent offenders at www.treatment.org/Taps/Tap11/tap11chap9.html.

The Marlatt Relapse Prevention Model

The work of Alan Marlatt has been enormously influential in addiction treatment and research. He provided a cognitive-behavioural framework with testable hypotheses and practical strategies for working with relapse.

Marlatt conceptualized relapse as a two-stage process, where the precipitants of substance use are distinct from the factors that prolong or sustain such use over time. Marlatt's research with people who experienced relapse (1980) led him to believe that relapse occurs as a result of a person's lack of coping skills to successfully avoid drinking or other drug use in certain challenging situations. Marlatt developed eight relapse determinants, or risk situations. These are:
• unpleasant emotions
• physical discomfort
• pleasant emotions

• tests of personal control
• urges and temptations
• conflict with others
• social pressure to use
• pleasant times with others.

Marlatt's approach to relapse prevention treatment focuses on providing coping skills training in the risk situations that are particular to each client.

Marlatt's taxonomy of risk situations is clinically useful in that it gives the therapist a "handle" on how to work with clients to prevent or discuss relapse. Relapse is therefore addressed

> in a pragmatic manner as an error, a lapse, a slip or temporary setback, and not an inevitable collapse on the road to recovery. Teaching people about high risk situations and how to cope with them more effectively is the essence of relapse prevention (Marlatt, 1996).

Marlatt's model, however, has some shortcomings. Saunders & Houghton (1996) point out that relapse precipitants may be multidimensional and highly complex. They note that additional variables, such as substandard housing, limited occupational opportunities, poor relationships and poverty can also impact behavioural change. Failure to cope may be evidence of a deficit in coping skills, but not necessarily. The person may choose not to employ coping skills because he or she is ambivalent about change. Saunders & Houghton (1996) also note that relapse can sometimes be helpful for clients who are ambivalent about change. The negative experience of a relapse can solidify intention to change. In addition, people with alcohol and other drug problems can have powerful attachments to their preferred substance, where giving up the substance can be compared to the ending of a love affair. Marlatt's taxonomy may not sufficiently capture the "magic" of the substance.

Marlatt (2002) has also conducted research and developed theory that applies Buddhist practices to relapse prevention. This groundbreaking work was inspired by his own experiences of the relaxing effects of transcendental meditation. Practices include the application of mindfulness to the internal monitoring of urges and cravings, accompanied by a lack of "attachment" to the urge to use. The efficacy of Buddhist practices such as mindfulness meditation in the prevention of relapse is supported by other research (Breslin et al., 2002), and interest in the compatibility of Buddhist teachings with cognitive-behavioural approaches is growing (see, for example, Campos, 2002, and Kumar, 2002). Buddhist thought and teachings, and related developments in relapse prevention theory and practice, are too complex to be done justice to here. Interested readers may wish to consult the articles cited. An on-line article by Parks & Marlatt (2000) on relapse prevention therapy can be found at http://nationalpsychologist.com/articles/art_v9n5_3.htm.

Structured Relapse Prevention: A Manual-Based Approach

The Structured Relapse Prevention treatment approach (SRP) developed by Helen Annis is designed for people with moderate to severe levels of alcohol or other drug dependence. Based on social learning theory developed by Albert Bandura, as well as on the work of Alan Marlatt (Marlatt & Gordon, 1985; Marlatt, 1996) and Prochaska & DiClemente (1992), the model provides a highly structured, manual-based approach to treatment.

SRP is currently used in addiction treatment centres throughout Ontario and is applied as both a group and an individual modality. Many adaptations, based on the populations served, sociocultural and linguistic considerations, as well as counsellor preferences, have been made to the model originally outlined in the manual (Annis et al., 1996). Such various iterations of SRP tend to conform to the basic two-phase approach, in which initiation-of-change strategies, such as avoidance and reliance on the support of others, are gradually complemented or replaced by more internalized coping strategies. SRP is also used by residential treatment centres to help prepare clients for their return to the community, and as part of after-care programs.

OVERVIEW OF STRUCTURED RELAPSE PREVENTION COUNSELLING

SRP counselling considers client readiness for change as defined by Prochaska and DiClemente's (1984) transtheoretical model. SRP comprises five components (see Table 8-1), each of which is matched to a stage of change. Clients progress through each component, advancing to the next level when they are ready. As indicated by the dotted-line arrows in Table 8-1, some clients may not progress through the stages in a linear fashion due to setbacks in their level of readiness for change.

At intake to SRP counselling, all clients receive a comprehensive assessment (Component 1), followed by feedback of results during one or more motivational interviewing sessions (Component 2). Clients who are willing to change their substance use will collaborate with their counsellor to develop an individually tailored treatment plan (Component 3). Only clients in the action stage of change—those who decide to try to implement the treatment plan and work toward change—sign a formal treatment contract and enter SRP counselling. The first phase of SRP focuses on powerful techniques designed to initiate and stabilize change (Component 4), while the second phase focuses on reducing clients' reliance on initiation strategies and substituting strategies that have greater potential for long-term maintenance of change in substance use behaviour (Component 5).

Each component of the treatment process is described in greater detail below, beginning with a discussion of the type of client for whom this treatment approach is likely to be most effective.

TABLE 8-1

Components of the Outpatient Counselling Program in Relation to Five Stages of Change

PROGRAM COMPONENT	STAGE OF CHANGE				
	Precontemplation	Contemplation	Preparation	Action	Maintenance
1. Assessment					
2. Motivational Interviewing					
3. Individual Treatment Plan					
4. SRP "Initiation" Counselling					
5. SRP "Maintenance" Counselling					

COMPONENT 1: ASSESSMENT

During the assessment component of SRP counselling, two treatment planning tools are administered. The first tool, the Commitment to Change Algorithm for Alcohol (CCA-A) and Drugs (CCA-D) is a brief and easy-to-use tool developed to assess clients' readiness to change (Schober & Annis, 1996a). The CCA is based on the trans-theoretical model (Prochaska & DiClemente, 1984) and classifies clients into one of five stages of change depending on recent drinking or other drug use, reported intention to change and recent quit/change attempts. Clients are placed in the highest stage for which they qualify. The second tool, the Inventory of Drug-Taking Situations (IDTS-50; Annis & Martin, 1985a) identifies any antecedents to alcohol and other drug use.

Examples of the CCA-A and CCA-D are shown in Table 8-2 on page 151, along with the definitions used for reduced drinking limits and quit attempts. Because the criteria for different stages are clear, a client's advancement to a higher stage, or regression to an earlier stage, can be readily tracked throughout treatment. High test-retest reliability for the CCA has been reported (Schober & Annis, 1996a).

The IDTS-50 is a 50-item assessment and treatment planning tool designed to provide a situational analysis of a client's substance use. This information is critical in understanding a client's motivation for substance use and in designing an individually tailored treatment program. The frequency of the client's past drinking or other drug use is assessed, following the classification system developed by Marlatt & Gordon (1980), across eight risk areas: unpleasant emotions, physical discomfort, pleasant emotions, tests of personal control, urges and temptations, conflict with others, social pressure to use and pleasant times with others.

The IDTS generates a personalized profile that provides a situational analysis of the client's substance use; Figure 8-1 shows a sample IDTS profile of a person who uses cocaine. This client is at high risk when experiencing unpleasant emotions and urges and temptations; thus, treatment planning would emphasize strategies targeted to these risk areas. The IDTS may be administered either in writing or by using computer interactive software.

COMPONENT 2: MOTIVATIONAL INTERVIEWING

The motivational interviewing approach is designed to help clients build commitment and readiness to change (Miller & Rollnick, 2002). Thus, motivation is not viewed as a static character trait, but rather as an expression of an individual's natural ambivalence toward change. In other words, motivation is a changeable state over which the counsellor can have considerable influence by actively engaging clients in changing their substance use. In SRP, the assessment process is conducted using techniques to build client motivation; for example, the personalized objective feedback of assessment results is excellent in building a client's commitment to change (Allsop, 1990; Saunders et al., 1991).

COMPONENT 3: INDIVIDUAL TREATMENT PLAN

One of the most important components of SRP counselling is treatment planning. We have found the following tools and techniques to be helpful in encouraging client collaboration in the development of a treatment plan for SRP counselling: goal setting and self-monitoring, identifying problem drinking or other drug use situations, identifying coping strengths and weaknesses, and contracting for treatment. Each step is described in more detail below.

Goal setting and self-monitoring can be useful ways of facilitating client participation in the treatment planning process. Clients use self-monitoring forms to note their substance use goal each week—including their level of confidence in achieving this goal—and keep a daily record of any substance use that took place, the circumstances surrounding that use, risky situations encountered and coping strategies used. Clients then discuss the self-monitoring with their counsellor during subsequent treatment sessions.

A fundamental part of planning for SRP treatment involves agreeing on the client's most problematic drinking or other drug use situations. The IDTS, which is given at assessment, provides this information in a systematic way, based on the types of situations that triggered substance use over the past year. After discussing the IDTS results and the daily monitoring, clients are asked to rank the three most problematic triggers to substance use that they want to work on in treatment, and to give specific examples of past drinking or other drug use experiences for each situation. This exercise allows clients to analyze past situations in detail in order to identify what they might do differently in similar situations in the future. In addition, because the maintenance phase of SRP counselling focuses on planned exposure to high-risk situations for substance use (see below), it is important that both client and counsellor have a detailed overview of past drinking or other drug use scenarios.

TABLE 8-2

Commitment to Change Algorithm (CCA): Tool Used to Classify a Client into One of Five Stages of Change

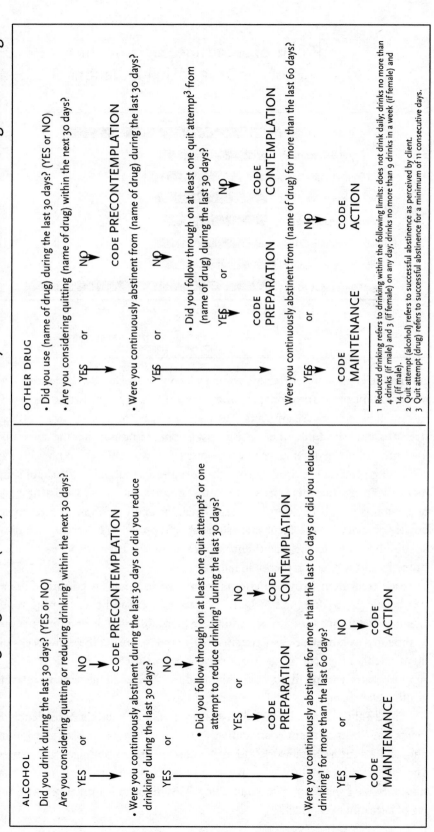

ALCOHOL

• Did you drink during the last 30 days? (YES or NO)

• Are you considering quitting or reducing drinking[1] within the next 30 days?

  YES   or   NO → CODE PRECONTEMPLATION

• Were you continuously abstinent during the last 30 days or did you reduce drinking[1] during the last 30 days?

  YES   or   NO

  • Did you follow through on at least one quit attempt[2] or one attempt to reduce drinking[1] during the last 30 days?

    YES   or   NO → CODE CONTEMPLATION

    CODE PREPARATION

• Were you continuously abstinent for more than the last 60 days or did you reduce drinking[1] for more than the last 60 days?

  YES   or   NO → CODE ACTION

  CODE MAINTENANCE

OTHER DRUG

• Did you use (name of drug) during the last 30 days? (YES or NO)

• Are you considering quitting (name of drug) within the next 30 days?

  YES   or   NO → CODE PRECONTEMPLATION

• Were you continuously abstinent from (name of drug) during the last 30 days?

  YES   or   NO

  • Did you follow through on at least one quit attempt[3] from (name of drug) during the last 30 days?

    YES   or   NO → CODE CONTEMPLATION

    CODE PREPARATION

• Were you continuously abstinent from (name of drug) for more than the last 60 days?

  YES   or   NO → CODE ACTION

  CODE MAINTENANCE

[1] Reduced drinking refers to drinking within the following limits: does not drink daily; drinks no more than 4 drinks (if male) and 3 (if female) on any day; drinks no more than 9 drinks in a week (if female) and 14 (if male).
[2] Quit attempt (alcohol) refers to successful abstinence as perceived by client.
[3] Quit attempt (drug) refers to successful abstinence for a minimum of 11 consecutive days.

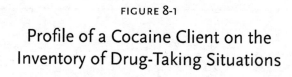

FIGURE 8-1

Profile of a Cocaine Client on the Inventory of Drug-Taking Situations

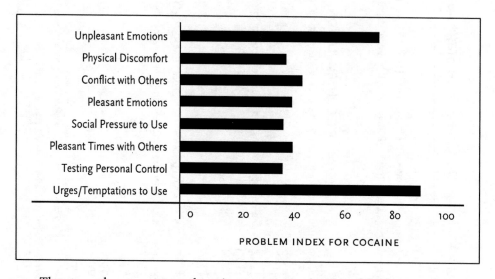

The strengths, supports and coping responses already available to a client are invaluable in preventing relapse, and they form the groundwork for developing successful homework assignments. The client must become more aware of his or her strengths and learn to use them effectively. Coping responses that the client may have used successfully in other areas may be quite effective, with only minor alterations, in addressing problematic drinking or other drug use situations. At this point in treatment planning, the therapist's task is to establish the client's existing repertoire of general coping behaviours, personal strengths and environmental resources. The process of reviewing the client's repertoire should provide a better appreciation of the possibilities open to the client, and should allow the client to focus on his or her strengths and successes rather than failures.

SRP treatment provides clients with a wide range of coping skills assignments, which are designed to help enhance and expand their coping repertoire. Clients select from a list of topics, which are then addressed during treatment sessions or provided as homework assignments. For example, during the early weeks of treatment clients often choose to work on coping with cravings or increasing social support. Later treatment sessions might address anger management, relaxation or healthy relationships.

Finally, the client is informed of the program's orientation, attendance requirements, the limits of client confidentiality and expectations for participation in planning and executing homework. Other possible treatment options are also presented. The client is then asked to decide whether he or she wishes to work toward change in substance use by entering SRP counselling. This decision is formalized with the signing of a treatment contract.

COMPONENT 4: INITIATION COUNSELLING

The "heart" of SRP counselling is divided into two major phases: initiation (Component 4) and maintenance (Component 5; Annis, 1990). The initiation phase focuses on counselling strategies suitable for clients in the action stage of change. That is, only clients who have decided to change and have signed a treatment contract enter this first phase of SRP counselling. This is because there is reason to believe that it can be detrimental to use action-oriented counselling procedures with clients who have not yet decided to change.

At the first treatment session and toward treatment discharge, the client should complete the Drug-Taking Confidence Questionnaire (DTCQ-50; Annis & Martin, 1985b), which is a 50-item self-report questionnaire designed to assess Bandura's concept of self-efficacy for alcohol- and other drug-related situations. Clients are asked to imagine themselves in a variety of situations derived from the work of Marlatt & Gordon (1980) and to indicate their level of confidence in their ability to resist the urge to drink or use other drugs in each situation. Levels of confidence are measured on the following six-point scale: zero (not at all confident), 20 (20 per cent confident), 40 (40 per cent confident), 60 (60 per cent confident), 80 (80 per cent confident), and 100 (very confident). A client's response on the DTCQ-50 allows the therapist to monitor the development of the client's self-efficacy in relation to coping with specific substance use situations over the course of treatment.

This initiation phase of SRP incorporates the substance use triggers identified by the client in the treatment plan. The focus is on assisting clients to anticipate substance use triggers for the coming week, and to identify and commit to alternative coping strategies that don't involve drinking or other drug use. Clients must begin to identify and plan for high-risk situations in advance, so that they can prepare alternative coping strategies.

Clients are encouraged to use coping plans that are known to be powerful strategies in initiating behavioural change. These strategies include avoiding risky situations (e.g., drug use settings and drug-using friends) and seeking out social support (e.g., from reliable friends or family members). Figure 8-2 shows the Weekly Plan (Initiation Phase) Form that clients complete to guide them in anticipating substance use triggers and using relatively safe initiation strategies, such as avoidance and social support, to cope.

FIGURE 8-2

Weekly Plan (Initiation Phase) Form

NAME: _____ SUBSTANCE: _____ DATE: _____

SRP WEEKLY PLAN — INITIATION PHASE

The early weeks of changing your alcohol or other drug use can be a challenging time. We call this early period of behaviour change the "Initiation Phase," which can last for anywhere from one month to much longer. Research has shown that "initiating" a change in your behaviour is easier and more effective when you use some of the following powerful strategies.

- Think about what you have to lose if you don't change. What are the factors "pushing" you to change your drinking or drug use at this time?
- Think about situations that could arise and present a risk for you. Plan ahead of time what you will do so that you aren't caught off guard.
- Avoid risky places and friends who use alcohol or other drugs.
- Involve your spouse, another family member, or a trusted friend or sponsor.
- During the first couple of weeks of changing your drinking or other drug use, living in a supportive environment can be especially helpful.
- If you want to stop drinking, consider discussing the use of alcohol-sensitizing or anti-craving medication (e.g., Antabuse®, Temposil® or Naltrexone®) with your doctor. These drugs can be a big help in getting you over those difficult first few weeks.
- Set a goal for your drinking or other drug use — make a commitment to yourself.

Below is some space for you to think about what you would like to accomplish in the coming week and how you will do so.

GOAL: _____

Confidence in achieving this goal: ❑ 0% ❑ 20% ❑ 40% ❑ 60% ❑ 80% ❑ 100%

Describe **two substance use triggers** that are likely to arise over the coming week: Indicate the following: Where will you be? What time of day? Who, if anyone, will be present? What will you be doing, thinking, feeling?	For each of the two triggers, describe **several coping strategies** that you will be prepared to use: You may want to use some of the strategies listed above, or plan other ways of coping that will work for you.

For clients who have difficulty stabilizing abstinence while attending SRP out-patient sessions, the use of a protective drug or an anti-craving medication may be considered as part of the initiation phase of SRP counselling. An example of the integration of a pharmacological agent (calcium carbimide) with SRP homework assignments is given in Annis (1991); the results of a randomized controlled trial are presented in Annis & Peachey (1992).

COMPONENT 5: MAINTENANCE COUNSELLING

This final phase of SRP counselling focuses on strategies suitable for clients in the maintenance stage of change. The Commitment to Change Algorithm identifies clients in the maintance stage as those who have successfully implemented a change in their substance use for a period of at least 60 days.

Although it can be argued that the term "relapse prevention" should be restricted to clients in the maintenance stage of change, in practice, clients do not progress from an exclusive use of initiation strategies (Component 4) to maintenance strategies (Component 5). Instead, clients tend to combine both action and maintenance strategies throughout treatment, coming to increasingly rely on maintenance phase strategies towards the end of treatment. The distinction between initiation and maintenance strategies is emphasized so that clients are aware of which strategies they are using. The objective is to encourage clients to rely less on initiation strategies and to gain confidence in the use of maintenance strategies before treatment ends. This last phase of treatment involves four stages: graduated real-life exposure to a client's high-risk situations for substance use; homework tasks within each type of risk situation; slowly reducing the client's reliance on initiation strategies (including reliance on pharmacological agents); and the design of homework tasks to promote self-attribution of control. These maintenance-of-change counselling strategies are discussed in greater detail in Annis (1990) and Annis & Davis (1989a; 1989b).

The Weekly Plan Form that is used to help clients to incorporate these maintenance strategies is shown in Figure 8-3. Several differences from the Weekly Plan (Figure 8-2) for initiation-phase sessions should be noted. While clients in the initiation phase are asked to focus on anticipating drug-use triggers that are likely to arise naturally over the coming week, clients in the maintenance stage are also asked to actually plan on entering self-identified high-risk situations.

Homework assignments must be designed so that clients experience success and begin to build confidence (self-efficacy) in their ability to cope in high-risk situations. Multiple homework assignments (i.e., three or more) should be agreed upon at each treatment session so that the client quickly learns that a high-risk situation does not automatically imply a relapse. These homework assignments should draw on a wide variety of the client's coping strengths and resources. As the client's confidence grows, he or she moves up the hierarchy to more difficult situations. At this later stage, a slip or lapse is unlikely to be the major setback it might have been early in treatment because the client has already begun a "snowball effect" in the growth of self-efficacy. By the end of treatment, the client should take most of the responsibility for designing his or her own homework assignments.

FIGURE 8-3

Weekly Plan (Maintenance Phase) Form

NAME: _____ SUBSTANCE: _____ DATE: _____

SRP WEEKLY PLAN — MAINTENANCE PHASE

Congratulations! You've successfully made some changes in your drinking or other drug use. The next step is to maintain those changes and prevent relapse. Research has shown that two of the most powerful strategies for maintaining behaviour change are to:

1. take stock of all of the high-risk situations that you are likely to encounter as a natural part of your lifestyle, and
2. gradually enter these situations, starting with a lower risk and working your way up.

The idea behind planning to enter situations in which you might be tempted to drink or use other drugs is that, if these situations are likely to arise at some point, it's better for you to be in control of where and when they do. The following are more tips for maintaining behaviour change.

• Experience each risk situation a few times before moving on to the next one.

• Make sure that you take the credit for success! For example, in the initiation phase of change, we encouraged you to seek the support of others. Now that you are learning to maintain change, it's important for you to know that you can "do it on your own" if you have to.

• Make sure that the situation you plan to enter is challenging, but not too challenging.

• If you are having difficulty with entering high-risk situations, you may be moving too quickly. Take your time! You can always go back to using some of the initiation strategies (like avoiding people, places and things, or relying on the support of others) until you feel more confident.

Two powerful strategies to help maintain changes in your drinking or other drug use are setting a goal and planning to enter risk situations. Below is space for you to plan what you would like to accomplish in the coming week.

GOAL: _____

Confidence in achieving this goal: ❑ 0% ❑ 20% ❑ 40% ❑ 60% ❑ 80% ❑ 100%

HOMEWORK ASSIGNMENT Planned Exposure to a Substance Use Trigger	OUTCOME REPORT
Describe triggering situation: _____ _____ _____ Planned experience: When? _____ Where? _____ Who present? _____ Coping plan (be specific, describe exactly what you will say and do, what you will be thinking, etc.): _____ _____ _____	Did you attempt this assignment? ❑ No ❑ Yes Were you successful? ❑ No ❑ Yes Comment: _____ _____ _____ Did you use? ❑ No ❑ Yes If Yes, how much? _____ What, if anything, might you try doing differently next time? _____ _____

In summary, clients who are in the action stage or initiation phase are encouraged to use avoidance (e.g., avoidance of drug use settings, drug-using friends), social support (e.g., a reliable friend or family member) and perhaps a protective or anti-craving medication. Clients who are in the maintenance stage, however, are expected to use a greater variety of coping alternatives that will make them more self-reliant. Consistent with research on the relationship of coping repertoire to outcome (Bliss et al., 1989; Curry & Marlatt, 1985; Moser, 1993) and the superiority of many active coping strategies compared with simple avoidance (Moser, 1993; Shiffman, 1985), clients in the maintenance stage are encouraged to develop a broad repertoire of coping alternatives that include active as well as avoidant cognitive and behavioural coping responses.

SUMMARY OF THE SRP APPROACH

Although SRP counselling has been presented as a highly structured, ordered sequence of five counselling components, in practice a dynamic interplay occurs between counselling components and a client's readiness to change. Counselling components are designed to enhance client readiness to change and client stage of change affects the choice of counselling components. While some clients may proceed in a linear fashion through the stages of change and counselling components, others may not. For example, an action-stage client who experiences a lapse to substance use while receiving initiation-stage counselling may need earlier counselling components such as continued assessment and motivational interviewing. Similarly, a preparation-stage client may experience uncertainty regarding the decision to change when faced with signing an individual treatment contract. If this occurs, further exploration of the costs and benefits of change through motivational interviewing is required. Thus, the SRP treatment model takes into account clients' readiness to change—the SRP components can be individually tailored to fit clients' ongoing needs.

The purpose of treatment is to effect a rise in self-efficacy across all areas of perceived risk. If the client fails to show growth of confidence in coping with a particular risk situation, further work in this area should be considered before the client is discharged from treatment. The therapist must consider possible reasons for the lack of development of confidence in the identified area. For example, has the client successfully performed homework assignments involving entry into situations of this type? If so, what self-inferences is the client drawing from those experiences? Such an inquiry by the therapist should uncover the reason for the client's lack of confidence in relation to the particular risk area and identify any further work that needs to be done before treatment completion.

RESEARCH FINDINGS FOR THE SRP MODEL

The SRP counselling process focuses heavily on the conduct of homework assignments, particularly in the initiation (or action) and maintenance phases. An early study by Annis and Davis (1988) that evaluated the homework component of SRP counselling found that clients successfully completed the vast majority of homework assignments. Ninety per cent of assignments generated by the client were completed successfully compared with 73 per cent of those generated by the therapist, emphasizing the importance of active client participation. Although homework assignments involve entry into risk situations for substance use, particularly during the maintenance phase, most clients were successful in adhering to their treatment goal. Typically, any slips (lapses) occurred outside of homework assignments. Interestingly, negative mood states and interpersonal conflict increased the likelihood that a lapse would become a serious relapse.

Clinical trials evaluating the effectiveness of SRP counselling for people with alcohol problems have supported the following conclusions:
• In the year following SRP treatment, most clients dramatically reduce their substance use (Annis & Davis, 1988; Graham et al., 1996).
• Group-delivered SRP counselling can be equally effective as individual SRP counselling for clients with both alcohol and other drug problems (Graham et al., 1996).
• Clients with well-differentiated profiles on the Inventory of Drug-Taking Situations do better in SRP counselling than clients with undifferentiated profiles, while the reverse is true with more traditional counselling (Annis & Davis, 1991).
• Clients with good outcomes show high confidence (self-efficacy) and make good use of coping strategies when faced with high-risk situations (Moser & Annis, 1996).
• The greater the number and variety of coping strategies used by the client, the lower the likelihood of relapse (Moser & Annis, 1996).

Further research is needed to establish the relative effectiveness of SRP counselling for clients with problems resulting from use of other substances, such as cocaine and opioids, and to evaluate the SRP counselling components in relation to client readiness for change.

RELAPSE PREVENTION WITH DIVERSE CLIENT POPULATIONS

In any treatment intervention, the needs of diverse client populations need to be considered and treatment strategies tailored accordingly. Although this is a major concern in the treatment of substance use problems, little research has been done with many special populations and marginalized groups. This section highlights a few key considerations from existing research and clinical practice implications of relapse prevention counselling, taking into account gender, age (youth and older adults), ethnocultural factors, sexual diversity and concurrent mental health disorders.

Gender

Studies of treatment populations have shown that married men have a lower rate of relapse than unmarried men. For women, marriage is protective for some, and is related to relapse for others (for example, if the woman is returning to a partner who uses alcohol or other drugs; Walton et al., 2001). Research has also shown that men tend to report more negative social influences, greater exposure to substances and poorer coping skills than women (Walton et al., 2001). Some research has suggested that a depressed mood is the most frequent determinant of relapse (Strowig, 1999) for men and that Caucasian men report the poorest coping when compared with a matched sample of Caucasian women and African-American men and women (Walton et al., 2001).

In general, women tend to report better coping mechanisms than men (Walton et al., 2001). Women also tend to see their substance use as secondary to more general problems, such as anxiety and depression. As a result, women use medical and psychiatric services more frequently than men and perceive these services as more effective (Osorio et al., 2002).

Youth

Few relapse prevention models focus on youth. However, some research has explored ways of adapting these models to best fit the needs of younger clients.

Relapse prevention for young people needs to focus on issues of youth-parent relationships and peer group membership, as these are central to the lives and experiences of younger clients. Illicit substance use by youth is strongly related to parental support as well as parental awareness and monitoring of the whereabouts and activities of their child (Miller & Plant, 2003). Peer influences, delinquency and re-offending behaviour are also strongly associated with youth substance use (Roget et al., 1998). In some cases, relapse prevention for youth may need to include liaison with the juvenile justice system, or a contract with a specific substance use treatment provider.

Roget and colleagues (1998) suggest that a relapse prevention program for youth should include assessment, incentive building, contract development and evaluation. Assessment that combines theories of adolescent development with Marlatt & Gordon's (1985) eight high-risk situations discussed earlier in this chapter may be helpful. In this view, high-risk situations for relapse are connected to the drive to meet developmental needs (Roget et al., 1998). For example, social pressure to use substances can be linked with peer acceptance in young adults. Building a high-risk "profile" that is particular to each client and takes into account the developmental tasks unique to youth can facilitate work on relevant coping skills.

In facilitating change in youth, research shows that alcohol and other drug education is not enough. Elkind (1984, in Roget et al., 1998) suggests that adolescents think and behave with the notion that nothing bad will happen to them—talking about the consequences of substance use gets cognitively re-interpreted to mean "others become addicted, but not me."

Clinicians need to make feedback personally relevant to young clients, and to avoid confrontation. In addition, they need to encourage youth to actively prepare for relapse and to practise coping strategies.

An important component of relapse prevention strategies with youth is the development of a behavioural contract, in this case a "relapse contract." This contract is

created by all parties involved and might include family rules, school or job requirements, probation requirements, treatment attendance, urinalysis, social supports
and relapse consequences. It is important to keep in mind that any relapse episodes
need to focus on what can be learned, as "learning by doing" is important in this stage
of life.

Older Adults

Most research exploring relapse has focused across the adult age range rather than
specifically on older adults. However, a few differences in treatment outcomes for older
adults have been noted (Barrick & Connors, 2002). For example, high-risk situations
among older adults tend to involve intrapersonal issues more frequently than among
younger adults (Barrick & Connors, 2002). In addition, several age-specific issues
were found to be relevant to relapse prevention in older adults. Negative emotional
states related to anxiety, interpersonal conflict, depression, loneliness, loss and social
isolation appear to be the highest-risk situations identified. Retirement, the death of a
partner or child and the stressors of aging represent a risky time for alcohol or other
drug use. Cognitive impairments associated with aging, no matter what the etiology,
need to be assessed and taken into consideration in relapse plans for older adults
(Barrick & Connors, 2002).

Schonfeld and his colleagues (2000) evaluated a 16-week relapse prevention
program called "Get Smart" and found that cognitive-behavioural programs that
focus on identifying high-risk situations, coping skills and relapse plans worked well
with older clients with significant medical, social and substance use problems.

Ethnocultural Factors

Many treatment programs have difficulty attracting and retaining clients from diverse
ethnocultural communities. Language, treatment philosophies and methods, clinician
demographics, and lack of agency knowledge or awareness of cross-cultural counselling implications create systemic barriers for many clients. Increasingly, the literature indicates that clinicians need to develop competence in working with clients
from diverse racial, cultural, ethnic and religious backgrounds (Straussner, 2002).
Ethnocultural competence, defined as "the ability of a clinician to function effectively
in the context of ethnocultural differences" (Straussner, 2002, p. 35) is a critical skill
in the application of relapse prevention strategies and techniques.

Although some research has been carried out on substance use patterns and
issues in different cultural groups, caution needs to be exercised in drawing particular
clinical implications from this work given the heterogeneity of ethnocultural groups.
In addition, more research is needed to help develop relapse prevention approaches
specific to different populations.

For example, little research exists regarding relapse prevention applications for Aboriginal peoples. Clients who live on reserves may face geographical barriers to accessing treatment. In addition, Western models of treatment may not fit with traditional Native healing approaches. This was found in the development of the Inventory of Drinking Situations questionnaire (Annis & Davis, 1991) when Aboriginal reviewers suggested the addition of a Native spirituality component to reflect a high-risk situation relevant to this population.

Sexual Diversity

Little has been written about relapse prevention specific to lesbian, gay, bisexual, transsexual or transgendered people. However, as with all counsellor-client interactions, mutual respect, unconditional positive regard, and attentiveness to the client's issues and goals should be paramount. Clients from sexually diverse groups will often have specific issues relating to discrimination (homophobia, biphobia, transphobia), coming out, openness about sexual orientation/gender identity, family issues, involvement in the community, body image and HIV/AIDS (Barbara et al., 2002). See Chapter 16 for specific suggestions on how to be intentionally inclusive with these client populations.

Concurrent Mental Health Disorders

It is estimated that 50 to 65 per cent of people with substance use problems also experience a co-occurring mental health disorder (Bellack & DiClemente, 1999). Excessive substance use in people with mental illness has all of the same adverse health, social, legal and financial consequences that it does for others, along with the additional complications of decreased treatment compliance, increased risk of exacerbating the symptoms of mental illness, increased risk of relapse and compromised efficacy of neuroleptic medications (Bellack & DiClemente, 1999). Because non-adherence to treatment among psychiatric patients who use substances can lead to a number of adverse consequences ranging from poor clinical outcomes to violent behaviour, efforts to increase adherence have been attempted (Swanson et al., 1999). An integrated approach drawing from both the addiction and mental health domains attempts to address both problem areas at the same time, explore how they interact and examine how substances are used to treat the negative symptoms of mental illness or the side-effects of treatments.

One such integrated approach is an adaptation of the motivational interviewing model by Bellack & DiClemente (1999). Their approach attempts to minimize the impact of the cognitive, motivational and social skill deficits associated with severe mental illness. The treatment protocol contains four modules: the first focuses on social skills and problem-solving techniques to help people deal with peers and to refuse substances; the second focuses on education in triggers, cravings, the reasons for use and the risk of using for people with severe mental illness; the third consists of motivational interviewing, goal setting and contingency plans such as urine screens; and the fourth focuses on relapse prevention strategies. The 90-minute sessions are held twice a week for approximately six months. The sessions are highly structured, and the concepts are broken down into smaller learning units. There is an emphasis on behavioural rehearsal and the repetitive learning of a small number of specific skills to use in a few key high-risk situations. There is also an extensive use of learning aids and content repetition.

EMPIRICAL SUPPORT FOR RELAPSE PREVENTION APPROACHES

In general, relapse prevention approaches, including the SRP model, fall under the category of cognitive-behavioural coping-skills therapy (CBST). These approaches are based on social learning theory, and have been well-validated in the research literature (Longabaugh & Morgenstern, 1999). The two core components shared by these approaches include (1) a theoretical foundation that examines deficits in one's ability to cope with overall life stressors and alcohol-related stimuli; and (2) the use of individualized coping skills training. These types of therapies were among the first to demonstrate efficacy in reducing drinking in randomized clinical trials and are "among those [interventions] having the most evidence for clinical and cost effectiveness" (Longabaugh & Morgenstern, 1999, p. 79). In addition, other authors (Dimeff & Marlatt, 1998) have noted that:

> relapse prevention may be particularly promising in reducing the severity of relapses when they occur, in enhancing the durability of treatment effects, and for patients who demonstrate higher levels of impairment across multiple dimensions. . . . In essence, while relapse prevention does not provide full inoculation against relapse, it significantly reduces the negative consequences and harm resulting from the fall (p. 516).

A meta-analysis of 26 studies supported the overall efficacy of relapse prevention in reducing substance use and improving psychosocial adjustment (Irvin et al., 1999). Thus, the relapse prevention approaches discussed in this chapter are suitable for a range of individuals with moderate to severe levels of alcohol and other drug dependence. Indeed, these interventions have made a significant contribution to the growing body of evidence-based interventions in the addiction field.

CONCLUSION

This chapter has highlighted a few of the many approaches used to address relapse to substance use. These treatment approaches must be considered against a backdrop of research findings and theorizing that may contradict or challenge accepted models of care. Overall, cognitive-behavioural approaches such as the SRP model demonstrate empirical support and can be used effectively with a variety of clinical populations. In all cases, it is critical to ensure that relapse prevention strategies are tailored to the unique needs of clients and that the particular issues of diverse populations are considered.

ADDITIONAL INFORMATION

The following materials are available from the Marketing Department, Centre for Addiction and Mental Health, 33 Russell Street, Toronto, ON M5S 2S1 (Telephone: 1 800 661-1111):

Annis, H.M., Herie, M.A. & Watkin-Merek, L. (1996). *Structured Relapse Prevention: An Outpatient Counselling Approach.* Includes all assessment instruments, homework assignments, and session-by-session checklists. Toronto: Addiction Research Foundation.

Annis, H.M. & Martin, G. (1985). *Inventory of Drug-Taking Situations (IDTS-50).* Computer interactive software is also available. Toronto: Addiction Research Foundation.

Annis, H.M. & Martin, G. (1985). *Drug-Taking Confidence Questionnaire (DTCQ-50).* Computer interactive software is also available. Toronto: Addiction Research Foundation.

Annis, H.M., Turner, N.E. & Sklar, S.M. (1997). *Inventory of Drug-Taking Situations (IDTS-50) User's Guide.* Toronto: Addiction Research Foundation.

Annis, H.M., Sklar, S.M. & Turner, N.E. (1997). *Drug-Taking Confidence Questionnaire (DTCQ-50) User's Guide.* Toronto: Addiction Research Foundation.

REFERENCES

Addiction Research Foundation. (1993). *Core Client Interview: Behaviour Change and Relapse Prevention Unit.* Toronto: author.

Allsop, S. (1990). Relapse prevention and management. *Drug and Alcohol Review, 9,* 143–153.

Annis, H.M. (1986). A relapse prevention model for treatment of alcoholics. In Miller, W.R. & Heather, N. (Eds.), *Treating Addictive Behaviors: Processes of Change* (pp. 407–421). New York: Plenum.

Annis, H.M. (1990). Relapse to substance abuse: Empirical findings within a cognitive-social learning approach. *Journal of Psychoactive Drugs, 22*(2), 117–124.

Annis, H.M. (1991). A cognitive-social learning approach to relapse: Pharmacotherapy and relapse prevention counselling. *Alcohol and Alcoholism, Suppl. 1,* 527–530.

Annis, H.M. & Davis, C.S. (1988). Self-efficacy and the prevention of alcoholic relapse: Initial findings from a treatment trial. In Baker, T.B. & Cannon, D.S. (Eds.), *Assessment and Treatment of Addictive Disorders* (pp. 88–112). New York: Praeger.

Annis, H.M. & Davis, C.S. (1989a). Relapse prevention. In Hester, R.K. & Miller, W.R. (Eds.), *Handbook of Alcoholism Treatment Approaches* (pp. 170–182). New York: Pergamon Press.

Annis, H.M. & Davis, C.S. (1989b). Relapse prevention training: A cognitive-behavioral approach based on self-efficacy theory. *Journal of Chemical Dependency Treatment, 2*(2), 81–103.

Annis, H.M. & Davis, C.S. (1991). Relapse prevention. *Alcohol Health and Research World, 15*(3), 204–212.

Annis, H.M. & Martin, G. (1985a). *Inventory of Drug-Taking Situations (IDTS-50).* Toronto: Addiction Research Foundation.

Annis, H.M. & Martin, G. (1985b). *Drug-Taking Confidence Questionnaire (DTCQ-50).* Toronto: Addiction Research Foundation.

Annis, H.M. & Peachey, J.E. (1992). The use of calcium carbimide in relapse prevention counselling: Results of a randomized controlled trial. *British Journal of Addiction, 87,* 63–72.

Annis, H.M., Schober, R. & Kelly, E. (1996). Matching addiction outpatient counselling to client readiness for change: The role of structured relapse prevention counselling. *Experimental and Clinical Psychopharmacology, 4,* 37–45.

Bandura, A. (1977). Self-efficacy: Toward a unifying theory of behavioral change. *Psychological Review, 84*(2), 191–215.

Bandura, A. (1978). Reflections on self-efficacy. *Advances in Behaviour Research and Therapy, 1*, 237–269.

Bandura, A. (1986). *Social Foundations of Thought and Action.* Englewood Cliffs, NJ: Prentice Hall.

Barbara, A.M., Chaim, G. & Doctor, F. (2002). *Asking the Right Questions: Talking about Sexual Orientation and Gender Identity During Assessment for Drug and Alcohol Concerns.* Toronto: Centre for Addiction and Mental Health.

Barrick, C. & Connors, G.J. (2002). Relapse prevention and maintaining abstinence in older adults with alcohol-use disorders. *Drugs & Aging, 19*(8), 583–594.

Bellack, A. & DiClemente, C.C. (1999). Treating substance abuse among patients with schizophrenia. *Psychiatric Services, 50*(1), 75–80.

Bliss, R.E., Garvey, A.J., Heinhold, J. & Hitchcock, J.L. (1989). The influence of situation and coping on relapse crisis outcomes after smoking cessation. *Journal of Consulting and Clinical Psychology, 57*, 443–449.

Bliss, P., Murphy, K. & Ricketts, T. (2002). Relapse prevention group-work: A clinical evaluation. *Journal of Substance Use, 7*, 78–84.

Breslin, F.C., Zack, M. & McMain, S. (2002). An information-processing analysis of mindfulness: Implications for relapse prevention in the treatment of substance abuse. *Clinical Psychology: Science and Practice, 9*(3), 275–299.

Campos, P.E. (2002). Integrating Buddhist philosophy with cognitive and behavioral practice. *Cognitive and Behavioral Practice, 9*, 38–40.

Curry, S.G. & Marlatt, G.A. (1985). Unaided quitters' strategies for coping with temptations to smoke. In Shiffman, S. & Wills, T.A. (Eds.), *Coping and Substance Use* (pp. 243–265). New York: Academic Press.

Dimeff, L.A. & Marlatt, G.A. (1998). Preventing relapse and maintaining change in addictive behaviours. *Clinical Psychology: Science and Practice, 5*(4), 513–525.

Gorski, T.T. (1989). *Passages through Recovery: An Action Plan for Preventing Relapse.* Center City, MN: Hazelden.

Graham, K., Annis, H.M., Brett, P.J. & Venesoen, P. (1996). A controlled field trial of group versus individual cognitive-behavioral training for relapse prevention. *Addiction, 91*(8), 1127–1139.

Hunt, W.A., Barnett, L.W. & Brach, L.G. (1971). Relapse rates in addiction programs. *Journal of Clinical Psychology, 27*, 455–456.

Irvin, J.E., Bowers, C.A., Dunn, M.E. & Wang, M.C. (1999). Efficacy of relapse prevention: A meta-analytic review. *Journal of Consulting and Clinical Psychology, 6*(4), 563–570.

Kumar, S.M. (2002). An introduction to Buddhism for the cognitive-behavioral therapist. *Cognitive and Behavioral Practice, 9*, 40–43.

Litman, G.K., Eiser, J.R., Rawson, N.S.B. & Oppenheim, A.N. (1979). Differences in relapse precipitants and coping behaviors between alcohol relapsers and survivors. *Behaviour Research and Therapy, 17*, 89–94.

Litman, G.K., Stapleton, J., Oppenheim, A.N., Peleg, M. & Jackson, P. (1984). The relationship between coping behaviors, their effectiveness and alcoholism relapse and survival. *British Journal of Addiction, 79*(3), 283–291.

Longabough, R. & Morgenstern, J. (1999). Cognitive-behavioural coping-skills therapy for alcohol dependence. *Alcohol Research and Health, 23*(2), 78–85.

Marlatt, G.A. (1996). Taxonomy of high risk situations for alcohol relapse: Evolution and development of a cognitive-behavioral model. *Addiction, 91* (Supplement), S37–S49.

Marlatt, G.A. (2002). Buddhist philosophy and the treatment of addictive behavior. *Cognitive and Behavioral Practice, 9*, 44–50.

Marlatt, G.A. & Gordon, J.R. (1980). Determinants of relapse: Implications for the maintenance of behavior change. In Davidson, P. & Davidson, S. (Eds.), *Behavioral Medicine: Changing Health Lifestyles* (pp. 71–127). New York: Brunner/Mazel.

Marlatt, G.A. & Gordon, J.R. (1985). *Relapse Prevention: Maintenance Strategies in the Treatment of Addictive Behaviors*. New York: Guilford Press.

Miller, P. & Plant, M. (2003). The family, peer influences and substance use: Findings from a study of UK teenagers. *Journal of Substance Use, 8*, 1475–9942.

Miller, W.R. (1996). What is a relapse? Fifty ways to leave the wagon. *Addiction, 91* (Supplement), S15–S27.

Miller, W.R. & Rollnick, S. (2002). *Motivational Interviewing* (2nd ed.). New York: Guilford Press.

Miller, W.R., Tonigan, J.S., Montgomery, H.A., Abbott, P.J., Meyers, R.J., Hester, R.K. et al. (1990). *Assessment of Client Motivation for Change: Preliminary Validation of the Socrates (Rev.) Instrument*. Albuquerque, NM: Center for Research on Addictive Behaviors, University of New Mexico.

Moser, A.E. (1993). *Situational Antecedents, Self-efficacy and Coping in Relapse Crisis Outcome: A Prospective Study of Treated Alcoholics*. Toronto: York University.

Moser, A.E. & Annis, H.M. (1996). The role of coping in relapse crisis outcome: A prospective study of treated alcoholics. *Addiction, 91*(8), 1101–1113.

Osorio, R., McCusker, M. & Salazar, C. (2002). Evaluation of a women-only service for substance misusers. *Journal of Substance Use, 7*, 41–49.

Parks, G.A. & Marlatt, A. (2000, September/October). Relapse prevention therapy: a Cognitive-behavioral approach. *The National Psychologist, 9*(5). Available: http://nationalpsychologist.com/articles/art_v9n5_3.htm.

Prochaska, J.O. & DiClemente, C.C. (1984). *The Transtheoretical Approach: Crossing Traditional Boundaries of Therapy.* Homewood, IL: Dow Jones/Irwin.

Prochaska, J.O. & DiClemente, C.C. (1992). Stages of change in the modification of problem behaviors. In Hersen, M., Eisler, R. & Miller, P.M. (Eds.), *Progress in Behavior Modification Series, 28, 184*–218. Sycamore, IL: Sycamore Publishing Company.

Roget, N.A., Fisher, G.L. & Johnson, M.L. (1998). A protocol for reducing juvenile recidivism through relapse prevention. *Journal of Addictions and Offender Counselling, 19*, 33–43.

Saunders, B. & Houghton, M. (1996). Relapse revisited: A critique of current concepts and clinical practice in the management of alcohol problems. *Addictive Behaviors, 21*(6), 843–855.

Saunders, B., Wilkinson C. & Allsop, S. (1991). Motivational interviewing with heroin users attending a methadone clinic. In Miller, W.R. & Rollnick, S. (Eds.), *Motivational Interviewing* (pp. 279–292). New York: Guilford Press.

Schober, R. & Annis, H.M. (1996a). Commitment to change in individuals seeking treatment for excessive drinking. Manuscript submitted for publication.

Schober, R. & Annis, H.M. (1996b). Stages and processes of change in individuals seeking treatment for excessive drinking. Manuscript in preparation.

Schonfeld, L., Dupree, L.W., Dickson-Fuhrmann, E., McKean Royer, C., McDermott, C.H., Rosansky et al. (2000). Cognitive-behavioural treatment of older veterans with substance abuse problems. *Journal of Geriatric Psychiatry Neurology, 13*, 124–129.

Shiffman, S. (1985). Preventing relapse in ex-smokers: A self-management approach. In Marlatt, G.A. & Gordon, J.R. (Eds.), *Relapse Prevention.* New York: Guilford Press.

Straussner, S.L. (2002). Ethnic cultures and substance abuse. *Counselor,* December 2002, 34–38.

Strowig, A.B. (1999). Relapse determinants reported by men treated for alcohol addiction: The prominence of depressed mood. *Journal of Substance Use Treatment, 19*, 469–474.

Swanson, A.J., Pantalon, M.V. & Cohen, K.R. (1999). Motivational interviewing and treatment adherence among psychiatric and dually diagnosed patients. *The Journal of Nervous and Mental Disease, 187*(10), 630–635.

Walton, M.A., Blow, F.C. & Booth, B.M. (2001). Diversity in relapse prevention needs: Gender and race comparisons among substance abuse treatment patients. *American Journal of Drug Alcohol Abuse, 27*(2), 225–240.

Wilson, G.T. (1980). Cognitive factors in lifestyle changes: A social learning perspective. In Davidson, P.O. & Davidson, S.M. (Eds.), *Behavioral Medicine: Changing Health Lifestyles* (pp. 3–37). New York: Brunner/Mazel.

Chapter 9

Mutual Aid Groups

JOHN KELLY, KEITH HUMPHREYS AND HELEN YOUNGSON

INTRODUCTION

Mutual aid groups (sometimes known as self-help groups) are an important resource for many people with substance use problems. They can help initiate, maintain and enhance the broad lifestyle changes, and major psychological and social adjustments, that typically accompany successful recovery from these problems. They also provide opportunities for people to make social contacts and form healthy relationships, practise life skills, learn to take responsibility and solve problems. Other group members can be valuable at potentially high-risk times, such as evenings and week-ends, when professional help is often not readily available. Indeed, one of the greatest strengths of mutual aid groups is that they can be available indefinitely, which is important because substance use problems usually are chronic (Humphreys & Tucker, 2002). Many substance use clients need frequent and/or long-term support that is beyond the mandate and resources of most treatment agencies.

Miller (1989) states that our role as professionals is to help our clients, where appropriate, link with the mutual aid groups of their choice, making sure they have been properly informed about their options. This chapter is intended to provide counsellors with background information, research evidence and clinical strategies to help them accomplish this goal.

Mutual Aid Groups and Their Potential Benefits

In this chapter, the term *mutual aid* refers to experiences that are "owned by the consumer" (Lavoie et al., 1994) and that bring people together with the common purpose of helping each other in their recovery. Mutual aid groups are synonymous with self-help groups, but not with other activities commonly labelled as self-help, such as using books, tapes, exercises, the Internet and other resources for self-directed recovery from a wide variety of problems.

The earliest of contemporary mutual aid groups, Alcoholics Anonymous (AA), was founded in 1935 in Akron, Ohio. AA came to public attention in the 1940s due to positive media coverage and its positive portrayal in several Hollywood movies (Kurtz, 1979/1991). Since then many other mutual aid organizations have emerged, either inspired by or in reaction to AA.

In the United States, people who had recovered from alcohol problems began to establish alcohol recovery homes. In Ontario, resources were found to study and treat alcohol misuse and, in 1949, the Alcoholism Research Foundation was established (later the Addiction Research Foundation, which eventually became part of the present Centre for Addiction and Mental Health). A treatment continuum began to develop, beginning with detoxification and initial intensive treatment, which was followed by outpatient and residential aftercare (e.g., halfway and three-quarter-way houses) and community mutual aid groups.

Research has shown the efficacy of mutual aid as part of aftercare (Humphreys, 2003; Fiorentine & Hillhouse, 2000). In the United States the clinical practice guidelines of the American Psychiatric Association and the Department of Veterans Affairs both recommend referral to mutual aid groups. Substance use counsellors often educate their clients on the merits of joining such a group, and use the client's subsequent group experience in the therapy (e.g., by exploring the client's responses to the group experience). A few agencies facilitate clients' involvement in mutual aid groups by providing meeting space. These groups are then available to the agencies' clients for as long as they are needed, even after treatment is over. Other counsellors start mutual aid groups to meet the needs of particular client populations.

Members of a mutual aid group come together to pool their knowledge and experiences, offer each other support, and discuss and create their own solutions. Identification with other people with similar problems, who are at various stages in recovery, often decreases clients' feelings of shameful "uniqueness" and instils hope that change is possible. Mutual aid groups such as AA are founded on the belief that "helping you helps me" (Hill, 1984; AA, 2001). This belief has been substantiated by research on the helper-therapy principle (Maton, 1988; Schwartz & Sendor, 1999). A feeling of being helpful to others often increases feelings of self-esteem, which is frequently low among people with substance-related problems. Research and practice show the need for a variety of mutual aid groups to address the needs of different populations (Kirkpatrick, 1978; Zweben, 1995; Bishop, 1995; Humphreys & Woods, 1993; Delgado & Humm-Delgado, 1993; Reissman & Carroll, 1995).

MUTUAL AID ORGANIZATIONS FOR PEOPLE WITH SUBSTANCE USE PROBLEMS

Eight mutual aid groups for people with alcohol and other drug problems are described in this chapter: Alcoholics Anonymous, Narcotics Anonymous (NA), Cocaine Anonymous (CA), Methadone Anonymous (MA), Moderation Management (MM), Self Management and Recovery Training (SMART Recovery), Secular Organizations for Sobriety (SOS) and Women for Sobriety (WFS). We devote the most space to AA, which is the oldest, largest mutual aid organization. AA has a large-scale publishing infrastructure (producing books, pamphlets, videos, etc.), and has been the subject of many studies and reviews. Many similar 12-step, substance-focused fellowships, such as those listed above, have emerged following in the traditions of AA. Contact information for all of these mutual aid fellowships is listed at the end of the chapter.

Other similar programs, including Overeaters Anonymous, Nicotine Anonymous, Gamblers Anonymous, Adult Children of Alcoholics, Al-Anon (for family members) and Alateen (for children of people with alcohol problems), are also available in many communities. These groups, which have formats similar to AA's, will not be covered here.

Room and Greenfield (1993) found that AA is the most frequently sought source of help for an alcohol-related problem in the United States, and the same may be true in Canada. Although all mutual aid groups described below exist internationally, no other is as accessible as AA, which is available in most communities in North America. The headquarters of the groups described are included at the end of this chapter. Metropolitan areas generally have the greatest variety of mutual aid groups, including groups for particular populations (e.g., women, gay men, diverse ethno-cultural communities). Of course, professionals can take the initiative, with the assistance of people in recovery, to establish a group aimed at meeting their clients' needs. The Internet can also be a useful resource, as most organizations now hold on-line mutual aid group meetings.

Alcoholics Anonymous

Alcoholics Anonymous has spread around the globe in the seven decades since its founding. Drawing on a variety of data sources, Humphreys (2004) recently estimated AA's worldwide membership at between four million and six million people, about half of whom live in Canada or the United States. AA is a fellowship of men and women who meet regularly to share experiences and increase understanding about practical application of the "12 steps." The 12 steps that comprise the program (listed below) lead people through a series of cognitive and behavioural exercises to promote a "spiritual awakening" or "psychic change" sufficient for recovery from alcohol problems. Although it is not impossible to recover and learn about the process of change through the 12 steps without attending AA meetings, many in AA believe it is difficult to do so.

MEETINGS

Depending on the size of the community, the number of meetings available ranges from one to hundreds. Locations include church basements, hospitals and recreation centres. The local AA office, whose number can be found in the telephone book, can direct people to the nearest and the most appropriate meeting.

Typical Format

Meetings typically last between 60 and 90 minutes. Nearly all begin with some type of reading from AA literature, such as from the fellowship's main text, *Alcoholics Anonymous*, more commonly referred to as the "Big Book" (AA, 2001). There is often also a short prayer at the beginning of the meeting. From that point, meetings vary greatly in focus and format, but almost always involve some type of verbal account of members' life experiences, past and present. At some meetings, chips or tokens are awarded to individuals who have reached early abstinence milestones, such as 30 days, 60 days or 90 days, or six months. Some members carry these tokens with them as a reminder of their recovery. Because AA has a distinct tradition of being fully self-supporting and declining outside contributions, a voluntary collection is taken, and members may make announcements of upcoming AA-related events. The main portion of the meeting may focus on a recovery topic, an AA reading or aspect of the recovery program (e.g., a particular step) or a speaker's story, which may be followed by open discussion. Proceedings are usually brought to a close with a prayer (often the Lord's Prayer), for those who wish to recite it. In some meetings, members join hands in a circle if they wish to do so.

Types of Meetings

As noted above, larger communities often have AA meetings serving particular sub-groups, for example women or men only, youth, gay men, and various professional groups (e.g., lawyers, doctors, police, pilots). Some offer meetings in languages other than English or French. AA meetings also vary in level of desired anonymity (e.g., "open" versus "closed" meetings), and format and focus (e.g., "speaker-discussion" or "speaker-only" meetings versus "step meetings").

Only members, or potential members with "a desire to stop drinking" (Alcoholics Anonymous, 1952), may attend AA's closed meetings. Because these meetings are not accessible to the general public, participants may feel more comfortable attending and disclosing information about themselves. These meetings may take any format and content focus. In contrast, anyone is welcome to attend open meetings. Thus, family members and friends, or other interested people such as students or health care professionals, may attend either as support or merely to understand more about the nature of the AA fellowship.

A common type of AA meeting format is the "speaker-discussion" meeting, in which an individual member recounts his or her story of how he or she became addicted to alcohol and subsequently recovered. This often includes how the person "works" the 12 steps in daily life and in his or her struggles and successes in recovery. This activity may promote identification, universality, and instillation of hope, dynamics also present in professional group therapies (Yalom, 1996). The presentation is followed by open discussion. In contrast, a "speaker" meeting is a meeting in which one person speaks at length about his or her own history and recovery experiences with no discussion by other members.

Other meetings focus on a particular piece of AA literature such as the *AA Grapevine* (a monthly magazine), *The Twelve Steps and Twelve Traditions* (AA, 1952) or *Alcoholics Anonymous* (AA, 2001), from which the fellowship takes its name. In these meetings a step or chapter is read and discussed, and its content related by members to past and current life contexts. These are most often closed meetings.

GUIDING PRINCIPLES

Alcoholics Anonymous adheres to the principles that are outlined in its "twelve traditions." Each tradition is a guiding principle resulting from the experiences of early AA groups (AA, 1952). For example, early groups had lists of criteria as to who was eligible for membership. This was eventually whittled down to a single simple requirement: a desire to stop drinking. All groups are autonomous and self-supporting. The collections taken at meetings pay for the rent, refreshments and celebrations of abstinence, and maintain the office and phones locally, regionally and internationally. Early in AA history, the organization decided not to accept contributions from people who are not AA members and to limit the yearly contributions of individual members. It was believed that too much money or property ownership (AA does not own any property) would distract the organization from its primary purpose of "helping alcoholics to achieve sobriety" (Alcoholics Anonymous, 1952).

AA believes that alcoholics respond most favourably when attracted rather than coerced (AA, 1994a). Although some treatment centres, judges and criminal lawyers may insist on clients attending AA meetings, AA lets its friends (counsellors, nurses, doctors, ministers, police, etc.) promote AA.

AA encourages members to maintain anonymity at the level of "press, radio, TV and film" (AA, 1952). Privacy, confidentiality and anonymity are expected for all involved in the program. To help protect members' privacy and anonymity, a card is sometimes read at meetings that states, "Who you see here, what you hear here, when you leave here, let it stay here."

AA's primary purpose is to carry its message to anyone who has alcohol problems. Despite many AA members' endorsement of the disease concept of "alcoholism," the AA organization itself does not endorse this concept (or any other). However, AA literature does often refer to alcoholism as an "illness" or "malady" (e.g., AA, 2001), although it is never formally referred to as a medical disease.

HOW DOES AA WORK?

From AA's perspective and experience, members achieve recovery through a combination of factors including sponsorship, work on the 12 steps, belief in a "higher power," and service.

Sponsorship

Sponsors are mentors who, by virtue of well-established abstinence, provide a model and help those they sponsor by listening and by relating their own experiences in similar situations. They also share how they use the tools of the program to help them cope effectively without drinking. The relationship is one of trust and acceptance, which develops over time.

Newcomers are encouraged to seek out an established member with whom they believe they could feel comfortable and whose sober lifestyle they admire. Newcomers then ask the chosen member to serve as a sponsor. AA recommends that the sponsor and sponsored person be of the same sex: "This custom usually promotes quick understanding and reduces the likelihood of emotional distractions that might take the newcomer's mind off the purpose of AA" (AA, 1994b).

When a sponsored person has abstained from alcohol for a certain time and worked the 12 steps, the person is often encouraged by his or her sponsor to also become a sponsor—to pass on what he or she has received. It is believed in AA that in giving, one receives. Long-term research studies have validated this premise in people with alcohol and other drug problems: serving as a sponsor appears strongly associated with prolonged abstinence (Crape et al., 2002; Cross et al., 1990).

Work on the 12 Steps

The program's 12 steps are suggested as a means to achieve continuous and contented abstinence. They are actually 12 statements describing the sequential process of how AA's first 100 members of the organization achieved sobriety. They are:

1. We admitted we were powerless over alcohol—that our lives had become unmanageable.
2. Came to believe that a Power greater than ourselves could restore us to sanity.
3. Made a decision to turn our will and our lives over to the care of God *as we understood Him.*
4. Made a searching and fearless moral inventory of ourselves.
5. Admitted to God, to ourselves and to another human being the exact nature of our wrongs.
6. Were entirely ready to have God remove all these defects of character.
7. Humbly asked Him to remove our shortcomings.
8. Made a list of all persons we had harmed, and became willing to make amends to them all.
9. Made direct amends to such people wherever possible, except when to do so would injure them or others.
10. Continued to take personal inventory and when we were wrong promptly admitted it.

11. Sought through prayer and meditation to improve our conscious contact with God *as we understood Him*, praying only for the knowledge of His will for us and the power to carry that out.

12. Having had a spiritual awakening as the result of these steps, we tried to carry this message to alcoholics and to practise these principles in all our affairs (Alcoholics Anonymous, 2001).

Following the realizations of personal "powerlessness" over the (alcohol) problem in step 1, and that the problem's solution lies in finding a "higher power" (step 2), members are asked to make "a decision" (step 3) about what to do next. If the decision is made to trust the AA process (i.e., "turn our life and will over to the care of God"), members then complete a self-assessment (step 4), discuss it with another person (often a sponsor; step 5) and begin to use steps 6 and 7 to address the issues, character traits and maladaptive behaviours uncovered in the self-assessment that may have contributed to, and may still contribute to, ineffective coping with life, and that could result in a return to alcohol use. It is then suggested that members continue the self-assessment process by making a list of people who they feel they have harmed, and then make direct amends to them, except when to do so would actually make things worse. This process is intended to help relieve shame, guilt and fear, and to decrease isolation from others. After completing these steps all the way through once, members are encouraged to use steps 10 to 12 for maintenance: to continue to take self-inventory, to increase contact with a "higher power" of their own understanding, and to help others. The entire process is designed to produce a "spiritual awakening" or "psychic change" sufficient to overcome alcohol addiction.

Concept of Higher Power

AA encourages members to develop the concept of a spiritual "higher power." For some members who have difficulty separating a personal spirituality as espoused in AA from prior or current religious preferences and experiences, a higher power can mean the AA group itself or, perhaps, a sponsor. By definition, this involves an admission that one is not the centre of the universe, that is, "not God" (Kurtz, 1979/1991). This notion of spiritual surrender bothers some potential AA members. Some are simply put off by AA's spiritual language and concepts, and may be more comfortable in one of the other less spiritually oriented groups described in this chapter. However, some AA members find that the process of ceasing efforts to control all aspects and events of their lives (many of which are of course beyond the control of anyone) actually *increases* their sense of control over alcohol and their lives, and provides a greater sense of freedom.

Initially for some AA members, their group becomes their higher power. Others rely on "Good Orderly Direction" (i.e., "GOD") in their lives to serve as a higher power. Lest AA sound too uniform in its spiritual views, some important caveats from research are in order. For instance, AA includes many members who are atheists or agnostics (Tonigan, Miller et al., in press). In fact, half of AA's original membership were in this class (AA, 2001). Although less religiously involved people may be more likely to drop out of 12-step groups like AA (Kelly & Moos, 2003), those who do continue benefit as much as those who are more religious (Winzelberg & Humphreys, 1999). In fact, many AA members benefit from the fellowship of AA while largely ignoring the program's spiritual aspects (Nealon-Woods et al., 1995).

Service

Alcoholics Anonymous was conceived by its co-founder, Bill Wilson, as having three legacies: recovery (embodied in the 12 steps), unity (embodied in the 12 traditions) and service (derived essentially from the last part of the 12th step, "…carry this message to other alcoholics.") Service work can, however, take many forms. It can be helping to set up the meeting, making coffee, being responsible for literature or looking after the group's finances. It can involve serving as the secretary of a meeting or being the group representative at regional events. From AA's perspective, this kind of service to the group is an indirect way of "carrying the message" by making sure that meetings occur and that they function satisfactorily. Service is also seen as part of a member's recovery, in that it helps members become more responsible for their personal success as well as that of the fellowship.

RESISTANCE TO AA

Counsellors or clients may object to some aspects of the AA program. They may find the spiritual approach unfamiliar, too religious sounding or not religious enough. They may find it repugnant to attend meetings with "alcoholics." They may feel that they are not as bad, crazy or down-and-out as others they see at meetings. They may not want to be in church basements or in groups, or want to ask for help or be willing to receive it. They may find meetings monotonous, boring or ritualistic. They may express fears of becoming dependent on AA and their Higher Power. They may still want to drink alcohol or use other drugs. Many meetings are now non-smoking, and some people may object to that. Some may be unwilling to believe that they are "powerless over alcohol." Some may find AA slogans (e.g., "Easy does it," "Keep it simple," "First things first") too simplistic.

Some of these objections to AA may be legitimate concerns specific to AA itself, or may represent a client's general reluctance to engage in any form of mutual aid or even formal treatment. Importantly, earlier clinical concerns regarding many objections to AA have not been borne out empirically. Increasingly rigorous research carried out during the past 10 to 15 years has consistently revealed that people who attend and become involved in AA and other similar 12-step substance-focused mutual aid groups have better outcomes. As mentioned in more detail later, clinicians can do much to help their clients give these groups a try.

Narcotics Anonymous and Cocaine Anonymous

Two other mutual aid 12-step programs for people with substance use problems are Narcotics Anonymous (NA) and Cocaine Anonymous (CA). NA has about 1,000 chapters in Canada; Canadian data for CA are not available (Humphreys, 2003). These groups were formed more recently than AA, and they serve the different needs and subcultures of their members.

These not-for-profit fellowships have a simple message: "We have found a way to live without using drugs and we are happy to share it with anyone for whom drugs are a problem" (NA, 1996b). The NA way offers a drug-free way of life, and "recovery in NA focuses on the problem of addiction, not on any particular drug" (NA, 1996a). NA and CA literature and books are available at the respective meetings. Much of the organizational detail we have discussed with respect to AA also applies to CA and NA.

Research findings suggest that participation in mutual aid groups by people who use substances may improve their outcomes independent of other factors (American Psychiatric Association, 1995; Humphreys, 2003; Weiss et al., 2000), by providing peer support for continued participation in treatment, helping them avoid drug-using peers and high-risk environments, and intervening early in patterns of thinking and behaviour that may lead to relapse.

Many CA and NA members attend AA, where they may find other members who have more months or years of abstinence and who thus provide the hope and example that newcomers seek. More often than not, CA and NA members also have alcohol use problems. People seeking to stop their drug use may also go to AA meetings because CA and NA do not exist in many smaller communities. A large-scale study of people with cocaine dependence found that clients attended mostly AA and NA, rather than CA (Weiss et al., 2000). One possible reason is that CA is a newer fellowship with fewer meetings available than AA and NA. NA is also inclusive in its membership, accepting people who use cocaine, alcohol and opioids. Further-more, many participants in this study also had comorbid alcohol-related problems and so, as mentioned above, would have legitimately attended AA and found it relevant. A major implication of this finding is that, although a person's primary drug of choice may not exactly match that of a specific substance-focused 12-step fellowship, a person's overall substance-use profile may mean he or she can still benefit from attending.

For many years, certain AA members were reluctant, at meetings, to identify with or entertain the stories of people who used other drugs. However, fewer and fewer newcomers to AA are dependent solely on alcohol, so many AA members may need to talk about issues related to drugs other than alcohol. The acceptance of this among AA members and groups is likely to vary, since the culture of AA groups varies con-siderably (Montgomery et al., 1993). As a result, counsellors may wish to prepare their clients for potential opposition to discussion of issues relating to drugs other than alcohol at AA meetings.

Information on local CA and NA meetings is available from the organizations' World Service Offices (listed at the end of this chapter) or from the telephone directory.

Methadone Anonymous

The use of methadone in the treatment of opioid dependence has increased in many regions of Canada and the United States. It is not only a very effective treatment for opioid dependence but is also highly cost-effective. One study examining daily opioid users in Toronto found the average social cost of an untreated illicit opioid user to be $49,000 per year, while methadone maintenance treatment can be provided for about $6,000 per year (Wall et al., 2000).

Methadone Anonymous (MA) is a relatively new fellowship of current or past methadone clients who together have formed a 12-step organization to help maintain recovery. Meetings are open (unless otherwise designated) to all those who wish to learn how to abstain from opioids and other drugs, including alcohol. MA recognizes that methadone is a drug (i.e., a medication), but considers it to be a tool of recovery. MA is based on the 12 steps and 12 traditions of AA. Anecdotal evidence suggests that because some people may perceive methadone as continued drug use, methadone clients may not feel welcome at traditional mutual aid meetings (e.g., Narcotics Anonymous), which are intended to facilitate total abstinence from drugs. The emergence of MA is therefore timely, especially given current efforts aimed at increasing access to and enrolment in methadone programs (Willenbring, 2001). Preliminary survey findings of MA members suggest this fellowship may be helpful and may offer unique benefits not available in professional treatment (Gilman et al., 2001), and so may serve as a useful adjunct in the treatment of opioid dependence.

Moderation Management

Moderation Management (MM) is the only alcohol mutual aid organization specifically targeted to people whose drinking problems have not reached the point of dependence (Kishline, 1994). It is a not-for-profit registered charity, with no dues or fees, that started in 1994 in the United States. It is not intended for people dependent on alcohol, or people who were once dependent and have stopped drinking. Its main aim is to help people who have drinking problems, but are not alcohol-dependent, to return to moderate alcohol consumption. Those who choose abstinence are referred to abstinence-based programs (e.g., AA, SMART Recovery or Women for Sobriety). MM's current North American membership is around 500 people, with perhaps several times that many having contact with the organization in any given year (Humphreys, 2004). Survey research indicates that the typical MM member is Caucasian, well-educated and employed; most members show no signs of physical dependence on alcohol and use no illicit drugs (Humphreys & Klaw, 2001).

MM offers the following:

1. A supportive mutual-help environment that encourages people who are concerned about their drinking to take action to change as soon as possible, before drinking problems become severe.

2. A nine-step professionally reviewed program, which provides information about alcohol, moderate drinking guidelines and limits, drink-monitoring exercises, goal-setting techniques and self-management strategies. Members also work on taking "small steps" toward finding balance and moderation in other areas of their lives.

3. Some free literature available at meetings, and mutual aid and professional books, audiotapes, videos and interactive computer programs that describe moderation programs available through the network. Individual groups are building small "libraries" for members' use.

4. An e-mail list to allow members to keep up on recent MM happenings, ask questions, make comments and suggestions, philosophize and locate groups is up and running and can be joined on the Web site (see Web site address at end of chapter).

5. Presentations and workshops for professionals and organizations.

MM guidelines and limits for moderate drinking are available free at meetings and in the organization's handbook, *Moderate Drinking* (MM, 1996), which is available at some public libraries. The book, and the MM program generally, differ from 12-step organizations in that they rely explicitly on recent findings from peer-reviewed scientific journals.

SMART Recovery

Self Management and Recovery Training (SMART Recovery) is an outgrowth of another mutual aid organization known as Rational Recovery (RR). In 1993–94, many of the psychologists involved as advisers in RR withdrew and formed the SMART Recovery Network. RR's founder subsequently repudiated the value of mutual aid groups (Humphreys, 2004). SMART Recovery, meanwhile, has grown and now has about 250 groups and 2,000 members in the United States and Canada (Humphreys, 2004). SMART Recovery is based on cognitive-behavioural training and rational thinking (Bishop, 1995). Like Moderation Management, SMART Recovery draws extensively on findings from research into treatment of substance use problems. It is a program of "sensible mutual aid" with trained co-ordinators. There are currently meetings in Calgary, Alberta; Sudbury, Ontario; Penticton, British Columbia; Montreal and St. Jérôme, Quebec (as well as Internet-based SMART Recovery resources accessible anywhere). As SMART Recovery expands, other meetings may appear in other communities. Again, the Web site (listed at the end of the chapter) keeps an updated list of meetings.

SMART Recovery is a free mutual aid program for recovery from substance dependency. The emphasis is on learning how to increase one's motivation to quit. The organization stresses learning to handle urges and developing new ways to cope.

The goal is to create a healthy, positive lifestyle. Permanent abstinence is regarded as the most rational, easy solution. When success is achieved, graduates may choose to leave or to stay with their group to help others (SMART Recovery, 1996).

MEETINGS

About 10 to 12 people usually attend meetings, which are frequently led by a trained co-ordinator who may be a professional. Each group has as an adviser, a professional therapist who may or may not attend every meeting. This person is available to the co-ordinator for guidance in group functioning, to teach a new rational-emotive behaviour therapy (REBT) strategy, or if a member is in trouble. Members are encouraged to read core books.

Groups meet once or twice weekly with the aim of helping participants overcome their addictive behaviours by gaining more control over their thinking, emotions and behaviour and by developing effective relapse-prevention skills. There is no standard format for meetings. Participants may talk (in some groups for up to 10 minutes each) about their problems in recovery and their fears about relapse. They are often taught, by the co-ordinator or adviser, strategies to avoid relapse and how to analyse their thinking, using Ellis's ABCDE formula (Bishop, 1995). Social skills training and practice (such as role-playing) may be part of the program. These strategies give direction to the discussion and questioning. Cross-talk is encouraged, and confrontation between members occurs as members try to help each other recognize the irrationality of their thinking and behaviour. Participants exchange phone numbers and keep in touch between meetings. A collection is taken to defray costs.

RESISTANCE TO SMART RECOVERY

Bishop (1995) reports that, because of the emphasis on rationality and the absence of a spiritual focus, many people find SMART Recovery helpful, but some find the confrontation upsetting. Some people may want to gain more self-control but to continue drinking, while others return to AA. Some may attend both AA and SMART Recovery. Some people who have tried SMART Recovery find it "as unsatisfactory as AA" (Bishop, 1995), which may reflect a generalized aversion to groups or a generalized aversion to stopping alcohol consumption.

Secular Organizations for Sobriety

Secular Organizations for Sobriety (SOS; also known as "Save Our Selves"), "a self-empowerment approach to sobriety" (SOS, 1996b), was launched in 1986 in co-operation with the United States Council for Democratic and Secular Humanism. It is a not-for-profit network of lay-led community groups with the sole aim of helping people maintain their abstinence and recovery from alcohol problems. SOS has about 350 active groups and 3,000 members and operates almost entirely in the United States and, to a lesser extent, Canada and the United Kingdom (Humphreys, 2003).

SOS is an alternative recovery method for people with substance-related problems who are uncomfortable with the spiritual content of 12-step programs. It credits the individual for achieving and maintaining his or her own abstinence and encourages the use of the scientific method to understand alcoholism. Like AA, it has no opinion on outside matters and does not wish to become embroiled in controversy (SOS, 1996a).

All who sincerely desire abstinence are welcome. Abstinence must be the main priority in the individual member's life—"the Sobriety Priority." Anonymity is respected, and honest, clear and direct communication of feelings and thoughts is encouraged. Members are expected to choose non-destructive, non-delusional, rational and sober approaches to living the "good life" (SOS, 1996c).

SOS groups have a maximum of 20 people, and leadership is shared. People with similar problems get together in a safe, non-judgmental environment. The structure and format of the meeting are established by the group. Abstinence anniversaries are acknowledged. New members are encouraged to attend meetings at least once a week for the first six months, followed by "booster" meetings as needed. Pamphlets and books are available at meetings, and the SOS National Clearinghouse publishes a quarterly newsletter.

SOS founder James Christopher (1992) describes the methods advocated by SOS in his most recent book, *SOS Sobriety: The Proven Alternative to 12-Step Programs*. Unfortunately, no empirical studies have been conducted to examine the effectiveness of SOS.

Women for Sobriety

Women for Sobriety (WFS) was established in 1975 by Jean Kirkpatrick, a woman in recovery, who found that AA did not meet all her needs as a woman. She believed that women need their own groups, free from men and role expectations, in which to share their experiences and grow stronger. Today, WFS has between 1,000 and 2,000 members in the Canada and the United States (Humphreys, 2003). Almost all these members are Caucasian, well-educated and middle class (Kaskutas, 1992).

The WFS program "is an affirmation of the value and worth of each woman," as is shown by its Thirteen Statements of Acceptance:

1. I have a drinking problem that once had me.
2. Negative emotions destroy only myself.
3. Happiness is a habit I will develop.
4. Problems bother me only to the degree I permit them to.
5. I am what I think.
6. Life can be ordinary or it can be great.
7. Love can change the course of my world.
8. The fundamental object of life is emotional and spiritual growth.
9. The past is gone forever.
10. All love given returns twofold.

11. Enthusiasm is my daily exercise.
12. I am a competent woman and have much to give to others.
13. I am responsible for myself and my sisters (Kirkpatrick, 1978).

Kirkpatrick (1978) maintains that these statements lead a woman to see herself positively and increase her self-confidence. She learns to see herself as able to overcome her drinking and other problems. The changes she experiences are reinforced by the group. WFS groups provide acceptance, nurturing and a sense of belonging, and are a place to release anxiety, share fears and learn to trust.

MEETINGS

Eight to 12 women usually attend meetings, which are held in places such as homes, women's treatment centres and shopping mall facilities. The discussion or "conversation" (Kirkpatrick, 1978) is led by one of the members. Most groups meet once a week but may meet more often as required. Meetings never last longer than 90 minutes.

MEMBERSHIP

Membership is open to any woman who has a problem with alcohol and who wants to stop drinking and find a new way of life. It is believed that a person's dependence on alcohol, acquired to overcome stress, loneliness and emotional deprivation, must be resolved through abstinence and personal change. A woman has to make the decision to take responsibility for herself and her actions. Unlike in AA, a recital of a woman's drinking history is not required, since there are no open speaker meetings. In the absence of a local WFS group, women can become part of the Pen Pal Program and correspond with recovered women. The office will notify members of the Pen Pal Program when a new group is starting near them (Women for Sobriety, 1996b). In addition, abundant literature, workbooks, videos and audiotapes are available at a nominal cost from WFS headquarters.

THE EFFECTIVENESS OF MUTUAL AID GROUPS

As mentioned above, the majority of empirical research on mutual aid groups has been conducted on AA and similar 12-step programs. This is mainly because of the sheer size and influence of these fellowships, which has drawn the attention of researchers and governmental scientific agencies such as the U.S Institute of Medicine and National Institutes of Health. Although there is currently a lack of research evidence supporting the effectiveness of similar (but non-12-step) substance-focused mutual aid organizations, anecdotal reports suggest they may hold similar promise. Large-scale reviews of studies completed on AA (Emrick et al., 1993; Tonigan et al., 1996), conducted mostly in the 1970s and 1980s, concluded that AA had beneficial effects on people's drinking behaviour and psychosocial functioning. However, much of the research covered in these reviews was not methodologically rigorous.

Consequently, some clinicians remained skeptical about the true benefits of mutual aid groups. Over the past decade, the quality and quantity of research on 12-step, substance-focused mutual aid groups has increased dramatically.

A large randomized controlled trial of treatment for alcohol dependence also examined the use of mutual aid groups (Project MATCH, 1993). This was the largest such trial of individual psychotherapies ever undertaken, comprising more than 1,700 male and female clients. A professionally delivered twelve-step facilitation (TSF) treatment was compared with motivational enhancement therapy (MET) and cognitive behaviour therapy (CBT). Although the TSF treatment should not be mistaken for a test of mutual aid groups, TSF is an intervention intended specifically to initiate and help maintain clients' use of mutual aid groups. In addition, the trial measured all clients' involvement in such groups both during and after treatment.

Results revealed the feasibility of the professional TSF approach, as well as its superior efficacy with respect to abstinence, relative to the more empirically supported CBT and MET (Project MATCH, 1997). Furthermore, the superior outcomes attained by clients treated in TSF were explained by their attending mutual aid groups during the follow-up period. In addition, the study found that regardless of which original treatment clients received, people who attended 12-step mutual aid groups had significantly better drinking outcomes (Tonigan, Connors et al., in press). Interestingly, after three years, 58 per cent of TSF clients had attended an AA meeting in the previous 90 days, but so had 45 per cent of MET clients and 39 per cent of those assigned to CBT. Consequently, mutual aid organizations appear to be a valuable adjunct to treatment for substance use problems, even in programs where they are not formally emphasized.

Similar findings were obtained in another large controlled study of 487 clients who were dependent on cocaine (Crits-Christoph et al., 1999). Again, although the study was not a test of mutual aid groups per se, a principal goal of one of the treatments (individual drug counselling) was to facilitate clients' involvement in 12-step mutual aid groups. Clients who received individual drug counselling had significantly better substance use outcomes than those who had other treatments.

Additional evidence comes from more naturalistic studies that assess nearly all clients in particular treatment programs, and thus are more representative of real treatment populations. In one such study of more than 3,000 male inpatient substance-use clients, those treated in professional 12-step-focused programs were more likely to be abstinent after one year than those treated in cognitive behavioural or eclectic programs. Furthermore, clients who attended mutual aid groups during the follow-up period had better substance-related and psychosocial outcomes, no matter which type of treatment they had received.

Counsellors often ask how many meetings they should recommend their clients attend. Some clinicians believe clients should attend as many meetings as possible, especially early in recovery. Others advocate for a meeting every day for a defined period, such as the first three months. Research suggests more frequent attendance is associated with less substance use, especially during the first year or two after professional treatment. However, research to date has not proven that the

"90 meetings in 90 days" approach necessarily has better results than would a similar period of regular attendance (e.g., three or four meetings a week for three months). One study found that clients who attended mutual aid meetings at least twice weekly, on average, during the first year after treatment, were significantly less likely to relapse during the same period (Etheridge et al., 1999). Nonetheless, some clients may want and benefit from a more total commitment, depending on their individual circumstances.

Some clinicians believe that clients do well in 12-step mutual aid groups because they are more motivated or have better prognoses to begin with. However, it appears that even when these factors are taken into account, people involved in 12-step mutual aid groups still have improved outcomes (McKellar et al., 2003). Also, when compared with people who do not enter treatment, have professional treatment only, or have a combination of professional treatment plus AA, those who attend AA only appear to do at least as well as those receiving more intensive treatments. People who try to change their substance use without *any* type of help tend to have the worst outcomes (Timko et al., 2000). Thus, for some clients, attending AA may be enough to help them achieve lasting recovery. However, most clients will need formal treatment in addition to mutual aid.

In summary, the current evidence, some of which is highlighted above, has grown in quality and quantity (for a more substantial review, see Kelly, 2003). When the old and new evidence is combined and viewed together, a consistently beneficial effect emerges for involvement in mutual aid groups, on various substance use and psychosocial outcomes measured at various time points. More research on other, non-12-step, mutual aid organizations may yield similar findings.

NON-ATTENDANCE AND DROPOUT

In general, as we discussed above, clients attending mutual aid groups have better results than those receiving other treatment. But are specific client subgroups more or less likely to attend, drop out or benefit from groups than others? An answer to this question could help counsellors facilitate clients' attendance at mutual aid groups. These issues are discussed next.

Despite the encouragement of their counsellors, many clients either decide not to attend mutual aid groups or drop out too quickly to realize benefits. About 40 per cent of clients who begin attending groups drop out within the first year (Kelly & Moos, 2003; Tonigan, Connors et al., in press). One U.S. study of nearly 3,000 male Veterans Affairs clients found that those who were less religious, less motivated for abstinence and had less prior 12-step experience at the time they entered treatment were the most likely to drop out (Kelly & Moos, 2003). However, the study also found that these clients were less likely to drop out of mutual aid groups within the first year if they perceived their treatment environments as relatively cohesive, supportive and spiritually oriented. Thus, treatment programs whose staff are encouraging, caring, helpful and empathic, and are comfortable discussing spiritual issues with clients, may help increase the likelihood that clients will follow treatment recommendations, such as attending mutual aid groups after treatment ends. This finding is important since, consistent with prior research, those clients who dropped out from groups were three times more likely to be using substances at follow-up.

Additionally, among the clients with the risk factors noted above, those who became actively involved in 12-step groups during treatment, including getting a sponsor, developing friends and reading program literature, were less likely to drop out. Consequently, treatment programs and counsellors that encourage and monitor such endeavours during treatment may witness lower group dropout rates among their clients after treatment ends (Kelly & Moos, 2003).

CONCERNS WITH SPECIFIC POPULATIONS

Clients with Concurrent Psychiatric Disorders

Many counsellors may be inclined not to refer certain clients to mutual aid groups, because they believe such groups may not be a good fit or, worse, may be harmful to their clients. Such clients may include the increasing numbers with concurrent substance use and mental health problems, including bipolar disorder, major depressive disorder or post-traumatic stress disorder (PTSD). The principal fear is that some mutual aid group members may persuade these clients to stop taking their psychotropic medication. Formal research in this area is scarce, but suggests that a small minority of group members oppose medication use for both emotional and substance use problems (Rychtarik et al., 2000; Tonigan & Kelly, in press). It is not clear why AA members do not actively endorse medication use in general, but anecdotal evidence suggests the reason may relate to generalized fears of cross-addiction, and/or a belief that dependency on any "drug" is bad. However, the level of prejudice against medication in 12-step groups seems no higher or lower than the level in other individuals with alcohol problems (Tonigan & Kelly, in press) or in society in general, so group members may simply be reflecting common cultural beliefs. More research is needed to assess the precise reasons. All the same, many clients with concurrent disorders may benefit from attending mutual aid groups, so counsellors may wish to prepare them to cope with potential opposition to psychotropic medication.

The degree to which clients with concurrent disorders attend and benefit from traditional mutual aid groups, such as AA or NA, may depend on their combination of disorders. For example, clients with both substance use problems and PTSD appear to participate in, and benefit from, 12-step groups as much as clients with substance use problems alone (Ouimette et al., 2001). In contrast, Noordsy and colleagues

(1996) found that outpatients with substance dependence and psychotic disorders (e.g., schizophrenia) do not appear to benefit from traditional 12-step mutual aid involvement as much as other clients, unless the group is tailored to clients with concurrent disorders. A larger study, with more than 350 clients, found similar rates of attendance at AA among people with any concurrent psychiatric diagnosis except schizophrenia (Tomasson & Vaglum, 1998). A further study by Bogenschutz and Akin (2000) found that clients with concurrent substance use problems and severe mental health problems attended mutual aid groups at rates comparable to those of substance use clients in general, but reported more difficulty fitting in at meetings. A study examining male substance use clients with concurrent major depressive disorder found that these clients may not become as socially involved in mutual aid groups as do clients with substance use problems alone, and may not benefit as much (Kelly et al., 2003). Thus, although more research is needed in this increasingly important area, different subgroups of clients with concurrent disorders will likely vary in how well they fit into groups and how much benefit they receive. Newer mutual aid organizations such as Double Trouble in Recovery (www.doubletroubleinrecovery.org) and Dual Recovery Anonymous (http://draonline.org) are increasing in number. These groups focus specifically on both substance abuse and mental health problems and so may be a better fit for clients with concurrent disorders (e.g., they explicitly encourage members to take their medication).

Youth

Adolescents have been shown to benefit from attending mutual aid groups such as AA or NA (Brown et al., 1994; Kelly et al., 2000 & 2002). However, some counsellors working with adolescents and young adults are concerned at the lack of meetings specifically for youth. In addition, youth tend to have much less chronic and severe problems than adults, which makes abstinence-focused groups less appealing to many.

Even if teens are motivated to attend mutual aid groups, the predominantly adult composition of most groups may hinder their identification with the group and present a barrier to continued attendance and involvement. (Demographic data from AA's latest triennial survey [AA, 2002] revealed members' average age to be 46 years, with only 2 per cent of members under age 21.) Age similarity may be particularly important for youth because of the influence of variables tied to their developmental status (Deas et al., 2000). Youth who attend meetings may not believe they have much in common with other participants and may have difficulty identifying with issues central to recovery (e.g., severity of substance dependence) and peripheral to recovery (e.g, employment concerns, marital relations). Consequently, youth may not perceive the sharing of specific experiences by older members as helpful or relevant in dealing with the recovery issues of their own life stage, and they may make fewer therapeutic gains. It is therefore prudent for counsellors to direct young clients to mutual aid meetings where other youth are in attendance.

HOW COUNSELLORS CAN HELP

1. **Recognize the validity and importance of mutual aid groups**. Most professionals recognize that people with substance use problems need support and encouragement if they are to maintain treatment gains. This belief has been supported by research (Lavoie et al., 1994; McCrady & Irvine, 1989; Reissman & Carroll, 1995). Thus, it is appropriate for the counsellor to introduce clients to the idea that people with substance use problems must have ongoing support for as long as is needed. Such support can be found at minimal cost in mutual aid groups. The counsellor can describe the groups that exist locally and, if choices don't exist, work with the client to overcome any resistance to the existing mutual aid group; help to establish a mutual aid group more to the client's liking; or work with the client to find support for abstinence through family, friends or other groups.

2. **Visit and become familiar with local mutual aid groups**. Though the descriptions in this chapter may be somewhat informative, counsellors often feel more confident discussing mutual aid groups with clients if they themselves have attended. In Project MATCH, for example, the TSF counsellors were encouraged to attend a minimum of ten 12-step meetings to become more familiar with format and process. Former clients may be a good resource to facilitate attendance.

   It is a good idea to become familiar with the various types and sizes of meetings, so you can help clients make good choices. Some research indicates that clients are good candidates for AA if they have a severe drinking problem, an affective rather than a cognitive focus, concerns about the purpose and meaning of life, good interpersonal skills and a high need to belong (McCrady & Irvine, 1989). Clients are also most likely to benefit from mutual aid if they join a group whose members are similar to them in age, culture and occupational status (American Psychiatric Association, 1995; Zweben, 1995).

3. **Make contacts and actively facilitate attendance**. Keep in touch with former clients who attend mutual aid groups, and develop a list of people who will keep you informed and will take a client to his or her first meeting. Additionally, be willing to actively put clients in contact with group members through counselling sessions. One study found that when therapists actively linked clients with members of mutual aid groups, rather than simply giving the clients information and encouraging them to attend, the clients were far more likely to attend (Sisson & Mallams, 1981). Specifically, of the clients who were only encouraged to attend, *not one* client attended a single 12-step meeting during the four weeks following referral. By contrast, where the counsellor telephoned willing group members and had the client speak to the member while in the office and make arrangements to attend a specific meeting, *every* client attended at least one meeting (2.3 meetings on average).

4. **Ask clients to become involved in mutual aid groups early in their therapy**. This strategy is helpful for several reasons. It allows the client to get used to groups, the members and the process before they leave therapy. It allows the counsellor time to explore the client's issues about the groups and to deal with

any resistance. Some counsellors ask clients to keep a log or journal of their experiences at meetings, including their thoughts and feelings, for discussion at counselling sessions (Nowinski et al., 1995).

5. **Try other resources available to complement your skills.** (1) By using the "stages of change" model in therapy (DiClemente & Prochaska, 1982; see Chapter 2 of this book), you can help clients discover where they are in their mutual aid participation and begin to work with them to move to the next stage. (2) Bishop (1995) describes how to integrate rational-emotive behaviour therapy (REBT) and addictive voice recognition techniques (AVRT) into your practice to prepare clients for SMART Recovery. (3) The *Twelve Step Facilitation Therapy Manual* (Nowinski et al., 1995) is a good guide to helping clients become involved in mutual aid groups. Although it focuses on 12-step groups, it contains many ideas that may be generalized to other mutual aid groups. It is free and available from the U.S. National Institute of Alcohol Abuse and Alcoholism (NIAAA). McCrady and Irvine (1989) and Zweben (1995) also offer an in-depth approach to integrating AA with professional practice.

6. **Keep an open mind.** Sometimes preconceived notions or negative anecdotes can interfere with the counsellor's open mind with regard to mutual aid groups. Research continues and new findings may suggest different approaches. Expending too much professional energy on defending one treatment approach or one particular mutual aid group may compromise optimal care and put the client at risk for relapse. It is wise to be sensitive to a client's reaction to, and preferences for, a particular group, while helping the client to give such groups a reasonable try.

7. **Direct clients to suitable meetings and prepare them for what to expect.** When recommending meetings to clients, it is best to have a sense of which groups may be a good fit. For example, if you are working with adolescents or young adults, suggest meetings where other young people may be present (e.g., AA lists "young persons'" meetings). If you are working with clients with concurrent substance use and psychiatric problems, direct them to "dual recovery" meetings, meetings that may be more "medication friendly" or meetings where similar clients will be present to provide support. It is wise to discuss the potential barrier of "poor fit" with clients at the outset of counselling. This may include discussing group members' possible resistance to psychotropic medication, and exploring ways to cope with it. It may also include assessing and discussing the client's resistance to "spiritual" issues and certain approaches to change.

CONCLUSION

A variety of substance-focused mutual aid groups exist, and groups of various kinds are becoming increasingly common. Current evidence suggests that clients who attend 12-step groups such as AA or NA have significantly better outcomes. Other mutual aid groups (e.g., SMART Recovery, SOS), although less widespread, may have similar benefits, but await more formal investigation. Counsellors can significantly increase the chance that their clients will attend and become involved in such groups by:

• educating themselves about these organizations
• attending groups
• preparing clients for what to expect
• remaining open-minded
• actively putting clients in touch with existing group members, and continuing to monitor and discuss clients' mutual aid experiences.

A mutual aid group member, who had been abstinent for 15 years, said her experience with mutual aid was similar to a group of geese flying south. Her story, as described by Kort and Smith (1993), noted that science has learned the following:

> As each bird flaps its wing, it creates uplift for the bird immediately following it. By flying in a V formation, the whole flock can fly at least seventy per cent farther in a day than if each bird flew on its own.... Whenever a goose falls out of formation, it feels how hard it is to try to fly against the wind on its own, and it quickly gets back into formation to fly with the flock.... When the lead goose gets tired, it rotates back in the wing and another goose flies in the front of the point.... The geese in the back honk to encourage those at the front to keep up their speed. When a goose weakens or is hurt and falls out of formation, two geese follow it down to help and protect it. They stay with the goose until it is able to fly or until it dies. Then they set out again, either on their own or with another formation, until they catch up with the group (p. 7).

Like the group member, we believe the goose analogy serves as a useful metaphor for mutual aid.

RESOURCES

Alcoholics Anonymous World Services, Inc.
Box 459, Grand Central Station
New York, NY 10163
U.S.A.
Phone: 212 870-3400
Fax: 212 870-3137
Web site: www.alcoholics-anonymous.org

Cocaine Anonymous World Service Office
3740 Overland Avenue, Suite G
Los Angeles, CA 90034
U.S.A.
Phone: 310 559-5833
Fax: 310 559-2554
E-mail: cawso@ca.org
Web site: www.ca.org

Methadone Anonymous
Advocates for the Integration of Recovery and Methadone (AFIRM), Inc.
Long Beach Medical Center—MMC
455 East Bay Drive
Long Beach, NY 11561
U.S.A.
Phone: 516 897-1330 (days)
          516 889-8142 (evenings)
Fax: 516 897-1149
E-mail: afirmfwc@aol.com
Web site: www.methadonetoday.org/m_isreco.htm

Moderation Management
c/o HRC
22 W. 27th Street
New York, NY 10001
U.S.A.
Phone: 212 871-0974
Fax: 212 213-6582
E-mail: mm@moderation.org
Web site: www.moderation.org

Narcotics Anonymous
P.O. Box 9999
Van Nuys, CA 91409
U.S.A.
Phone: 818 773-9999
Fax: 818 700-0700
E-mail: lynnl@sprynet.com
Web site: www.wsoinc.com

Narcotics Anonymous Canada
World Service Office
150 Britannia Rd. East, Unit 21
Mississauga, ON L4Z 2A4
Phone: 905 507-0100
Fax: 905 507-0101

SMART Recovery Network
24000 Mercantile Blvd. Suite 11
Beachwood, OH 44122
U.S.A.
Phone: 216 292-0220
Fax: 216 831-3776
Web site: www.smartrecovery.org

SOS
P.O. Box 5
Buffalo, NY 14215
U.S.A.
Phone: 716 636-7571

SOS National Clearinghouse
The Centre for Inquiry—West
5521 Grosvenor Blvd.
Los Angeles, CA 90066
U.S.A.
Phone: 310 821-8430
Fax: 310 821-2610
E-mail: sosa@loop.com
Web site: www.secularhumanism.org/sos

Women for Sobriety
P.O. Box 618
Quakertown, PA 18951
U.S.A.
Phone and fax: 215 536-8026
E-mail: wfsobriety@aol.com
Web site: www.womenforsobriety.org

AUTHORS' NOTE

John Kelly and Keith Humphreys are affiliated with the Veterans Affairs Health Care System and Stanford University School of Medicine in Palo Alto, California. Their work on this chapter was supported in part by grants from the U.S. Veterans Affairs Health Services Research and Development Service.

REFERENCES

Alcoholics Anonymous. (1952). *The Twelve Steps and Twelve Traditions*. New York: Alcoholics Anonymous World Services.

Alcoholics Anonymous. (1994a). *About AA: A Newsletter for Professionals* (Fall/Winter ed.). New York: Alcoholics Anonymous World Services.

Alcoholics Anonymous. (1994b). *Questions and Answers on Sponsorship*. New York: Alcoholics Anonymous World Services.

Alcoholics Anonymous. (2001). *Alcoholics Anonymous: The Story of How Many Thousands of Men and Women Have Recovered from Alcoholism* (4th ed.). New York: Alcoholics Anonymous World Services.

Alcoholics Anonymous. (2003). *2001 Membership Survey: A Snapshot of A.A. Membership*. New York: AA World Services.

American Psychiatric Association. (1995). Practice guidelines for the treatment of clients with substance use disorders: Alcohol, cocaine, opiates. *American Journal of Psychiatry, 152*(11), 63–80, supplement.

Bishop, F.M. (1995). Rational-Emotive Behavior Therapy and two mutual aid alternatives to the 12-step model. In A.M. Washton (Ed.), *Psychotherapy and Substance Abuse* (pp. 141–160). New York: Guilford.

Bogenschutz, M.P. & Akin, S.J. (2000). 12-Step participation and attitudes toward 12-step meetings in dual diagnosis patients. *Alcoholism Treatment Quarterly, 18*(4), 31–45.

Brown, S.A., Myers, M.G., Mott, M.A. & Vik, P. (1994). Correlates of successful outcome following treatment for adolescent substance abuse. *Journal of Applied & Preventive Psychology, 3*, 61–73.

Christopher, J. (1992). *SOS Sobriety: The Proven Alternative to 12-Step Programs.* New York: Prometheus Books.

Crape, B.L., Latkin, C.A., Laris, A.S. & Knowlton, A.R. (2002). The effects of sponsorship in 12-step treatment of injection drug users. *Drug and Alcohol Dependence, 65*, 291–301.

Crits-Christoph, P., Siqueland, L., Blaine, J., Frank, A., Luborsky, L., Onken, L.S. et al. (1999). Psychosocial treatments for cocaine dependence: National Institute on Drug Abuse Collaborative Cocaine Treatment Study. *Archives of General Psychiatry, 56*(6), 493–502.

Cross, G.M., Morgan, C.W. et al. (1990). Alcoholism treatment: A ten-year follow-up study. *Alcoholism: Clinical and Experimental Research, 14*(2), 169–173.

Deas, D., Riggs, P., Langenbucher, J., Goldman, M. & Brown, S. (2000). Adolescents are not adults: Developmental considerations in alcohol users. *Alcoholism Clinical and Experimental Research, 24*(2), 232–237.

Delgado, M. & Humm-Delgado, D. (1993). Chemical dependence, mutual aid, and the Hispanic community. In R.S. Mayer, A.L. Kail & T.D. Watts (Eds.), *Hispanic Substance Abuse* (pp. 424–445). Springfield, IL: Charles C. Thomas.

DiClemente, C. & Prochaska, J.O. (1982). Self-change and therapy change of smoking behavior: A comparison of processes of change in cessation and maintenance. *Addictive Behaviors 7*(2), 133–142.

Emrick, C.D., Tonigan, J.S., Montgomery, H. & Little, L. (1993). Alcoholics anonymous: What is currently known? In B.S. McCrady & E.R. Miller (Eds.), *Research on Alcoholics Anonymous: Opportunities and Alternatives* (pp. 41–76). New Brunswick, NJ: Alcohol Research Documentation Inc.

Etheridge, R.M., Craddock, S.G., Hubbard, R.L. & Rounds-Bryant, J.L. (1999). The relationship of counselling and self-help participation to patient outcomes in DATOS. *Drug and Alcohol Dependence, 57*, 99–112.

Fiorentine, R. & Hillhouse, M.P. (2000). Drug treatment and 12-step program participation: The additive effects of integrated recovery activities. *Journal of Substance Abuse Treatment, 18*(1), 65–74.

Gilman, S.M., Galanter, M. & Dermatis, H. (2001). Methadone Anonymous: A 12-step program for methadone maintained heroin addicts. *Substance Abuse, 24*(4), 247–256.

Hill, K. (1984). *Helping You Helps Me: A Guide Book for Mutual Aid Groups*. Ottawa: Canadian Council on Social Development.

Humphreys, K. (2004). *Circles of Recovery: Mutual Aid Organisations for Addictions*. Cambridge, U.K.: Cambridge University Press.

Humphreys, K. & Klaw, E. (2001). Can targeting non-dependent problem drinkers and providing internet-based services expand access to assistance for alcohol problems? A study of the Moderation Management mutual aid/mutual aid organization. *Journal of Studies on Alcohol, 62*, 528–532.

Humphreys, K. & Tucker, J. (2002). Towards more responsive and effective intervention systems for alcohol-related problems. *Addiction, 97*, 126–132.

Humphreys, K. & Woods, M.D. (1993). Researching mutual help group participation in a segregated society. *Journal of Applied Behavioral Science, 29*(2), 181–201.

Kaskutas, L.A. (1992). *An analysis of Women for Sobriety*. Doctoral dissertation available from University Microfilms (UMI), Order Number 9330441.

Kelly, J.F. (2003). Self-help for substance use disorders: History, effectiveness, knowledge gaps and research opportunities. *Clinical Psychology Review, 23*(5), 639–663.

Kelly, J.F., McKellar, J.D. & Moos, R.H. (2003). Comorbid major depression in patients with substance use disorders: Effects on 12-step self-help participation and substance use outcomes. *Addiction, 98*, 499–508.

Kelly, J.F. & Moos, R. (2003). Dropout from self-help groups: Prevalence, predictors and counteracting treatment influences. *Journal of Substance Abuse Treatment, 24*(3), 241–250.

Kelly, J.F., Myers, M.G. & Brown, S.A. (2000). A multivariate process model of adolescent 12-step attendance and substance use outcome following inpatient treatment. *Psychology of Addictive Behaviors, 14*(4), 376–389.

Kelly, J.F., Myers, M.G. & Brown, S.A. (2002). Do adolescents affiliate with 12-step groups? A multivariate process model of effects. *Journal of Studies on Alcohol, 63*(3), 293–304.

Kirkpatrick, J. (1978). *Turnabout: Help for a New Life*. New York: Doubleday.

Kishline, A. (1994). *Moderate Drinking: The Moderation Management Guide for People Who Want to Reduce Their Drinking*. New York: Crown.

Kort, M. & Smith, S. (1993). *Stop Smoking Program: Facilitators Guide*. Toronto: Addiction Research Foundation.

Kurtz, E. (1979/1991). *Not-God: A History of Alcoholics Anonymous*. Center City, MN: Hazelden.

Lavoie, F., Borkman, T. & Gidron, B. (Eds.). (1994). *Mutual aid and Mutual Aid Groups: International and Multicultural Perspectives. Part 1, 11*(1). New York: Haworth Press.

Maton, K.I. (1988). Social support, organizational characteristics, psychological well-being, and group appraisal in three mutual aid group populations. *American Journal of Community Psychology, 16*(1), 53–77.

McCrady, B.S. & Irvine, S. (1989). Mutual aid groups. In R.K. Hester & W.R. Miller (Eds.), *Handbook of Alcoholism Treatment Approaches* (pp. 153–169). New York: Pergamon Press.

McKellar, J.D., Stewart, E. & Humphrey, K.N. (2003). Alcoholics Anonymous involvement and positive alcohol-related outcomes: Cause, consequence, or just a correlation? A prospective 2-year study of 2,319 alcohol-dependent men. *Journal of Consulting and Clinical Psychology, 71*(2), 302–308.

Miller, W.R. (1989). Increasing motivation for change. In R.K. Hester & W.R. Miller (Eds.), *Handbook of Alcoholism Treatment Approaches* (pp. 67–80). New York: Pergamon Press.

Moderation Management. (1996). *Moderate Drinking*. Ann Arbor, MI: author.

Montgomery, H.A., Miller, W.R. & Tonigan, J.S. (1993). Differences among AA groups: Implications for research. *Journal of Studies on Alcohol, 54*, 502–504.

Narcotics Anonymous. (1996a). *Am I an Addict?* Van Nuys, CA: Narcotics Anonymous World Service Office.

Narcotics Anonymous. (1996b). *Welcome to Narcotics Anonymous*. Van Nuys, CA: Narcotics Anonymous World Service Office.

Nealon-Woods, M.A., Ferrari, J.R. & Jason, L.A. (1995). Twelve-step program use among Oxford House residents: Spirituality or support in sobriety? *Journal of Substance Abuse, 7*, 311–318.

Noordsy, D.L., Schwab, B., Fox, L. & Drake, R.E. (1996). The role of self-help programs in the rehabilitation of persons with severe mental illness and substance use disorders. *Community Mental Health Journal, 32*(1), 71–81; discussion 83–76.

Nowinski, J., Baker, S. & Carroll, K.M. (1995). *Twelve Step Facilitation Therapy Manual: A Clinical Research Guide for Therapists Treating Individuals with Alcohol Abuse and Dependence*. Project MATCH Monograph Series, Vol. 1. DHHS Publication No. 94-3722. Rockville, MD: NIAAA.

Ouimette, P., Humphreys, K., Moos, R.H., Finney, J.W., Cronkite, R. & Federman, B. (2001). Self-help group participation among substance use disorder patients with posttraumatic stress disorder. *Journal of Substance Abuse Treatment, 20*(1), 25–32.

Project MATCH Research Group. (1993). Project MATCH (Matching Alcoholism Treatment to Client Heterogeneity): Rationale and methods for a multisite clinical trial matching patients to alcoholism treatment. *Alcohol Clinical Experimental Research, 17*(6), 1130–1145.

Project MATCH Research Group. (1997). Matching alcoholism treatments to patient heterogeneity: Project MATCH posttreatment drinking outcomes. *Journal of Studies on Alcohol, 58*, 7–29.

Reissman, F. & Carroll, D. (1995). *Redefining Mutual Aid: Policy and Practice*. San Francisco: Jossey-Bass.

Room, R. & Greenfield, T. (1993). Alcoholics Anonymous, other 12-step movements and psychotherapy in the U.S. population 1990. *Addiction, 88*, 555–562.

Rychtarik, R.G., Connors, G.J., Dermen, K.H. & Stasiewicz, P.R. (2000). Alcoholics Anonymous and the use of medications to prevent relapse: An anonymous survey of member attitudes. *Journal of Studies on Alcohol, 61*(1), 134–138.

Schwartz, C.E. & Sendor, R.M. (1999). Helping others helps oneself: Response shift effects in peer support. *Social Science and Medicine, 48*, 1563–1575.

Secular Organizations for Sobriety. (1996a). *Home Page*. Los Angeles: SOS National Clearing House.

Secular Organizations for Sobriety. (1996b). *A Self-Empowerment Approach to Recovery*. Buffalo, NY: Secular Organizations for Sobriety.

Secular Organizations for Sobriety. (1996c). *The Sobriety Priority*. Buffalo, NY: Secular Organizations for Sobriety.

Sisson, R.W. & Mallams, J.H. (1981). The use of systematic encouragement and community access procedures to increase attendance at Alcoholics Anonymous and Al-Anon meetings. *American Journal of Drug & Alcohol Abuse, 8*(3), 371–376.

SMART Recovery. (1996). *Alcohol or Drug Problem? Now There Is a Scientific Alternative!* Beachwood, OH: Alcohol and Drug Abuse Mutual Aid Network.

Timko, C., Moos, R.H., Finney, J.W. & Lesar, M.D. (2000). Long-term outcomes of alcohol use disorders: Comparing untreated individuals with those in Alcoholics Anonymous and formal treatment. *Journal of Studies on Alcohol, 61*(4), 529–540.

Tomasson, K. & Vaglum, P. (1998). Psychiatric co-morbidity and aftercare among alcoholics: A prospective study of a nationwide representative sample. *Addiction, 93*(3), 423–431.

Tonigan, J.S., Connors, G.J. & Miller, W.R. (in press). Participation and involvement in Alcoholics Anonymous. In T.F. Babor & F.K. Del Boca (Eds.), *Matching Alcoholism Treatments to Client Heterogeneity: The Results of Project MATCH*. New York: Cambridge University Press.

Tonigan, J.S. & Kelly, J.F. (in press). Beliefs about AA and the use of medications: A comparison of three groups of AA-exposed alcohol dependent persons. *Alcoholism Treatment Quarterly*.

Tonigan, J.S., Miller, W.R. & Schermer, C. (in press). Atheists, agnostics and Alcoholics Anonymous. *Journal of Studies on Alcohol.*

Tonigan, J.S., Toscova, R. & Miller, W.R. (1996). Meta-analysis of the literature on Alcoholics Anonymous: Sample and study characteristics moderate findings. *Journal of Studies on Alcohol, 57*(1), 65–72.

Wall, R., Rehm, J., Fischer, B., Brands, B., Gliksman, L., Stewart, J., Medved, W. & Blake, J. (2000). Social costs of untreated opioid dependence. *Journal of Urban Health, 77*(4), 688–722.

Weiss, R.D., Griffin, M.L., Gallop, R., Onken, L.S., Gastdriend, D.R., Daley, D. et al. (2000). Mutual aid group attendance and participation among cocaine dependent patients. *Drug and Alcohol Dependence, 60,* 169–177.

Willenbring, M.L. (2001, December). *Opioid Agonist Translation Project: Progress to date.* Paper presented at the 2001 Veterans Affairs National QUERI Conference, Orlando, FL.

Winzelberg, A. & Humphreys, K. (1999). Should patients' religious beliefs and practices influence clinicians' referral to 12-step mutual aid groups?: Evidence from a study of 3,018 male substance abuse patients. *Journal of Consulting and Clinical Psychology, 67,* 790–794.

Women for Sobriety. (1996a). *Women and Addictions: A Way to Recovery.* Quakertown, PA: Women for Sobriety.

Women for Sobriety. (1996b). *"New Life" Literature.* Quakertown, PA: Women for Sobriety.

Yalom, I.D. (1996). *The Theory and Practice of Group Psychotherapy* (4th ed.). New York: Basic Books.

Zweben, J.E. (1995). Integrating psychotherapy and 12-step approaches. In A.M. Washton, (Ed.), *Psychotherapy and Substance Abuse* (pp. 124–140). New York: Guilford.

Chapter 10

Physical Effects of Alcohol and Other Drugs

MELDON KAHAN

Substance use counsellors can play an important role in maintaining their clients' physical health. They are frequently called upon to explain the health risks of alcohol and other drugs, and to inform clients of ways to minimize these risks. They often communicate with the client's family physician and other health care providers. Counsellors may be the first professionals to become aware of signs and symptoms of impending illness in a client. For these reasons, counsellors need to be familiar with the physical effects of alcohol and other drugs. This chapter briefly summarizes the health effects of the major drugs of abuse.

KEY CONCEPTS

Tolerance

Psychoactive (mood- or consciousness-altering) drugs tend to have a diminished effect with repeated use, a phenomenon known as tolerance. Tolerance is most marked in sedative and opioid use. Tolerance occurs when the nervous system adapts to heavy drug use. For example, alcohol activates GABA, a neurotransmitter that inhibits the activity of the central nervous system (CNS). It also inhibits NMDA, a neurotransmitter responsible for increasing CNS activity. These two actions cause the

CNS to slow down, resulting in sedation, the primary effect of alcohol. With repeated use, the CNS compensates by increasing the number and sensitivity of NMDA receptors on nerve cells. The NMDA system is thus able to overcome the sedating effects of alcohol, allowing a person who drinks heavily to act almost normally despite having consumed large amounts of alcohol.

Withdrawal

The nervous system requires days or weeks to adjust to the sudden cessation of drug use, causing a set of signs and symptoms known as withdrawal. For example, tolerance makes the NMDA system of people who drink heavily more active (see above), so when the person quits drinking, he or she experiences symptoms of an overactive nervous system. Withdrawal (like tolerance) is most common and severe with sedative and opioid use. While physical symptoms of withdrawal usually resolve in a week or two, people who use substances heavily over the long-term may experience mood disturbances and craving for weeks and months, due to semi-permanent changes in the nervous system.

Physical Dependence

"Physical dependence" refers to tolerance and withdrawal. Physical dependence often, but not always, accompanies psychological dependence. For example, people psychologically dependent on cocaine experience little or no physical withdrawal, while people taking high doses of opioids for chronic pain typically experience physical withdrawal when they stop taking the drug, but are not usually psychologically dependent; they take the drug for analgesia only and do not experience reinforcing psychoactive effects.

Dependence Liability

The ability of a drug to produce reinforcing states, such as pleasure or euphoria, is known as dependence liability. Drugs within the same class may vary in their dependence liability; for example, among opioids, heroin and oxycodone have a higher dependence liability than codeine. Dependence liability is affected by pharmacological factors, such as how quickly the drug reaches the brain. Genetic, social and psychological factors are also important, and individuals vary widely in their response to particular drugs. For example, most people do not particularly like the psychoactive effects of opioids, but a few people like them very much, placing them at higher risk for becoming dependent. Recent research suggests that drugs cause euphoria by increasing the concentration of the neurotransmitter dopamine in the brain, which in turn activates a bundle of nerves in the mid-portion of the brain known as the brain reward circuit (Kahan et al., 2000).

Intoxication and Overdose

Intoxication refers to the immediate psychoactive and physical effects of a drug. Intoxication results in overdose when it threatens vital functions of the nervous system, such as respiration and heart rate. The severity of intoxication and overdose depends on the amount of drug used; the route of administration; the person's age, gender, tolerance and concurrent drug use; and environmental cues. The most dangerous overdoses occur when people without tolerance use a mixture of opioids and sedatives.

Pharmacotherapy

Pharmacotherapy—the use of medications—in the treatment of substance dependence works in a number of ways. In agonist substitution therapy, the prescribed drug is in the same class as the addicting drug, and is therefore able to relieve craving and withdrawal symptoms. Examples include methadone for heroin dependence and the nicotine patch for nicotine dependence. In anti-craving therapy, prescribed drugs (such as naltrexone and acamprosate, which are used to treat alcohol dependence) modify the neurotransmitters involved in drug craving and withdrawal. Antagonist therapy medication blocks the action of the addicting drug, thus reducing its reinforcing effect (as with naltrexone for opioid dependence). Finally, in aversive therapy, the medication induces unpleasant physical symptoms if the addicting drug is taken (as with disulfiram [Antabuse®] and alcohol).

Pharmacotherapy varies widely in effectiveness. Methadone is highly effective. Medications for alcohol and nicotine dependence are modestly effective, but are nonetheless important adjuncts to psychosocial treatment. No pharmacotherapy has yet proven effective for cocaine dependence.

ALCOHOL

Most adults in our society who drink alcohol do so moderately and without problems. However, excess alcohol use creates a huge burden of sickness, death and health care costs, outweighing the combined effects of all other drugs of abuse except tobacco (Single et al., 1999). The following is a discussion of some common alcohol-related problems.

Intoxication

While consuming one or two drinks has a mild disinhibiting and relaxing effect, consuming four or more drinks typically causes increased sedation with impaired judgment, slurred speech, staggering gait and slow response time. Intoxication also affects mood and behaviour, causing emotional lability, impulsivity, anger and depression. Ten or more drinks can cause coma and death from decreased breathing or choking on vomit. The risks of acute alcohol intoxication are greatest among women, adolescents and elderly people, and when alcohol is consumed along with other drugs. Women reach a blood alcohol level one-third higher than men for a given rate of alcohol consumption; adolescents have little experience with the intoxicating effects of alcohol and are more likely to engage in risky behaviours; and the elderly have less tolerance to alcohol.

Cardiovascular Effects and Low-Risk Drinking Guidelines

Alcohol has a U-shaped mortality curve, which means that light drinkers tend to live longer than abstainers or heavy drinkers. Alcohol prevents clumping of platelets—tiny particles in the blood that form clots—and elevates levels of high-density lipoprotein, a type of cholesterol that protects against heart disease. As a result, alcohol prevents heart attacks and strokes.

Currently recommended low-risk guidelines advise no more than 14 drinks per week for men and nine per week for women, with no more than two drinks per day for men or women (Bondy et al., 1999). A lower weekly amount is suggested for women because they have a lower volume of blood and so, as noted above, will have a higher blood alcohol level than men for a given rate of alcohol consumption.

Clients should not be advised to drink if they currently abstain. Many abstainers have good reasons not to drink, and there are other ways to obtain the same cardiovascular benefit (such as exercise or quitting smoking). Most of the cardiovascular benefits of alcohol are obtained with less than one drink per day. While older adults who drink moderately may live longer on average, the mortality rate for young people increases directly with the amount consumed due to death from accidents, violence and suicide (Andreasson et al., 1988).

At higher doses, alcohol can harm the cardiovascular system. Intoxication or withdrawal can trigger an irregular heart beat, which in some cases can cause sudden death. Three drinks or more per day can raise blood pressure, causing strokes and other problems. Heavy alcohol use can damage the heart muscle, causing a condition known as cardiomyopathy. The weakened heart muscle is unable to pump blood efficiently, causing fatigue and shortness of breath.

Alcoholic Liver Disease

Alcoholic liver disease occurs in three stages. The first is called fatty liver, in which the liver accumulates fat and becomes enlarged. This stage usually lacks observable symptoms. The second stage is alcoholic hepatitis, or inflammation of the liver. This stage may also be asymptomatic, but sometimes people become seriously ill. They may develop jaundice, the signs of which are yellow skin, dark urine and whitish stools. They may also develop vomiting, fever and pain in the liver area (i.e., the right upper abdomen below the ribs).

Repeated or prolonged episodes of alcoholic hepatitis lead to the third stage, cirrhosis, in which large portions of the liver have died and been replaced by scar tissue. Cirrhosis is a major cause of death in Canada. The risk of developing cirrhosis is between 10 and 20 per cent for men who consume six drinks per day for 10 to 20 years. Women face an equivalent risk if they have three drinks per day (Kahan et al., 2002). Chronic daily drinking is worse for the liver than binge drinking.

With advanced cirrhosis, the liver cannot fully metabolize proteins, which creates the buildup of intermediate chemicals containing ammonia. These chemicals are toxic to the brain and may cause a condition called hepatic encephalopathy. In the early stages of encephalopathy, people are fatigued, forgetful and accident-prone. They may experience day-night reversal (sleeping during the day while being up at night). In the later stages, people become drowsy and may sink into a coma.

Encephalopathy can be triggered by sedating drugs, infections, electrolyte disturbances, gastrointestinal bleeding and other causes. People with encephalopathy should avoid sedatives such as benzodiazepines, avoid high-protein meals and report any new illness to their doctor right away. Encephalopathy is treated with a low-protein diet and laxatives, such as lactulose (which prevents the ammonia compounds from being absorbed). Sometimes hospitalization is required.

Cirrhosis also causes death through internal bleeding. Blood normally flows from the intestines into the portal vein, which enters into the liver. The scar tissue in the cirrhotic liver impedes blood flow in the portal vein, causing it to back up into veins in the esophagus. These veins then become swollen and engorged, a condition called esophageal varices. Varices sometimes burst, causing profuse and often fatal bleeding. Bleeding varices can be prevented with beta blockers, which lower the blood pressure in the esophageal veins.

Ascites, a condition in which the abdomen fills with fluid, is also due in part to obstructed blood flow. Ascites is often the first sign of severe cirrhosis and impending liver failure. Ascites is controlled with diuretics and a low-salt diet.

While mortality from cirrhosis can be reduced through medication such as propylthiouracil, the mainstay of treatment is reduced drinking. Clients with alcoholic liver disease should be told that fatty liver and alcoholic hepatitis are reversible with abstinence or reduced drinking; the liver is one of few organs in the body with cells that can regenerate. While cirrhosis is not reversible, the liver can function normally even if large portions are permanently scarred. People with cirrhosis can often lead normal lives as long as they stop drinking completely. Reduced drinking strategies are not recommended for these people, since even moderate alcohol consumption may promote liver damage.

People with advanced cirrhosis sometimes require a liver transplant for survival. Most transplant programs will place an alcohol-dependent patient on their waiting list only if he or she has participated in a treatment program, has been abstinent for at least six months to two years and has strong social supports. The person's counsellor often has a key role in advocating for his or her client with transplant programs. Only 10 per cent of people who have undergone a transplant relapse to drinking (Maldonado & Keeffe, 1997).

Gastritis, Esophagitis and Pancreatitis

Gastritis is a common complication of heavy alcohol consumption. Alcohol causes irritation and erosion of the stomach lining, producing discomfort and pain in the upper abdominal area. Gastritis is potentially serious because it can result in internal bleeding, the symptoms of which are bloody or dark-brown vomit and bloody or black, tarry stools. Gastritis often heals quickly with abstinence. A wide variety of medications promote healing by reducing the production of acid in the stomach.

Alcohol also causes inflammation in the esophagus (esophagitis) and pancreas (pancreatitis). Symptoms of esophagitis include heartburn and vomiting. Pancreatitis causes severe abdominal pain and vomiting, often requiring hospitalization. The condition can become chronic, causing prolonged or recurrent abdominal pain. People with chronic pancreatitis may require frequent hospitalizations and surgery, and regular use of pain killers. Chronic pancreatitis does not always fully resolve itself with abstinence.

Trauma

Alcohol consumption is a major cause of trauma-related death and injury, including motor vehicle crashes, work-related injuries and violence (assaults and suicide). Even moderate alcohol consumption can impair driving ability (Lowenstein et al., 1990).

Cancer

Moderate alcohol consumption (two drinks per day) is associated with a modestly elevated risk of breast cancer, perhaps due to the effects of alcohol on estrogen metabolism (Bradley et al., 1998). Alcohol also acts as a carcinogen and co-carcinogen (i.e., it increases the effect of other carcinogens) for esophageal, colorectal, pancreatic and laryngeal cancers (Brown & Devesa, 2002).

Dementia

Heavy drinking is associated with a number of neurological disorders. (For more details on the cognitive effects of alcohol, see Chapter 23.) One common and serious disorder is dementia, defined as a global decrease in cognitive functioning (Williams & Skinner, 1990). Alcoholic dementia differs from the most common form of dementia, Alzheimer's disease, in that it is potentially reversible with abstinence (although only some recover and recovery may only be partial). The cognitive changes of alcoholic dementia may be subtle, such as decreased ability to think abstractly. Counsellors who suspect dementia should refer the client to a neurologist or psychologist for neuropsychological testing and possibly a brain (CT) scan. Clients should be advised of the diagnosis and of the potential for recovery with abstinence.

Cerebellar Disease

Alcohol can damage the cerebellum, a part of the brain that controls balance and equilibrium. People with cerebellar disease have tremors of the hands and walk with a wide-based gait, as if they were on a moving ship. Sometimes they require a cane or walker to maintain their balance.

Peripheral Neuropathy

Alcohol may damage the nerves in the feet and legs, causing a condition known as peripheral neuropathy. People with this syndrome may experience decreased sensation and painful burning sensations in their feet.

Wernicke-Korsakoff Syndrome

People who drink heavily often eat poorly, and the metabolism of alcohol depletes the body's stores of the B vitamins. This can lead to a severe deficiency of vitamin B1 (thiamine), causing Wernicke-Korsakoff syndrome. In the Wernicke's phase of this syndrome, people become drowsy, unresponsive and their walking and eye movements become uncoordinated. Wernicke's is a medical emergency, requiring prompt administration of intravenous thiamine. If not treated in time, such people typically develop Korsakoff's syndrome, in which they exhibit marked impairment of short-term memory. People with Korsakoff's may not remember an event that occurred 10 minutes earlier. Those with Korsakoff's rarely recover and frequently require institutionalization.

Blackouts

A blackout is a type of amnesia in which the person is unable to remember events that took place during the previous evening's drinking binge. People may on occasion behave in a bizarre or dangerous manner during a blackout.

Alcohol Withdrawal

People are at risk for alcohol withdrawal if they consume at least six drinks per day for more than a week. Withdrawal becomes more severe with larger amounts and longer duration of drinking and with increased age (Brower et al., 1994), although there are large individual variations.

Withdrawal begins between six and 24 hours after the person's last drink. Physical symptoms usually resolve within three to seven days, but some people have insomnia, anxiety and dysphoria for weeks afterward. Symptoms include tremors, sweating, fast pulse, high blood pressure, vomiting and anxiety. Grand mal seizures are common in the first two to three days of withdrawal. Other complications include irregular heartbeat, hallucinations and delirium tremens.

Delirium tremens (DTs) occurs after three to four days of severe, untreated withdrawal. People who are hospitalized due to a medical illness such as pneumonia are at greatest risk for developing DTs. Symptoms include extreme confusion and disorientation, with vivid visual and auditory hallucinations and sometimes fever, sweating and tremor. Deaths can occur from electrolyte disturbances and an irregular heartbeat.

Alcohol withdrawal is effectively treated by providing a calm, supportive environment; most people do not require medication. Benzodiazepines are the treatment of choice for those who do need medication, because they are highly effective and very safe (Holbrook et al., 1999). There is some evidence that anticonvulsants, such as carbamazepine, are as effective as benzodiazepines and are associated with a lower risk of relapse (Malcolm et al., 2002), although more research is needed to establish their safety and their efficacy in preventing complications such as DTs.

Treatment of withdrawal can be greatly facilitated by use of the 10-item Clinical Institute Withdrawal Assessment (CIWA) scale, which measures the severity of withdrawal (Holbrook et al., 1999; Devenyi & Harrison, 1985; Erstad & Cotugno, 1995). The scale is administered every one to two hours by a nurse or other health care worker. The nurse asks about symptoms of withdrawal (such as anxiety) and observes for signs of withdrawal (such as tremor). Patients are given benzodiazepines (e.g., 20 mg of diazepam [Valium®]) when they score 10 or above. Additional doses are not needed once the CIWA score is less than eight, because diazepam lasts for many hours in the blood stream. Elderly patients and those with advanced liver disease are typically given lorazepam (Ativan®) rather than diazepam.

TREATMENT SETTING

Counsellors are sometimes in personal or telephone contact with a client who is in withdrawal or about to go into withdrawal. Withdrawal can be managed in the emergency department, withdrawal management service or residential treatment facility, or through a "day detox" or "home detox." Clients should be urgently referred to a physician on-site or to the emergency department if they have had a seizure, have clearly visible tremors when reaching for an object or walking, or are confused, disoriented or hallucinating. This is especially important if the person has had withdrawal seizures or delirium in the past, is elderly, lives alone, has serious medical problems such as heart disease or is dependent on other medications such as benzodiazepines.

Clients should be offered admission to a withdrawal management service ("detox centre") if they are intoxicated and might go into withdrawal some hours later, or if their withdrawal is mild and no longer requires medical attention. Staff at these centres are usually experienced at assessing withdrawal and know when a client requires urgent medical care. All withdrawal management services are affiliated with a nearby emergency department.

A planned medical detoxification is useful for people who are having difficulty abstaining from alcohol because of withdrawal symptoms. It can be done in a medical clinic, at home or in a residential treatment facility. Planned medical detoxification should be undertaken as part of a comprehensive treatment plan, since by itself it is not likely to result in long-term abstinence.

"Day detox" can be done in a treatment facility or physician's office. Clients are advised to have their last drink the night before and attend the facility the next morning. They are given diazepam every hour according to their CIWA score, and may be sent home or to a withdrawal management service after completing treatment. Most people complete treatment in a few hours.

Some alcohol and other drug treatment facilities provide inpatient medical detoxification. This is usually an elective, pre-booked procedure, and is often (but not always) followed by participation in a formal inpatient or outpatient program.

"Home detox" is useful for clients who are unable or unwilling to attend a treatment facility, medical clinic or withdrawal management service. Elderly clients in particular can benefit from home detoxification. The person should be assessed daily by a nurse or physician for the first two or three days. If benzodiazepines are required, they should be dispensed by a nurse or responsible family member, and a physician should be available for urgent phone consultation if needed.

COUNSELLOR'S ROLE

Counsellors should ask all clients with alcohol problems about withdrawal symptoms. Clients sometimes mistakenly attribute withdrawal symptoms to anxiety. Withdrawal-induced anxiety occurs at a set time of day (usually morning or afternoon), is accompanied by physical symptoms such as tremor and is quickly relieved by alcohol. Once withdrawal is identified, the counsellor and client should decide on the most appropriate setting, in consultation with a nurse or physician if necessary.

Reproductive Effects

Drinking during pregnancy can cause fetal alcohol spectrum disorder (FASD), the features of which are delayed growth, cognitive impairment and facial abnormalities, such as short eye openings. Affected children may also have cognitive-behavioural problems such as hyperactivity, speech disorders and deficits in learning and memory. These problems can persist into adolescence and adulthood.

FASD varies widely in severity, depending on the amount and timing of maternal alcohol consumption and other factors. For example, a child may have only cognitive deficits with no facial abnormalities. A safe level of alcohol consumption during pregnancy has not been established and abstinence is the most prudent recommendation (Bradley et al., 1998; Eustace et al., 2003). Alcohol consumption in the first trimester of pregnancy is thought to be particularly dangerous. See Chapter 22 for further information on this topic.

Alcohol use during pregnancy is also associated with low-birthweight infants, hypertension and other problems. Other reproductive effects include erectile dysfunction in men, irregular menstrual cycles in women and infertility in both men and women.

Psychiatric Effects

Heavy drinking can induce depression. Alcohol-induced depression usually resolves itself within two to four weeks of abstinence, distinguishing it from a primary mood disorder (Freed, 1981). Heavy drinkers are at high risk for suicide, partly because of alcohol-induced depression and the impulsivity and emotional volatility associated with acute intoxication (Freed, 1981; Inskip et al., 1998). Heavy drinking can also induce or exacerbate anxiety disorders and psychosis (Soyka, 1994).

Laboratory Detection of Alcohol

One common abnormality that may be detected in people who drink heavily is an elevated level of gamma-glutamyl transferase (GGT), a liver enzyme (Mihas & Tavassoli, 1992). Another is an increase in the size of red blood cells, as measured by a test called mean cell volume (MCV). At least four drinks per day are usually needed to produce elevations in these tests.

Blood tests such as GGT and MCV are not as sensitive as a clinical interview in detecting alcohol problems. However, periodic tests can be used to confirm clients' self-reports of reduced alcohol intake. With abstinence or reduced drinking, GGT usually returns to normal within four to eight weeks, and MCV within three months.

Pharmacological Treatment of Alcohol Dependence

Medications for alcohol dependence can be a useful adjunct to psychosocial treatment. Naltrexone (ReVia®) has been shown in several controlled trials to reduce the intensity and frequency of alcohol binges and cravings (Anton et al., 1999; Garbutt et al., 1999). Naltrexone diminishes the pleasurable and reinforcing effects of alcohol by blocking the action of neurotransmitters such as endorphins or dopamine. Naltrexone cannot be used with people who take opioids regularly, as it will trigger severe withdrawal. Acamprosate has also been shown to be effective in the treatment of alcohol dependence. It blocks the neurotransmitter glutamate, relieving craving and mood instability caused by prolonged alcohol withdrawal (Garbutt et al., 1999). Ondansetron and topiramate may also be effective in the treatment of alcohol dependence (Johnson et al., 2000; 2003).

Disulfiram acts by inhibiting a liver enzyme that metabolizes alcohol, causing the buildup of a toxic metabolite called acetaldehyde (Garbutt et al., 1999; Wright & Moore, 1990). People who drink alcohol while on disulfiram experience chest pain, headache, flushed face, vomiting and an irregular heartbeat. The reaction is potentially fatal, because blood pressure can drop precipitously and the heart can go into a dangerous rhythm. The person should not drink for at least seven days after taking disulfiram. There is limited evidence for the efficacy of disulfiram, but it may be a useful treatment adjunct in highly motivated patients who take the medication under the supervision of a spouse.

NICOTINE

For a detailed discussion of working with clients who are dependent on nicotine, see Chapter 31.

Psychoactive Effects

Nicotine is known as the "chameleon drug"; it acts as an anxiolytic when the smoker is anxious and a stimulant when the smoker is fatigued (Brands et al., 2000). It reaches the brain within seconds, and the average smoker takes up to 200 puffs a day. The potent psychoactive effect, rapid onset of action, frequent administration and wide availability make nicotine dependence by far the most common substance use disorder.

Withdrawal

Nicotine withdrawal is characterized by fatigue, irritability, gastrointestinal upset and craving for cigarettes. While the acute withdrawal resolves in five days, craving can last for many months, and relapse rates are high. Withdrawal is likely in those who smoke within half an hour of waking, and who smoke a pack a day or more. See Chapter 31 for a description of the health effects of cigarettes and an approach to counselling and medical treatment.

OPIOIDS

Opioids (also known as narcotics) act on receptors in brain cells to create a sense of euphoria and tranquility. Tolerance builds up quickly; people who use heroin chronically often report that the drug no longer gets them "high," but merely staves off withdrawal symptoms. Commonly misused oral opioids include oxycodone (contained in Percocet® and Percodan®), codeine (Tylenol #3®), hydromorphone (Dilaudid®) and morphine. Injectable opioids include morphine, meperidine (Demerol®) and heroin. Oxycodone and hydromorphone have a higher dependence liability than codeine.

Overdose

Opioids in high doses suppress the brain centres that control respiration and heartbeat, with potentially fatal results. People are at greatest risk for opioid overdose if they are not fully tolerant, have injected opioids or have also taken benzodiazepines or other sedating drugs. Signs of overdose include pinpoint pupils; slow, drawling speech; and "nodding off" (brief episodes of falling asleep). Such clients should be referred for immediate medical evaluation.

Withdrawal

Opioid withdrawal causes flu-like symptoms such as muscle aches, sweating, chills and goosebumps, runny nose and eyes, nausea and diarrhea. Muscle aches are the most common symptom. Psychological symptoms include insomnia, anxiety, depression and strong cravings for opioids. Pyschological symptoms usually cause considerably greater distress than physical symptoms. Withdrawal begins between six and 24 hours after the last use, depending on whether the opioid is short- or long-acting. Physical symptoms peak at two to three days and are resolved within five to seven days. Insomnia, dysphoria and drug craving may persist for months.

Opioid withdrawal does not have medical complications, except during pregnancy (see below). However, opioid withdrawal is by no means benign. It is associated with a severe organic mood syndrome and all clients in withdrawal should be assessed for suicidal ideation. Also, people lose much of their tolerance after a few days of abstinence and are at risk for overdose if they relapse.

Opioid withdrawal can be treated with methadone (see Chapter 29) or with clonidine, a non-narcotic drug that blocks the nervous impulses in the brain that cause withdrawal symptoms. Treating withdrawal with opioids other than methadone should only be done if the risk of double-doctoring (visiting more than one physician to get multiple prescriptions) is remote, or if the client is in a carefully supervised inpatient setting. Treatment of withdrawal by itself rarely results in long-term abstinence and should be combined with methadone maintenance and psychosocial treatment.

Reproductive Effects

Pregnant women who are dependent on heroin have a high infant mortality rate, due to delayed growth of the fetus and premature labour. Opioid withdrawal during pregnancy can induce uterine contractions, causing miscarriage in the first trimester or premature labour during the third trimester. To avoid these risks, pregnant women dependent on opioids should, as a rule, be offered methadone maintenance. Women who are dependent on heroin have better prenatal care, improved nutrition and substantially lower infant mortality rates when placed on methadone (Kaltenbach et al., 1998).

Infants born to mothers who are dependent on opioids are at risk for withdrawal, characterized by irritability, vomiting and poor feeding. Unrecognized neonatal withdrawal can cause seizures and death, so pregnant clients should be encouraged to disclose their opioid use to their caregivers. Withdrawal is treated with small, tapering doses of morphine (Osborn et al., 2002).

Opioids for Chronic Pain

Sustained release opioids are being increasingly prescribed for chronic pain in recent years. Examples include MS-Contin® (morphine), OxyContin® (oxycodone) and Duragesic® (transdermal fentanyl patch). These agents are probably less addictive than short-acting preparations such as Percocet® (oxycodone) because they have a slower onset of action and therefore less psychoactive effect. However, sustained release preparations can be misused by taking more than prescribed, crushing the pills before swallowing, or mixing them with water and injecting.

Prevalence of Opioid Dependence

Psychological dependence on opioids is not common in people who take opioids for chronic pain. Tolerance to the analgesic effects of opioids develops slowly and patients are often able to remain on the same dose for months or years. Most patients do not like the psychoactive effects of opioids and take the drug only for analgesia. The majority of those who do become dependent on prescribed opioids have a current or past history of dependence on other drugs (Reid et al., 2002).

Physical versus Psychological Dependence

People who are physically dependent take opioids daily for chronic pain, and experience withdrawal if the opioids are suddenly discontinued. Those who are psychologically dependent take opioids for their reinforcing psychoactive effects and have trouble controlling their use. While many psychologically dependent people are also physically dependent, the reverse is not true: as noted above, most patients take opioids for analgesia only and do not experience pleasurable psychoactive effects from them.

Distinguishing Opioid Use from Opioid Dependence

It can be difficult for counsellors and physicians to distinguish opioid use from opioid dependence, and sometimes patients who use opioids appropriately for legitimate pain are unfairly labelled as addicts. Opioid dependence should be suspected in patients who:
• take opioids far in excess of what would normally be required for their pain condition
• rapidly escalate their dose
• are dependent on alcohol, cocaine or other drugs
• take the medication in a binge rather than scheduled pattern
• exhibit drug-seeking behaviours (such as running out early or double-doctoring)
• refuse alternative methods of pain management
• undergo severe withdrawal.
While any patient who uses opioids regularly may experience withdrawal, those dependent on opioids experience more severe withdrawal with marked psychological symptoms.

Such cases require assessment by addiction and pain specialists. Patients with chronic pain who are dependent on opioids should be considered for methadone treatment (see Chapter 29). Methadone is a potent analgesic and can effectively relieve pain, withdrawal symptoms and craving.

Laboratory Detection

Laboratory detection of opioids through the use of urine drug screens (UDS) can be very complex, and consultation with a medical expert in the testing laboratory is advised, particularly if the result has legal consequences.

Immunoassay and chromatography are the two main laboratory techniques used to detect opioids in urine. The immunoassay detects some opioids up to seven days after the last use, although three to five days is average. Immunoassay does not distinguish between different types of opioids. Chromatography only detects opioids for one or two days, but it can identify specific opioids. For further information, see Chapter 29 and the Appendix to Chapter 3.

BENZODIAZEPINES

Benzodiazepines are among the most commonly prescribed of all drugs. Their main action is to diminish anxiety and induce sleep, but they are also used to treat alcohol withdrawal and prevent certain types of seizures. People become tolerant to the sleep-inducing effects of benzodiazepines, but do not develop significant tolerance to their anxiety-reducing effects. Most patients take the medication as prescribed, and benzodiazepine dependence is not common.

A number of benzodiazepines are available. They differ in their duration of action and dependence liability. For example, diazepam (Valium®) and chlordiazepoxide (Librium®) are long-acting, while triazolam (Halcion®) and alprazolam (Xanax®) are short-acting. Diazepam, triazolam and lorazepam (Ativan®) have higher dependence liabilities than oxazepam (Serax®), chlordiazepoxide or clonazepam (Rivotril®).

Intoxication and Overdose

Intoxication on large doses of benzodiazepines is clinically similar to alcohol intoxication. There is little risk of lethal overdose, unless the drug is used in combination with other psychoactive drugs such as opioids or alcohol.

Rebound Insomnia

Benzodiazepines suppress the deep and the rapid eye movement stages of the sleep cycle. When the drug is withdrawn suddenly, people experience fitful sleep interrupted by vivid dreams. This "rebound insomnia" occurs after about three weeks of nightly use, and may take several weeks to resolve.

Other Effects

Benzodiazepine use increases the risk of motor vehicle accidents, and can cause falls and confusion in elderly people. Long-acting benzodiazepines such as diazepam, flurazepam and chlordiazepoxide are particularly hazardous for elderly people.

Psychiatric Effects

Benzodiazepines can contribute to depression, particularly with high doses and in people with a pre-existing mood disorder. Benzodiazepines sometimes have a disinhibiting effect on people with psychosis or with certain personality disorders.

Laboratory Detection

Long-acting benzodiazepines such as diazepam can be detected for up to 20 days or longer with some immunoassay methods. Certain benzodiazepines such as clonazepam are difficult to detect on UDS.

Withdrawal

Withdrawal symptoms begin one to two days after stopping short-acting benzodiazepines, and two to five days after stopping long-acting benzodiazepines. Withdrawal is more severe with high doses of short-acting benzodiazepines, with long duration of use, and in people who are older or have concurrent anxiety, mood or substance use disorders. Withdrawal resolves itself within a few weeks for most people, but for some it may persist for months (Petursson, 1994; Lader, 1994; Pimlott & Kahan, 2000).

Patients who abruptly stop their benzodiazepines are at risk for seizures, delirium and hallucinations if they have used large amounts for prolonged periods (50 mg or more of diazepam, or the equivalent dose of another benzodiazepine, daily for more than a few weeks). Those who suddenly stop therapeutic doses (30 mg or less of diazepam, or the equivalent dose of another benzodiazepine) tend to experience two groups of symptoms: anxiety-related symptoms (emotional lability, insomnia, irritability, poor concentration and panic attacks) and subtle neurological symptoms (mild distortions of visual and auditory stimuli, blurry vision, unsteadiness of gait, depersonalization or déjà vu sensations; Busto et al., 1986).

The Decision to Taper

Patients who are dependent on high doses of benzodiazepines should be tapered off the drug, because the risks of continued use far outweigh the benefits. However, because therapeutic use does not generally result in severe social disruption or physical harm, and because withdrawal can be prolonged and difficult, the decision to taper a patient should be made only after a careful assessment of the risks and benefits (including psychiatric assessment if necessary). The risks, outlined above, include a possible increase in anxiety, depression and suicidal ideation. The benefits might not be apparent until tapering is well under way. People who are tapered off benzodiazepines frequently report feeling more alive, energetic and clear-thinking. They may be better able to make important life decisions and obtain greater benefit from psychotherapy.

Approach to Tapering

People taking very high doses should be tapered daily until their dose approaches the therapeutic range. Tapering should be done with long-acting sedatives such as diazepam or phenobarbital, preferably in an inpatient setting.

Those on therapeutic doses should be tapered slowly as outpatients over a period of several weeks or months (Dupont, 1990). It is medically easiest to taper the patient with the benzodiazepine he or she is taking, but people who are psychologically dependent on that drug might have greater success with another benzodiazepine. Tapering with long-acting agents such as diazepam or clonazepam may allow for a smoother withdrawal, although diazepam can be misused and is not a safe option for elderly people or those with liver disease. Patients taking alprazolam or triazolam should be tapered with these agents, or with clonazepam. Use of adjunctive agents such as carbamazepine, valproic acid or anxiolytic antidepressants may be helpful in difficult cases.

For physicians who are tapering patients, a weekly reduction of no more than 5 mg of diazepam (or equivalent) is suggested. The daily dispensing schedule (two, three or four times per day) should be kept the same until near the end. Clients should be advised not to miss doses or speed up the taper on their own, as this will generate withdrawal symptoms and "detoxification fear." The taper should be slowed near the end, as people often find the last pill the most difficult to discontinue. The patient should have a say in the rate of the taper; there is usually no need to complete the taper in a set time period. Frequent pharmacy pick-up might be necessary if the patient repeatedly runs out of pills.

A program of therapeutic support must be in place before tapering is attempted. Frequent follow-up visits should be organized, weekly if necessary. The client should be asked whether he or she feels any benefits of the tapering, as well as any withdrawal symptoms. Counsellors should watch for signs of depression and suicidal ideation during tapering.

SEDATIVES

Sedatives such as Seconal® have been largely replaced by benzodiazepines, although Fiorinal® use problems and dependence are still occasionally seen. Fiorinal, a drug used to treat headaches, is a combination of ASA, codeine and a barbiturate known as butalbital.

Sedatives can induce depression, and overdoses with these drugs are more dangerous than benzodiazepine overdoses. Patients who abruptly stop high doses of sedatives (such as 10 tablets per day of Fiorinal) can develop a dangerous and potentially fatal withdrawal that can include seizures, psychosis, delirium and an irregular heartbeat. The treatment drug of choice is phenobarbital used in an out-patient tapering program for people who use sedatives moderately, or in an inpatient setting for those who use them heavily.

SOLVENTS

Inhalation of solvents, such as gasoline or glue, produces intoxication similar to that of alcohol, with slurred speech, sedation and disinhibition. Distortions of vision and sense of time can also occur. Death can occur from suffocation, an irregular heartbeat or accidents.

Prolonged use of solvents can result in tolerance, withdrawal and dependence. The most serious medical consequence of solvent use is permanent brain damage, which is similar to alcohol-related brain damage but more severe and with a younger age of onset. As with alcohol, solvents damage the cerebellum (responsible for balance) and cerebrum (cognition and memory). Solvent use during pregnancy can cause premature birth and birth defects. Psychiatric effects of prolonged solvent use include depression, suicidal ideation and paranoia.

COCAINE

Cocaine causes a rapid buildup of several neurotransmitters in the brain, including dopamine (which causes euphoria) and epinephrine and norepinephrine (which stimulate the heart and nervous system). The euphoria usually lasts no more than 20 minutes with smoking and injection, but longer with oral or nasal use. The effects on the heart and nervous system last for hours. The first few uses of cocaine produce the most intense euphoria with feelings of elation, boundless energy and confidence. Dopamine becomes depleted with heavy use over time, so the person experiences a brief "rush" followed by agitation and paranoia.

Cocaine can be injected into the vein, smoked, inhaled through the nose ("snorting") or taken orally. Nasal inhalation irritates the lining of the nose and creates a milder euphoria than injecting or smoking, so people who use cocaine heavily tend to inject or smoke the drug. Such people often "binge" on cocaine, injecting or smoking it multiple times over several days, followed by days or weeks of abstinence.

"Crack" is made by mixing cocaine with baking soda, forming a small, solid rock that makes a popping sound when heated. Heating releases pure cocaine vapour, which circulates through the lungs and reaches the brain within seconds. Crack reaches a wider market than cocaine powder because it can be sold in small $10 to $20 packets.

Withdrawal

Cocaine withdrawal occurs in three phases. The first phase is the "crash," in which people who have just finished a cocaine binge sleep deeply for one to two days. This is followed by one or more weeks of intense cravings for cocaine, depression, insomnia with nightmares, and feelings of emptiness and irritability. Following this is the "extinction" phase, in which the person experiences episodic cravings for cocaine that gradually diminish in intensity and frequency over a period of months. Whether these phases represent a true physiological withdrawal remains controversial.

Overdose

Cocaine overdose produces seizures, severe hypertension and rapid heartbeat, fever and delirium, and eventually coma and death.

Cardiovascular Effects

Cocaine can trigger a marked rise in blood pressure, a rapid and irregular heartbeat, and spasms of the blood vessels (Warner, 1993). This can result in strokes, brain hemorrhages, heart attacks and ruptured aneurysms. While people with underlying hypertension or heart disease are at greatest risk, these complications have been reported to occur even in young, healthy adults taking small doses of cocaine. Combined cocaine and alcohol use creates a metabolite called cocaethylene, which appears to enhance cardiovascular toxicity (Pennings et al., 2002).

Reproductive Effects

Cocaine taken during pregnancy can cause the placenta to separate from the uterus, resulting in severe hemorrhage and the death of the fetus (Keller & Snyder-Keller, 2000). Cocaine can also trigger premature labour. Regular use of cocaine during pregnancy may cause delayed growth of the fetus, due to poor blood supply through the placenta. People who use cocaine often receive inadequate prenatal and medical care (Kaltenbach & Finnegan, 1998). Some studies suggest that cocaine use during pregnancy causes learning disabilities and delays in language development. However, these studies have been hampered by small sample size and inadequate control for variables such as nutrition, the use of other drugs (including smoking) and prenatal care. Well-controlled, long-term studies are currently under way (Lester et al., 2003).

Other Physical Effects

Grand mal seizures are very common among those who use cocaine, typically occurring within minutes of use. Like other stimulants, cocaine suppresses the appetite, leading to marked weight loss (Warner, 1993).

Psychiatric Effects

Cocaine can have profound psychiatric effects. People who are acutely intoxicated on cocaine display a wide variety of psychiatric symptoms, including delusions, paranoia, hallucinations (especially tactile), delirium and severe anxiety. Paranoid delusional disorders and other types of psychoses have been linked with chronic cocaine use. Symptoms may persist for months after the person has stopped using cocaine, and antipsychotic medication is often required. Cocaine can induce severe depression, and people who use cocaine heavily are at high risk of suicide. Concurrent cocaine and alcohol use increases the risk of depression, violence and suicide (Cornelius et al., 1998; Salloum et al., 1996).

Laboratory Detection

The metabolite of cocaine, benzoylecgonine, is detected in urine by immunoassay methods for three to seven days after use. See Chapter 3: Appendix for more information on drug screening.

CANNABIS

Cannabis (marijuana and hashish) is the most commonly used illicit drug in Canada. It is usually smoked but may be taken orally. Cannabis causes relaxation and a feeling of well-being accompanied by mild hallucinogenic effects, such as distortion in the sense of time, difficulty with abstract thinking and concentration, and vivid visual and auditory perceptions. Effects last several hours. While the risk of dependence is low compared with alcohol and many other drugs of abuse, cannabis dependence is a common reason for people to seek addiction treatment because its use is so widespread (Dennis et al., 2002).

Medical Uses

An oral, synthetic form of cannabis (Marinol®) is available for treating nausea caused by chemotherapy. Smoked cannabis has been suggested as an analgesic, muscle relaxant or appetite stimulant in the treatment of various conditions including multiple sclerosis and HIV, but to date there is little evidence to support its medical use (Killestein et al., 2002; Gurley et al., 1998; Watson et al., 2000). Given the risk of cannabis dependence and cannabis-induced psychiatric disorders, counsellors and physicians should await results of controlled trials before recommending cannabis for therapeutic use.

Withdrawal

People who suddenly stop using cannabis after taking high doses for long periods will sometimes experience a mild withdrawal syndrome consisting of several days of irritability, insomnia and decreased appetite (Weisdorf, 2000). Daily cannabis use over a long period is often motivated by mood control rather than by the drug's mild hallucinogenic effects, and people who use it in this way may experience a rebound in anxiety and emotional volatility after stopping use. Medical intervention is generally not needed.

Psychiatric Effects

Evidence suggests that cannabis can exacerbate depression (Rey et al., 2002), induce psychosis (Basu et al., 1999), trigger schizophrenia in people who are predisposed (Hambrecht & Hafner, 2000) and worsen symptom control in those with schizophrenia (Caspari, 1999). Adolescents and those with primary psychiatric disorders appear to be particularly vulnerable to the psychiatric effects of cannabis (Fergusson et al., 2002; Rey et al., 2002; Johns, 2001).

Acute Health Effects

Cannabis intoxication can trigger panic attacks and an irregular heartbeat. Epidemiological and pathological studies suggest that the long-term health effects of chronic cannabis use can cause or accelerate chronic obstructive lung disease (chronic bronchitis), induce pre-malignant changes in the lungs and other organs, and accelerate coronary artery disease (Henry et al., 2003). However, these studies are small, and results should be viewed as preliminary. Cannabis may lower infant birthweight for women who smoke at least four times per week during pregnancy (English et al., 1997). Chronic cannabis use may impair cognitive function and memory, but these effects appear to resolve within a few weeks of abstinence (Fried et al., 2002).

Laboratory Detection

Regular use of cannabis is detected in the urine for 20 days or longer. Second-hand cannabis smoke is generally not detectable on UDS.

HALLUCINOGENS

Hallucinogenic drugs such as LSD, mescaline and psilocybin can cause a psychotic reaction that usually resolves itself once the drug has worn off, but that may persist for months after use and, in some cases, may be permanent. Some people also have "bad trips," during which they experience extreme panic. Tolerance and withdrawal do not occur with hallucinogens.

In the weeks and months after stopping use, a small percentage of people may experience "flashbacks," in which they briefly relive past episodes of drug use. Though vivid and disturbing, flashbacks tend to last only minutes, and diminish in frequency and intensity over time.

ANABOLIC STEROIDS

Anabolic steroids are derived from the male sex hormone testosterone (Kahan & Wilson, 2002).They are used by athletes and body builders to enhance performance and increase muscle bulk and by adolescent males to improve their appearance. Anabolic steroids are rarely prescribed by physicians; the drugs are acquired illicitly from veterinary sources. They are frequently taken in heavy doses followed by reduced dosing or abstinence ("cycling" or "stacking"). Steroids are taken orally or by injection. Long-term steroid use has serious health effects (Bolding et al., 2002; Parssinen & Seppala, 2002).

Dependence

Steroids can induce euphoria, perhaps through the release of endorphins in the central nervous system, and there have been case reports of steroid dependence. Abruptly stopping heavy steroid use can cause withdrawal, which is characterized by fatigue, depression and craving.

Psychiatric Effects

People who use steroids can develop symptoms of aggression ("steroid rage"), depression and suicidal ideation, hypomania and psychosis. Most symptoms resolve themselves with abstinence, but depression may persist for months.

Health Effects

Steroids raise cholesterol levels and promote the formation of blood clots, resulting in heart attacks and strokes. Those who use steroids may be at higher risk for liver cancer. Women may experience irregular periods and masculinizing effects such as acne, deepened voice and facial hair. Men can develop small testicles, low sperm count, decreased sex drive and enlarged breasts. Steroids can stop bone growth in adolescents. Needle sharing can cause viral hepatitis or HIV.

CLUB DRUGS

The drugs described below, sometimes referred to as "club drugs" or "rave drugs," are classified as sedatives (GHB, flunitrazepam), stimulants (amphetamines), hallucinogenic stimulants (MDMA) and dissociative anesthetics (ketamine and PCP; Kahan & Wilson, 2002). They are relatively new and little is known about long-term health effects. They are usually taken in oral form and their effects last for several hours. They are usually not detectable on standard urine drug screens.

MDMA

The psychoactive effects of MDMA (3,4-methylenedioxymethamphetamine; commonly called "ecstasy") are due to the release of serotonin and dopamine in the brain. People who use ecstasy report feeling more sensual and affectionate, hence its other names "empathy" or "love drug." Tolerance develops quickly but it does not appear to cause withdrawal.

The acute toxic effects of ecstasy are due to the release of serotonin. People who take antidepressants or other drugs that elevate serotonin are at greatest risk. Symptoms and signs include fever, sweating, fast pulse, muscle rigidity and twitching, seizures and jaw clenching. Some of the medical complications of ecstasy are due to the circumstances in which it is used—prolonged dancing in a hot room without adequate fluid replacement can lead to dehydration and electrolyte imbalances, which have potentially serious consequences (Gowing et al., 2002).

LONG-TERM EFFECTS
Early studies suggest long-term memory impairment, but results are inconsistent and further research in this area is needed (Simon & Mattick, 2002; Dafters et al., 2003; Gouzoulis-Mayfrank et al., 2003). Regular ecstasy use is also associated with depression (Verheyden et al., 2003), and case reports suggest that it can trigger psychosis (Vecellio et al., 2003).

Amphetamines

Drugs in this class include amphetamine, methamphetamine (speed) and crystal methamphetamine (ice). Amphetamines are stimulants that are very similar to cocaine in their intoxication, withdrawal and psychiatric and medical effects. The main difference is that they are often taken orally and have a longer duration of action (several hours).

Gamma Hydroxybutyrate

Gamma hydroxybutyrate (GHB) is a potent sedative, with effects similar to alcohol. There is a small margin between the intoxicating dose and the dose that can cause coma and death. Combining GHB with alcohol is particularly dangerous.

WITHDRAWAL
GHB causes dependence and withdrawal. The withdrawal syndrome is similar to that of alcohol, but longer (up to 15 days) and more severe (Bowles et al., 2001; Craig et al., 2000; Dyer et al., 2001). Symptoms include tremors, seizures, hallucinations, paranoia and delirium. Barbiturates such as phenobarbital are the treatment drug of choice.

Flunitrazepam

Flunitrazepam (Rohypnol®) is a potent, short-acting benzodiazepine. Because it has pronounced sedative effects, it has been used as a "date rape" drug. Other sedating drugs have also been used for this purpose, including alcohol and GHB.

Ketamine

Ketamine (commonly known as "special K") is a dissociative anesthetic. Those who use the drug experience a dream-like state with confusion and hallucinations, out-of-body sensations and a distorted sense of time. Ketamine use can lead to coma and decreased respiration, particularly if taken with alcohol or other sedatives. It can also have serious cardiovascular and neurological complications, such as irregular heart-beat and seizures.

Phencyclidine

Phencyclidine (PCP) is also a dissociative anesthetic. It is smoked or "snorted." It can cause disorientation, acute psychotic symptoms including hallucinations and delusions, and violent behaviour. Like ketamine, it has serious medical complications such as seizures.

CONCLUSION

Alcohol and other drug problems are associated with a wide variety of serious physical and psychiatric problems. Counsellors should inform their clients of these health risks, and need to be alert to the symptoms and signs of physical and psychiatric illness in their clients.

REFERENCES

Andreasson, S., Allbeck, P. & Romelsjo, A. (1988). Alcohol and mortality among young men: Longitudinal study of Swedish conscripts. *British Medical Journal, 296*, 1021–1025.

Anton, R.F., Moak, D.H., Waid, L.R., Latham, P.K., Malcolm, R.J. & Dias, J.K. (1999). Naltrexone and cognitive behavioral therapy for the treatment of outpatient alcoholics: Results of a placebo-controlled trial. *American Journal of Psychiatry, 156*(11), 1758–1764.

Basu, D., Malhotra, A., Bhagat, A. & Varma, V.K. (1999). Cannabis psychosis and acute schizophrenia. A case-control study from India. *European Addiction Research, 5*(2), 71–73.

Bolding, G., Sherr, L. & Elford, J. (2002). Use of anabolic steroids and associated health risks among gay men attending London gyms. *Addiction, 97*(2), 195–203.

Bondy, S., Rehm, J., Ashley, M., Walsh, G., Single, E. & Room, R. (1999). Low-risk drinking guidelines: The scientific evidence. *Canadian Journal of Public Health, 90*(4), 264–270.

Bowles, T.M., Sommi, R.W. & Amiri, M. (2001). Successful management of prolonged gamma-hydroxybutyrate and alcohol withdrawal. *Pharmacotherapy, 21*(2), 254–257.

Bradley, K., Badrinath, S., Bush, K., Boyd-Wickizer, J. & Anawalt, B. (1998). Medical risks for women who drink alcohol. *Journal of General Internal Medicine, 13*(9), 627–639.

Brands, B., Kahan, M., Selby, P. & Wilson, L. (Eds.) (2000). *Management of Alcohol, Tobacco and Other Drug Problems: A Physician's Manual.* Toronto: Centre for Addiction and Mental Health.

Brower, K.J., Mudd, S., Blow, F.C., Young, J.P. & Hill, E.M. (1994). Severity and treatment of alcohol withdrawal in elderly versus younger patients. *Alcohol Clinical Experimental Research, 18*(1), 196–201.

Brown, L.M. & Devesa, S.S. (2002). Epidemiologic trends in esophageal and gastric cancer in the United States. *Surgical Oncology Clinics of North America, 11*(2), 235–256.

Busto, U., Sellers, E.M., Naranjo, C.A., Cappell, H., Sanchez-Craig, M. & Sykora, K. (1986). Withdrawal reaction after long-term therapeutic use of benzodiazepines. *New England Journal of Medicine, 315*(14), 854–859.

Caspari, D. (1999). Cannabis and schizophrenia: Results of a follow-up study. *European Archives of Psychiatry and Clinical Neuroscience, 249*(1), 45–49.

Cornelius, J.R., Thase, M.E., Salloum, I.M., Cornelius, M.D., Black, A. & Mann, J.J. (1998). Cocaine use associated with increased suicidal behavior in depressed alcoholics. *Addictive Behaviors, 23*(1), 119–121.

Craig, K., Gomez, H.F., McManus, J.L. & Bania, T.C. (2000). Severe gamma-hydroxybutyrate withdrawal: A case report and literature review. *Journal of Emergency Medicine, 18*(1), 65–70.

Dafters, R.I., Hoshi, R. & Talbot, A.C. (2003). Contribution of cannabis and MDMA ("ecstasy") to cognitive changes in long-term polydrug users. *Psychopharmacology (Berl).*

Dennis, M., Babor, T.F., Roebuck, M.C. & Donaldson, J. (2002). Changing the focus: The case for recognizing and treating cannabis use disorders. *Addiction, 97 Suppl. 1*, 4–15.

Devenyi, P. & Harrison, M.L. (1985). Prevention of alcohol withdrawal seizures with oral diazepam loading. *Canadian Medical Association Journal, 132*(7), 798–800.

DuPont, R.L. (1990). A physician's guide to discontinuing benzodiazepine therapy. *Western Journal of Medicine, 152*(5), 600–603.

Dyer, J.E., Roth, B. & Hyma, B.A. (2001). Gamma-hydroxybutyrate withdrawal syndrome. *Annals of Emergency Medicine, 37*(2), 147–153.

English, D.R., Hulse, G.K., Milne, E., Holman, C.D. & Bower, C.I. (1997). Maternal cannabis use and birth weight: A meta-analysis. *Addiction, 92*(11), 1553–1560.

Erstad, B.L. & Cotugno, C.L. (1995). Management of alcohol withdrawal. *American Journal of Health-System Pharmacy, 52*(7), 697–709.

Eustace, L.W., Kang, D.H. & Coombs, D. (2003). Fetal alcohol syndrome: A growing concern for health care professionals. *Journal of Obstetric, Gynecologic, and Neonatal Nursing, 32*(2), 215–221.

Fergusson, D.M., Horwood, L.J. & Swain-Campbell, N. (2002). Cannabis use and psychosocial adjustment in adolescence and young adulthood. *Addiction, 97*(9), 1123–1135.

Freed, E.X. (1981). Changes in weekly self-ratings of depression by hospitalized alcoholics. *Journal of Psychiatric Treatment and Evaluation, 3*, 451–454.

Fried, P., Watkinson, B., James, D. & Gray, R. (2002). Current and former marijuana use: Preliminary findings of a longitudinal study of effects on IQ in young adults. *Canadian Medical Association Journal, 166*(7), 887–891.

Garbutt, J.C., West, S.L., Carey, T.S., Lohr, K.N. & Crews, F.T. (1999). Pharmacological treatment of alcohol dependence: A review of the evidence [see comments]. *Journal of the American Medical Association, 281*(14), 1318–1325.

Gouzoulis-Mayfrank, E., Thimm, B., Rezk, M., Hensen, G. & Daumann, J. (2003). Memory impairment suggests hippocampal dysfunction in abstinent ecstasy users. *Progress in Neuro-psychopharmacology and Biological Psychiatry, 27*(5), 819–827.

Gowing, L.R., Henry-Edwards, S.M., Irvine, R.J. & Ali, R.L. (2002). The health effects of ecstasy: A literature review. *Drug and Alcohol Review, 21*(1), 53–63.

Gurley, R.J., Aranow, R. & Katz, M. (1998). Medicinal marijuana: A comprehensive review. *Journal of Psychoactive Drugs, 30*(2), 137–147.

Hambrecht, M. & Hafner, H. (2000). Cannabis, vulnerability, and the onset of schizophrenia: An epidemiological perspective. *Australian and New Zealand Journal of Psychiatry, 34*(3), 468–475.

Henry, J.A., Oldfield, W.L. & Kon, O.M. (2003). Comparing cannabis with tobacco. *British Medical Journal, 326*(7396), 942–943.

Holbrook, A.M., Crowther, R., Lotter, A., Cheng, C. & King, D. (1999). Meta-analysis of benzodiazepine use in the treatment of acute alcohol withdrawal. *Canadian Medical Association Journal 160*(5), 649–655.

Inskip, H.M., Harris, E.C. & Barraclough, B. (1998). Lifetime risk of suicide for affective disorder, alcoholism and schizophrenia. *British Journal of Psychiatry, 172*, 35–37.

Johns, A. (2001). Psychiatric effects of cannabis. *British Journal of Psychiatry, 178*, 116–122.

Johnson, B.A., Ait-Daoud, N., Bowden, C.L., DiClemente, C.C., Roache, J.D., Lawson, K. et al. (2003). Oral topiramate for treatment of alcohol dependence: A randomised controlled trial. *Lancet, 361*(9370), 1677–1685.

Johnson, B.A., Roache, J.D., Javors, M.A., DiClemente, C.C., Cloninger, C.R., Prihoda, T.J. et al. (2000). Ondansetron for reduction of drinking among biologically predisposed alcoholic patients: A randomized controlled trial. *Journal of the American Medical Association, 284*(8), 963–971.

Kahan, M., Selby, P. & Wilson, L. (2000). Pharmacotherapy in treatment. In B. Brands (Ed.), *Management of Alcohol, Tobacco and Other Drug Problems: A Physician's Manual* (pp. 54–56). Toronto: Centre for Addiction and Mental Health.

Kahan, M. & Wilson, L. (Eds.). (2002). *Management of Alcohol, Tobacco and Other Drug Problems: A Pocket Guide for Physicians and Nurses.* Toronto: Centre for Addiction and Mental Health.

Kaltenbach, K., Berghella, V. & Finnegan, L. (1998). Opioid dependence during pregnancy: Effects and management. *Obstetrics and Gynecology Clinics of North America, 25*(1), 139–151.

Kaltenbach, K. & Finnegan, L. (1998). Prevention and treatment issues for pregnant cocaine-dependent women and their infants. *Annals of the New York Academy of Sciences, 846,* 329–334.

Keller, R.W., Jr. & Snyder-Keller, A. (2000). Prenatal cocaine exposure. *Annals of the New York Academy of Sciences, 909,* 217–232.

Killestein, J., Hoogervorst, E.L., Reif, M., Kalkers, N.F., Van Loenen, A.C., Staats, P.G. et al. (2002). Safety, tolerability, and efficacy of orally administered cannabinoids in MS. *Neurology, 58*(9), 1404–1407.

Lader, M. (1994). Anxiolytic drugs: Dependence, addiction and abuse. *European Neuro-psychopharmacology, 4*(2), 85–91.

Lester, B.M., Lagasse, L., Seifer, R., Tronick, E.Z., Bauer, C.R., Shankaran, S. et al. (2003). The Maternal Lifestyle Study (MLS): Effects of prenatal cocaine and/or opiate exposure on auditory brain response at one month. *Journal of Pediatrics, 142*(3), 279–285.

Lowenstein, S.R., Weissberg, M.P. & Terry, D. (1990). Alcohol intoxication, injuries, and dangerous behaviors—and the revolving emergency department door. *Journal of Trauma, 30*(10), 1252–1258.

Malcolm, R., Myrick, H., Roberts, J., Wang, W., Anton, R.F. & Ballenger, J.C. (2002). The effects of carbamazepine and lorazepam on single versus multiple previous alcohol withdrawals in an outpatient randomized trial. *Journal of General Internal Medicine, 17*(5), 349–355.

Maldonado, J.R. & Keeffe, E.B. (1997). Liver transplantation for alcoholic liver disease: Selection and outcome. *Clinics in Liver Disease, 1*(2), 305–321.

Mihas, A.A. & Tavassoli, M. (1992). Laboratory markers of ethanol intake and abuse: A critical appraisal. *American Journal of Medical Sciences, 303*(6), 415–428.

Osborn, D.A., Cole, M.J. & Jeffery, H.E. (2002). Opiate treatment for opiate withdrawal in newborn infants. *Cochrane Database Systematic Reviews, 3,* CD002059.

Parssinen, M. & Seppala, T. (2002). Steroid use and long-term health risks in former athletes. *Sports Medicine, 32*(2), 83–94.

Pennings, E.J., Leccese, A.P. & Wolff, F.A. (2002). Effects of concurrent use of alcohol and cocaine. *Addiction, 97*(7), 773–783.

Petursson, H. (1994). The benzodiazepine withdrawal syndrome. *Addiction, 89*(11), 1455–1459.

Pimlott, N. & Kahan, M. (2000). Management of benzodiazepine dependence and withdrawal. In B. Brands (Ed.), *Management of Alcohol, Tobacco and Other Drug Problems: A Physician's Manual* (pp. 154–170). Toronto: Centre for Addiction and Mental Health.

Reid, M.C., Engles-Horton, L.L., Weber, M.B., Kerns, R.D., Rogers, E.L. & O'Connor, P.G. (2002). Use of opioid medications for chronic noncancer pain syndromes in primary care. *Journal of General Internal Medicine, 17*(3), 173–179.

Rey, J.M., Sawyer, M.G., Raphael, B., Patton, G.C., & Lynskey, M. (2002). Mental health of teenagers who use cannabis. Results of an Australian survey. *British Journal of Psychiatry, 180,* 216–221.

Salloum, I.M., Daley, D.C., Cornelius, J.R., Kirisci, L. & Thase, M.E. (1996). Disproportionate lethality in psychiatric patients with concurrent alcohol and cocaine abuse. *American Journal of Psychiatry, 153*(7), 953–955.

Simon, N.G. & Mattick, R.P. (2002). The impact of regular ecstasy use on memory function. *Addiction, 97*(12), 1523–1529.

Single, E., Robson, L., Rehm, J. & Xie, X. (1999). Morbidity and mortality attributable to alcohol, tobacco, and illicit drug use in Canada. *American Journal of Public Health, 89*(3), 385–390.

Soyka, M. (1994). Alcohol dependence and schizophrenia: What are the interrelationships? *Alcohol and Alcoholism, Suppl. 2,* 473–478.

Vecellio, M., Schopper, C. & Modestin, J. (2003). Neuropsychiatric consequences (atypical psychosis and complex-partial seizures) of ecstasy use: Possible evidence for toxicity-vulnerability predictors and implications for preventative and clinical care. *Journal of Psychopharmacology, 17*(3), 342–345.

Verheyden, S.L., Henry, J.A. & Curran, H.V. (2003). Acute, sub-acute and long-term subjective consequences of 'ecstasy' (MDMA) consumption in 430 regular users. *Human Psychopharmacology, 18*(7), 507–517.

Warner, E.A. (1993). Cocaine abuse. *Annals of Internal Medicine, 119*(3), 226–335.

Watson, S.J., Benson, Jr., J.A. & Joy, J.E. (2000). Marijuana and medicine: Assessing the science base—A summary of the 1999 Institute of Medicine report. *Archives of General Psychiatry, 57*(6), 547–552.

Weisdorf, T. (2000). Cannabis. In B. Brands (Ed.), *Management of Alcohol, Tobacco and Other Drug Problems: A Physician's Manual* (pp. 203–208). Toronto: Centre for Addiction and Mental Health.

Williams, C.M. & Skinner, A.E.G. (1990). The cognitive effects of alcohol abuse: A controlled study. *British Journal of Addiction, 85*, 911–917.

Wright, C. & Moore, R.D. (1990). Disulfiram treatment of alcoholism. *American Journal of Medicine, 188*, 647–655.

Chapter 11

Working in a Harm Reduction Framework

WAYNE SKINNER AND VIRGINIA CARVER

INTRODUCTION

Harm reduction policies and programs first appeared in the 1980s, and have since come to play a prominent role in the substance use field. Though the term "harm reduction" can be interpreted in different ways, in this chapter harm reduction policies and programs are those that are "designed to reduce drug related harm without requiring the cessation of drug use" and through which "interventions may be targeted at the individual, the family, community or society" (Centre for Addiction and Mental Health, 2002).

The growth of harm reduction policies and programs has paralleled other significant changes in the way that substance use problems are perceived and addressed. Over the past two decades, we have seen the substance use treatment field grow from its traditional focus on cessation and abstinence to include helpful interventions for those who want to reduce substance use to non-problematic levels. Though abstinence is the goal for the majority of clients, and most treatment settings still work within an abstinence framework, services have become more flexible in working with clients who have other treatment goals. New approaches by practitioners and services serve to engage and work with clients whose goal is to moderate but not stop their substance use, or who are not willing to change their use at all. Now the field is being challenged again to address the needs of people who have not benefited from and who might never be willing to enter the formal addiction treatment system. Factors that have contributed to the development of harm reduction approaches in Canada and elsewhere are discussed in the following section.

The Emergence of Harm Reduction Practices

Recognition of the threat posed by the spread of HIV/AIDS among people who use illicit drugs has been a major catalyst for the adoption of harm reduction policies and programs in Canada and other countries. More recently, recognition of the extent of hepatitis, particularly hepatitis C (HCV), infection among people who inject drugs has increased the urgency of efforts to reduce the spread of these diseases and others, such as tuberculosis (TB). Essentially, this has involved acknowledging that some conditions pose a greater threat to individuals and communities than illicit substance use and that the risk of becoming infected with one of these diseases is less related to the use of the drug per se and more to do with the way the drug is used and the circumstances under which the use occurs. For example, the spread of HIV/AIDS and HCV is more about the multiple use of contaminated needles than about injection drug use per se, just as the development of abscesses and infected areas is more about injection technique than about using the drugs themselves, or car or boat crashes are more about driving when intoxicated than about intoxication itself. Thus, the goal of harm reduction policies and programs is to reduce these adverse consequences of drug use rather than necessarily reduce drug use itself. The guiding harm reduction principle of the city of Amsterdam captures the pragmatic nature of the approach: People who cannot or will not give up their drug use should be given help to reduce the harm caused to themselves or others.

Initial strategies to prevent the spread of HIV/AIDS among people who inject drugs were pioneered in the Netherlands, though harm reduction in the form of heroin prescriptions for people using opioids existed in the United Kingdom prior to the HIV/AIDS crisis. Harm reduction strategies have since been adopted by a number of other countries, for example, the United Kingdom, Germany, Switzerland, Australia and Canada. As early as 1987, Canada's National Drug Strategy proposed wide-scale adoption of a harm reduction philosophy to drug use and harm reduction continues to be a key ingredient in our national drug strategy (Single, 2000a).

The cities of Amsterdam and Frankfurt, in particular, have developed model harm reduction strategies at the municipal level that involve collaboration between a wide range of stakeholders, but particularly between the health and law enforcement sectors. These models have been adopted by the City of Vancouver with the "Vancouver Agreement," a three-party agreement signed in 2000 among the Vancouver municipal government, the BC provincial government and the federal government to improve the social and economic conditions in all Vancouver communities, with the initial focus on the Downtown East (BC Ministry of Community, Aboriginal and Women's Services, 2000).

Model drug strategies, such as Vancouver's, have adopted a "Four-Pillar Approach," which integrates initiatives in prevention, treatment, enforcement and harm reduction. Successful strategies also ensure that the key harm reduction programs, such as methadone maintenance treatment and needle exchange services, are complemented by a range of other services that include medical and social care, shelter and housing, crisis intervention, outreach and counselling.

Though harm reduction strategies are associated primarily with injection drug use, they can be used to reduce the risks or harms associated with a wide range of potentially harmful behaviours. Examples include promoting condom use to reduce the risk of sexually transmitted diseases, encouraging the practice of appointing "designated drivers" to reduce driving while impaired, training staff in the hospitality industry to recognize and intervene when a customer has had too much to drink in order to reduce public intoxication, introducing environmental controls that do not permit smoking in public places and providing shelter for homeless individuals that does not require them to stop drinking.

Within the addiction treatment field, however, some practitioners feel abstinence-based approaches fall under the definition of harm reduction because their goal is to reduce harm. However, this view of harm reduction is broader than the intent of this chapter.

THE HARM REDUCTION DEBATE

Despite the growth of harm reduction approaches over the last two decades, harm reduction is still the subject of much debate among those with a stake in how a society addresses drug use—addiction professionals, politicians, bureaucrats, law enforcement officers, international agencies and the general public. Some believe that any let-up in "The War on Drugs" will inevitably lead to increased drug consumption and drug problems; others think that an emphasis on drug prohibition and criminal sanctions is an ineffective, harmful and costly approach.

Critics of harm reduction believe that initiatives such as needle exchange programs are anti-abstinence, but this is not necessarily the case. Others are concerned that harm reduction "enables" people who use drugs to continue unhealthy or illegal habits, and that this flies in the face of the belief that people need to experience the consequences of their drug use in order for behavioural change to occur. Also, they believe that it may send the wrong message to youth that drug use is acceptable. Even among those who support and practise harm reduction, views differ on how far to push the harm reduction agenda—is anything that reduces harmful individual consequences of drug use acceptable, or are there wider community or societal harms that may result from the implementation of harm reduction policies and programs? For example, legalizing drugs that are currently illegal could be perceived as reducing law enforcement, social and health costs to both the person who uses drugs and to society as a whole; alternatively, it could be perceived as resulting in increased rates of use and harm with consequent increased law enforcement health and social costs.

It is significant in this regard to note that all of the national and international legislation and regulations, the criminalization of use and the overall focus on abstinence have failed to reduce the level of opioid use in society. In contrast, studies have found that harm reduction initiatives such as methadone maintenance and needle exchange programs do indeed work and result in reductions in opioid dependence, the use of other substances, criminal activity, incarceration, mortality and the risk of acquiring HIV infection and potentially HCV, while improvements are seen in physical, mental and social functioning, quality of life and pregnancy outcomes (when combined with prenatal care) (Canadian HIV/AIDS Legal Network, 1999; Health Canada, 2002a). When harm reduction options such as methadone maintenance treatment are made available, the costs to society (health, criminal justice, employment, etc.) are actually reduced (Health Canada, 2002a)—results that stand in stark contrast to the effects of exclusively prohibitionist policies.

Thus, we hold an integrative view that looks at the important complementary relationship between abstinent and non-abstinent orientations. Harm reduction challenges us to go beyond existing helping paradigms for working with people with addictions. Usually addiction treatment is offered in community, office-based and institutional settings, open to all comers who qualify. Unfortunately these settings effectively exclude the most needy and at-risk clients who are neither able nor willing to participate in structured addiction treatment. Harm reduction invites us to think of ways that addiction treatment services can actively reach out to the most marginalized, disadvantaged and intractable populations. It is those populations, who continue to be the highest risk because they continue to use substances, to which harm reduction seeks to draw our attention.

While a drug-free lifestyle may be the best choice for people who have serious drug-related problems, many people will not accept a treatment goal of abstinence. For those who reject treatment that requires abstinence, harm reduction measures may still be effective. For clients at high risk of drug-related problems who are not inclined to stop or reduce their addictive behaviours, a counsellor's continued support might not only help them to reduce harmful effects of substance use, but might also lead to reduced use or to eventual abstinence. Change is a process, rather than a single step or action; harm reduction efforts encompass a willingness to offer support and resources, including education and information, as well more tangible things that can help people change their behaviour, such as housing, food, clothing and medical care. But harm reduction is not about change as a requirement for care and assistance. Whether or not a person continues an addictive behaviour, harm reduction asserts the human right to supportive care and services and to the need to focus on reducing harm even when a risky behaviour continues.

HARM REDUCTION APPROACHES FOR PEOPLE WHO INJECT DRUGS

Introduction

In Canada, the most commonly injected drugs are cocaine and heroin, though people who use anabolic steroids to improve athletic performance or enhance body image may also inject their drugs and be at risk of similar harms. Injecting drugs can lead to a variety of harms. Sharing injection equipment such as straws, cookers, swabs, filters, spoons, tourniquets or water that is contaminated with infected blood is a major risk factor for HIV and HCV. People who use cocaine may be particularly at risk because they inject several times a day and may not always have access to clean injecting equipment. Also at risk are people whose sexual partner uses injection drugs or who share drug injecting equipment with their partner. Some do not realize that sharing a needle with their partner may be as risky as sharing with someone else. People who inject steroids or other performance-enhancing drugs are at risk from sharing needles (National Institute on Drug Abuse, 2000). Other groups at risk include young people living on the street, Aboriginal people and offenders in correctional institutions. (Canadian HIV/AIDS Legal Network, 1999; Health Canada, 2002b).

In addition to the direct risk from sharing contaminated injecting equipment, people who inject drugs are also at high risk for early death from accidental overdoses, drug-related accidents and violence (Health Canada, 2002b). People who inject drugs may also be poor, homeless, have concurrent mental health problems, not eat well and have a range of other lifestyle problems that put them at risk. Illicit drug use fuels crime, particularly property crime, and criminal offences such as possession, trafficking, and production of illicit substances. Communities are concerned about the public aspect of illicit drug use, such as the open drug scene and discarded needles.

Rates of HIV among people who inject drugs increased rapidly in the '90s in large urban centres; in Canada, those centres particularly affected were Vancouver, Montreal, Toronto and Ottawa. In Vancouver, the prevalence of HIV infection among people who inject drugs was one to three per cent in 1988/89, and increased to 23 to 30 per cent by 1998/99 (Health Canada, 2001). Though not as dramatic, similar increases have occurred in other large Canadian cities. Health Canada estimates that 70 per cent of new HCV infections each year are related to sharing needles, syringes and other injecting equipment, with 80 per cent prevalence rates of HCV and HBV among people who inject drugs in Canada (Health Canada, 2001).

Methadone Maintenance Treatment

Described as the gold standard, methadone maintenance treatment (MMT) is the most commonly used strategy for opioid dependence (Federal/Provincial/Territorial

[F/P/T] Advisory Committee on Population Health, F/P/T Advisory Committee on Alcohol and Other Drug Issues, F/P/T Advisory Committee on AIDS and F/P/T Heads of Corrections Working Group on HIV/AIDS, 2001). A recent Health Canada report (Health Canada, 2002a) on best practices for MMT includes recommendations that address program development and design, program policies, delivery modes, program staff and environment, meeting the needs of special groups, and research and evaluation designed to make MMT more available and accessible and to keep people in the program. Methadone is one of the most researched and evaluated drugs in the world. Its efficacy has been demonstrated by numerous trials and few interventions in addiction have been proven to be as effective. It has been found to reduce morbidity and mortality, criminal involvement and the spread of HIV, and to help people who are opioid dependent "to gain control of their lives" (Single, 2000b). For pregnant women who are opioid dependent, it is the treatment of choice.

Methadone maintenance resolves the conundrum faced by many people who are opioid dependent—wanting to change, but being unable to discontinue opioid use. MMT is a substitution therapy, replacing other opioids with a medication that has well-developed protocols and is supervised by health care staff. MMT brings people who are opioid dependent into medical care, and allows them to stabilize their lives socially and to better attend to physical and mental health issues they might have. It reduces the likelihood that people will re-offend, and increases the chances that people who are unemployed might find employment or schooling. Many people in methadone maintenance elect to stay on methadone, often citing the life-transforming effects of the intervention as benefits they do not want to tamper with. Today, people may decide how long they wish to remain on methadone; in the pre-HIV era, they were often obliged to withdraw, with the usually predictable result that they would relapse to injection drug use.

While its efficacy would justify its inclusion high on the list of successful addiction treatments, MMT is often classified as a harm reduction intervention because it is a substitution therapy. It is important to note that the efficacy of methadone maintenance is optimal when provided in treatment contexts that include enhanced psychosocial treatment services (Ball & Ross, 1991).

Methadone is still a flashpoint in the ongoing public debate about what is addiction and what is recovery. As one methadone client who also works as a peer counsellor explained, "On methadone treatment, I am no longer an addict—I am not living an addictive lifestyle. I am taking a medication that stabilizes my life, allowing me to be a loving husband and father and self-supporting and productive member of society."

Alternative Substitution Drugs

Other substitution drugs such as buprenorphine, codeine and slow release morphine have been authorized for use in a number of European countries and Australia. In Canada, buprenorphine is available only through Health Canada's Special Access

Program under the Food and Drug Regulations (Health Canada, 2001). Trials of prescribed heroin for people who inject drugs and who have not been successfully maintained on methadone are being undertaken in Switzerland and the Netherlands and are also being considered in Australia. In Canada, the North American Opiate Medication Initiative (NAOMI) is developing a proposal for a clinical heroin trial (Health Canada, 2001). Currently three cities in Canada (Vancouver, Toronto and Montreal) are involved in this project. The focus of the research is to find methods for initiating people who have not been helped by existing strategies, including methadone maintenance, into drug use behaviours that reduce the harm to the person and to the community. Approaches being explored in this project include providing the addictive substance (heroin) in ways that ensure that the dose amounts and administration of the drug are supervised and that the person is brought into closer contact with supportive health care and social service resources.

Needle Exchange Programs

The main purpose of needle exchange programs (NEPs) is to ensure that people who inject drugs use only sterile needles and syringes, which helps control the spread of HIV/AIDS, hepatitis and other blood-borne diseases. Studies have found that NEPs decrease needle sharing and reduce the spread of HIV (Single, 2000b). As well as clean needles and syringes, needle exchange programs may also provide the following: other materials to improve the safety of injecting drugs, such as bottle caps, tourniquets and sterile water; collection of used needles for safe disposal; education on safer injecting practices and safer sexual practices; bleach kits and condoms or other protective devices; access to testing for HIV, hepatitis or other STDs; and linkage with services such as medical, health care, nutrition, housing, employment and substance use treatment. The first needle exchange program in Canada was established in 1989 in Vancouver; it is estimated that there are now over 200 NEPs across the country (Health Canada, 2001). Some needle exchange programs operate out of vans in order to better reach their clients; others are located at fixed sites, often along with other services for drug users.

Though NEPs are the main source of sterile injecting equipment for people who inject drugs, pharmacies may be the only source for those who live in areas far from city centres, where most NEPs are located. A survey of a random sample of Canadian community pharmacies (Cockerill et al., 1996) found that most pharmacies would sell needles and syringes to non-diabetics in some cases, while a quarter would sell to non-diabetics in all cases.

People who inject drugs may still have difficulty obtaining enough clean needles. Accurate estimates of the number of needles required by people who inject drugs are hard to obtain, but many experts feel that the number of needles distributed is significantly lower than the number required. This may be because there is no NEP or other outlet for clean needles in the community or that access to needles is restricted by distribution policies, such as only exchanging a clean syringe for a dirty one, or by the hours or location of distribution sites. If the person is incarcerated, there may be no access to clean needles. Lastly, drug use itself may impair the ability of the person who uses to get clean needles. Recognizing the need to increase the availability of clean needles, some NEPs have "flooded" their communities with large numbers of clean needles and created separate collection points for used needles, lifting the one-to-one exchange restriction. As long as a syringe has a use life greater than one injection, it has the potential to transfer infectious disease from one person to another. The goal of NEPs is to eliminate this risk and to encourage and support the safe disposal of injection equipment.

Supervised Injection Sites

Supervised injection sites (SIS) are facilities "where drug users can bring their own drugs and inject them in a supervised, safer environment" (F/P/T Advisory Committee on Population Health, F/P/T Advisory Committee on Alcohol and Other Drug Issues, F/P/T Advisory Committee on AIDS and F/P/T Heads of Corrections Working Group on HIV/AIDS, 2001). Supervised injection sites provide sterile injecting equipment and advice on safer injecting practices, as well as other services such as condom distribution, medical attention, etc.; they do not provide the drugs—these are brought by the person who uses them. Sites have been established as part of the continuum of services for people who inject drugs in the Netherlands, Switzerland, Germany and Australia, and are being considered by other European countries. Generally, SISs are established in districts where there is a substantial drug scene and, like NEPs and other harm reduction programs, they are another way to reach people who inject drugs.

SISs have been credited with reducing overdose deaths and HIV infections among people who inject drugs, and decreasing public nuisance by reducing the open drug scene and public injecting as well the number of discarded needles (Single, 2000b; Canadian HIV/AIDS Legal Network, 2002).

Though concerns have been raised that SISs condone drug use, the federal government and a parliamentary committee have supported their establishment in Canada. Recently, the federal government issued interim guidelines that establish a legal framework under the *Controlled Drugs and Substances Act* (CDSA) that would allow jurisdictions to apply for an exemption under Section 56 of CDSA for scientific purposes "for a pilot supervised injection site research project." (Health Canada, 2002c). Without such an exemption, the operation of an SIS would be illegal as would the activities of its customers (people who use drugs) who would be in possession of illegal substances while in the SIS. In 2003, Vancouver became the first Canadian city to establish such a site.

Information and Education about Safer Drug Use

Providing information and education to people who inject drugs is an important component of helping them reduce the risks associated with injecting. Information and educational materials can teach people who inject drugs about how to inject more safely, have safer sex and reduce the risk of transmission of HIV and HCV and other blood-borne diseases. A recent example can be found in Toronto where agencies working with the street population collaborated with groups of people who use drugs to develop and distribute safer crack-smoking equipment in "crack kits" to reduce burns to the mouth, face and hands when smoking crack. The kits also include other harm reduction supplies, such as condoms (Canadian Harm Reduction Network, undated). Similar approaches are being considered in Vancouver (Drug Policy Alliance, 2003). In Wales, life-saving techniques, such as heart massage, are being taught to people who use drugs as a strategy to reduce overdose deaths (BBC News, 2003).

Drug User Groups and Networks

Countries with well-developed harm reduction strategies have recognized the importance of involving the people who use drugs themselves; Australia, for instance, has funded drug user groups, which have played a central role in developing Australia's response to HIV/AIDS and injection drug use (Health Canada, 2001). In Canada, cities such as Vancouver, Montreal and Toronto have drug user groups. Peer education is a powerful mechanism for reaching people who inject drugs who may be less trusting of professionals. VANDU in Vancouver, one of the most active groups in Canada, has worked with health professionals and researchers to produce educational materials and develop proposals for new harm reduction initiatives.

Diversion Programs

Diversion programs are intended to divert people with drug problems away from the justice system and into treatment. The rationale for these programs is that people with drug problems who commit crimes often do so to obtain drugs, and will continue to commit crimes unless the drug problem is addressed. If they are sent to prison, drug use may continue, increasing the likelihood that the person will return to drug-related crime on release. In some countries, such as Australia and the United Kingdom, people with drug problems are identified at the time of their arrest and referred to treatment. In countries such as Canada and the United States, people with drug problems who commit crimes are referred to special drug courts that offer treatment rather than a custodial sentence. In Canada, drug treatment courts have been established in Toronto and Vancouver with funding under the National Crime Prevention Strategy for non-violent offenders who are addicted to opioids or cocaine. The court offers court-supervised treatment as an alternative to a custodial sentence. Participants who successfully complete treatment usually receive a non-custodial sentence or may have their charges withdrawn (National Crime Prevention Strategy, 2003).

The principle here is to see problems related to addictive behaviours as health issues rather than criminal justice issues alone. By offering people who break the law a therapeutic remedy, the goal is to reduce rates of recidivism and help the person achieve a healthier, more socially integrated lifestyle. There is evidence that these programs produce better outcomes than the traditional "crime and punishment" methods. That said, there is some criticism, even among harm reduction advocates, of the way these programs are operated. The concern is that to qualify the person has to admit guilt to be eligible, which might be a forced choice. If the person does not succeed in the intervention, he or she could be brought back before the courts and subject to sentence without the benefit of usual legal process. These concerns address the process of court diversion more than they address the principle of providing a therapeutic (not correctional) response to people with drug problems who commit crime.

Remedial measures programs for people convicted of impaired driving employ a similar approach of balancing legal sanctions with an educational or therapeutic intervention which addresses the offenders' substance use behaviour and provides them with information and strategies to avoid future high risk behaviours.

HARM REDUCTION APPROACHES FOR OTHER POPULATION GROUPS

Though harm reduction strategies are generally associated with injection drug use, a harm reduction approach is also commonly used with older adults with substance use problems (see Chapter 15 for more information) and with youth, particularly those who are hard to reach, such as street-involved youth (see Chapter 17 for more information). And though they do not inject their drugs, people who have severe and chronic problems with alcohol and other substances may also experience a wide spectrum of harms, particularly homelessness, physical and mental health problems, poverty, family breakdown, unemployment and violence.

Some people who are homeless and who do not wish to stop using alcohol or other drugs may choose to sleep outside rather than to use shelters that do not allow such substances on the premises. However, in many parts of Canada, exposure during the winter months can result in serious harm. A number of communities have recognized the need for harm reduction approaches with those who are homeless and have substance use problems. In Toronto, for example, one shelter offers overnight bottle storage for its clients, eliminating the need for them to finish the contents of the bottle before coming into the shelter. Evaluation of this program indicated a high degree of satisfaction with the program by clients, staff, administrators and associated service providers (Research Group on Drug Use, 2001). In Ottawa, a service for the homeless provides an "alcohol maintenance program" to shelter residents. Residents are provided with one standard drink an hour as well as food, clothing and access to other services such as dental and medical care and referral to substance use treatment (Canadian Medical Association Journal, 2001, Logan, 2001; Shepherds of Good Hope Web site, undated). In Toronto, the Mayor's Task Force on Homelessness called for the provision not just of "dry" housing, where abstinence is required, but also "damp" housing (people can use outside their residence, but not inside) and "wet" housing (use is allowed inside the house, and often active supervision and support is required). Like other harm reduction initiatives, these programs can be a first step for some people in a process of reducing or stopping their substance use and improving their health and well-being.

IMPLEMENTING HARM REDUCTION APPROACHES IN CLINICAL PRACTICE

In looking at addiction, we have moved beyond a binary model, which reduces addiction to something that you either have or do not have, to seeing drug use—and addictive behaviour in general—as existing along a continuum. The original treatment tradition, which still thrives today, was built on an abstinence model. Countless individuals have benefited from this approach, and more will use it effectively in the future. The second therapeutic tradition has involved what could be called "moderation management"— helping people whose use has become problematic to moderate their use to non-problematic levels. These two traditions have usually been provided in community or institutional contexts where the client seeks out and is accepted into treatment. We are now in the process of creating what might become a third tradition in responding to addiction problems. Harm reduction is a more outreaching, pragmatic way of working with people who use substances that is particularly concerned with people who have not benefited from existing approaches and who are at greatest risk to harm from addictive behaviour. Harm reduction as a philosophy of care calls on practitioners to go beyond the traditional models of care to find innovative and unconventional ways of applying client-centred principles to people whose lives are most negatively affected by substance use. This challenges health care and social service workers on what had here-tofore been automatic assumptions about how to work with addiction problems. It also provides a new lens through which to understand and work with people with addiction problems.

Individual practitioners, substance use treatment services and other service settings can adopt harm reduction approaches in their work with clients with substance use problems. Here are some suggestions:
• Negotiate non-abstinent treatment goals as a way station for clients who are not ready to give up substances. Reducing substance use even by small amounts or switching to a less harmful mode of use (e.g., from injecting to smoking cocaine) demonstrates to clients that they can successfully make changes. For those clients who believe that they don't need to quit, reduced use may also convince them to consider abstinence when they continue to experience problems. It is always a

judgment call as to whether a counsellor is "enabling" a client to continue to use substances harmfully. However, if the client is making positive changes for better health, the counsellor may wish to continue to provide support in addition to non-judgmental feedback on the links between substance use and problems in other life areas.

- Explore high-risk behaviours such as injection drug use, sharing needles or other drug-taking equipment, and unsafe sexual practices as part of a comprehensive assessment. Provide clients with information about safer sex and safer drug use, either in-house or through referral (e.g., to an STD clinic).

- Provide syringes, safe-use equipment, condoms and other protective devices and make clients aware of how they can access sterile injecting equipment in the event of a future relapse.

- Develop linkages with services that provide methadone maintenance treatment to ensure that clients also receive substance use counselling and support and are not denied access to substance use treatment services.

Borrowing generously from some principles that Denning (2000) outlined as at the heart of "harm reduction psychotherapy," here are some broad points to consider when looking at helping practices that are in the spirit of harm reduction. (Note that some of these principles are not exclusive to harm reduction, but are part of client-centred approaches to addiction in general.)

- Connect. At the core of therapeutic effectiveness is the ability to engage and build a respectful and committed connection with a person in need.

- Do no harm. (The old adage is, "First, do no harm," but here we give precedence to engagement.) Many interventions, at the level of care and of policy, have presumed to have the person's best interests at stake, but have ended up doing more harm than good.

- See addiction as a complex phenomenon that has biological, psychological, social and spiritual dimensions. Solutions are more likely to be found by engaging a wide set of situational and societal factors rather than by seeing it as a problem that resides solely in the body and brain of the person who uses.

- Understand the ways drug use is a behaviour that has value to the person who uses. Harm reduction work involves respecting and being curious about the ways that the addictive behaviour has become important to the person; understanding the meaning of the behaviour for the person doing it can help set the stage for looking with him or her at the merits of alternative solutions.

- Recognize that drug use is not governed by rules of fate or inevitability. Use is not doomed to progress to dependence. Patterns of drug use in individuals vacillate over the life course and there are many pathways to change, just as there also are risks and hazards.

- Accept that for most people changing substance use behaviour is an extended process that involves episodes and periods of relapse that benefit from a long-term helping approach. Indeed, it might take some time before any change at all in substance use is even considered by the person. Harm reduction work in addiction differs from other intervention approaches because it does not require the client to have a goal of stopping or reducing addictive behaviour. The client's eligibility rests on his or her risk of harm and the need to look at ways of reducing that risk without changing his or her addictive behaviour.

• Make assessment (the identification of needs) a client-centred process. Clients sometimes want to call the shots; other times they want to be guided. Make it possible for the client to tell you what his or her needs are, then negotiate what you will work on together and how it will happen (Sobell et al., 1992).

• Involve the client as an active participant in all phases of the process, extending the focus of your work to his or her needs beyond the addictive behaviours.

• Build self-efficacy by helping the client to recognize his or her own strengths and by helping the client to become connected to social supports that are reliable and trustworthy.

• Focus on drug-related harms rather than on drug use in itself: "Any change in drug-related harm is a change in the right direction" (Demming, 2002, p.11).

• Be a prepared, committed practical helper concerned with the pragmatic realities of the client's life and situation, including health, housing, legal, income, relationship and leisure issues.

• Stay engaged and use outreach strategies that demonstrate continuing concern and availability to help support, guide and be guided by the client. For the most marginalized and disadvantaged clients, the journey through and out of substance use problems is likely to be a long, bumpy and frustrating one.

Harm reduction cannot be reduced to these principles, but they do illustrate harm reduction work in front-line practice. It is anchored in a basic commitment to the human rights and dignity of people who are substance users. It insists that there are basic rights and entitlements that are frequently denied but need to be extended in special ways because of the vulnerability of this population. And finally, it indicates the inevitable public health consequences that come from keeping members of our society marginalized and disadvantaged. Although this work has advanced dramatically in the past two decades, it still is in a formative stage; we will continue to learn more about it in the future. An important point to make, and a fitting endnote, is the need to evaluate harm reduction. Because this work is grounded in a commitment to working pragmatically with people affected by substance use problems, it is vital that it be evidence-based and that we continue to measure its effectiveness against the alternatives that are available.

REFERENCES

Ball, J.C. & Ross, A. (1991). *The Effectiveness of Methadone Maintenance Treatment: Patients, Programs, Services, and Outcomes.* New York: Springer-Verlag.

BBC News. (2003). *Addicts given life-saving courses.* Available: news.bbc.co.uk/1/hi/wales/28757405.stm.

BC Ministry of Community, Aboriginal and Women's Services. (2000). *The Vancouver Agreement*. Available: www.mcaws.gov.bc.ca/vancouver-agreement/pdf2.htm.

Canadian Harm Reduction Network. (undated). *Crack Kits*. Available: http://canadianharmreduction.com/facts.php.

Canadian HIV/AIDS Legal Network. (1999). Injection drug use and HIV/AIDS: Legal and ethical issues. Background Paper. Available: www.aidslaw.ca/Maincontent/issues/druglaws/e-iduback/graphics/e-background.pdf.

Canadian HIV/AIDS Legal Network. (2002). *Establishing Safe Injection Facilities in Canada: Legal and Ethical Issues*. Available: www.aidslaw.ca/Maincontent/issues/druglaws/safeinjectionfacilities/toc.htm.

Canadian Medical Association Journal. (2001). Harm-reduction initiative provides alcohol to Ottawa's street alcoholics. *Canadian Medical Association Journal, 165*(7), 937. Available: www.cma.ca/cmaj/vol-165/issue-7/093b.asp.

Centre for Addiction and Mental Health. (2002, September). CAMH position on harm reduction: Its meaning and application for substance use issues. Available: www.camh.net/best_advice/harm_reduction_pos0602.html.

Cockerill, R.W., Myers, T., Worthington, C., Millson, M. & Rankin, J. (1996). Pharmacies and their role in the prevention of HIV/AIDS. *Journal of Social and Administrative Pharmacy, 13*(2), 46–53.

Denning, P. (2000). *Practicing Harm Reduction Psychotherapy: An Alternative Approach to Addictions*. New York: Guilford Press.

Drug Policy Alliance. (2003). *Canadian Health Officials Considering Safe Smoking Kits for Crack Users*. Available: www.lindesmith.org/library/03_25_03crack.cfm.

F/P/T Advisory Committee on Population Health, F/P/T Advisory Committee on Alcohol and Other Drug Issues, F/P/T Advisory Committee on AIDS and F/P/T Heads of Corrections Working Group on HIV/AIDS. (2001). *Reducing the Harm from Injection Drug Use in Canada* (Cat. No. H39-589/2001E). Ottawa: Minister of Public Works and Government Services.

Health Canada. (2001). *Harm Reduction and Injection Drug Use: An International Comparative Study of Contextual Factors Influencing the Development and Implementation of Relevant Policies and Programs*. Available: www.hc-sc.gc.ca/hppb/hepatitis_c/caredisc.html.

Health Canada. (2002a). *Literature Review Methadone Maintenance Treatment* (Cat. No. H49-162/2002E). Ottawa: Minister of Public Works and Government Services.

Health Canada. (2002b). *Best Practices Methadone Maintenance Treatment* (Cat. No. H39-164/2000E). Ottawa: Minister of Public Works and Government Services.

Health Canada. (2002c). *Application for an Exemption under Section 56 of the Controlled Drugs and Substances Act for a Scientific Purpose for a Pilot Supervised Injection Site Research*

Project (Interim Guidance Document). Ottawa: Drug Strategy and Controlled Substances Programme, Healthy Environments and Consumer Safety Branch.

Logan, J. (2001). Drinking from the bottle of redemption. *Insight.* Available: www.carleton.ca/ctown/archiv/apr1301/insite1.htm.

National Crime Prevention Strategy. (2003). Drug treatment court program information. Available: www.prevention.gc.ca/en/index.html.
National Institute on Drug Abuse. (2000). *NIDA Community Drug Alert Bulletin: Anabolic Steroids.* Available: http://165.112.78.61/SteroidAlert/Steroidalert.html.

RGDU Research Group on Drug Use. (1999). An evaluation of the Seaton House Annex Harm Reduction Shelter, *Fax on Drugs, 3*(2). Available: www.city.toronto.on.ca/drugcentre/fax0302.htm.

Shepherds of Good Hope. (undated). Available: http://members.rogers.com/shepherdsofgoodhope/prog.html.

Single, E. (2000a). *Harm reduction as the basis for drug policy: What does it mean and how does it matter?* Paper presented at the Addictions Millennium 2000 conference, Toronto.

Single, E. (2000b). *The effectiveness of harm reduction and its role in a new framework for drug policy in British Colombia.* Paper presented at the 2000 National Federal/Provincial/Territorial Meeting on Injection Drug Use, Vancouver. Available: www.ccsa.ca/docs/vancouver.htm.

Meeting Clients' Needs

Chapter 12

Working with Women

SUSAN HARRISON AND EVA INGBER

INTRODUCTION

Most women with substance use problems do not present themselves for addiction treatment; those who do have often experienced a range of problems, from physical and psychological health consequences to family, job, financial, legal and other problems. If we, as counsellors, are to help these women recover and develop their potential, we must understand and empathize with them. We must know the treatment issues that are specific to women and match each client to the types of treatment that best meet her needs. Although we are beginning to see women coming for help earlier—as health promotion, prevention and early intervention efforts take hold in communities—we will likely continue to work with women who have been severely damaged by their substance use and abuse.

Stephanie Covington writes that gender-responsive treatment means creating an environment through site selection, staff selection, program development, content and material that reflects an understanding of the realities of women's lives, and is responsive to the issues of the clients (Covington, 2001). Our goal in this chapter is to explore issues from a gender-responsive approach.

This chapter begins by discussing how attitudes affect women's development of substance use problems, treatment barriers for women and women's process of recovery. We discuss both the physical and psychological factors involved in women's use of substances. The last section addresses important issues in recovery, including beginning the treatment process, skill development during recovery, treatment approaches and counsellor characteristics. We discuss the relationship and interdependence of gender, socialization and substance use, and look at effective and meaningful ways to help women address their recovery needs.

ATTITUDES AFFECTING WOMEN'S DEVELOPMENT OF SUBSTANCE USE PROBLEMS AND THEIR RECOVERY

When working with women who have alcohol and other drug problems, the importance of attitudes cannot be overemphasized. Societal attitudes toward women in general, and toward these women in particular, have an impact on many levels. Attitudes of people in these women's worlds—life partners, other family members, employers, friends, counsellors—and of the client herself may determine when and if a woman decides to seek help and whether she finds supports or obstacles in her road to recovery.

Societal Attitudes toward Women in General

To help female clients, we must understand and empathize with each client individually. To empathize with them as women is even more basic and important than to understand and empathize with their substance use problems, because, as Beth Glover Reed (1985) states so simply and powerfully, "women are women long before they become involved in chemical misuse or dependency." Women's reality differs greatly from men's reality. We must truly appreciate the fabric woven from the various threads in women's lives.

Women still hold secondary status in our society, and even more so if they are of a race, ethnic group, language or sexual orientation other than the white heterosexual majority. Women devalued in this way often become victims of violence and have lower self-esteem and lower aspirations than do men.

A few statistics from *Women in Canada 2000: A Gender-Based Statistical Report* (Statistics Canada, 2000), covering various social, health and economic conditions, are illustrative:
• In 1996–97, 62 per cent of females aged 12 and over reported having some form of chronic health condition as diagnosed by a health care professional.
• Women continue to make up the large majority of lone parents in Canada. In 1996, 83 per cent of all single-parent families were headed by women.
• 56 per cent of all families headed by lone parent mothers had incomes that fell below the Low Income Cut-Offs.
• In 1997, the average annual pre-tax income, from all sources, of women aged 15 and over was $19,800—just 62 per cent of the average income of men.
• Even when employed, women are still largely responsible for looking after homes and families. In 1998, employed women with a spouse and at least one child under age 19 spent an hour and a half a day more than men performing household duties.

• 32 per cent of women murdered in 1998 were killed by their spouse, versus three per cent for men.
• In 1998, 78 per cent of all female victims of crime were victimized by someone they knew (54 per cent for men).

Studies have documented the detrimental effects of these social conditions on the mental and physical health of women. Researchers in the fields of women's health and women with addictions have found that the stress resulting from social conditions such as violence (Groeneveld & Shain, 1989) may lead to problematic use of alcohol and other drugs as a coping mechanism.

Attitudes toward Women with Alcohol and Other Drug Problems

Women's use of alcohol has always been judged more harshly than that of men. In ancient Rome, drinking by a woman was punishable by death. In most areas of our society, it is acceptable for women to drink moderately. However, disapproval of drunkenness in women is greater than for men. A national survey in 1991 found that respondents (who themselves would be more critical of female than male drunkenness at a party) felt that others would have even stronger disapproval (Wilsnack, 1996, as stated in Vogeltanz & Wilsnack, 1997).

The greater stigma that surrounds women who have substance use problems delays or prevents their seeking assistance—they internalize society's negative attitudes and feel guilty and responsible for their situation. These feelings can be a double-edged sword. They may produce the anxiety and discomfort necessary to motivate the women toward change. However, these feelings of guilt and shame can also be overwhelming and serve as a trigger for further problematic substance use.

Attitudes in Research

Counsellors working with women should keep in mind that what we read is rarely free of attitudinal bias. Generally, theories of human development, therapeutic models and techniques, and even what are considered acceptable research models, were developed predominantly by and for men. These are then often generalized to female populations.

When reading studies, be skeptical and question whether they apply to women. Be aware of whether these studies include both males and females. If both sexes are included, are the data for women analysed separately to see if there are any gender differences? Brett et al. in 1995 reviewed specialty journals on alcohol, drugs and addictive behaviours and found that it was still common for studies using exclusively male populations to generalize findings to both sexes.

Counsellor Attitudes

Women with substance use problems may be perceived as sicker and harder to treat. There have been enough treatment studies over the past 10 years to demonstrate that this is not the case. When they come for treatment, women may be experiencing more problems as a result of their use of substances, but they recover as well as, if not better than, men when provided with appropriate treatment. Sometimes they struggle because of environmental factors and barriers, such as child or elder care responsibilities, a spouse who uses substances heavily or is abusive, or post-traumatic stress symptoms. If women are dropping out of treatment, try to find out what barriers they are experiencing and consider what your service could do to help.

BELIEF SYSTEMS
Those of us who work in the addiction field may unconsciously stigmatize women. We need to explore our own belief systems and consider how they influence our work with clients. We are not unaffected by the society in which we live.

We need to begin by asking ourselves the most basic question: "Do I even like women, let alone value and respect them?" In other words, "Do I have a 'positive regard' for women, or have I internalized negative societal attitudes toward them? For example, does it matter to me whether my first-born child is a boy or a girl?"

REACTING TO COMMON SITUATIONS
Next, we need to ask ourselves more specific questions related to situations we will likely face if working with women. Could you work effectively with a woman who:
• told you she had abused her children either physically or verbally?
• was neglecting her children?
• had given up her children or was expressing indifference or hostility toward them?
• revealed heavy drinking and/or other drug use during pregnancy?
• you felt had inadequate parenting skills?
• wishes to end a marriage where there are school-aged children?
• has been married several times?
• insists on staying in an abusive relationship?
• talks about the difficulties in her relationship with her same-sex partner?
• tells you she has had or is contemplating an abortion?
• spends most of her time with you in tears?
• makes sexual advances towards you?
• is grieving the death of a child/spouse/parent?
• has killed or assaulted someone?
• is just starting to acknowledge being a lesbian?
• earns money as a sex-trade worker?
• has begun to have memories of childhood sexual abuse?
• has divulged plans to commit suicide?

- is often angry in interviews?
- is obese?
- is HIV-positive or has AIDS or another blood-borne disease, such as hepatitis C?

Visualize yourself working with a client in one of these situations—how do you feel toward her? Could you be supportive, and create a therapeutic environment conducive to client growth? Or do you recognize personal values or biases that would affect your feelings toward her? Participating in clinical consultation is necessary so that these issues or judgments can be explored and addressed so as to not cause harm to clients. Attitudes and empathy are the two key ingredients for effective recovery when working with women who have substance use problems—the parentheses within which all other knowledge and skills are held. See below for further discussion of counsellor attributes and the role of empathy in recovery.

BARRIERS THAT WOMEN FACE

In addition to the attitudes just discussed, women face other barriers to treatment.

Isolation

The loneliness and isolation common to so many women point out the lack of a close support system. The catalysts that often connect a man to the help he needs to recover, such as an employer, family physician, justice system or spouse threatening to leave, are not as common for a woman. Women less often have a life partner; and if they do, he or she often does not support the woman's recovery efforts.

A sense of belonging, of being valued and respected, is crucial to the health of human beings. People who feel good about themselves, who feel connected to other people, valuable and whole, have much less need to seek these feelings—or numb the lack of them—through substance use.

The isolation that women with alcohol and other drug problems experience can be seen not only as a barrier to recovery, but also as a major health risk. In his classic work on suicide, Durkheim (1951) pinpointed several common elements among those who take their own lives: alienation, no sense of belonging, not feeling valued or useful, and low self-esteem. A meta-analysis of studies that looked at 37,000 people in the United States, Finland and Sweden found that individuals who are cut off from others are much more likely to die prematurely than are those with a strong social network (House et al., 1988).

A Woman's Focus on Others

Women are socialized to attend to the needs of others, but they are often not good at identifying their own needs. In fact, a woman with substance use problems rarely feels that she has legitimate needs. She is often not alone in this belief. Her family, partner, children, friends, employer and doctor may explicitly or implicitly convey the same message.

We have worked with many women who were emphatic in their need to schedule appointments around other people's needs, such as hockey practices, partners wanting to bring guests home from work or children needing help with a project. However, even as they became stronger in their recovery, and more able to acknowledge their right to have their own needs met, these women still felt very guilty over the one evening a week they came for their support group. A woman's connection with her treatment program may always remain somewhat tentative because of this ongoing dynamic of feeling both responsibility and guilt.

Child-Care Responsibilities and Concerns

A widely quoted idea states, "No one likes to think that the hand that rocks the cradle is a shaky one" (Curlee, 1970). Because of the greater stigma attached to women with alcohol and other drug problems, people often assume that a mother who has substance use problems is unfit to parent. This stigma cannot help but create a barrier to treatment for a woman who has child-care responsibilities.

Through our clinical experience, we have seen that, even when they are using alcohol and other drugs, women work very hard to take care of their children. Women often try to figure out how their children's lives will be least compromised by their own struggles. A woman may try to avoid using until her children are at school, or only when other caregivers can be present. Women will often compromise their own self-care when working to take care of their children the best way they can, while struggling with their substance use. As most treatment programs do not provide child-care, a woman may find, if she cannot pay for child-care, and no one in her family network would be a safe alternative caregiver, that she is faced with an additional barrier to seeking help.

A woman's treatment program may need to be flexible, allowing mothers to take children to school, attend doctors' appointments and tend to sick children. With flexibility in these areas, a woman can address her own treatment needs without feeling she is compromising the needs of her children.

Diversity Issues for Women

While they share some common characteristics, women who have substance use problems are a very diverse group, with different needs. Addiction is always part of a larger portrait that includes a woman's history and the social, cultural and economic factors that create the context of her life (Covington, 2002). Understanding this context means considering women's needs related to age (both younger and older women), sexual orientation, homelessness, living in rural communities, incarceration, ethnocultural background, Aboriginal status, the presence of HIV/AIDS or hepatitis C, pregnancy and concurrent mental health disorders. Barriers, related to these needs, within treatment programs and systems can make it less likely that women with diverse needs will find the help they need.

When women come together in group counselling programs, differences in backgrounds need to be named, including differences in substance use, reasons for using and lifestyles connected to the use, in order to help women express their individual and shared experiences.

Health Care System

Surprisingly, the primary health care and mental health care systems sometimes prevent or delay women from getting appropriate help for substance use problems. As has been found in many studies, Vogeltanz & Wilsnack (1997) explain that many more women than men go to mental health or medical settings to seek help for problems. It is common knowledge that women visit physicians much more often than men do (even taking into account women's trips related to children). However, substance use problems are often not identified in these settings, either because of inadequate knowledge or because of stigma. Unfortunately, it can also happen that mental health professionals may not know enough about addiction issues; a woman may receive a variety of mental illness diagnoses without having her problem with alcohol and other substances recognized and addressed.

SPECIAL CONSIDERATIONS IN SUBSTANCE USE AMONG WOMEN

Effects of Substance Use

Chapter 10 of this book goes into detail about the physical effects of substance use. For our purposes here, we will highlight a few considerations that are specific to women.

Most women who come for treatment will have been using multiple substances—usually alcohol in combination with benzodiazepines and/or opioid painkillers. Clients may be unaware of the potential risk of becoming dependent on these medications. Some combinations may also include illicit substances, predominantly cannabis and cocaine.

Women sometimes decide to withdraw themselves from benzodiazepines, opioids or antidepressants, not realizing the medical and psychological risks of withdrawal. Women need to be encouraged to seek medical support when trying to stop using these medications.

Many of the women we have worked with were taking antidepressants prescribed by their family doctors. Adlaf & Ialomiteanu (2002) found that women in Ontario were still significantly more likely to use anxiety medication, and twice as likely to report use of medications for depression, compared with men. It is important when working with women to tease out whether the depression is the primary problem, or whether it is the result of alcohol use.

Women were not included in early tests that looked at therapeutic benefits and side-effects of older-generation antidepressants. More recent medications, such as the SSRIs, can also differ in their effect on and effectiveness between men and women. Studies point to the need for more research on potential gender differences in areas such as pharmacodynamics, dosage, side-effects and withdrawal effects (Stewart, 1998).

Alcohol Use

Women's use of psychoactive substances in general has traditionally been lower than that of men. Young women, though they drink less often and in smaller quantities, are almost as likely to be drinkers (having consumed alcohol in the past 12 months) as young men are.

For example, a 2003 survey of Ontario students (Adlaf & Paglia, 2003) showed a small significant difference between adolescent males and adolescent females in the percentage of drinkers: 68.3 per cent and 64.3 per cent, respectively. In the 1998 Canadian Campus Survey, the authors concluded that: "Even if women drink less, do so less often and less heavily than men, few differences were observed in the rates of problems due to alcohol . . . no gender differences were observed in the rates of dependence" (Gliksman et al., 2000, p. 57).

Given the same amount of alcohol, women get more intoxicated, get intoxicated faster and stay intoxicated longer than their male counterparts (York & Welte, 1994). A woman who consumes two-thirds as much alcohol as a man will likely get the same effect. This difference is due to factors such as:
• percentage of body fat (women have a higher percentage and therefore have less body water to dilute the alcohol)
• hormones (alcohol generally has more effect on women premenstrually)
• metabolism (including diminished activity of the stomach enzyme that breaks down alcohol), as reported by Frezza et al. (1990) and Seitz et al. (1993).

The long-term effects of drinking differ for women, as well (women experience serious health problems after a shorter period of long-term drinking than men do, often referred to as "telescoped" effects):

- **Liver disease**: Women who drink two to three drinks a day have significant risk for developing cirrhosis of the liver. Women also develop other types of alcoholic liver disease at a faster rate than men (Gavaler & Arria, 1995).
- **Cancer**: Women are particularly vulnerable to cancer of the lips, tongue, pharynx and esophagus. Studies have also associated alcohol consumption with breast cancer—that is, there is a significantly elevated risk of developing breast cancer at levels of consumption of two or three drinks a day (Longnecker et al., 1988; Schatzkin et al., 1987; Katsouyanni et al., 1994).
- **Brain damage**: Women are more susceptible to alcohol-related brain damage than men (Jacobson, 1986).
- **Heart disease**: Even though, among people who have a drinking problem, women consume less alcohol than men do, they are at as much or more risk for alcohol-associated heart muscle disease (cardiomyopathy) (Urbano-Marquez et al., 1995; Kahan & Wilson, 2002).

Sexual Issues

Stephanie Covington, an expert in the area of women, sexuality and addiction, reported at a conference in Winnipeg in 1990 that she had found 74 per cent of women in recovery had sexual problems. Interestingly, these women often reported having sexual problems before developing substance use problems. This same observation has been made by others, as noted by Vogeltanz & Wilsnack (1997). In fact, longitudinal data suggests that sexual problems may be a strong predictor of continued problem drinking over time (Wilsnack et al., 1991), and, in this sense, sexuality becomes a recovery issue (see below and also Chapter 24).

Psychological Factors

COPING WITH EMOTIONS

The most common reasons given by women for seeking treatment for substance use problems, according to researchers cited by Health Canada (2001a), are "depression, medical problems, problems with family relationships and feelings related to children leaving the home" (p. 25), with anxiety, depression and stressful events as contributing factors.

Finding ways to cope with emotions can be a challenge for many women in recovery. Women seeking help often use substances to help them cope with their emotions. Research has shown that women's highest-risk situations are negative emotions and conflict with others (Annis & Graham, 1995; Annis et al., 1996). Substance use helps women to escape from these difficult feelings, as well as numb themselves from situations and feelings that may be overwhelming.

Through our experience, we have seen that one of the biggest challenges for women in recovery is learning how to be with their emotions without using or self-harming in any way. Women have learned that substance use can help them temporarily escape from painful feelings.

Recovery involves a shift from acting out destructive behaviours (to displace feeling or rid oneself of feeling) to accepting and integrating feelings. This process involves learning to calm oneself through self-soothing techniques and sharing with others (Covington, 2002).

SENSE OF SELF

It has been widely documented that women with drinking problems have lower self-esteem than their male counterparts (Beckman & Amaro, 1986). Not only do they have very low self-esteem, but many have little or no sense of self and no sense of purpose in life (Schlesinger et al., 1990). They often feel powerless, with no control over their lives, and yet they take total responsibility and blame for anything that is wrong in their lives. Their problem, as Covington (1990) so succinctly stated, is not grandiosity, but invisibility.

Concurrent Disorders

Health Canada's best practice guidelines on concurrent disorders define concurrent disorders as "any combination of mental health and substance use disorders" (Health Canada 2001b, p. 7). The guidelines also state that people who are in treatment for substance use problems have higher rates of mental health problems than people in the general population (Health Canada, 2001b).

A high percentage of women who enter substance use treatment have histories of depression, anxiety, post-traumatic stress disorder and bulimia. It is important to assess a woman for concurrent disorders to determine which services are needed to help address her needs and goals. Symptoms of anxiety and depression may not only interfere with optimum outcomes from substance use treatment, but are often also reported as triggers for relapse (Health Canada, 2001b).

SERVICE DELIVERY CHALLENGES

One of the challenges of working with women with substance use problems is offering services that meet the individual needs of the women seeking help. People with a history of concurrent disorders may have the experience of seeking out many health care services, in an effort to get their needs met. A woman may have a negative experience when she enters a treatment program that does not meet her needs; such an experience may further stigmatize her. She may consequently feel more discouraged and frustrated, and may feel like a failure.

However, not all programs can meet the needs of every woman presenting for treatment. Counsellors need to know the strengths of a program, as well as knowing when a client would benefit more from a modification of the program or a referral to another service. Referring a woman to an inappropriate program may be more harmful than helpful. Unfortunately, long waiting lists for specialized concurrent disorder programs can make it hard to match a client to the programs that would best address her needs.

ASSESSMENT FOR CONCURRENT DISORDERS

If you are working with women who have concurrent disorders, you must develop working relationships with mental health practitioners in your community. Women often present at assessment with previous diagnoses that may or may not be accurate. It is important to reassess each woman, even when a thorough evaluation has been conducted in the past (Cohen, 2000). In early recovery, it may be difficult to assess if a woman's symptoms of depression and anxiety are connected to the effects of the substances, withdrawal and/or mental health issues. Chapters 18 and 26 give more detail on assessing these issues.

SELF-HARM AND BORDERLINE PERSONALITY DISORDER

A major challenge for counsellors working with women is clients who present with self-harming behaviours (Linehan, 1993). Clinicians often mistake these behaviours for symptoms of the substance use problem when, in fact, they may be related to borderline personality disorder and/or borderline traits.

Best practice guidelines for concurrent substance use and borderline personality disorders report that the best empirically supported treatment is Dialectical Behaviour Therapy (Health Canada, 2001b). Women with the diagnosis of borderline personality disorder may present as highly competent and at the same time lack skills to process emotional issues that are addressed in a treatment program. Dialectical Behaviour Therapy programs help women develop skills to regulate their emotions while helping them address harmful behaviours such as parasuicidal behaviour and substance use, among others.

Suicide Risk

People with concurrent dependence on substances and mood/anxiety disorders are at increased risk for suicide (Health Canada, 2001b). Women who have a drinking problem are at greater risk of suicide than women who do not—as much as five times (Gomberg, 1989). Many of the female clients we have worked with attempted suicide, and many of those had tried more than once. Because of this increased risk, all counsellors should remember to regularly assess women with concurrent disorders for suicide risk (Cohen, 2000). Counsellors need to:
• have skills to do a suicide risk assessment
• work with staff as a team
• seek regular supervision on these issues.

Trauma

Counsellors need to be aware of a strong connection between substance use and trauma. Women often use substances to cope with the memories of abuse, as well as the symptoms of trauma. Treatment programs must be able to address this connection.

To address this connection effectively, counsellors must be familiar with first-stage trauma work. First-stage work does not involve working with memories of trauma or delving into the past. It does involve validating a women's trauma history. Connections to substance use need to be established while women focus on safety and developing coping strategies.

Some women may find mutual aid groups and meetings very helpful, and some may find them unsafe. If a woman discloses her personal history, she may feel uncomfortable and also may be at risk for flashbacks and dissociation.

For women with a diagnosis of Post-Traumatic Stress Disorder (PTSD), the research recommends an integrated treatment model that addresses both substance use and PTSD (Health Canada, 2001b). Najavits (2002) uses a cognitive-behavioural model to address both PTSD and substance use issues in implementing first-stage trauma work. This treatment program is probably the most widely studied for this population and is associated with high retention rates and reduced substance use, as well as reduced post-traumatic stress syndrome symptoms (Health Canada, 2001b).

BEGINNING THE TREATMENT PROCESS

Assessment

An effective treatment plan or program must begin with a comprehensive assessment. Any instruments should be checked for their reliability, validity and appropriateness for use with women. To know what services a client will need, the assessor should ask more than the standard questions about substance use, by exploring:
• any consequences the client may experience after even low amounts of substance use
• circumstances under which she uses
• whether she uses and shares needles or lives with someone who injects drugs
• whether she smokes
• health status and medical problems, and any mental health concerns
• history of violence/abuse, including current safety issues
• legal issues
• suicide attempts
• self-harming behaviours, including disordered eating

- safer sex practices
- sexual orientation
- substance use by the client's partner
- what, if any, social supports she already has in place
- if there are other health care providers with whom she is working (this includes asking for signed consent from the woman, as there may be a need to communicate with these professionals)
- whether the client has children or other dependants (including pets) for whom she will need care arrangements
- financial resources, including money for transportation
- safe housing
- educational/vocational background (there might be a need for upgrading or retraining)
- her current and past coping and self-care strategies, with an emphasis on her strengths.

Creating a Safe Environment

The environment in which the assessment and core services take place may influence a woman's decision about whether she engages in the treatment process. The physical environment needs to reflect the needs of the clients, by addressing issues of diversity, as well as safety. Because many women in substance use treatment have a history of violence, an immediate sense of safety in and around the environment is crucial. Consider the following factors:

- Is public transit very close by?
- Are streets well lit?
- Is her privacy assured—are meetings with her counsellor structured to protect the confidentiality of their discussions?
- Are her personal belongings accessible only to her?
- Is there (in the case of mixed programs) adequate physical separation from male participants?

Once in treatment, a woman should be offered a range of treatment options, including separate space where she can be free of the pressures to interact with men, particularly during the early stages of recovery (Cohen, 2000). In agencies that offer services for men and women, safety issues need extra attention, and clients may need to consider the limitations of the setting.

Safety also includes having appropriate boundaries between the client and the clinician, and knowing that the environment is free of physical, emotional and sexual harassment (Covington, 2002). Some women may want to seek treatment in all-women settings that have more options around safety.

Developing Stronger Boundaries

Women are socialized to care for others. When women come together in a group setting, one often hears such responses as "I know what you mean; I feel that way too." There is a lot of support, sharing and connecting.

However, in a group setting, boundaries can be blurred, and women can fall into the roles of becoming caregivers for each other. In a group-focused treatment program, women may benefit from learning about how to support other clients while staying focused on their own recovery needs.

One challenge is to help women have clear boundaries and practise their assertiveness. Some women may not feel comfortable discussing their own issues, feeling that their own problems are not as important or serious as another group member's concerns.

In addition, women may not know how much information to share about themselves in a group setting; they benefit from a discussion about the importance of sharing at a pace that feels comfortable for each individual.

For women with a history of trauma, the timing of information-sharing is an important consideration. Beyer & Carnabucci emphasize empowering women to act intuitively on when and where they feel comfortable talking about their issues. However, they caution that:

> Traumatized women who have not developed a cohesive sense of self and boundaries may want to express their pain at the earliest opportunity, before sufficient relational experience and trust have been developed within the group. Group members may not know how best to support the woman, leaving her feeling alienated (Beyer & Carnabucci, 2002, p. 524).

For this reason, women should have the option of working with individual counsellors while in a group program. A woman may feel more comfortable addressing some issues with an individual therapist.

Communicating with Professionals in Other Systems

Women seeking treatment for substance use are often involved with professionals from many other systems, such as probation officers, child welfare workers and lawyers. Clients of substance use services often have difficulty asserting themselves, particularly in situations that involve power imbalances. Women often feel judged when dealing with other systems and are often in vulnerable positions; for example, a woman may be going through a custody battle with an ex-partner, who may be exposing the woman's substance use history to judge her as an unfit mother. Women may benefit from learning how to ask questions, prepare for meetings and practise asserting themselves.

Carolyn DeMarco writes about a Women's Health Bill of Rights that focuses on women's choices when seeing their physician (DeMarco, 1995). These women's rights include statements such as "I have the right to choose the types of treatment I prefer from among the options offered to me by my doctor."

DEVELOPING SKILLS IN RECOVERY

The first task for a counsellor is to help a client identify and work on her treatment goals and avoid harmful behaviours. The client also needs to learn to feel better about herself—this work in itself is a journey that usually follows a path such as the following:
• confronting her self-hate
• moving through despair to hope
• developing a sense of self, upon which self-esteem will be built slowly over the rest of her life.
She also needs to learn to express anger safely. The expression of anger in women in our society is barely tolerated, let alone encouraged. But the client must learn ways to express anger if she is to develop strength, self-esteem, some sense of control over her life and, perhaps most of all, avoid depression.

Self-Care

Learning self-care strategies helps a woman reduce her vulnerability. One of the challenges for counsellors is helping women assess when it is safe to be with their feelings and when they need to use various coping strategies to safely take a break from intense, overwhelming feelings.

In environments that have been physically and emotionally abusive, women and girls have usually lacked validation of their emotional and physical needs. Self-invalidation occurs when a person adopts the characteristics of the "invalidating environment" and tends to invalidate or ignore her or his own thoughts, beliefs and emotional responses, and to rely on others for accurate information about internal and external reality (Linehan, 1993). In recovery, women slowly learn to identify and authenticate their own feelings and respond to their own needs in ways that make sense to them.

Observing Feelings through Self-Monitoring

Women can learn to become more aware of their feelings through self-monitoring. This model focuses on women's individual strengths. By observing her thoughts and feelings, a woman can learn when she is most at risk to use substances or to behave in other harmful ways. This process of observing and recording feelings helps women to become their own therapist and see their patterns of risk. Women can be asked to record their coping strategies that help them avoid substance use. Women can therefore learn what is most useful for ongoing self-care and for developing relapse prevention plans. Cravings are seen as learning opportunities. When they experience cravings, women should be encouraged to seek support and discuss coping strategies.

Helping Women to Stay Present

When entering treatment, many women want to tell their stories of past trauma. This can be challenging for the therapist who wants to respond to the needs of the client and at the same time evaluate if sharing of her trauma history will be safe and therapeutic for the woman. Of course therapists want the recovery process to be empowering for the client, yet when a woman does not have the coping skills to deal with the feelings that arise from opening up these stories, the outcome can be harmful to her. See Chapter 18 for an explanation of the stages involved in trauma work.

Grounding Techniques

Therapists working with women in recovery must be skilled at teaching grounding techniques. This education helps women know what may happen to them when they are no longer using and memories begin to arise.

As Judith Herman states, women in early recovery often swing from feelings of being overwhelmed to feeling numb (Herman, 1992). Women will express fear that they are "going crazy" or will state, "I don't know who I am." Women may feel as though they are on an emotional roller-coaster. When women learn that others are having similar experiences, they often feel relieved and much less frightened.

For more detail on this crucial work, see Chapter 18 and the resources at the end of this chapter.

Educating Clients in Mindfulness Skills

Research has shown that mindfulness is helpful in addressing substance use problems. "Mindfulness is cultivated by assuming a stance of an impartial witness to your own experience. To do this requires that you become aware of the constant stream of judging and reacting to inner and outer experiences, and learn to step back from it" (Kabat-Zinn, 1990, p. 33).

Mindfulness skills are particularly helpful to women in recovery who are carrying many negative labels and judgments of themselves, preventing them from being in the present. Developing mindfulness skills requires ongoing practice. For resources on this topic, see the work of Jon Kabat-Zinn and Marsha Linehan. Staff who facilitate mindfulness programs must be properly trained and supervised.

TREATMENT APPROACHES

Gender of Group Participants

Because of the constellation of factors usually found among women seeking treatment, gender-specific group treatment, at least in early recovery, is often most appropriate. However, women need to choose what makes sense for them as full participants in developing their treatment plan.

MIXED GENDER GROUPS

Many clinicians and studies (e.g., Brody, 1987; Holmes, 2002) have observed that mixed gender groups are less effective for women than for men. Some of the challenges for women in mixed groups may include the following:
• Interaction reinforces traditional gender role stereotypes.
• Women speak less often and for less time than men.
• Women are often interrupted.
• Women do not defend their ideas vigorously.
• Issues of body image and sexuality are not discussed, or may be discussed in sexist ways.
• Women may compete and may not develop closeness with each other.
• Women communicate in more passive styles, talk softly and may tend to withdraw.
• Women overtly and covertly defer to men and encourage male participation and interactions.
• Men's language patterns predominate.

Deborah Tannen, a sociolinguist, has analysed the conversational dynamics between men and women, and describes them as "cross-cultural communication, prey to a clash of conversational styles" (Tannen, 1991, p. 42).

However, some women may be reluctant to engage in an all-women group because they dislike other women; these women may choose mixed-gender groups.

When a woman is progressing well in her recovery, there can be some specific benefit to participation in mixed-gender groups, co-led by male and female therapists. Skilled facilitators, themselves fully aware of different interaction patterns between men and women, and healthy in their own gender roles and interactions, can model for participants and provide a safe setting for women to practise what may be new assertive interactions with men.

Project MATCH studied three different treatment interventions with men and women and found that they all worked relatively equally, with only one client attribute, psychiatric severity, having a significant interaction with treatment type. However, further study is needed, because, in all cases, very experienced therapists and close monitoring and interaction with clients were consistent components of the study groups (Project MATCH Research Group, 1997).

WOMEN-SPECIFIC GROUPS

Women-specific groups facilitated by women counsellors allow clients to develop a sense of self through validation of their experiences and perceptions. In these groups, women:
• can explore personal, behavioural and attitudinal changes, as well as express difficult feelings such as anger and shame
• discuss the social determinants of problems specific to women
• can learn to please themselves instead of others and learn to trust and value women. For many women, these groups also provide the safety necessary to take risks (an exception may be those who have been abused by mothers or lesbian partners).

Women can now access all-women Alcoholics Anonymous and Women for Sobriety groups, as well as all-women groups within some treatment programs and services.

Copeland & Hall's 1992 study found that a women's service, in comparison with traditional mixed-sex services, attracted significantly more:
• women with dependent children
• lesbian women
• women who had a maternal history of substance use problems
• women who were sexually abused in childhood.

At the Women's Program, originally at the Addiction Research Foundation (now part of the Centre for Addiction and Mental Health), staff found that retention rates for women were higher than in the mixed program. The Women's Program grew and developed as a result of clients' expressing feelings of safety and comfort in the women's groups and asking for increased women-specific services. Clearly, further thought and analysis is necessary in this area.

Cognitive Behaviour Therapy

When working with clients with substance use issues, cognitive behaviour therapy (CBT) helps a client:
• explore the function of the substance use
• understand her thoughts and feelings leading to triggers
• focus on developing alternative coping strategies.

According to Beck et al. (1993), CBT considers the substance use in terms of its sociological, interpersonal and psychological dimensions. It is collaborative (building trust), active, based on open-ended questioning, and highly structured and focused.

The characteristics of CBT—its focus on the whole person and emphasis on affective, cognitive and behavioural change—make it particularly suited to the needs of women in treatment for substance use. "Women's treatment needs to be based on the premise of the whole person, incorporating the holistic model of addiction and emphasizing affective, cognitive and behavioural change. The affective aspect is especially important for females because their substance abusing behaviour needs to be understood in the context of their emotional lives" (Covington, 2002, p. 64). One needs to make connections to women's affective experiences; through collaboration, the therapist develops a partnership with the client, empowering her to manage her urges through individual self-care techniques.

COUNSELLOR CHARACTERISTICS AND GENDER

We began this chapter by stating that, if we are to help women recover and develop their potential, we must understand and empathize with each woman individually. The relational bond between the client and her therapist is the one essential ingredient in all treatment approaches. Put another way, we expect that further treatment outcome research in the substance use field will confirm what psychotherapy research has—that one of the key prognostic variables in treatment is the empathic qualities of the therapist.

EMPATHY AND SELF-EXPLORATION

Empathy means profoundly valuing and understanding the client's reality. It also involves knowing yourself intimately, so you can be with the client every step of the way and not lose yourself in the process. We offer the following list of questions, based on those used by the authors of Women's Ways of Knowing (Belenky et al., 1986), for some self-exploration from a perspective you may not have considered:

• How do you express your anger?
• What are your deepest fears? How do you deal with them?
• Do you seek nurturance for yourself? How, in what ways and from whom?
• Have you experienced intimate group sharing with other women or men?
• Have you been through your own therapy?
• Do you know who you are? Could you describe yourself to someone?
• In your own family, how are roles assigned? How are finances handled; who makes money decisions? How are household duties handled?
• If you have children, how are they growing up vis-à-vis traditional male/female roles, ways of interacting, etc.?
• What would you (or did you) look for in a helping person?
• What stands out for you in your life over the last few years?
• What is your life like right now? What do you care about and think about?
• Is the way you see yourself now different from the way you saw yourself in the past? What led to the changes? How do you see yourself changing in the future?
• What does being a woman/man mean to you?

- Do you think there are any important differences between women and men?
- How has your sense of yourself as a woman/man been changing?
- What relationships have been really important to you in your life? Why? How would you describe those relationships? How would the other person describe them?
- Have you had a relationship with someone who helped you shape the person you have become?
- Have you had a really important relationship where you were responsible for taking care of another person? How would you describe this? How important was that in your life?

We hope you can see some connection between your own answers to these questions and your ability to walk in step with women clients.

The odds are good that a woman therapist will understand, better than a male therapist, the world a female client describes. This is not to say that a male therapist can never empathize with the experiences of female clients. A study reported by Kaplan (1985) found that very experienced men could achieve the same rate of therapy outcome as moderately experienced or experienced female therapists. Whether male or female, the counsellor needs to see that substance use by the client was a coping strategy that has been used to deal with very challenging situations and feelings. The therapist needs to observe her or his judgments and consider that this use made sense to the woman at the time and helped her cope, using the skills she had available to her at that time. A woman's substance use is often about lack of learned coping strategies, rather than denial or resistance.

CONCLUSION

Women use substances as a way of coping with their life situations, feelings and thoughts. When women have a history of using substances, they carry a tremendous amount of guilt and shame. They often feel loss over what they had hoped for in relationships and expectations of themselves. Women speak about what their lives would have looked like if they had not been using.

It is the work of counsellors to help women learn to validate themselves and focus on their strengths. Women with substance problems carry society's stigma of women substance users. The women we work with often have tremendous empathy for others, but carry many self-judgments—even when they are working so hard to care for themselves the best way they can, they find it hard to accept that their own substance use made sense for them at the time, given their life situation and abilities to cope.

When men stop using substances, they often speak about feeling better. For women, substance use is often a symptom or coping strategy that covers the underlying feelings and issues. When women stop using, many feelings emerge and much work is needed to help a woman learn to both identify and cope with her feelings. In early recovery, women's emotions often swing from feeling numb to feeling overwhelmed. Recovery for women is about learning to cope with emotions, and about learning to care for oneself in ways that are not self-harming.

It is an honour to work with women who present for treatment and are at various stages in their recovery process. Observing these women's struggles, strengths and determination is a privilege. It is so important, as counsellors, to communicate to women a sense of hope: that changing one's behaviour and addressing one's issues is possible and can lead to many positive outcomes.

Accompanying an addicted woman on the long journey to recovery—through self-loathing, guilt and despair to self-understanding, self-acceptance, self-respect and control over her own life—is like being a midwife. The client sets the pace, and you move forward with her when she has the strength; sit quietly beside her while she catches her breath; encourage her, guiding her to push again, telling her the pain won't last, that the destination is worth it, that you've seen many other women go through this, and you know she has the strength to push again. And, ultimately, she gives birth to herself, seeing her potential finally becoming reality.

REFERENCES

Adlaf, E.M. & Ialomiteanu, A. (2002). *CAMH Monitor eReport: Addiction and Mental Health Indicators among Ontario Adults in 2001, and Changes since 1977.* Toronto: Centre for Addiction and Mental Health.

Adlaf, E.M. & Paglia, A. (2003). *Drug Use among Ontario Students 1977–2003: Detailed OSDUS Findings.* CAMH Research Document Series No. 13. Toronto: Centre for Addiction and Mental Health.

Annis, H.M. & Graham, J.M. (1995). Profile types on the inventory of drinking situations: Implications for relapse prevention counselling. *Psychology of Addictive Behaviors, 9,* 176–182.

Annis, H.M., Turner, N.E. & Sklar, S.M. (1996). *Inventory of Drug-Taking Situations: User's Guide.* Toronto: Addiction Research Foundation.

Beck. A.T., Wright, F.D., Newman, C.F. & Liese, B.S. (1993). *Cognitive Therapy of Substance Abuse.* New York: Guilford Press.

Beckman, L.J. & Amaro, H. (1986). Personal and social difficulties faced by women and men entering treatment. *Journal of Studies on Alcohol, 47,* 135–145.

Belenky, M.F., Clinchy, B.M., Goldberger, N.R. & Tarule, J.M. (1986). *Women's Ways of Knowing.* New York: Basic Books.

Beyer, P.B. & Carnabucci, K. (2002). Group treatment of substance abusing women. In S.L. Ashenberg Straussner & S. Brown (Eds.), *The Handbook of Addiction Treatment for Women* (pp. 515–538). San Francisco: Jossey-Bass.

Brett, P.J., Graham, K. & Smythe, C. (1995). An analysis of specialty journals on alcohol, drugs and addictive behaviors for sex bias in research methods and reporting. *Journal of Studies on Alcohol, 56*, 24–34.

Brody, C. (1987). *Women's Therapy Groups.* New York: Springer Publishing Co.

Cohen, M. (2000). *Counseling Addicted Women: A Practical Guide.* Thousand Oaks, CA: Sage Publications.

Copeland, J. & Hall, W. (1992). A comparison of women seeking drug and alcohol treatment in a specialist women's and two traditional mixed-sex treatment services. *British Journal of Addiction, 87*, 1293–1302.

Covington, S.S. (1990). Unpublished conference presentation at Women and Substance Abuse: Strategies for the 90s, Winnipeg, Manitoba.

Covington, S.S. (2001, Feb.). Creating gender-responsive programs: The next step for women's services. *Corrections Today, 63*, 85-87.

Covington, S.S. (2002). Helping women recover: Creating gender-responsive treatment. In S.L. Ashenberg Straussner & S. Brown (Eds.), *The Handbook of Addiction Treatment for Women* (pp. 52–73). San Francisco: Jossey-Bass.

Curlee, J. (1970). A comparison of male and female patients at an alcoholism treatment centre. *Journal of Psychology, 74*, 239–247.

DeMarco, C. (1995). *Taking Charge of Your Body: A Woman's Guide to Health (rev. ed.).* Winlaw, BC: Well Woman.

Durkheim, E. (1951). *Suicide.* New York: Free Press.

Frezza, M., Di Padova, C., Pozzato, G., Terpin, M., Baraona, E. & Lieber, C.S. (1990). High blood alcohol levels in women: The role of decreased gastric alcohol dehydrogenase activity and first-pass metabolism. *New England Journal of Medicine, 322*(2), 95–99.

Gavaler, J.S. & Arria, A.M. (1995). Increased susceptibility of women to alcoholic liver disease: Artifactual or real? In P. Hall (Ed.), *Alcohol Liver Disease: Pathology and Pathogenesis* (2nd ed.) (pp. 123–133). London, U.K.: Edward Arnold.

Gliksman, L., Demers, A., Adlaf, E.M., Newton-Taylor, B. & Schmidt, K. (2000). *Canadian Campus Survey 1998.* Toronto: Centre for Addiction and Mental Health.

Gomberg, E.S. (1989). Suicide risk among women with alcohol problems. *American Journal of Public Health, 79*, 1363–1365.

Groeneveld, J. & Shain, M. (1989). *Drug Use among Victims of Sexual Abuse.* Toronto: Addiction Research Foundation.

Health Canada. (2001a). *Best Practices: Treatment and Rehabilitation for Women with Substance Use Problems.* Ottawa: Minister of Public Works and Government Services Canada.

Health Canada. (2001b). *Best Practices: Concurrent Mental Health and Substance Use Disorders.* Ottawa: author.

Herman, J.L. (1992). *Trauma and Recovery.* New York: Basic Books.

Holmes, L. (2002). Women in group and women's groups. *International Journal of Group Psychotherapy, 52*(2), 171–188.

House, J., Landis, K. & Umberson, D. (1988). Social relationships and health. *Science, 241,* 540–545.

Jacobson, R. (1986). The contribution of sex and drinking history to the CT brain scan changes in alcoholics. *Psychological Medicine, 16,* 547–559.

Kabat-Zinn, J. (1990). *Full Catastrophe Living, Using the Wisdom of Your Body and Mind to Face Stress, Pain and Illness.* New York: Dell Publishing.

Kahan, M. & Wilson, L. (Eds.). (2002). *Managing Alcohol, Tobacco and Other Drug Problems: A Pocket Guide for Physicians and Nurses.* Toronto: Centre for Addiction and Mental Health.

Kaplan, A.G. (1985). Female or male therapists for women patients: New formulations. *Psychiatry, 48*(May), 111–121.

Katsouyanni, K., Trichopoulou, A., Stuver, S., Vassilaros, S., Papadiamantis, Y., Bournas, N. et al., (1994). Ethanol and breast cancer: An association that may be both confounded and causal. *International Journal of Cancer, 58,* 356–361.

Linehan, M.M. (1993). *Skills Training Manual for Treating Borderline Personality Disorder.* New York: Guilford Press.

Longnecker, M.P., Berlin, J.A., Orza, M.J. & Chalmers, T.C. (1988). A meta-analysis of alcohol consumption in relation to risk of breast cancer. *Journal of the American Medical Association, 260,* 652–656.

Project MATCH Research Group. (1997). Matching alcoholism treatments to client heterogeneity: Project MATCH Posttreatment drinking outcomes. *Journal of Studies on Alcohol, 58*(1), 7–29.

Reed, B.G. (1985). Drug misuse and dependency in women: The meaning and implications of being considered a special population or minority group. *The International Journal of the Addictions, 20*(1), 13–62.

Schatzkin, A., Jones, D.Y., Hoover, R.N., Taylor, P.R., Brinton, L.A., Ziegler, R.G. et al. (1987). Alcohol consumption and breast cancer in the epidemiologic follow-up study of the first national health and nutrition examination survey. *The New England Journal of Medicine, 316,* 1169–1173.

Schlesinger, S., Susman, M. & Koenigsberg, J. (1990). Self-esteem and purpose in life: A comparative study of women alcoholics. *Journal of Alcohol and Drug Education, 36*(i), 127–141.

Schober, R. & Annis, H.M. (1996). Barriers to help-seeking for change in drinking: A gender-focused review of the literature. *Addictive Behaviors, 21*(1), 81–92.

Seitz, H.K., Egerer, G., Simanowski, U.A., Waldherr, R., Eckey, R., Agarwal, D.P. et al. (1993). Human gastric alcohol dehydrogenase activity: Effect of age, sex, and alcoholism. *Gut, 34*, 1433–1437.

Statistics Canada. (2000). *Women in Canada 2000: A Gender-Based Statistical Report.* Ottawa: author.

Stewart, D.E. (1998). Are there special considerations in the prescription of serotonin reuptake inhibitors in women? *Canadian Journal of Psychiatry, 43*, 900–904.

Tannen, D. (1991). *You Just Don't Understand.* New York: Ballantine Books.

Urbano-Marquez, A., Estruch, R., Fernandez-Sola, J., Nicolas, J.M., Pare, J.C. & Rubin, E. (1995). The greater risk of alcoholic cardiomyopathy and myopathy in women compared with men. *Journal of the American Medical Association, 274*, 149–154.

Vogeltanz, N. & Wilsnack, S.C. (1997). Alcohol problems in women: Risk factors, consequences, and treatment strategies. In S.J. Gallant, G.P. Keita & R. Royak-Schaler (Eds.), *Health Care for Women. Psychological, Social, and Behavioral Influences* (pp. 75–96). Washington, DC: American Psychological Association.

Wilsnack, S.C., Klassen, A.D., Schur, B.E. & Wilsnack, R.W. (1991). Predicting onset and chronicity of women's problem drinking: A five year longitudinal analysis. *American Journal of Public Health, 81*, 305–318.

York, J.L. & Welte, J.W. (1994). Gender comparisons of alcohol consumption in alcoholic and nonalcoholic populations. *Journal of Studies on Alcohol, 55*, 743–750.

ADDITIONAL READINGS AND RESOURCES

Addiction Research Foundation. (1996). *The Hidden Majority: A Guidebook on Alcohol and Other Drug Issues for Counsellors Who Work with Women.* Toronto: author.

British Columbia Ministry of Health and Ministry Responsible for Seniors. (undated). *Women's Day Treatment Manual.* Victoria: author. (Contact: Adult Clinical and Addictions Services Branch, 3rd Floor, #1810 Blanshard Street, Victoria, BC V8T 4J1. Telephone: 604 952-0800.)

Center for Substance Abuse Treatment. (1994). *Practical Approaches in the Treatment of Women Who Abuse Alcohol and Other Drugs.* Rockville, MD: author.

Harris, M. & Fallot, R.G. (Eds.). (2001). *Using Trauma Theory to Design Service Systems.* San Francisco: Jossey-Bass.

Haskell, L. (2001). *Bridging Responses. A Front-Line Worker's Guide to Supporting Women Who Have Post-Traumatic Stress.* Toronto: Centre for Addiction and Mental Health.

Najavits, L. (2002). *Seeking Safety: A Treatment Manual for PTSD and Substance Abuse.* New York: Guilford Press.

For a catalogue of resources (books, manuals, videos) on women and substance use or to place an order, visit the CAMH Web site at www.camh.net or, in North America, call toll-free 1 800 661-1111. In Toronto or outside North America, call 416 535-501 ext. 6059. You can also e-mail: marketing@camh.net.

Chapter 13

Working with Men

TIM GODDEN

Because men predominate in substance dependence treatment programs, one might assume that any effective addiction treatment program would benefit male clients. However, clinical experience and a growing body of literature suggest that clinicians can forge a more productive therapeutic relationship with male clients by addressing barriers that often stop men in particular from engaging in treatment. These barriers include the influence of traditional male values and the client's relative social stability.

This chapter will briefly review the shifting conceptions of the masculine role in North American society, how traditional ideas of manhood have influenced substance use—particularly alcohol consumption—and how a male client's relative degree of social stability can affect his chances of engaging in treatment. In addition, this chapter will explore an approach—based on the motivational interviewing and stages of change frameworks—that clinicians can use to anticipate and address potential barriers in working with male clients in addiction programs. To provide context, the opening section presents a brief profile of men with substance use problems.

CHARACTERISTICS OF MEN'S SUBSTANCE USE

Over the years, many surveys have demonstrated differences between male and female substance use. A recent investigation by the Centre for Addiction and Mental Health, of substance use among Ontario adults from 1977 to 2000, found that men were more likely than women to drink alcohol daily, consume more drinks weekly, drink "hazardously or harmfully," smoke cigarettes, use cannabis during the past year, use cocaine in their lifetime and use ecstasy in their lifetime (Adlaf & Ialomiteanu, 2001).

A Health Canada analysis of a large-scale survey on use of alcohol and other drugs found that being male was the strongest predictor of drinking behaviour, including high-volume consumption (Single et al., 1995). That same analysis concluded that "the portrait of the individual most likely to report a drinking problem is that of a young adult male, single or divorced, who is unemployed and/or has relatively low income," (Single et al., 1995, p. 1) and further that "the use of cannabis and other illicit drugs is strongly associated with being young, male and single" (Single et al., 1995, p. 2).

In addition, men are heavily represented in substance use mortality and morbidity figures. For example, of the total 6,507 deaths caused by alcohol use in Canada in 1996, 4,685 of those who died were men. These figures include 787 men killed by alcohol-related motor vehicle accidents, compared with 357 women. Of the 805 people whose deaths were attributed to illicit drugs in 1996, 86 per cent were male (Single, 2000). Perhaps statistics such as these, which underline the severe consequences of male substance use, explain, at least in part, why more men than women find their way into treatment programs. Ellis and Rush (1993) estimate that the ratio of men to women in treatment services ranges from 2:1 to 4:1, depending on the type of service.

Given that research points to a strong association between the male gender and substance use, it seems fitting to explore what is known about the sociological context of this association.

SHIFTING CONCEPTIONS OF THE NORTH AMERICAN MALE

In charting the progress of modern masculinity, writers generally have described a list of traditional male values and discussed how social forces have given rise to alternative styles of manhood. Traditional masculinity has been described in a variety of ways—many in contrast to traditional femininity. For example, O'Neil (1982) speaks about the "masculine mystique," which discourages any ways of thinking or being that could be interpreted as feminine. Real (1997) defines masculinity as "a negative achievement," suggesting that boys approach mainstream manhood not by moving towards something valued but by moving away from something devalued—namely the traditional feminine values such as dependence, expressiveness and affiliation. In addition, Eisler and Skidmore (1987) present the concept of "masculine gender role stress," describing five situations in which men experience stress in their male identity:
1. inadequate physical performance
2. having to express emotions
3. subordinating to women
4. inferior intellectual performance
5. work and sex performance failure.

A common feature of many descriptions of the traditional male include the need to be strong and in control. Van Wormer (1989) suggests three influences that may predispose men to alcohol dependence:
• the "male drinking culture"
• pressures to be productive and excel
• sexual orientation.

Van Wormer claims, "Traditional male values not only encourage alcoholics to drink, but also later make it hard to seek the help they need to stop. Male alcoholics are said to drink to prove their masculinity and sense of power" (p. 233). Some effective interventions to address these challenges can be based on methods such as anger and stress management, outlined in later sections of this chapter.

Since the 1960s in North America, traditional male values seem to have evolved offshoots in response to social forces. Zeth (1997) outlines five major societal influences which have affected views of masculinity:
• the feminist men's movement
• men's rights groups
• mythopoetic groups
• addiction/recovery groups
• heroic male values.

At various times during the 20th century, the pro-feminist men's movement arose in response to societal changes advanced by the women's movement. This vision deplored the negative aspects of traditional masculine behaviour—manifested by power and control often referred to by feminist writers as the "patriarchy"—and favoured values more compatible with equality between the sexes. Men's rights groups have been formed in reaction to a perception that the gains made by women's rights groups—mainly in the legal system—have come at the expense of men. Generally, these groups are organized around advocacy for the elimination of perceived gender discrimination against men. Zeth (1997) suggests that mythopoetic and addiction/recovery groups share core values, which identify community, storytelling and the pursuit of spirituality as important activities in encouraging positive masculinity and a healthy lifestyle. The last major societal influence cited by Zeth, heroic male values, refers to the concept that, in order to achieve an adequate level of masculinity, men are expected to be heroic: to be strong and resilient in the face of any circumstance and to hide any emotional or physical pain they experience. Kipnis (1991) suggests that the expectations of women may reinforce these heroic values and the male behaviour associated with them.

Robert Bly (1990), who is widely recognized as a leader in what Zeth called the mythopoetic men's movement, succinctly describes how mainstream American masculinity had evolved in the mid-to-late 20th century. On the surface, "the '50s male" was optimistic, hard-working, disciplined, dedicated and concerned for his wife and children, but underneath was isolated, deprived, lacking in compassion and awareness of what was important to women. In the '60s, a new style of man arose who questioned the mainstream male values of the previous decade and paid more attention to women's issues and values. Next, in Bly's evolutionary map, "the soft male" of the '70s demonstrated the positive traits of gentleness, thoughtfulness and receptivity, but lacked vitality and life-satisfaction. Using this historical framework, Bly explored the ways men can access the most positive aspects of traditional masculinity seen in many cultures, and thus gain vitality and meaning in the process.

Writers in the fields of mythology and Jungian psychology have described a positive model for masculinity. This model is based on the idea that men can find energy and meaning by developing the right relationships with the archetypes of the male psyche. Archetypes—discussed at length in the literature of Jungian psychology—are "the bedrock structures that define the human psyche's own nature, and make it the same regardless of the culture in which an individual lives" (Moore & Gillette, 1992, p. 33). Jungian theory suggests that archetypes channel psychic energy in ways that either enhance or diminish a man's life and the lives of those around him. Moore and Gillette believe there are four "foundational" archetypes of the masculine psyche— King, Warrior, Magician and Lover. Based on their exploration of the King archetype, Moore and Gillette describe the characteristics of the "generative" man in this way: "Because he is himself secure and centred, the generative man can allow others to be themselves. He does not experience them as extensions of himself, but recognizes when he is confusing his own motives and values, his own hopes or fears, with those of others. He is not easily thrown off balance by others.… He can manage in most situations to defend his legitimate personal boundaries firmly, and without hostility" (Moore & Gillette, 1992, pp. 151–152).

INFLUENCE OF TRADITIONAL MALE VALUES

While there seems to be little consensus about the extent to which newer conceptions of masculinity have penetrated into the consciousness of male clients with substance use problems, many believe that traditional male values still operate within treatment programs. Recently, in a discussion in an all-male preparation group about coping with powerful emotions, clients were asked whether it was okay for men to cry in the presence of others. One client commented, "Any guy I see crying, I just laugh in his face." This response seems to indicate, at least, rejection of male expression of emotion and, at most, incomprehension of an entire range of feeling responses. If we accept that traditional male values continue to operate, we must ask how these values influence both the substance use among males and the decision whether or not to seek treatment.

The literature on the issue of traditional male values strongly suggests a link between conceptions of manhood and alcohol use (Isenhart, 1993, 2001; Lemle & Mishkind, 1989; McCreary, Newcomb & Sadava, 1999; Williams & Ricciardelli, 1999). There has been limited discussion of how the mainstream male identity is related to the use of other substances.

McCreary, Newcomb and Sadava (1999) found that the more strongly men held traditional attitudes, the more alcohol they consumed. Williams and Ricciardelli (1999) determined that high scores on alcohol use for both men and women were associated with high scores on "negative masculinity." Also Lemle and Mishkind (1989) asserted that consuming alcohol was in keeping with expected male behaviours such as risk taking, challenging convention and being aggressive.

Guided by traditional conceptions of manhood, a male client may not only drink more but may also be unwilling to engage in and complete substance use treatment. From his extensive review of the relevant literature, Isenhart (2001) summed up the ways in which traditional male values represent barriers to seeking treatment:

- Men tend to drink heavily to fit in with other men.
- Men tend to drink heavily when they have difficulty living up to the traditional masculine role.
- Men may believe that seeking help is inconsistent with the traditional male role.
- If men seek out health care, they generally do not follow the advice they receive.
- Many substance use interventions require men to behave in ways that are inconsistent with the traditional male role (e.g., sharing feelings) and that run counter to years of socialization.

When working with male clients from initial assessment through to continuing care, clinicians would be wise to adapt their approaches to circumvent the potential barriers to accessing treatment, which appear to be embedded in traditional masculinity. Later, this chapter will explore some suggested adaptations, which can create space in treatment sessions for discussion of the influence of traditional male values on behaviour.

At this point, we will examine another factor, social stability, that may influence whether men can participate fully in substance use programs.

SOCIAL STABILITY AND MALE SUBSTANCE USE

Much research and clinical experience has emphasized the importance of a male client's relative social stability in determining whether he can successfully participate in a treatment program. Variables used to measure a client's social stability include marital and employment status and degree of social isolation (Rabinowitz & Marjefsky, 1998) and family, legal and employment status (McLellan et al., 1983). Kissin et al. (1970) determined that a male research subject was socially stable if he had higher ratings on a list of "social variables," which include marital status, education, occupational stability, whether he had ever been arrested and where he drank (e.g., at home versus in a park or alley). Building on the three formulations listed above, this chapter proposes that a male substance use client is socially stable if he has the following characteristics: a stable spousal relationship, regular contact with one or more family members or close friends, access to recreational opportunities unrelated to high-risk substance use situations, and regular volunteer or paid employment.

Several studies indicate that a lack of social stability can contribute to non-completion of substance use treatment and, conversely, that attending to key elements of a client's social stability during treatment can enhance the outcome (Milby et al., 1996; Rabinowitz & Marjefsky, 1998). Rabinowitz and Marjefsky (1998) did a retrospective analysis of 676 first-time male admissions to an inpatient alcohol treatment program and found support for "the important role of social isolation and marginality as risk factors for poor treatment outcomes among males" (p. 189). Milby et al. (1996) examined the efficacy of a treatment approach for people who are homeless and use crack and alcohol that rewarded abstinence with access to furnished apartments and job-training opportunities. After six months, study participants who received four months of the "contingency management" benefits had 18 per cent fewer positive cocaine tests than did "conventional care" clients.

Both clinical experience and research results suggest that the following elements contribute to poor social stability for male clients:
• homelessness
• unemployment
• anger and violence
• legal difficulties
• poor family and relationship functioning
• mental health issues.

These elements are discussed in more detail below.

Homelessness

No clear link has been established in the literature between substance use and homelessness. In exploring the relationship between these two issues, Johnson et al. (1997) proposed "a multi-directional model that recognizes substance abuse and homelessness to be risk factors for one another" (p. 442), a model that is equally applicable to men and women. This team of researchers—who based their model on an investigation of 303 substance users, who were either homeless or at risk for being so—observed that:
• other drug use may have displaced problem alcohol use as an important precursor of homelessness for many people
• prior periods of homelessness predicted the onset of problem use of both alcohol and other drugs
• access to social and economic resources can help the individual avoid both homelessness and substance use problems.

In addition, Odell and Commander (2000) concluded that substance use and the absence of family support contribute strongly to homelessness in people with a psychotic disorder.

Unemployment

Irregular employment and unemployment have been linked to substance use in both survey data and a substantial number of research studies. A Canadian survey (Single et al., 1994) found that the highest average levels of alcohol consumption were among unemployed and unskilled people. Brewer et al. (1998) identified unemployment as one variable predicting continued opioid use during and after treatment. Rabinowitz and Marjefsky (1998) identified unemployment as being associated with non-completion of treatment.

Anger and Violence

As with homelessness, the literature reveals no clear-cut relationship between anger, violence and substance use. However, some studies have shown that people with drinking problems are more likely than non-drinkers to abuse their relationship partners (Potter-Efron & Potter-Efron, 1991), and that men are more likely than women to resort to violence (Miedema, 1996). Given the association between anger and substance use, it seems sensible to explore the need for anger management counselling during the early stages of substance use treatment. Clancy (1996) accepted the link between anger and addiction and developed a treatment approach designed to address both issues at the same time. The approach proposes that a client's risk of substance use relapse is connected to his or her inability to constructively express emotions, and seeks to help clients identify "strategies to modify self-destructive feelings, thoughts, and behaviors and select response choices that allow him or her to escape the anger-addiction-relapse cycle," (p. 11). In escaping this cycle, clients learn how to recognize that anger is building up by identifying the physical, behavioural, emotional and cognitive signs; they can then intervene before the anger triggers acting out or substance use. The interventions that Clancy suggests for clients include taking a "time out" to consider available options; using positive self-talk; using effective communication skills to express feelings and needs; applying problem-solving principles; applying stress management techniques; and managing resentments.

Legal Difficulties

Many referrals to substance use treatment programs originate in court orders. However, researchers have not yet reached a consensus on how a legal mandate influences a client's treatment outcome. After reviewing the existing literature on the subject, Health Canada (1999) stated that " it would be improper to conclude that legally mandated clients are necessarily less suitable candidates for treatment than others," (p. 34). In the United States, the National Institute on Drug Abuse (NIDA) has suggested that mandates—legal and other types—can improve a client's chances of connecting with support. "Treatment does not need to be voluntary to be effective. Sanctions or enticements in the family, employment setting, or criminal justice system can significantly increase treatment entry, retention and success" (NIDA, 1999b, pp. 1–2).

Family and Relationship Functioning

Many substance use programs have developed active family programs because they recognize that the adverse effects of a client's substance use often spill over into the lives of partners and family members. Pursuing the proposition that clients have better outcomes in treatment programs that include a family-couples component, Stanton and Shadish (1997) did a meta-analysis of 1,571 cases that compared family-couples therapy with non-family substance use interventions. They found that family therapy yielded better results, and concluded that the outcomes of already effective non-family therapy approaches may be improved by adding a family or couples component. These investigators observed that studies that compared the effectiveness of family therapy in men versus women showed no differences in outcome. However, in a meta-analysis of 21 studies of "family-involved therapy" for alcohol dependence, Edwards and Steinglass (1995) found that the client's gender seems to be related to the effectiveness of treatment. Also, they concluded that in studies with a larger majority of male clients, family therapy was likely to be more effective than non-family interventions. This suggests that for the main phase of treatment—between engagement and aftercare—established family interventions may be more effective for men than for women. However, in situations where the female partner has been abused, it is generally recognized that family therapy may be unsafe and is not recommended.

Mental Health

Chapter 26 discusses the treatment implications of concurrent disorders. Clinicians working with men should be aware that many male clients have both substance dependence and mental health symptoms. Recently many authors have stressed the importance of addressing both issues at the same time (Bellack & Gearon, 1998; Carey, 1995; Martino et al., 2002). The concurrent disorders literature also suggests that substance use by the client can complicate the process of accurately diagnosing underlying psychiatric conditions (Carey & Correia, 1998; Drake et al., 1996).

ADAPTING TREATMENT TO MALE VALUES

As suggested earlier, clinicians need to carefully consider their approaches to male clients because men may be subject to traditional male values that run counter to the norms of substance use treatment, and because social instability may work against program participation. Unfortunately, little research has been done to evaluate the effectiveness of male-targeted substance use programs. In one study, Bartholomew et al. (2000) evaluated a psychoeducational group intervention called "Time Out! For Men," which addressed communication skills, sexuality, gender socialization and intimacy. The investigators concluded that clients who participated found the program content "salient and meaningful," and that this type of intervention might increase the effectiveness of a treatment protocol. An example of a specific exercise from the program is a worksheet consisting of incomplete sentences such as "The one thing I most need from my partner is..." and "I know I hurt my partner when...." Completing and discussing this exercise gives clients an opportunity to examine their needs for intimacy and how these needs have been affected by traditional male norms.

The following section will outline one overall approach to engage male clients in treatment, which can help to avoid or reduce the potential impediments described above.

AN OVERALL APPROACH FOR MALE CLIENTS

Two overarching theoretical frameworks are widely considered to be powerful and broadly applicable: the transtheoretical, or "stages of change," model of intentional human behaviour change (Prochaska et al., 1994; Prochaska, DiClemente & Norcross, 1992) and motivational interviewing (MI; see Chapter 2). The influence of these two frameworks will be evident throughout this section; their value is affirmed by clinical experience and by treatment outcome literature. For specific examples of how MI principles can apply to men with substance use problems, see Appendix 1 of this chapter.

In working with male clients, it may be helpful to consider three phases of the therapeutic relationship: early, middle and late. Each of these phases can be connected to the stages in the transtheoretical model of change—the early phase corresponds roughly to the precontemplation and contemplation stages, the middle phase to the preparation and action stages, and the late phase to the maintenance stage.

In their application of the motivational interviewing framework, Miller and colleagues have organized work with clients into "therapeutic tasks" contingent on each stage of change. This helps to avoid what has been called the "premature focus trap" (Miller & Rollnick, 2002a), namely broaching an issue that a client is not yet ready to discuss, thereby eliciting resistance.

Early Phase

Two vital tasks may be identified in the early phase of working with male clients: building the therapeutic alliance and exploring sources of ambivalence. Many authorities emphasize the importance of spending the necessary time and effort to establish a good working relationship (Ackerman & Hilsenroth, 2003; Health Canada, 1999; Moos, 2003; Shonfeld-Ringel, 2001). Perhaps the most important aspect of "getting off on the right foot" is to avoid making any assumptions about the client's reasons for seeking treatment. As much as possible let the client tell his own story, even if he hesitates and appears reticent. This can be achieved by beginning an assessment or first appointment with an "engagement piece," in which the clinician asks the client open-ended questions about why he has come. If the client feels he was coerced into attending, his response to the open-ended questions may be short and not so sweet. Expressions of anger can be met effectively using the "roll with resistance" strategy, which helps to avoid any direct confrontations. "Resistance that a person offers can be turned or reframed slightly to create a new momentum toward change" (Miller & Rollnick, 2002b, p. 40). It can be effective to empathically reflect back the client's feelings of frustration for being forced to do something against his wishes, while carefully probing to discover how the client's concerns could be addressed in future sessions. Other ways of building a therapeutic alliance with male clients include appropriate self-disclosure (Van Wormer, 1989) and acknowledgment of the client's challenges and successes (Ackerman & Hilsenroth, 2003).

The second task in the early phase of working with male clients—exploring sources of ambivalence—requires much patience. From an MI standpoint, the guiding principle is to enable the client to give a detailed description of why change is difficult. These sources of ambivalence, which fuel mixed feelings about the prospect of change, may be common to all clients regardless of gender (e.g., fear and shame) or they may be specific to the male context (e.g., a general aversion to seeking help for fear that this process would "gamble one's masculinity"; Thom, 1986, p. 784). Ambivalence may also derive from eroded self-efficacy—the client's belief that he can achieve change—arising from his low social stability. For this reason, if the treatment agency's mandate includes case management, conditions such as homelessness and unemployment should be addressed as part of the total effort to tackle the substance use. The U.S. National Institute on Drug Abuse suggests that this type of service is a crucial part of the treatment of problem substance use for many clients (NIDA, 1999a). For a discussion of case management, see Chapter 3.

A large body of literature within the MI movement strongly suggests that little progress can be made until the reason for the client's ambivalence is identified, discussed and, to some extent, resolved.

Middle Phase

Once the counsellor and the male client have come to terms with these barriers to progress, they can move on to the middle stage. The major tasks of this stage include working with any resurgent feelings of ambivalence, continuing case management and problem solving around social stability issues, and addressing treatment planning. If the client and counsellor have forged a strong therapeutic alliance, the first two tasks should be readily identified in the course of any particular session. However, treatment planning for male clients deserves special consideration. Even though the concept of treatment matching has been widely studied within the addiction field, no simple treatment-matching scheme has materialized and little work has been done to develop an approach to help clinicians select treatment programs based on the particular attributes of male clients as a group. In spite of this, Health Canada, in its report entitled *Best Practices—Substance Abuse Treatment and Rehabilitation*, concludes, "Although the literature does not yet provide strong evidence by which to match clients to specific treatment interventions, it does not mean that all clients require the same types of services. A variety of flexible and individualized services is required and guidelines for the selection of appropriate services are needed" (Health Canada, 1999, p. 25). In the absence of such guidelines for male clients, each clinician does his or her best to develop a treatment plan that will address as many client needs as possible. Insights from motivational interviewing teach us that we should present clients with as many suitable options as possible because those who perceive they have choice are more likely to follow through with the chosen plan (Miller & Rollnick, 1991). A few general principles from Health Canada's *Best Practices* document, supplemented with material from other sources, may be helpful in developing a list of treatment options (see Appendix 2).

COGNITIVE BEHAVIOURAL TOOLS

Several practical cognitive behavioural tools may produce progress with male clients: decisional balance, used in both the Guided Self-Change (GSC) program (Sobell, 1994) and the Structured Relapse Prevention (SRP) program (Annis et al., 1996); the ABC exercise and the use of a self-monitoring log.

The decisional balance exercise helps a client organize his thoughts on the advantages and disadvantages of, on the one hand, continuing problem substance use and, on the other hand, meeting a well-defined treatment goal. Male clients often find that the process helps them identify male-specific sources of ambivalence (e.g., loss of time with "the boys") and reveals core issues (e.g., leisure time not associated with problem substance use) they need to address to increase the likelihood of meeting a substance use goal.

The ABC exercise, also known as "functional analysis," can be carried out during a group or individual counselling session, or assigned as homework. The simple model helps clients to understand the function of substance use and to identify its triggers and consequences. This enables them to develop strategies to avoid using

TABLE 13-1

Functional Analysis

A (ACTIVATORS OR TRIGGERS)	B (BEHAVIOUR)	C (CONSEQUENCES)	
		SHORT TERM	LONGER TERM
Got in argument with partner over not having a job	Went to meet buddy	Temporary escape from pressures/stress	Hangover/next day a "write-off"
Feeling bad because a man should have a job	Drank 10 pints at pub	Fun to see old friend	Partner even more angry after I stayed out all night
Frustration: partner doesn't understand how hard it is to find work			Loss of sleep
Feeling overwhelmed by feelings and unsure of how to cope with them			Problems/stress still there (maybe worse)
Feeling that if I were a man I'd be able to handle all this			Risk of drinking and driving
Financial pressure (too many bills, not enough money)			Triggered to use secondary substance
Anger: "Why me?"			Guilt: broke promise to myself that I'd control my drinking
Got call from old buddy asking me to come out for a beer			Guilt: broke promise to partner about not going to pub

alcohol or other drugs in the future. The ABC model encourages clients to view substance use as a behavioural pattern or habit that they can change. For an example of how a male client might complete the exercise, see Table 13-1.

By identifying the activators or triggers (A) that lead to substance use behaviours (B) which in turn have problematic consequences (C), clients can highlight the chain of events that leads to episodes of problem substance use, and increase the likelihood that an assertive approach can change the outcome in a high-risk situation (Annis et al, 1996).

The activity of self-monitoring, which captures many details that correlate with urges to use or with episodes of problem use, can identify triggers that, in turn, can be linked to male-specific concerns in treatment.

Late Phase

Once a male client has achieved stability in his substance use goal, the therapeutic alliance can focus on such tasks as continuing to help the client increase his social stability, identifying and planning countermeasures to avoid or effectively manage potential relapse, and fostering the client's independence and his connections to informal supports in the community. For the second of these late-stage tasks, specifically planning relapse countermeasures, two cognitive behavioural tools from SRP may help male clients. In the first, the relapse warning signs exercise, clients list the signs of an impending relapse under the headings of thoughts, feelings and actions, and develop strategies for coping with the triggers those signs represent. Some of the signs can reflect a client's experience of traditional masculine values (e.g., "If he can handle a drink, I can."). In the second exercise, "If I were to relapse," clients can develop realistic strategies for pulling out of a relapse, if it happens.

A valuable part of community integration with male clients is the identification of what has been called "the third place" (Oldenburg, 1989; Rheingold, 1995). This is a place where men have traditionally gathered to satisfy their desires for fun, light conversation and physical activity. Clinical experience is rich with examples of abstinent male clients who return to a favourite pub for a coffee or soft drink because it is the only place they know where they can enjoy a sense of camaraderie. Finding an alternative "third place" may help male clients meet important social needs while eliminating exposure to a potentially high-risk situation. There is no simple recipe to guide a client in creating a new third place. Zeth (1997) suggests that 12-step meetings cannot fully address this need but that the destinations men go to after meetings, such as coffee houses or diners, can have attributes of a third place. In his comprehensive exploration of the subject called *The Great Good Place*, Ray Oldenburg (1989) cites the following characteristics of a third place: the freedom to come and go as one pleases and assurance of access throughout a wide range of times of day; a comfortable, informal, "playful" and inclusive environment; and a regular crowd, accepting of new people, engaged in the main activity of conversation. Oldenburg points to a disturbing decline in the numbers of third places in modern society. Thus, counsellors can play an important role in helping male clients identify such places in their post-treatment lives. In this respect, it is worth noting Oldenburg's observation that places clients might visit casually in their immediate neighbourhood, such as grocery stores, might become third places, eventually providing clients with "daily doses of novelty, diversion and social support" (Oldenburg, 1989, p. 289).

GENDER OF THE COUNSELLOR

Another issue that has been examined for its effect on the efficacy of treatment for male clients is the gender of the counsellor. To date, no research has asserted that counsellor gender is an important determinant of treatment outcomes for men with substance use problems. After investigating client conceptions of ideal male and female counsellors, Jonker et al. (2000) concluded that it might be more useful to consider the attributes of the ideal addiction counsellor, regardless of gender. In this investigation, the respondents perceived the ideal male and female counsellors almost identically—dominant, extraverted and responsible. Also, Bowman (1993) and Nelson (1993) could not demonstrate a clear advantage in matching clients and counsellors by gender. Clinical experience shows that some male clients are more comfortable working with female counsellors and, especially when working through male-based issues such as gender roles and sexuality, others are more comfortable with male counsellors. Thus, if possible, it might be productive to have a male and a female counsellor co-lead treatment groups.

SUGGESTIONS FOR MALE TREATMENT GROUPS

Van Wormer (1989) made a detailed case for including well-organized, all-male groups as part of a range of treatment services. She said that such groups can "provide a supportive network of men helping men explore their innermost cares and feelings, and . . . an avenue for the discussion of concerns related to the masculine gender role," (p. 230). This therapist described five key themes that commonly emerge in men's treatment groups:
1. self-esteem
2. trust
3. sex and sexuality
4. identifying and expressing feelings
5. male gender identity and stereotyping
(Van Wormer, 1989).

Ingber (1997) made the following suggestions for ensuring that treatment groups involving men adequately address male-specific issues:

• Actively acknowledge and discuss men's gender issues in the group, making the connection between these issues and the function of substance use in their lives.

• Acknowledge that many men have been socialized not to disclose feelings, especially with other men, and help them do so in group and, if necessary, help them identify specific feelings.

• Create group norms and a sense of ownership for the group, to establish permission to share varied life experiences and to create expectations for a respectful, non-judgmental climate.

Any complete set of norms should emphasize respect for all the differences that clients may bring to a group, including class, culture and sexual diversity. For a detailed exploration of this latter difference, please see Chapter 16.

Many clinicians have also argued that if substance dependence treatments do not include a module on stress management, clients will miss a crucial component that could greatly increase their chances of success. This proposition is based on the idea that clients experience a great deal of stress upon entering treatment and after discharge, as a result of the negative consequences of substance use—for instance, criminal charges and relationship distress. Some counsellors believe that stress management skills are particularly important for male clients, given their tendency to suppress and ignore not only strong emotions but also chronic muscular tension—both of which can be linked to increased risk of relapse. The results of many investigations have demonstrated that stress is an important consideration in addiction treatment (Brown et al. 1995; Lamon & Alonzo, 1997; Sinha et al. 2000). For many years, Ontario's Centre for Addiction and Mental Health has included a major stress management component in a popular outpatient treatment program called Evening Health Service (EHS). After educating clients about the importance of the mind-body connection, EHS therapists teach a variety of stress-reduction skills, promoting healthier breathing, muscle relaxation, enhanced blood flow, use of positive imagery, and better concentration and more effective decision making. In addition, EHS emphasizes the importance for stress management of aspects of a client's lifestyle, such as exercise, diet, sleep and social support.

Clinical experience has illuminated a number of other topics worthy of exploration in male treatment groups, such as grief, loneliness, feelings of inadequacy, difficulty in adapting to changes in family and societal expectations, and social isolation. Unfortunately there is not enough space to cover them all here.

SUGGESTIONS FROM PSYCHODYNAMIC APPROACHES

It is beyond the scope of this chapter to undertake an extensive exploration of the literature on psychodynamic approaches to male substance use. A brief overview of this body of work follows.

Psychodynamic theories on male addiction are diverse and detailed. Levin (1997) surveys the field starting with the 19th-century theorist Thomas Trotter, who wrote about alcoholism as a disease with two causes, heredity and premature weaning, and Sigmund Freud, who asserted that a dependence on any substance was a replacement for the "primary addiction" of masturbation. After surveying a number of other psychodynamic theories, including the ideas that addiction is rooted in childhood rage, arrested psychological development, "chronic suicide" and "ego inflation," Levin presents one concept, "pathological narcissism," as a helpful, integrated model of addiction. Hans Kohut defined pathological narcissism—which manifests itself as feelings of emptiness, poor self-regulation, arrogance or grandiosity and a tendency to isolate—as the regression or fixation to an early stage of development. On the assumption that pathological narcissism is a driving force in addiction, Levin suggests a number of key issues to be addressed in treatment. They include emphasizing that substance dependence is not a defect of the self; addressing chronic feelings of emptiness and lack of identity; building the capacity to be alone; addressing a client's tendency to idealize the effects of the substance; dealing with low self-esteem and grandiosity; and addressing feelings of shame.

CONSIDERATIONS IN WORKING ACROSS CULTURES

Some investigations have examined how male values from diverse ethnocultural groups play out in substance use treatment. For example Goldberg (1997) explored the concept of machismo among Spanish-speaking American men with substance use problems. She asserts that the term "machismo" has been widely misinterpreted outside the Spanish-speaking community as meaning "brutal hypermasculinity," as manifested in chauvinism and aggressiveness. Within the community, the term has many positive connotations—"a kind of daring and control where the male meets challenge, risks or threats with coolness and self-composure," (pp. 456–457). Goldberg suggests that a proper understanding of machismo and other important cultural concepts that unify Spanish-speaking American communities, such as spiritualism, will enhance the therapeutic environment by helping clinicians avoid the perpetuation of stereotypes, especially during the engagement process. This general principle applies whenever a counsellor works with a client with a different cultural background.

However, even an extensive knowledge of cultural norms includes a potential pitfall. If a clinician working cross-culturally treats a norm as a universal, he or she might also misinterpret an individual client's experience and values. Goldberg suggests that one way to reduce this risk is to assess a client's relative degree of acculturation—the process by which members of a specific cultural group learn, acquire and integrate overt and covert cultural characteristics of a host culture. Other investigators agree that acculturation is an important consideration. For example, Shoshana

Shonfeld-Ringel (2001) has explored the cross-cultural dynamics between Asian clients and European-American counsellors.

It is not easy for counsellors to achieve "cultural competence"—the ability to work effectively across cultures—but, fortunately, the issue has recently been receiving more attention in the research community. Shonfeld-Ringel (2001) suggests that important ingredients of a collaborative cross-cultural treatment relationship include: empathy (the ability "to be open to multiple perspectives of both personal and cultural realities"; p. 54), mutuality (the power and authority shared by client and counsellor) and an appreciation of the subtleties of both verbal and non-verbal communication. Shonfeld-Ringel also underlines the importance for counsellors of learning about their own cultural biases, for instance the Western concepts of individuation and autonomy, and how these may conflict with values from other cultures, such as interdependence with family and community.

SUMMARY AND CONCLUSIONS

Counsellors and therapists have a greater likelihood of meeting the needs of a male client if they explore the client's unresolved ambivalence, which may be rooted in the influence of traditional male values and in the client's relative social instability. When men feel safe talking about their concerns, they speak about issues such as an inability to cope with powerful emotions that may be central to their risk of dependence on substances. However, how safe men feel in a treatment setting can depend on how strongly traditional ideas of masculinity operate in their lives. Thus, when working with male clients, clinicians must make space for an exploration of how various conceptions of manhood may help or hinder life-enhancing behavioural change. Also, researchers in the substance use field could make a valuable contribution to clinical practice by further developing and evaluating interventions that address the barriers to male participation in treatment.

APPENDIX 1: EXAMPLES OF MOTIVATIONAL INTERVIEWING WITH MALE CLIENTS

The literature on motivational interviewing (MI) does not explore how the model can be applied in work with men. However, certain MI strategies can help male clients explore the issues, rooted in their experience of masculinity, that may stand in the way of behavioural change. Examples of these strategies are exploring male fears and the techniques of reframing and shifting focus.

MI suggests that fear often rests at the heart of a person's ambivalence. For men, fear can be based in what change means in terms of their relationships with peers. In some cases, a man's social network may revolve entirely around substance use. Thus, making significant changes could mean a risk of even more social isolation. And even if a man continues to see "high-risk" people while maintaining his substance use goal, he may perceive a loss of status amongst his peers (i.e., not feeling like "one of the boys"). For these reasons, it may be important for the clinician to resolve ambivalence by helping male clients envision and build a new or adapted social network.

MI further suggests that a clinician's effectiveness is enhanced if he or she handles clients' resistance in a way that does not spark more resistance. Two strategies that seem to be particularly useful with male clients are reframing and shifting focus. If a male client considers entering treatment a sign of weakness and cowardice (i.e., he believes it means that he lacks the wherewithal to solve personal problems on his own), the counsellor can "reframe" or encourage the client to shift perspective by suggesting that the client's presence actually represents courage in taking a new path and facing up to serious life issues. If a client is expending time and energy in a session trying to prove his manhood, a counsellor can effectively sidestep the issue and shift the focus onto something the client has identified as important and aligned with the goals of treatment.

APPENDIX 2: PRINCIPLES FOR TREATMENT PLANNING

Individual versus Group Treatment

Although research has not shown either individual or group treatment to be clearly more effective, the group setting has the potential to provide the client with more role modelling, peer support and information sharing, and more opportunities to develop interpersonal skills. However, clinicians should watch for circumstances that favour a one-on-one intervention, for instance transportation challenges or scheduling conflicts due to shift work (Graham et al., 1996). In addition, issues such as sexual orientation, a history of trauma and concurrent disorders may lead the clinician to recommend individual treatment.

Outpatient versus Inpatient

Neither outpatient nor inpatient treatment is deemed more effective in measurements of overall treatment outcome (Finney et al., 1996). However, specific client characteristics, such as severe social instability, may suggest an inpatient admission as the preferred first option. If there is no firm indication in either direction, the clinician can be guided by the "stepped care" approach, which indicates choices based on the optimal balance between intensity and lack of invasiveness (Sobell & Sobell, 2000).

Continuing Care

Health Canada (1999) has reached no firm conclusion about the merits of continuing care but suggests that clients who are less socially stable and more dependent on substances may benefit from a longer course of treatment, which could include participation in an outpatient treatment program and some form of aftercare.

12-Step Group Participation

Health Canada suggests that we need more research before we can answer the question "for whom and under what conditions might a referral to self-help be most beneficial." However, it concludes that "some attempts to link substance users with self-help groups may be appropriate unless clearly contraindicated by personal preference or local conditions," (Health Canada, 1999, p. 61).

Choice of Treatment Based on a Theoretical Foundation

Health Canada (1999) states that the literature supports the effectiveness of:
• behavioural approaches, including relapse prevention, which help clients identify high-risk situations and develop related coping strategies
• "self-control therapy," which provides instruction in specific self-management skills aimed at reducing or avoiding substance use
• a community reinforcement approach, which employs several methods to change the client's environment to make abstinence more rewarding (and which has been particularly promising with clients who have fewer social supports and more severe alcohol use)
• marital therapy
• stress management interventions and social skills training (teaching clients interpersonal and intrapersonal coping skills)
• brief motivational counselling, which typically includes one to three sessions of feedback and advice drawn from an individual assessment and presented to the client in a motivational way.

Health Canada (1999) concludes that the many and diverse psychotherapeutic approaches used in the field are difficult to evaluate using experimental methods.

After conducting a literature review of 25 treatment modalities, the Correctional Service of Canada (1996) concluded that the following approaches were promising:
• assertion training
• controlled drinking strategies
• employment training
• methadone maintenance treatment for clients who use opioids
• provision of aftercare
• problem solving
• recognizing high-risk situations
• relapse (prevention) techniques
• social skills training.

ACKNOWLEDGMENTS

I would like to thank Pam Hubley, Faculty of Nursing, University of Toronto, and Lorna Sagorsky and Marg Beardwood of the Brief Treatment team, CAMH, for their support in my writing of this chapter. I would also like to acknowledge Eva Ingber of CAMH for providing encouragement and a solid foundation for the chapter, and CAMH library co-ordinator Sheila Lacroix for her research support. Finally, I would like to thank John O. Godden, of Toronto, for his indispensable feedback.

REFERENCES

Ackerman, S.J. & Hilsenroth, M.J. (2003). A review of therapist characteristics and techniques positively impacting the therapeutic alliance. *Clinical Psychology Review, 23*, 1–33.

Adlaf, E.M. & Ialomiteanu, A. (2001). CAMH Monitor eReport: Addiction & Mental Health Indicators among Ontario Adults, 1977–2000. (CAMH Research Doc. Series No. 10). Centre for Addiction and Mental Health, Toronto. Available: www.camh.net/research/population_life_course.html.

Annis, H.M., Herie, M.A. & Watkin-Merek, L. (1996). *Structured Relapse Prevention: An Outpatient Counselling Approach.* Toronto: Addiction Research Foundation.

Bartholomew, N.G., Hiller, M.L., Knight, K., Nucatola, D.C. & Simpson, D. (2000). Effectiveness of communication and relationship skills training for men in substance abuse treatment. *Journal of Substance Abuse Treatment, 18*, 217–225.

Bellack, A.S. & Gearon, J.S. (1998). Substance abuse treatment for people with schizophrenia. *Addictive Behaviors, 23*(6), 749–766.

Bly, R. (1990). *Iron John: A Book about Men.* Reading, MA: Addison-Wesley.

Bowman, D. (1993). Effects of therapist sex on the outcome of therapy. *Psychotherapy, 30*(4), 678–684.

Brewer, D.D., Catalano, R.F., Haggerty, K., Gainey, R.R. & Fleming, C.B. (1998). A meta-analysis of predictors of continued drug use during and after treatment for opiate addiction. *Addiction, 93*(1), 73–92.

Brown, S.A., Vik, P.W., Patterson, T.L., Grant, I. & Schuckit, M.A. (1995). Stress, vulnerability and adult alcohol relapse. *Journal of Studies on Alcohol, 56*(5), 538–545.

Carey, K. (1995). Treatment of substance use disorders in schizophrenia. In A.F. Lehman & L.B. Dixon (Eds.), *Double-jeopardy: Chronic Mental Illness and Substance Use Disorders.* Longhorne, PA: Harwood Academic Press.

Carey, K.B. & Correia, C.J. (1998). Severe mental illness and addictions: Assessment considerations. *Addictive Behaviors, 23*(6), 735–748.

Clancy, J. (1996). *Anger and Addiction: Breaking the Relapse Cycle. A Teaching Guide for Professionals.* Madison, CT: Psychosocial Press.

Correctional Service of Canada. (1996). *Literature Review—Substance Abuse Treatment Modalities.* Available: www.csc-scc.gc.ca/text/pblct/litrev/treatmod/toce_e.shtml.

Drake, R.E., Rosenberg, S.D. & Mueser, K.T. (1996). Assessing substance use disorder in persons with severe mental illness. In R.E. Drake & K.T. Mueser (Eds.), *Dual Diagnosis of Major Mental Illness and Substance Abuse. Volume 2: Recent Research and Clinical Implications.* (pp. 3–17). San Francisco: Jossey-Bass.

Edwards, M.E. & Steinglass, P. (1995). Family therapy treatment outcomes for alcoholism. *Journal of Marital and Family Therapy, 21*(4), 475–509.

Eisler, R.M. & Skidmore, J.R. (1987). Masculine gender role stress. Scale development and component factors in the appraisal of stressful situations. *Behavior Modification, 11*(2), 123–136.

Ellis, K. & Rush, B.R. (1993). *Alcohol and Other Drug Services in Ontario: Results of a Provincial Survey, 1992.* Toronto: Addiction Research Foundation.

Finney, J.W., Hahn, A.C. & Moos, R.H. (1996). The effectiveness of inpatient and outpatient treatment for alcohol abuse: The need to focus on mediators and moderators of setting effects. *Addiction, 91*(12), 1773–1796.

Goldberg, E.V. (1997). Hispanic substance abusing men and machismo. In S.L.A. Straussner & E. Zelvin (Eds.), *Gender and Addictions: Men and Women in Treatment* (pp. 287–309). Northvale, NJ: Jason Aronson.

Graham, K., Annis, H.M., Brett, P.J. & Venesoen, P. (1996). A controlled field trial of group versus individual cognitive-behavioural training for relapse prevention. *Addiction, 91*(8), 1127–1139.

Health Canada. (1999). *Best Practices. Substance Abuse Treatment and Rehabilitation.* Ottawa: Minister of Public Works and Government Services of Canada.

Ingber, E. (1997). Working with men. In S. Harrison & V. Carver (Eds.), *Alcohol & Drug Problems. A Practical Guide for Counsellors* (2nd ed.; pp. 245–257). Toronto: Addiction Research Foundation.

Isenhart, C. (2001). Treating substance abuse in men. In G.R. Brooks & G.E. Good (Eds.), *The New Handbook of Psychotherapy and Counseling with Men: A Comprehensive Guide to Settings, Problems, and Treatment Approaches* (Vol. 1; pp. 246–262). San Francisco: Jossey-Bass.

Isenhart, C.E. (1993). Masculine gender role stress in an inpatient sample of alcohol abusers. *Psychology of Addictive Behaviors, 7*, 177–184.

Johnson, T.P., Freels, S.A., Parsons, J.A. & Vangeest, J.B. (1997). Substance abuse and homelessness: Social selection or social adaptation? *Addiction, 92*(4), 437–445.

Jonker, J., De Jong, C.A.J., de Weert-van Oene, G.H. & Gijs, L. (2000). Gender-role stereotypes and interpersonal behavior. How addicted inpatients view their ideal male and female therapist. *Journal of Substance Abuse Treatment, 19*, 307–312.

Kipnis, A. (1991). *Knights without Armor.* New York: Jeremy Tarcher/Pedigree.

Kissin, B., Platz, A. & Su, W.H. (1970). Social and psychological factors in the treatment of chronic alcoholism. *Journal of Psychiatric Research, 8*, 13–27.

Lamon, B.C. & Alonzo, A. (1997). Stress among males recovering from substance abuse. *Addictive Behaviors, 22*(2), 195–205.

Lemle, R. & Mishkind, M.E. (1989). Alcohol and masculinity. *Journal of Substance Abuse Treatment, 6,* 213–222.

Levin, J.D. (1997). Psychodynamic perspectives on substance-abusing men. In S.L.A. Straussner & E. Zelvin (Eds.), *Gender and Addictions: Men and Women in Treatment* (pp. 285–309). Northvale, NJ: Jason Aronson.

Martino, S., Carroll, K., Kostas, D., Perkins, J. & Rounsaville, B. (2002). Dual diagnosis Motivational Interviewing: A modification of Motivational Interviewing for substance-abusing patients with psychotic disorders. *Journal of Substance Abuse Treatment, 23,* 297–308.

McCreary, D.R., Newcomb, M.D. & Sadava, S.W. (1999). The male role, alcohol use, and alcohol problems: A structural modeling examination in adult women and men. *Journal of Counseling Psychology, 46,* 109–124.

McLellan, A.T., Luborsky, L., Woody, G.E., O'Brien, C.P. & Druley, K.A. (1983). Predicting response to alcohol and drug abuse treatments: Role of psychiatric severity. *Archives of General Psychiatry, 40,* 620–625.

Miedema, J. (1996). *Changing Ways Counsellor's Manual: Challenging Men toward Safety and Equality in Their Primary Relationships.* London, ON: Changing Ways.

Milby, J.B., Schumacher, J.E., Raczynaski, J.M., Caldwell, E., Engle, M., Michael, M. & Carr, J. (1996). Sufficient conditions for effective treatment of substance abusing homeless persons. *Drug and Alcohol Dependence, 43,* 39–47.

Miller, W.R. & Rollnick, S. (1991). Brief intervention: More pieces of the puzzle. In W.R. Miller & S. Rollnick (Eds.), *Motivational Interviewing. Preparing People to Change Addictive Behavior* (pp. 30–35). New York: Guilford Press.

Miller, W.R. & Rollnick, S. (2002a). Phase 1: Building motivation for change. In W.R. Miller & S. Rollnick (Eds.), *Motivational Interviewing. Preparing People for Change* (2nd ed.; pp. 52–84). New York: Guilford Press.

Miller, W.R. & Rollnick, S. (2002b). What is Motivational Interviewing? In W.R. Miller & S. Rollnick (Eds.), *Motivational Interviewing. Preparing People for Change* (2nd ed.; pp. 33–42). New York: Guilford Press.

Moore, R.L. & Gillette, D. (1992). *The King Within: Accessing the King in the Male Psyche.* New York: W. Morrow.

Moos, R.H. (2003). Addictive disorders in context: Principles and puzzles of effective treatment and recovery. *Psychology of Addictive Behaviors, 17*(1), 3–12.

National Institute on Drug Abuse. (1999a). *Principles of Drug Addiction Treatment: A Research Based Guide.* Available: www.drugabuse.gov/PODAT/PODAT4.html.

National Institute on Drug Abuse. (1999b). Thirteen principles of effective drug addiction treatment. In *NIDA Notes, 14*(5), 1–2. Available: www.drugabuse.gov/NIDA_ Notes/NNVol14N5/tearoff.html.

Nelson, M.L. (1993). A current perspective on gender differences: Implications for research in counseling. *Journal of Counseling Psychology, 40*(2), 200–209.

Odell, S.M. & Commander, M.J. (2000). Risk factors for homelessness among people with psychotic disorders. *Social Psychiatry and Psychiatric Epidemiology, 35*, 396–401.

Oldenburg, R. (1989). *The Great Good Place: Cafes, coffee shops, community centers, beauty parlors, general stores, bars, hangouts and how they get you through the day.* New York: Paragon House.

O'Neil, J.M. (1982). Gender-role conflict and strain in men's lives: Implications for psychiatrists, psychologists, and other human-service providers. In K. Solomon & N.B. Levy (Eds.), *Men in Transition: Theory and Therapy* (pp. 5–44). New York: Plenum.

Prochaska, J.O., DiClemente, C.C. & Norcross, J.C. (1992). In search of how people change. *American Psychologist, 47*(9): 1102–1114.

Prochaska, J.O., Velicer, W.F., Rossi, J.S., Goldstein, M.G., Marcus, B.H., Rakowski, W. et al. (1994). Stages of change and decisional balance for 12 problem behaviors. *Health Psychology, 13*(1), 39–46.

Potter-Efron, P.S. & Potter-Efron, R.T. (1991). *Anger, Alcoholism and Addiction. Treating Individuals, Couples, and Families.* New York: Norton.

Rabinowitz, J. & Marjefsky, S. (1998). Alcohol & drug abuse: Predictors of being expelled from and dropping out of alcohol treatment. *Psychiatric Services, 49*(2), 187–189.

Real, T. (1997). *I Don't Want to Talk about It. Overcoming the Secret Legacy of Male Depression.* New York: Scribner.

Rheingold, H. (1995). The virtual community. *Utne Reader, 68*, 61–64.

Shonfeld-Ringel, S. (2001). A re-conceptualization of the working alliance in cross-cultural practice with non-Western clients: Integrating relational perspectives and multicultural theories. *Clinical Social Work Journal, 29*(1), 53–63.

Single, E. (2000). *The Canadian Community Epidemiological Network on Drug Use: Overview Report, 2000.* Canadian Centre on Substance Abuse. Available: www.ccsa.ca/ccendu/Reports/2000national.htm.

Single, E.W., Brewster, J., MacNeil, P. & Hatcher, J. (1994). *Alcohol and Drug Use: Results from the General Social Survey, 1993.* Ottawa: Health Canada.

Single, E., Brewster, J., MacNeil, P. Hatcher, J. & Trainor, C. (1995). *Alcohol and drug use: Results from the 1993 General Social Survey.* Report prepared for the Studies Unit, Health Promotion Directorate, Health Canada, January 1995. Available: www.ccsa.ca/docs/gsseng.htm.

Sinha, R., Fuse, T., Aubin, L.R. & O'Malley, S.S. (2000). Psychological stress, drug-related cues and cocaine craving. *Psychopharmacology, 152,* 140–148.

Sobell, L.C. (1994). *Guided Self-Change Clinical Training Manual.* Toronto: Addiction Research Foundation.

Sobell, M.B. & Sobell, L.C. (2000). Stepped care as a heuristic approach to the treatment of alcohol problems. *Journal of Consulting and Clinical Psychology, 68*(4), 573–579.

Stanton, M.D. & Shadish, W.R. (1997). Outcome, attrition, and family-couples treatment for drug abuse: A meta-analysis and review of the controlled, comparative studies. *Psychological Bulletin, 122*(2), 170–191.

Thom, B. (1986). Sex differences in help-seeking for alcohol problems 1. The barriers to help-seeking. *British Journal of Addiction, 81,* 777–788.

Van Wormer, K. (1989). The male-specific group in alcoholism treatment. *Small Group Behavior, 20*(2), 228–242.

Williams, R.J. & Ricciardelli, L.A. (1999). Gender congruence in confirmatory and compensatory drinking. *Journal of Psychology, 133,* 323–331.

Wilson, V.E. & Cummings, M.S. (2003). *Owner's Manual for Self-Regulation of Your Brain and Body.* Toronto: YSAM Inc.

Zeth, J. (1997). Incorporating Men's Values into Substance Abuse Treatment. In S.L.A. Straussner & E. Zelvin (Eds.), *Gender and Addictions. Men and Women in Treatment* (pp. 311–332). Northvale, NJ: Jason Aronson.

Chapter 14

Clients with Physical Disabilities

KEITH WALKER

INTRODUCTION AND OVERVIEW

Estimates of the prevalence of disabilities can vary widely depending on how disability is defined. But even by conservative estimates, people with disabilities constitute a significant minority in most societies. In Canada about 12 per cent of people living in the community (3.6 million) report impairments that restrict their activities. Since disability rates increase with age, we can expect growing numbers of people with disabilities as the population continues to age (Ostir, 1999; Statistics Canada, 2001).

There is now a substantial body of evidence indicating a high prevalence of alcohol problems within some disability groups. Linkages between disability issues and addiction issues have been reported since the early 1980s, when Rasmussen & Boer (1980) found that a disproportionately large number of the clients of a vocational rehabilitation centre had experienced serious alcohol problems. Addiction-disability issues gained prominence throughout the 1980s; in 1989, *Alcohol Health & Research World* devoted a special issue to substance use and disability. Since that time, we have seen:
- a growing volume of studies investigating the distribution and causes of alcohol and other drug problems among various groups of people with disabilities
- the development of interventions aimed at helping people with disabilities who are at risk for substance use problems
- the emergence of an advocacy movement aimed at advancing the cause of people with disabilities, who continue to be poorly served by mainstream addiction services.

A comprehensive review of the research literature on substance use and disability has recently been made by Heinemann (in press). This chapter will not attempt a detailed account of this literature, but will highlight findings to provide an overview of the current disability-addiction field. It will also provide some historical context to our understanding of disability issues, review some salient issues in working with clients with concurrent physical disabilities and substance use problems, and provide some direction for accessing further information.

The title of this chapter refers to clients with "physical disabilities," a term that is usually used to designate disabilities such as spinal cord injury, spina bifida, amputation, diabetes and arthritis. However, many of the issues addressed are also relevant to other categories of disabilities, including disabilities arising from cognitive, sensory and affective impairments. As the author's experience is primarily in the area of spinal cord rehabilitation, most examples are from that field.

The objectives of the chapter are to:

1. review the meanings of disability from the various perspectives of the health system, disability advocates and disability writers; and discuss the evolution in thinking about disability, which has led to a better understanding of the social determinants of disability and a broader acknowledgment of the rights of people with disabilities

2. discuss why it is important to be particularly sensitive to issues of autonomy when working with people with disabilities

3. provide a brief review of the literature on substance use among people with disabilities

4. discuss some of the clinical and ethical issues in working with clients who use potentially addictive medications

5. describe developments in substance use services for people with disabilities, and discuss ways to improve service delivery.

THE MEANINGS OF DISABILITY

It is important to consider how we define disability—the constructs we use to describe it, how we view its root causes, and the values and beliefs we hold about people with disabilities—since our conceptions can affect our ability to work with clients with disabilities. In addition, counsellors need to explore the personal meanings implicit in the language used by clients with disabilities, and to attempt to understand clients' behaviour within the context of both their physical and social environments (Altman, 2001; Crisp, 2002).

Disability as Impairment

There is no widely accepted way of classifying disabilities. In epidemiological studies, disabilities are classified sometimes by the underlying health condition causing the impairment (e.g., stroke, diabetes, spinal cord injury, multiple sclerosis) and sometimes by the impairment itself (e.g., paralysis, blindness, deafness). The use of broad disability groupings (e.g., physical, sensory, intellectual, psychiatric) also involves some arbitrariness since many health conditions can result in multiple impairments that cut across categories (Altman, 2001). The lack of international standards for collecting epidemiological data may partially explain the wide variance in disability rates reported across countries.

Disabilities vary widely in cause, severity, age of onset, and duration/progression. Some disabilities remain relatively static throughout the lifespan; others are progressive and may have periods of remission or exacerbation. The severity of disabilities can range from conditions that mildly, occasionally or temporarily interfere with one's activities to conditions that severely interfere with many activities of daily living. People living in the community with very severe disabilities usually need extensive help with personal care and modifications to the environment, including assistive devices and accessible housing. Statistics Canada (2001) reports that 8.6 per cent of Canadians live with disabilities of mild-to-moderate severity and 5.9 percent with severe-to-very-severe disabilities.

Multiple Impairments

CONCURRENT PHYSICAL IMPAIRMENTS

Most people who report having a disability have more than one disability. For many types of disabilities, multiple impairments are the norm. For example, most people with mobility impairments due to spinal cord injury (SCI) or multiple sclerosis (MS) will also have impairments in multiple body systems, some of which can be more disabling than the mobility impairment (e.g., Hawkins & Heinemann, 1998). Many will lose bladder and bowel control and will experience loss of sexual function. In addition, most people with mobility impairments will be at risk for a multitude of other medical complications (including spasms, urinary tract infections, skin breakdown, fractures, burns and other health problems) that can lead to further disability. Many will also encounter age-related impairments earlier than the able-bodied population due to factors such as disease progression, medical complications and wear-and-tear on body joints.

In the case of disabilities resulting from catastrophic injuries, multiple disabilities are common. For example, up to 50 per cent of people who sustain an SCI also sustain a mild-to-moderate brain injury (Elovic & Kirshblum, 1999; Watanabe et al., 1999). In some instances, it can be hard to tell the extent to which cognitive deficits may be due to pre-injury factors such as brain damage related to heavy substance use (Ham & Parsons, 2000).

CONCURRENT MENTAL HEALTH PROBLEMS

There is evidence of a high concurrence between (1) some physical disabilities and some mental health problems and (2) between substance use problems and mental health problems. Mental health challenges, like substance use problems, can either play a causal role in physical disabilities or can occur in response to the stresses of coping with disabilities.

Examples of pre-existing mental health problems that increase the risk of traumatic injury include mood disorders, some personality disorders, some learning disorders and psychoses (Radnitz et al., 1996; Stewart, 1988)—that is, any mental health issue that is likely to increase the incidence of risk-taking or self-injury.

The most common psychological problems that occur in response to catastrophic injuries are depression, some anxiety disorders, adjustment disorders and post-traumatic stress disorder (Anson & Shepherd, 1996). Suicide rates among people with catastrophic injuries are several times those found in the general population (DeVivo et al., 1999).

The International Classification of Functioning, Disability and Health

For over two decades, the International Classification of Impairments, Disabilities, and Handicaps (ICIDH) served as the authoritative disability classification system (World Health Organization, 1980). Although it has since been replaced, its terminology continues to be used widely in legislation and policies affecting people with disabilities. The ICIDH used a multidimensional system to classify disablement. It distinguished among three causally related disablement concepts:

• **impairment**: "any loss or abnormality of a psychological, or anatomical structure or function"
• **disability**: "any restriction or inability (resulting from an impairment) to perform an activity in the manner or with the range considered normal for a human being"
• **handicap**: "any disadvantage for a given individual, resulting from an impairment or disability, that limits or prevents the fulfillment of a role that is normal for that individual."

Thus, for example, a person who loses his eyesight (an impairment) will be unable to read printed material (a disability) and could be severely disadvantaged in pursuing his career as a newspaper editor (a handicap).

In 2001 the World Health Organization (WHO) revised the ICIDH to incorporate contemporary thinking about population health and the importance of environmental factors in the causation of disability. The new ICIDH-2 (WHO, 2001)—subsequently renamed the International Classification of Functioning, Disability and Health (ICF)—classifies both health and disablement along three dimensions that are closely related to those in the original ICIDH. However, in order to move away from a disease-based conceptualization of disability, the ICF dimensions focus on constituents of health rather than on the consequences of disease. They include components related to the body, to the person and to society. "Disability" in the ICF serves as an umbrella term that can describe:

- impairments in body functions or structures (Body component)
- limitations in activities, which can range from basic activities of daily living, such as dressing and feeding oneself, to complex instrumental activities, such as planning one's schedule for the day, driving to work or attending school (Activity component)
- restrictions on social participation, which includes participation in societal roles and opportunities related, for example, to work, recreation or access to services (Participation component).

In addition to these three "components of health," the ICF includes a list of environmental (i.e., physical and social) factors that can influence any of these components. In our example of the man who recently lost his sight, the extent to which his activities and social participation are restricted will depend on a number of physical and social environmental factors (e.g., the willingness of his employer to invest in the technology required to allow him to pursue his occupation, or the availability of a seeing-eye dog to enable him to get to work). Being aware of the impact of environmental factors on the three health components can help us understand how two people with the same health condition can experience disability in very different ways.

The ICF acknowledges that personal factors (e.g., personal health practices, individual capacities and coping skills) can also play important moderating roles in disability, but it does not attempt to classify them because of the large variance in social and cultural standards across populations.

Social Models of Disability

The study of the social determinants of disability has evolved into a relatively new branch of academia known as disability studies. This interdisciplinary school of study is based on a model of disability that defines disability as a social rather than a biological phenomenon. While there are a number of differing versions of the social model of disability (Pfeiffer, 2002), most include the following central themes (Asch & Fine, 1988; Barnes et al., 1999; Oliver, 1990, 1996; Winter, 2003):

- Disability is created by society's response to impairment rather than the impairment itself. It results from society's failure to accommodate the needs of people with impairments to enable them to participate fully in society.
- Impairment does not equal abnormality. "Normality" is a value-based construct that reflects social judgments about what constitutes acceptable variations in biology and functioning.
- Impairment does not imply personal tragedy. People with disabilities should not be held as objects of pity.
- Disability is not synonymous with the need for assistance and social support.

Everybody requires services in order to live independently in the community.
• People with disabilities constitute a marginalized minority who frequently encounter both systemic and interpersonal discrimination.

Disability as a Human Rights Issue

Social models of disability date back to the civil rights movements of the 1960s and 1970s, when disability rights advocates began to challenge the discriminatory treatment of people with disabilities (Zames Fleischer & Zames, 2001). Subsequently disability advocates associated with the Independent Living Movement (ILM) have campaigned relentlessly for civil rights, including antidiscrimination legislation, access to the built environment and access to the supports and services required to live independently in the community. The ILM's most significant achievement is the U.S. *Americans with Disabilities Act* (ADA). Enacted in 1991, the ADA prohibits discrimination and requires employers and providers of goods and services to make reasonable accommodations to the needs of people with disabilities.

The ILM in Canada has aligned itself closely with the American ILM. The Canadian *Charter of Rights and Freedoms* protects people with disabilities against discriminatory treatment, as do a number of legislative acts. However, Canada does not have any legislation with the specificity or legal power of the ADA. In 2001, Ontario passed the *Ontarians with Disabilities Act* (ODA), which stipulates that all publicly funded services must be made accessible to people with disabilities. Unfortunately, its scope is much more limited than that of the ADA and it has no enforcement provisions.

Disability Culture and Identity

While the community identity of people with disabilities was forged through their status as a disadvantaged minority (Linton, 1998), the expression of the community's cultural identity has evolved through a burgeoning body of literature, art and music (Brown, 1995, 2000; Shakespeare, 1994). The identity of the community has also been strengthened through the development of a broad range of adapted sports (including individual sports such as wheelchair racing, tennis, skiing, sailing, scuba diving and hang gliding, and team sports including hockey, soccer and basketball). The promotion of adapted sports through national and international competition, particularly the Paralympics, has also increased public awareness of a positive disability identity.

Most people with disabilities, like most people without disabilities, identify with more than one culture (Brown, 2000; Shakespeare, 1994). The extent of their identification with different cultures may vary over the course of their lives. Some people with disabilities identify with other groups that have experienced discrimination (e.g., women, gays and lesbians, and some racial, ethnic and religious groups). Some identify with other cultures that hold non-mainstream values and beliefs that can shape their experience of disability.

Many people with disabilities appear to identify more closely with people who have similar impairments to theirs than they do with the broader disability community. People differ widely with respect to their degree of interest in disability politics. They also differ in:
• the extent to which they have been able to accept their impairments
• their ability to assert their rights and advocate on their own behalf
• the values and personal philosophies they hold with respect to individual autonomy.

The Deaf community provides perhaps the quintessential example of the evolution of the concept of disability as culture and the rejection of a medical or impairment model of disability. It may also illustrate the need for care providers to attend closely to cultural issues when relating to people with disabilities.

Proponents of deafness as a culture vehemently dispute the portrayal of deafness as impairment (Padden & Humphries, 1988; Roots, 1999). They contend that deafness is a positive personal trait and that the deaf community is a linguistic minority group with a distinct culture, including a strong sense of belonging and its own unique values, social norms and arts. The Deaf community uses the capitalized form of "deaf" to designate its status as a linguistic and cultural minority.

Sign language is central to the identity of the Deaf culture. Many Deaf advocates condemn the use of hearing aids and cochlear implants. They protest educators imposing or promoting oral training, speech-language therapy, and English- or French-based signing systems. They view these interventions as threats to their language and to the viability of the Deaf culture itself.

The Disability Experience

The transformation in the meaning of disability from an individual problem to a social problem has been important to the successes of the disability rights movement. It has also been instrumental in restoring a sense of dignity, purpose and belonging to the lives of many people with disabilities.

While social factors are clearly important determinants of the extent to which people are disadvantaged by impairment, biological and psychological factors can also play an important role in disability. Defining disability solely in terms of societal barriers fails to acknowledge the role that impairment and illness play in the lives of many people with disabilities (Costa & VandenBos, 1990; Marinelli & Dell Orto, 1999). Focusing only on structural and systemic issues ignores the devastating effects of stigmatization and social exclusion on the person's well-being (Goffman, 1963; Oyserman & Swim, 2001). The statements of some disability activists—in reacting to what is often termed "ableist" stereotyping—can sound almost dismissive of the pain, suffering and emotional distress that many people with disabilities live with daily.

The psychological adjustment and well-being of people with disabilities is not directly related to their degree of impairment. Social role expectations and social supports appear to be more important determinants of adjustment than physical factors. Hartkopp et al. (1998), for example, found that suicide rates among people with SCI were highest among those with less severe impairments.

Psychological adjustment to disability can be influenced by a number of psychosocial and socioeconomic variables (e.g., DeLoach & Greer, 1981; Trieschmann, 1980). For people who have had a catastrophic injury, life in the early months and years can be particularly difficult. In addition to physical and functional losses and complications, the person may also lose his or her home, job and income. It can be enormously hard to adapt to significant role changes in vocational and inter-personal areas, including relationships with friends, family and sexual partners. Over the first few weeks and months after the injury, people may have to make numerous decisions with respect to finding or renovating housing, buying and funding adaptive equipment, and arranging for personal support services. Because of reductions in length of stay in acute rehabilitation programs, patients and families feel increasingly pressured to make decisions more quickly and to seek interim solutions to housing problems (e.g., placement in a nursing home) or to delays and shortages in community support services. For people with high needs who are not wealthy, there may be no viable alternatives to long-term care. For those who are eligible for disability compensation through motor vehicle insurance, the adversarial and lengthy nature of the insurance and legal systems can be highly stressful and can have negative effects on rehabilitation.

A catastrophic injury usually has detrimental effects on the lives of the person's immediate family members, who may share many of the losses and role dislocations. The strength of relationships can be seriously tested, particularly in cases where the spouse must provide care and, in some cases, bear the brunt of the person's anger and frustration. Marital breakdown and loss of friendships are common.

While the person's capacity to cope is more likely to be overwhelmed during the early years of disability, chronic depression and other psychological problems may be found among people who have lived with disability for many years. Frequently these are people who are experiencing "disability burn-out" in response to their unrelenting struggle to overcome seemingly insurmountable barriers.

The disability experience is likely to be very different for the person who was born with impairments or who acquired impairments early in life. For people who encounter early disability, childhood experiences such as bullying and social exclusion can inflict deep insecurities about their self-worth.

As many disability advocates have expressed, disability can also bring benefits. Counsellors to people with severe physical disabilities encounter clients (most of whom have been living with disability for a number of years) who say their disability has had positive life-altering or even life-saving effects. For example, some people with severe injuries related to substance use describe the experience as a "wake-up call" to the need to make lifestyle changes (Bombardier, 2000; Heinemann, in press). Disability can make some people rethink their personal values and priorities, which can lead to a more meaningful and fulfilling life. For a few people, who in their pre-disability days had been struggling to fulfil roles and expectations, disability can provide a socially acceptable "out" (Parsons, 1951; Winter, 2003). However, the people we most frequently encounter as clients are struggling to cope, and some are struggling to find any semblance of meaning, justice or hope in the hand that life has dealt them.

We health and social service providers without disabilities must be mindful of being "outsiders" with respect to disability culture, and limited in our ability to comprehend the lived experience of disability (Dembo, 1969, 1970; Wright, 1991). We must be wary of our personal fears regarding illness and disability and our tendencies to view disability as more tragic than do people who live with disability (Gerhart et al., 1994). Numerous studies suggest that most people with severe physical disabilities assess their quality of life almost as highly as do those with no disability (Bach & Tilton, 1994). However, this observation has been so difficult for health providers to accept that it is sometimes referred to as the "disability paradox" in the rehabilitation literature (e.g., Albrecht & Devlieger, 1999).

Disability and Disadvantage

As discussed thus far, disability is primarily about disadvantage—an insight that was first made several decades ago by people living with disability, and one that has slowly gained acceptance by health institutions, governments, courts and academics across the world.

A broad body of evidence in the field of population health suggests that inequalities in wealth and power have strong negative effects on the health status of less advantaged people within a society (e.g., Hayes & Dunn, 1998; Wilkinson, 1996). The poverty rate among people with disabilities in Canada in 1995 was estimated to be approximately double the rate among people without disabilities (Fawcett, 2000). The prevalence of disabilities is higher among the most impoverished groups. Disability rates among Aboriginals, for example, have been estimated at 30 per cent (Government of Canada, 2002).

While people with disabilities are economically disadvantaged as a group, there are also growing disparities within the group with respect to income and the availability of housing, equipment, supports and services. In many Canadian jurisdictions, the degree to which a person is disadvantaged will depend on both the person's financial and employment status at the time of disability and the cause of the disability (e.g., motor vehicle crash, workplace injury, non-work-related accident or illness). These factors determine who pays for the services, equipment and supports needed for the person to integrate into the community (e.g., auto insurance, workers' compensation, medical insurance benefits, or the person); they also determine the availability and comprehensiveness of the benefits provided. In many jurisdictions, people with minimal or no insurance are faced with long waiting periods for accessible housing and community supports. Growing numbers of people with disabilities are forced to live in institutions because the support services that would enable them to live in the community are not available.

Autonomy and Empowerment

Of all the losses that accompany disability, the loss of personal independence and autonomy is often the most significant and dehumanizing (Winter, 2003). Many people with severe disabilities must depend on others for their most basic personal needs, including toileting, washing, dressing, cooking and eating. Personal autonomy, however, should not be confused with personal independence, as many people in the rehabilitation field are wont to do (Cardol et al., 2002; Kuczewski & Fiedler, 2001; Oliver, 1990). Personal autonomy refers to "the ability to be in control and make decisions, rather than doing things alone or without help" (Oliver, 1990, p. 91). Personal autonomy is diminished when people are required to conform to the schedules set by their caregivers and other service providers. It is also diminished by the necessity to conform to a regimented lifestyle, which restricts opportunities for social participation and spontaneity—when, for example, even the simplest outings must be planned well in advance. As a result, many people with severe disabilities perceive that they have true decisional autonomy in very few areas in their lives. In counselling people with disabilities, it is thus important to be particularly sensitive to issues of autonomy and to work collaboratively with the client in developing treatment goals and strategies.

RESPECT AND DIGNITY

Treating clients with respect and dignity is fundamental to effective practice with any clientele, but these issues demand particular attention when working with clients who experience frequent intrusions into their personal space by health and personal care providers. The foundation for an effective therapeutic relationship is summed up by the phrase *respect not pity, partnership not paternalism*. We cannot expect to empower our clients to strive for greater participation in society if we do not ourselves encourage them to participate actively in treatment planning. Counsellors must be self-reflective and self-critical, and attentive to their own psychological needs, limitations, fears and foibles. They need to be aware of the substantial power imbalances in relationships with clients who are socially disadvantaged.

Guidelines to "disability etiquette" are available at a number of disability Web sites. The Canadian Centre on Disability Studies has published a comprehensive set of guidelines that include communication tips for many types of disabilities (Jones, 1997). Some principles underlying disability etiquette are as follows:

• Do not define people in terms of their disabilities. Put the person first, not the disability. For example, it is preferable to refer to "people with disabilities" rather than "disabled people" or to "people who are blind" or "people with vision impairments" rather than "the blind."

• Be sensitive to cultural issues. For example, in exception to the above rule, many people with deafness prefer to be referred to as *Deaf people*.

• Unless otherwise directed, communicate directly with the person, not through his or her attendant or companion.

• Be prepared to offer assistance but do not assume it is needed or wanted. Many people with disabilities find overly solicitous behaviour irksome and a violation of their space and dignity.

How we refer to people with disabilities should be determined not by political correctness but by respect. The use of the word "challenged," for example, (an invention of service providers) is considered patronizing by most people with disabilities. Preferred terms do change over time, as they do for other minority groups, often in response to a term having taken on a pejorative meaning.

PERSONAL MEANING AND IDENTITY

Severe disability is life-altering. Some clients tend to speak about life before disability and life after disability as two separate existences. After disability, most people will experience a period of grieving. Like people grieving other significant losses, such as the loss of a loved one, a person may experience a variety of emotional states, including anxiety, depression, denial, anger, withdrawal and resignation. However, there are no identifiable stages of grieving that most or all people must go through, nor is there a "normal" period for completing the grieving process (Wortman & Cohen Silver, 2001). Unlike most other major losses, disability may entail a series of losses experienced over the course of months or years.

The self-esteem of people who cannot work can be undermined by the emphasis our society places on gainful employment as a measure of self-worth and identity. Although strides have been made in addressing some barriers to employment, a web of systemic and attitudinal impediments still keeps most people with disabilities out of the labour market. The unemployment rate for people with severe disabilities has stayed stubbornly at about 70 per cent in both Canada and the United States for many years (Canadian Paraplegic Association, 2000; Harris Interactive, 2000). While it is important to continue to work toward reducing employment barriers, it may also be important to critically examine the values we and our clients hold with respect to employment. Some authors in the vocational rehabilitation field have argued that vocation should be redefined to include unpaid activities that are personally meaningful or socially beneficial (Ernst & Day, 1998; Ravelshoot, 1996; West, 1995).

The experience of disability often brings up significant existential questions for the first time in a person's life. Disability can shatter basic beliefs and assumptions about justice and fairness, one's own safety and security, the meaningfulness of life, trust in others and self-worth (e.g., Meichenbaum, 1994). The struggle to regain a new, positive self-identity involves creating meaning from tragedy, gaining resilience through pain and suffering, and taking pride in achievements once considered inconsequential—a process that can be fraught with paradox (Keyes & Haidt, 2002; Neimeyer & Raskin, 2000).

The role of the counsellor is not to provide ready-made answers but to provide support and guidance as the client struggles to accommodate new realities into his or her life narrative. A strengths-based approach that focuses on abilities rather than disabilities and on choice rather than victimization can help some clients develop a positive self-image (e.g., Mackelprang & Salsgiver, 1998).

People who have lived successfully with disability for a number of years can serve as invaluable positive role models for clients with disabilities and as allies to the counsellor. Peer support and mentorship programs are available through a number of national and provincial disability associations.

Addiction as Disability

Addiction can be considered a disability in its own right, since it can result directly in impairments in physical and social functioning that restrict the person's participation in societal roles and opportunities. Functional impairments related to substance use can extend long beyond the time the person has stopped using.

For people with substance use problems, as for those with physical disabilities, societal barriers to inclusion can sometimes be the primary determinants of disability. Indeed, the social stigma attached to addiction and to the use of some substances can be more damaging than the stigma attached to most physical disabilities. Addiction is recognized as a disability in most civil rights legislation. Yet in legislation intended specifically to protect the rights of people with disabilities, addiction is typically not accorded equal status with other disabilities (de Miranda, 2002). For example, under the ADA in the United States, people with substance use disabilities do not have the same rights as most other disability groups with respect to employment protection. Their rights to employment and to social assistance are often made conditional upon remaining abstinent and/or seeking treatment. In the United States, people can lawfully be made to submit to urinalyses as a condition of employment or social assistance. In Ontario, disability pensions and other benefits are denied even to people with substance use disabilities who are clearly unemployable and have little hope of gaining control over their substance use.

SUBSTANCE USE AMONG PEOPLE WITH DISABILITIES

Prevalence and Cause of Substance Use Problems

As noted earlier, problem substance use can be either a cause or a consequence of disability. In developed countries, alcohol use has been identified as the leading cause of disabilities among men and the 10th largest among women (Murray & Lopez, 1991). Injuries continue to be the leading cause of alcohol-related disabilities in the developed world. However, disease is gradually catching up as the population ages (WHO, 2000) and more people become susceptible to a host of medical conditions that can be related to chronic heavy alcohol use (e.g., diabetes, organic brain damage, peripheral neuropathies).

Although some studies suggest a high rate of substance use problems among mixed populations of people with disabilities (e.g., Moore & Li, 1994; Rasmussen & DeBoer, 1980), prevalence most likely varies widely across different types of disabilities. Consumption patterns are likely to be influenced by cultural and environmental factors that affect the availability and social desirability of various substances. For example, cannabis can be expected to be more accepted and more readily available in disability groups that use marijuana to treat symptoms such as pain, spasticity and nausea.

We must be cautious about generalizations in evaluating findings that suggest a high rate of substance use problems among people with disabilities. It is important to bear in mind that people with disabilities are as heterogeneous as the population at large. Like the general population, people with disabilities who use alcohol or other drugs do so for a variety of reasons, some of which may and some of which may not be related to their disabilities. Cultural dissimilarities between different disability groups, as well as regional differences in patterns of substance use, can affect the prevalence of substance-related problems.

The most thorough studies of substance use among people with disabilities have been carried out by researchers in the fields of acquired brain and spinal cord injuries. Some highlights of the findings, reviewed by Bombardier (2000) and Heinemann (in press) follow. For both traumatic brain injury (TBI) and spinal cord injury (SCI) in the United States:

- A significant proportion of people sustaining injuries are intoxicated at the time: between 29 per cent and 86 per cent for TBI and between 17 per cent and 49 per cent for SCI.
- Alcohol is more frequently implicated than other drugs as a contributing factor to TBI and SCI. It is involved in between 40 per cent and 60 per cent of catastrophic injuries resulting from motor vehicle crashes. The severity of injuries is related to blood alcohol level at the time of the crash.
- Significant numbers of people with TBI (16–66 per cent) or SCI (35–49 per cent) report a history of substance use problems that predates their injuries.
- Health risks related to problem substance use after injury (although different for the two groups) can be serious and even life-threatening. For people with TBI, substance misuse is associated with higher rates of seizures, aggression and mental health problems. For SCI, health risks include an increased risk of medical complications, depression and suicide.
- For people with a pre-existing drinking problem, alcohol consumption tends to decline over the initial months following injury but for some it returns to problematic levels within 12 to 18 months. Like those with alcohol problems in the general population, many people with disabilities achieve sobriety for extended periods with occasional periods of relapse.
- Although most post-injury alcohol problems reflect the resumption of pre-injury drinking practices, a significant proportion of people develop alcohol problems for the first time after becoming disabled.
- Problem substance use following injury is associated with poorer rehabilitation outcomes, higher rates of depression, difficulties in reintegrating into the community and increased risks of reinjury.

- Abstinence rates after injury are higher (about 50 per cent) than in the general population, but moderate-to-heavy drinking is also more common (about 40 per cent). Interestingly, among people with disabilities, abstainers with a long history of drinking problems are more likely to experience poor outcomes, including an increased risk of medical complications among people with SCI and lower employment rates among people with TBI.
- As the population ages, we are seeing fewer substance-related "accidents of youth" (e.g., diving accidents, motorcycle accidents) and a growing number of injuries and medical conditions associated with chronic substance use and higher dependency levels.

Most of the published epidemiological data on substance use among people with traumatic injuries are from the United States. The wide range in estimates of prevalence may reflect not only methodological differences in measurement and case detection, but also regional and cultural variations in substance use patterns (e.g., differences between inner-city, suburban and rural areas).

Very little has been published about the incidence and prevalence of substance use problems among Canadians with TBI or SCI. Canadian traffic fatality data (e.g., Beirness et al., 1995) and research carried out at a Toronto hospital trauma unit (Kapur, 1974) provide figures similar to those from the United States (Waller et al., 1997) with respect to substance involvement in serious motor vehicle crashes. Canadian statistics regarding the cause of TBI and SCI (Liberman et al., 2003) are also similar to those described in studies from the American TBI & SCI Model System hospitals (e.g., Elovic & Kirshblum, 1999), except for violence-related injuries, which are much less common in Canada.

Evidence is scarce about the substance consumption patterns of disability groups other than people with TBI or SCI.

Medications and Disability

Many people with disabilities take multiple medications to treat pain, spasticity and other complications. Many of these medications can interact with alcohol and some other drugs (Weathermon & Crabb, 1999); some have potential for misuse and addiction; and some have negative side-effects such as fatigue and cognitive impairment, which can contribute to depression and disability. In advising clients with disabilities about low-risk substance use, counsellors should consider whether there may be risks uniquely related to their disabilities. For example, among people with SCI, substance misuse can increase risks for secondary complications (e.g., Heinemann & Hawkins, 1998); it can lead to bladder and kidney damage, stroke, skin breakdown, reinjury and further functional impairments.

It is beyond the scope of this chapter to discuss the risks and benefits of all medications used to treat the medical complications associated with different disabilities. However, two categories of drugs—opioids and cannabis—deserve some mention because of the controversies surrounding their use.

OPIOID USE IN THE MANAGEMENT OF PAIN

Pain is often regarded as a secondary disability, since it so frequently accompanies other disabilities. Nonetheless, for many people with disabilities, pain is the most significant disabling aspect of their medical condition (e.g., Westgren & Levi, 1998). For many pain conditions, including those with causes that are still poorly understood, pain may be the only disabling factor. Thus, pain has emerged as a disability in its own right.

In 2002, pain was the second most prevalent disability among Canadians. Statistics Canada estimates that about 10 per cent of people over the age of 15 are disabled by pain.

Many people with chronic severe pain can only get adequate relief through opioid medications. However, physicians are often reluctant to prescribe opioids for pain management because of concerns about creating addiction and concerns about the heavy hand of governmental regulators and professional governing boards (Joranson & Gilson, 1994).

Some studies have found a substantial proportion of patients in pain medicine settings misuse opioids or other substances (e.g., Fishbain et al., 1986; Katon et al., 1985). However, most reviewers believe the risks of opioid addiction have been exaggerated because of confusion about the meaning of addiction. Porter & Jick (1980), for example, in a large-scale epidemiological study of pain patients, found the prevalence of iatrogenic (doctor-caused) addiction to be less than 0.1 per cent, a finding that has since been confirmed in several other studies. Based on a review of the available literature in 1990, the WHO Expert Committee on Cancer Relief and Palliative Care concluded that the medical use of opioids rarely leads to the development of psychological dependence (WHO, 1990).

Pain specialists argue that unrealistic fears about the risks of opioid addiction stem from widespread misperceptions equating addiction with physical dependence or tolerance (Friedman, 1990; Loder et al., 2003; Von Roenn et al., 1993). Anyone who uses large doses of opioids for a long time will develop physical dependence (i.e., they will experience withdrawal symptoms when they stop taking the drug); some, but not most, will develop tolerance and need larger doses. Physical dependence per se cannot be considered harmful. Patients also develop dependence on other prescribed drugs such as beta-blockers, corticosteroids and antidepressants, which are not usually associated with addictive disorders. Rarely do pain patients lose control over opioids, use them compulsively for their psychic effects or continue to use them despite harm— behavioural patterns that are characteristic of addiction. Many pain patients maintained for years on the same dose of opioids do not develop tolerance; in many cases, the need to increase dosage appears to be related to disease progression rather than the development of tolerance (Foley, 1991; Schug et al., 1992). The safety profile of opioids is more positive than most other medications used to treat pain, such as non-steroidal anti-inflammatory drugs (NSAIDs). Fears about inducing respiratory depression are largely unwarranted (e.g., American Academy of Pain Medicine and American Pain Society, 1997).

Patients whose pain is inadequately controlled are often mislabelled as "addicted" because of drug-seeking behaviours, such as "clock-watching," cravings, concerns about availability and unsanctioned dose escalations. This pattern of "aberrant" behaviour, sometimes referred to as "pseudo-addiction" (Weissman & Haddox, 1989), will typically resolve itself when the patient's pain is adequately relieved.

Fear of addiction affects not only the prescribing behaviour of physicians but also the behaviour of people who are disabled by pain, many of whom refuse opioids or take less than the effective dose because they are afraid of becoming addicted (Cleeland, 1987; Ward et al., 1993).

Most epidemiological data on the concurrence between pain disorders and substance use problems have come from studies carried out in pain clinics. It is difficult to know how representative pain-clinic patients are of the broader population of people with coexisting pain and substance use problems. The literature provides little information about the prevalence of pain disorders among people seeking addiction treatment. However, a recent study of addiction treatment programs in the state of New York found that 37 per cent of outpatients enrolled in methadone maintenance programs and 24 per cent of inpatients admitted to residential treatment programs reported chronic severe pain (Rosenblum et al., 2003). A large proportion of the patients with chronic severe pain had received no prescription medication for pain over the previous three months. The authors stress the need for addiction treatment centres to develop comprehensive pain management programs.

Obtaining adequate pain treatment can be particularly hard for people with a known history of substance use problems. Undertreatment of pain for these people arises not only from misperceptions about the nature of addiction, but also from bias (Talmadge, 2003). Discriminatory treatment can arise either from punitive attitudes toward addiction (e.g., practitioners are overly concerned about being conned) or from overly paternalistic concerns about "enabling" the patient's addiction.

There are yet no evidence-based practice guidelines for working with patients with concurrent pain disorders and substance use problems. The most frequently cited recommendations in the literature come from Portenoy (1996) and Portenoy & Payne (1997), who suggest that opioids should be prescribed only when other, more conservative, methods of treatment have failed. However, more recent recommendations from the American Association for Addiction Psychiatry (Talmadge, 2003) suggest that people with concurrent pain disorders and substance use problems should be treated like anyone else. Risks arising from withholding or under-prescribing opioids are likely to be greater among people with substance use problems: the failure to adequately control pain may increase the incidence of illicit drug behaviours, psychopathology and suicide. Where there are concerns that the patient is at increased risk for addiction, they should be addressed with the patient as part of the treatment plan.

Patient contracts for opioids are currently used by many pain centres, although their efficacy has not been demonstrated in clinical studies (Fishman et al., 1999). An example of an opioid contract can be found on Web site for the American Academy of

Pain Medicine (www.painmed.org). How a patient contract is negotiated is probably as important as what it says.

MEDICAL MARIJUANA AND SYMPTOM CONTROL

It has been claimed that marijuana can be an effective treatment for symptoms of many disabling medical conditions, including chronic pain, chemotherapy-induced nausea and vomiting, wasting syndrome in patients with HIV, epilepsy, glaucoma, muscle spasticity related to spinal cord injury and multiple sclerosis, and movement disorders related to a number of neurological conditions (Benson & Watson, 1999; National Institutes of Health, 1997). The movement in many countries to decriminalize marijuana has been based on claims for its medical benefits, its relative safety compared with other legal drugs such as alcohol and tobacco, and concerns about the extensive societal harm that has resulted from its criminalization.

Although there is a growing body of clinical research into medical marijuana, controlled clinical trials have been scarce. Clinical trials are currently being conducted for some uses, but researchers have had difficulty standardizing doses and have faced legal and regulatory obstacles. There has been much more research into the health and social effects of marijuana use. The most recent reviews of short- and long-term health effects can be found in Benson & Watson (1999) and Kalant et al. (1999). Other, more current, information can be found in expert testimony provided to the Canadian Senate (Senate Special Committee on Illegal Drugs, 2002).

Health professionals working with people with disabilities are likely to see more clients and patients willing to discuss their marijuana use and more requesting marijuana prescriptions. Many marijuana users are skeptical about information concerning risks because of misinformation disseminated by some proponents of the "war on drugs." Nonetheless, some long-term users indicate that they are concerned about negative effects on their health, lifestyle and social relationships. Some are concerned about having developed dependence. Some acknowledge having marijuana use problems, but report that marijuana is more effective than prescription drugs, that they have fewer or lesser side-effects, or that they believe its long-term use is safer. Some say they use marijuana to counteract the side-effects of other medications or to enhance the effectiveness of other medications. Some use it to treat emotional symptoms as well as physical ones—for example, depression, anxiety, boredom, anger or fatigue. Many people who use marijuana for medical reasons have previously used it recreationally. Many, of course, continue to use it for social as well as medical reasons, which for some can lead to problems.

In working with clients who use large quantities of marijuana for medicinal purposes, it can be hard to assess the extent to which physical, psychological or social impairments might be related to the marijuana use, to the use of other substances (including prescription drugs), to the underlying medical condition or to psycho-social factors. It is sometimes possible to obtain worthwhile information by encouraging clients to experiment with trial periods of reduced use or abstinence and to investigate alternative medications and non-pharmacological methods of relieving symptoms. However, the counsellor must bear in mind that marijuana might be serving important psychic functions in addition to pain management.

Depending on the client's concerns, possible ways to reduce health risks might be to modify inhalation practices, use water filtration or vaporization devices, or use ingestible preparations.

TREATMENT ISSUES

Treatment Approaches and Outcomes

Despite evidence that people with some types of disabilities are at greater risk for substance use problems and are under-represented in treatment programs, the physical rehabilitation and addiction fields have been somewhat slow to develop appropriate services. Interventions based on traditional recovery-oriented approaches have not been well received in most TBI and SCI rehabilitation settings (Walker, 1996). Unlike clients in an addiction treatment setting, patients in a physical rehabilitation setting are likely to differ widely with respect to:
• degree of substance dependence
• kinds and severity of substance use problems
• awareness of substance use problems
• willingness to acknowledge problems
• current concerns and priorities.

Focusing on people who are severely dependent ignores the needs of those who are less dependent but who, nonetheless, may be at risk for serious substance use problems. Although many patients with substance use problems say they want to change, only a small percentage shows interest in receiving addiction treatment (Bombardier & Rimmele, 1998).

Patients in acute rehabilitation may be particularly resistant to treatment for substance use problems, because of
• the dual stigma of being identified as both "addicted" and "disabled"
• heightened sensitivity to intrusions into their personal lives, perhaps in response to the loss of privacy in so many other areas of their lives.

Although many inpatient TBI and SCI rehab facilities have policies and procedures for addressing substance use issues, they often seem to be aimed more at managing risk and containing intoxication problems than at promoting lifestyle change. Many facilities, if not most, do provide some information about alcohol and other drugs as part of their patient education programs; some provide screening and referral to community-based substance use services or support groups; and a few provide specialized addiction counselling services. Interest in substance-related issues in rehabilitation settings has waxed and waned over the past two decades. The organizational response to people at risk for substance use problems too often has swung from denial and "benign" neglect at one end of the spectrum to authoritarian and intrusive interventions at the other.

On a more positive note, the U.S.-based National Institute on Disability and Rehabilitation Research has funded a centre at Wright State University in Dayton, Ohio, dedicated to program development, research and professional training to meet the needs of people with coexisting substance use and physical or mental health problems. The centre (referred to as SARDI—Substance Abuse Resources and Disability Issues) is currently assessing the use of a consumer advocacy model to provide community-based outpatient substance use and mental health services to people with physical disabilities (SARDI, 2003).

One promising development in rehabilitation-based substance use programs is the introduction of brief interventions that aim to enhance patients' awareness of substance use issues and motivate them to change their substance-related behaviour. Bombardier and colleagues have carried out several studies supporting the clinical observation that experiencing disability can motivate lifestyle change. They suggest that the period of inpatient rehabilitation might be an opportune time to engage newly injured SCI and TBI patients in a dialogue about change (Bombardier & Rimmele, 1998, 1999). They have adapted Miller & Rollnick's (1991) motivational interviewing techniques for use during inpatient rehabilitation. Preliminary results for a small number of TBI subjects suggested that the treatment has a positive effect (Bombardier & Rimmele, 1999).

Another promising approach is the adaptation by Heinemann and colleagues of Cox & Klinger's (1988, 1990, 2003) counselling techniques. These techniques aim to modify the client's motivational basis for substance use, with the objective of helping the client find a more satisfying life free of alcohol or other drugs. TBI patients receiving this treatment showed positive changes on motivational measures compared with no-treatment controls, and their substance use was reduced by 50 per cent by the end of the program (Heinemann, in press; Cox et al., 2003). However, these differences were not maintained at follow-up.

A third hopeful development is a skills-based counselling approach developed by Langley (1992) and Langley & Ridgely (1994) that teaches TBI patients to recognize high-risk situations, improve problem-solving skills and develop adaptive coping responses. Part of the appeal of this approach is that it addresses substance use issues in the context of other lifestyle issues and integrates substance use treatment with other rehab interventions. A 12-month outcome study found evidence that the treatment helped clients.

The U.S.-based National Clearinghouse for Alcohol and Drug Information has published a Treatment Improvement Protocol (TIP) for people with physical and cognitive disabilities. The TIP provides best-practice consensus-based guidelines aimed at reducing barriers and improving substance use services (Moore, 1998).

Improving Accessibility to Substance Use Services

Accessibility issues in the provision of substance use services concern more than simply physical accessibility (U.S. National Association on Alcohol, Drugs and Disability, 1999). Accessibility is about more than ramps, doorways, washrooms and Braille elevator buttons. It also include the following:

• **Geographic accessibility**: The location of the treatment centre and the availability of accessible transportation can determine whether the client can get to the services he or she needs.

• **Program accessibility**: Can the program accommodate special needs such as slower pacing, scheduling (e.g., to allow for the extra time required for morning care or for days when the client cannot attend because of health needs), attendant care needs and special language or learning requirements (e.g., for people with deafness or hearing impairments, blindness or visual impairments, or learning impairments)?

• **Social accessibility**: These accessibility issues include attitudes, myths and stereotypes that affect the person's ability to participate fully. They include policies on and attitudes to the use of prescription drugs such as opioids, sedatives and anxiolitics. They also include staff attitudes and knowledge about disability issues. A "disability friendly" environment is both welcoming and inclusive.

The Need for a Continuum of Accessible Services

Early debates about service needs discussed whether we should modify mainstream addiction treatment services to accommodate the needs of people with disabilities, or provide specialized addiction treatment services for specific disability groups. Most authors argued for the importance of integrating people with disabilities into mainstream programs.

We now recognize the need for a broad and flexible continuum of accessible services aimed not only at dependent users but at all people who are at risk of substance use problems. Whether services can best be provided by the addiction system or by disability health service providers may vary from region to region, depending on geographic factors and the availability of other support services. We need to use resources efficiently and creatively to maximize the impact of scarce health care dollars. We need to tailor services to the needs and resources of different communities. We need to develop alternative cost-effective approaches, such as outreach services, telephone counselling services and Internet-based services. Substance use issues should be addressed at multiple points of access to the health care system. Finally, we need to do more to encourage people with disabilities to seek careers in health and social service fields. Recruiting people with disabilities into these fields may be one way to ensure that the needs of this population are better understood.

Partnerships

Improving the delivery of substance use treatment to people with disabilities will require better coordination between the addiction-service and disability-service sectors. It will require the development of partnerships and resources to address the training needs of treatment providers from both fields (e.g., Lamb et al., 1998). It will require the development of evidence-based practice guidelines for the provision of substance use services in the community. Some examples of effective partnerships can be found at the Web site for the SARDI program (SARDI, 2003).

Personal Commitment

Addressing issues of disability and substance use can be difficult and complex. Doing so effectively requires a commitment to learning and to reflection in practice. You may need to learn about your client's disabling condition to understand the role that substance use plays in his or her life. A wealth of information is available from disability associations and other advocacy groups. Disability literature can help you gain insight into disability culture and the experience of living with disability. The most authoritative source very often will be your client. Because of the health risks of living with disability, many clients will be well educated about their health condition.

Organizational Commitment

Whether interventions for people with disabilities are located within the addiction treatment sector, the disability sector or elsewhere, health providers must be willing to make real efforts to adapt their services to meet the special needs of clients with concurrent physical disabilities and substance use problems. While legislation recognizes that people with disabilities have a right to services, organizations can be resistant to accommodating the special needs of people with concurrent disabilities. Organizations must commit to working with counterparts and decision makers in the mental health, addiction and rehabilitation sectors to establish referral practices that are based on the needs of clients rather than the needs of institutions.

To effectively address the needs of residents or patients, physical rehabilitation settings and other institutions need to balance their policies and procedures for risk management with clinical considerations. For some patients in TBI and SCI rehabilitation settings, a substance use problem can be considered the primary disability (Heinemann, in press), even though programs are designed to address only the physical disability. In developing institutional policies and programs on substance use issues, we may sometimes face ethical dilemmas in balancing the rights of the person with those of others. In developing policy, institutions should consider:
• evidence of the potential harms and benefits of the substances in question—
  including those specific to the patient's/client's disabilities

• the availability of alternatives to the drug of choice—including alternative medications, therapies, recreational outlets and lifestyles.

Addressing the health and behavioural concerns that arise from problem substance use raises complex ethical and clinical issues, not only for the client but also for other patients and staff. People who continue to misuse substances during their hospitalization can be particularly problematic, since their behaviour can affect others. How do we respect the person's rights to rehabilitation services while ensuring the safety and well-being of others? How do we strike a reasonable balance between the extremes of neglect and paternalism?

One approach is to address substance use problems within the context of other risky behaviours (Walker, 1997). Substance use problems can be seen as a subset of overlapping categories of risk-related behaviours encountered in the rehabilitation setting (Figure 14-1). In responding to problem substance use, our focus should be on the consequences of use rather than on use itself—i.e., on harm and the risk of harm rather than on consumption. Our response to the person should depend on the nature of the risks—on whether we are primarily concerned about risks to the individual patient, to other patients, to staff or to the organization.

FIGURE 14-1

Relationship of Substance Misuse to Other Risk-Related Behaviours in Inpatient Rehabilitation Settings

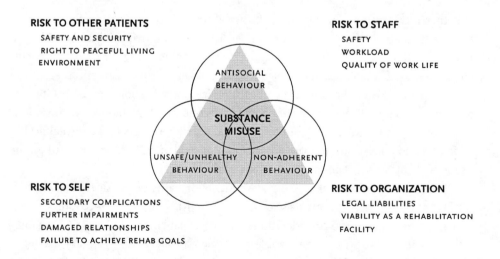

RISK TO OTHER PATIENTS
SAFETY AND SECURITY
RIGHT TO PEACEFUL LIVING
ENVIRONMENT

RISK TO STAFF
SAFETY
WORKLOAD
QUALITY OF WORK LIFE

ANTISOCIAL BEHAVIOUR

SUBSTANCE MISUSE

UNSAFE/UNHEALTHY BEHAVIOUR

NON-ADHERENT BEHAVIOUR

RISK TO SELF
SECONDARY COMPLICATIONS
FURTHER IMPAIRMENTS
DAMAGED RELATIONSHIPS
FAILURE TO ACHIEVE REHAB GOALS

RISK TO ORGANIZATION
LEGAL LIABILITIES
VIABILITY AS A REHABILITATION
FACILITY

Adapted from Walker (1997)

CONCLUDING COMMENTS

As addiction service providers, we have the moral and legal obligation to accommodate the needs of people with disabilities. Addressing their needs may require us to make fundamental changes in how we provide services. In many instances, however, the major accommodation required may be attitudinal and motivational rather than physical.

As discussed in the introduction to this chapter, people with disabilities are as heterogeneous as the population at large. However, the disability community includes some of the most disadvantaged and marginalized people in our society and some of the most challenging to the health provider. The role of the addiction counsellor in many cases is to attempt to mitigate some of the harm caused to clients by barriers to their full participation in society. Client advocacy is often a prerequisite for fostering a change in the client's lifestyle.

ACKNOWLEDGMENTS

The author gratefully acknowledges the valuable feedback provided by Allen Heinemann and by Karmick in reviewing this chapter. Dr. Heinemann is a professor at the Department of Physical Medicine and Rehabilitation in the Feinberg School of Medicine, Northwestern University in Chicago, and Associate Director of Research at the Rehabilitation Institute of Chicago. He is widely published in the field of substance use–disability research. Karmick is a writer from Toronto who has been living with spinal cord injury for about two years.

REFERENCES

Albrecht, G. & Devlieger, P. (1999). The disability paradox: High quality of life against all odds. *Social Science and Medicine*, 48, 977–988.

Altman, B.M. (2001). Disability definitions, models, classification schemes, and applications. In G.L. Albrecht, K.D. Seelman & M. Bury (Eds.), *Handbook of Disability Studies* (pp. 97–122). Thousand Oaks, CA: Sage Publications.

American Academy of Pain Medicine and American Pain Society. (1997). *The Use of Opioids for the Treatment of Chronic Pain.* Available: www.painmed.org/productpub/statements/pdfs/opioids.pdf.

Anson, C.A. & Shepherd, C. (1996). Incidence of secondary complications in spinal cord injury. *International Journal of Rehabilitation Research*, 19, 55–66.

Asch, A. & Fine, M. (1988). Disability beyond stigma: Social interaction, discrimination, and activism. *Journal of Social Issues*, 44, 3–22.

Bach, J.R. & Tilton, M. (1994). Life satisfaction and well-being measures in ventilator support-ed traumatic tetraplegics. *Archives of Physical and Medical Rehabilitation, 75*, 626–632.

Barnes, C., Mercer, G. & Shakespeare, T. (1999). *Exploring Disability: A Sociological Introduc-tion.* Cambridge, England: Polity Press.

Beirness, D.J., Mayhew, D.R., Simpson, H.M. & Lefebvre, J.L. (1995). *Alcohol-Involved Motor Vehicle Fatalities in Ontario.* Ottawa: Traffic Injury Research Foundation of Canada.

Benson, J.A., Jr. & Watson, S.J., Jr. (1999). *Marijuana and Medicine: Assessing the Science Base.* Washington, DC: National Academy Press.

Bombardier, C.H. (2000). Alcohol and traumatic disability. In R.G. Frank & T.R. Elliott (Eds.), *Handbook of Rehabilitation Psychology* (pp. 399–416). Washington, DC: American Psycho-logical Association Press.

Bombardier, C. & Rimmele C. (1998). Alcohol use and readiness to change after spinal cord injury. *Archives of Physical Medicine & Rehabilitation, 79,* 1110–1115.

Bombardier, C. & Rimmele, C. (1999). Motivational interviewing to prevent alcohol abuse after traumatic brain injury. *Rehabilitation Psychology, 44,* 52–67.

Brown, S.E. (1995). *Investigating a Culture of Disability: Final Report.* Las Cruces, NM: Institute on Disability Culture.

Brown, S.E. (2000). *A Celebration of Diversity: An Annotated Bibliography about Disability Culture.* Las Cruces, NM: Institute on Disability Culture.

Canadian Paraplegic Association. (2000). *Workforce Participation Survey of Canadians with Spinal Cord Injuries.* Toronto: Canadian Paraplegic Association.

Cardol, M., DeJong, B.A. & Ward, C. (2002). On autonomy and participation in rehabilita-tion. *Disability and Rehabilitation, 24,* 970–974.

Cleeland, C.S. (1987). Barriers to the management of cancer pain. Oncology, *1,* 19–26.

Costa, P.T., Jr. & VandenBos, G.R. (Eds.). (1990). *Psychological Aspects of Serious Illness: Chronic Conditions, Fatal Diseases, and Clinical Care.* Washington, DC: American Psycho-logical Association Press.

Cox, W., Heinemann, A., Miranti, S., Schmidt, M., Klinger, E. & Blount, J. (2003). Outcomes of Systematic Motivational Counseling for substance use following traumatic brain injury. *Journal of Addictive Diseases, 22,* 93–110.

Cox, W. & Klinger, E. (1988). A motivational model of alcohol use. *Journal of Abnormal Psychology, 97,* 168–180.

Cox, W. & Klinger, E. (1990). Incentive motivation, affective change, and alcohol use: A model. In W. Cox (Ed.), *Why People Drink: Parameters of Alcohol as a Reinforcer* (pp. 291–314). New York: Gardener Press.

Cox, W. & Klinger, E. (Eds.). (2003). *Handbook of Motivational Counseling: Concepts, Approaches, and Assessment.* Chichester, U.K.: Wiley.

Crisp, R. (2002). A counselling framework for understanding individual experiences of socially constructed disability. *Disability Studies Quarterly, 22,* 20–32. Available: www.cds.hawaii.edu.

de Miranda, J. (2002). Discrimination against addicts and alcoholics persists. *Alcoholism and Drug Abuse Weekly*, December 17, 2001. Available: www.naadd.org/resources.html.

DeLoach, C. & Greer, B.G. (1981). *Adjustment to Severe Physical Disability: A Metamorphosis.* New York: McGraw Hill.

Dembo, T. (1969). Rehabilitation psychology and its immediate future: A problem of utilization of psychological knowledge. *Rehabilitation Psychology, 16,* 63–72.

Dembo, T. (1970). The utilization of psychological knowledge in rehabilitation. *Welfare Review, 8,* 1–7.

DeVivo, M.J., Krause, J.S. & Lammertse, D.P. (1999). Recent trends in mortality and causes of death among persons with spinal cord injury. *Archives of Physical Medicine & Rehabilitation, 80,* 1411–1419.

Elovic, E. & Kirshblum, K. (1999). Epidemiology of spinal cord injury and traumatic brain injury: The scope of the problem. *Topics in Spinal Cord Injury Rehabilitation, Dual Diagnosis: SCI-TBI, 5,* 1–20.

Ernst, J.L. & Day, E.H. (1998). Reducing the penalties of long-term employment: Alternatives in vocational rehabilitation and spinal cord injury. *Journal of Vocational Rehabilitation, 10,* 133–139.

Fawcett, G. (2000). *Bringing Down the Barriers: The Labour Market and Women with Disabilities in Ontario.* Ottawa: Canadian Council on Social Development.

Fishbain, D., Goldberg, M., Meagher, B., Steele, R. & Rosomoff, H. (1986). Male and female chronic pain patients categorized by DSM-III psychiatric diagnostic criteria. *Pain, 26,* 181–197.

Fishman, S.M., Bandman, T.B., Edwards, A. & Borsook, D. (1999). The opioid contract in the management of chronic pain. *Journal of Pain and Symptom Management, 18,* 27–37.

Foley, K.M. (1991). Clinical tolerance to opioids. In A.I. Basbaum & J.M. Besson (Eds.), *Towards a New Pharmacotherapy of Pain* (pp. 181–204). New York: John Wiley & Sons.

Friedman, D.P. (1990). Perspectives on the medical use of drugs of abuse. *Journal of Pain Symptom Management, 5*(1 Suppl.), 2–5.

Gerhart, K.A., Koziol-McLain, J., Lowenstein, S.R. & Whiteneck, G.G. (1994). Quality of life following spinal cord injury: Knowledge and attitudes of emergency care providers. *Annals of Emergency Medicine, 23,* 807–812.

Goffman, E. (1963). *Stigma: Notes on the Management of Spoiled Identity.* Englewood Cliffs, NJ: Prentice Hall.

Government of Canada. (2002). *Advancing the Inclusion of Persons with Disabilities: A Government of Canada Report—December 2002.* Ottawa: Government of Canada Available: www.hrdc-drhc.gc.ca/hrib/sdd-dds/odi/documents/AIPD/.

Ham, H.P. & Parsons O.A. (2000). Predicting cognitive performance in alcoholics and nonalcoholics: Specification of affective, childhood behavior disorders, and antisocial variables. *Applied Neuropsychology, 7,* 90–95.

Harris Interactive, Inc. (2000). *2000 N.O.D./Harris Survey of Americans with Disabilities.* New York: Harris Interactive, Inc.; Washington, DC: National Organization on Disability. Available: www.nod.org.

Hartkopp, A., Brønnum-Hansen, H., Seidenschnur, A. & Biering-Sørensen, F. (1998). Suicide in a spinal cord injured population: Its relation to functional status. *Archives of Physical & Medical Rehabilitation, 79*, 1356–1361.

Hayes, M.V. & Dunn, J.R. (1998). *Population Health in Canada: Systematic Review.* CPRN Study No. H*01. Ottawa: Renouf.

Hawkins, D. & Heinemann, A. (1998). Substance abuse and medical complications following spinal cord injury. *Rehabilitation Psychology, 43*, 219–231.

Heinemann, A.W. (In press). Disability and rehabilitation issues. In J. Lowinson, P. Ruiz, R.B. Millman & J.G. Langrod (Eds.), *Substance Abuse: A Comprehensive Textbook* (4th ed.). Baltimore, MD: Lippincott, Williams & Wilkins.

Heinemann, A.W. & Hawkins, D. (1998). Substance abuse and medical complications following spinal cord injury. (Revised). *Rehabilitation Psychology, 43*, 219–231.

Jones, M.H. (1997). *People with Disabilities.* Winnipeg, MB: The Canadian Centre on Disability Studies. Available: http://dawn.thot.net/disability_guide.html.

Joranson, D.E. & Gilson, A.M. (1994). Controlled substances, medical practice and the law. In H.I. Schwartz (Ed.), *Psychiatric Practice under Fire: The Influence of Government, the Media and Special Interests on Somatic Therapies* (pp. 173–194). Washington, DC: American Psychiatric Press.

Kalant, H., Corregal, W., Hall, W. & Smart, R. (Eds.). (1999). *The Health Effects of Cannabis.* Toronto: Centre for Addiction and Mental Health.

Kapur, B.M. (1974). Patterns of drug abuse and their relationship to traffic accidents. In S. Israelstam & S. Lambert (Eds.), *Alcohol, Drugs, and Traffic Safety: Proceedings of the Sixth International Conference on Alcohol, Drugs and Traffic Safety, Toronto, September 8–13, 1974* (pp. 69–72). Toronto: Addiction Research Foundation.

Katon, W., Egan, K. & Miller, D. (1985). Chronic pain: Lifetime diagnoses and family history. American *Journal of Psychiatry, 142*, 1156–1160.

Keyes, C.L.M. & Haidt, J. (Eds.). (2002). *Flourishing: Positive Psychology and the Life Well-Lived.* Washington, DC: American Psychological Association.

Kuczewski, M. & Fiedler, I. (2001). Ethical issues in rehabilitation: Conceptualizing the next generation of challenges. *American Journal of Physical Medicine & Rehabilitation, 80*, 848–851.

Lamb, S., Greenlick, M.R. & McCarty, D. (Eds.). (1998). *Bridging the Gap between Practice and Research: Forging Partnerships with Community-based Drug and Alcohol Treatment.* Washington, DC: National Academy Press.

Langley, M. (1992). Prevention of substance abuse in persons with neurological disabilities. *Neurorehabilitation, 2*, 52–64.

Langley, M. & Ridgely, M. (1994). *Skills-Based Substance Abuse Prevention Counseling: Behavioral Interventions for Clients with Neurological Disabilities.* Austin, TX: National Center for the Dissemination of Disability Research.

Lee, K.K. (2000). *Urban Poverty in Canada: A Statistical Profile.* Available: www.ccsd.ca/pubs/2000/up/.

Liberman, M., Mulder, D., Lavoie, A., Denis, R. & Sampalis, J.S. (2003). Multicenter Canadian study of prehospital trauma care. *Annals of Surgery, 237*, 153–160.

Linton, S. (1998). *Claiming Disability*. New York: New York University Press.

Loder, E., Witkower, A., McAlary, P., Huhta, M. & Matarrazzo, J. (2003). Rehabilitation hospital staff knowledge and attitudes regarding pain. *American Journal of Physical Medicine & Rehabilitation, 82*, 65–68.

Mackelprang, R.W. & Salsgiver, R.O. (1998). *Human Services and Person with Disabilities*. New York: Thomson Learning.

Marinelli, R.P. & Dell Orto, A.E. (1999). *The Psychological and Social Impact of Disability*. New York: Springer.

Meichenbaum, D. (1994). *A Clinical Handbook/Practical Therapist Manual for Assessing and Treating Adults with Post-Traumatic Stress Disorder* (PTSD). Waterloo, ON: Institute Press.

Miller, W. & Rollnick, S. (Eds.). (1991). *Motivational Interviewing: Preparing People for Change*. New York: Guilford Press.

Moore, D. (1998). *Substance Use Disorder Treatment for People with Physical and Cognitive Disabilities: Treatment Improvement Protocol* (TIP) Series 29. Rockville, MD: National Clearinghouse for Alcohol and Drug Information, U.S. Department of Health and Human Services.

Moore, D. & Li, L. (1994). Substance use among applicants for vocational rehabilitation services. *Journal of Rehabilitation, 60*, 48–53.

Murray, C.J. & Lopez, A.D. (Eds.). (1991). *The Global Burden of Disease: A Comprehensive Assessment of Mortality and Disability from Diseases, Injuries, and Risk Factors in 1990 and Projected to 2020*. Geneva, Switzerland: World Health Organization.

National Association on Alcohol, Drugs and Disability. (1999). *Access Limited Substance Abuse Services for People with Disabilities: A National Perspective*. Washington, DC: National Association on Alcohol, Drugs and Disability.

National Council of Welfare. (2000). *Welfare Incomes 1999*. Ottawa: Minister of Public Works and Government Services Canada.

National Institutes of Health. (1997). *Workshop on the Medical Utility of Marijuana: Report to the Director, National Institutes of Health, by the Ad Hoc Group of Experts*. Available: www.nih.gov/news/medmarijuana/MedicalMarijuana.htm.

Neimeyer, R.A. & Raskin, J.D. (Eds.). (2000). *Constructions of Disorder: Meaning-Making Frameworks for Psychotherapy*. Washington, DC: American Psychological Association.

Oliver, M. (1990). *The Politics of Disablement*. Basingstoke, England: Macmillan and St. Martin's Press.

Oliver, M. (1996). *Understanding Disability: From Theory to Practice*. New York: St. Martin's Press.

Ostir, G.V. (1999). Disability in older adults 1: Prevalence, causes, and consequences. *Behavioral Medicine, 24*, 147–157.

Oyserman, D. & Swim, J.K. (2001). Stigma: An insider's view. *Journal of Social Issues, 57*, 1–14.

Padden, C. & Humphries, T. (1988). *Deaf in America: Voices from a Culture.* Cambridge, MA: Harvard University Press.

Parsons, T. (1951). *The Social System.* New York: The Free Press.

Pfeiffer, D. (2002). The philosophical foundations of disability studies. *Disability Studies Quarterly, 22,* 3–23. Available: www.cds.hawaii.edu.

Portenoy, R.K. (1996). Opioid therapy for chronic nonmalignant pain: Clinicians' perspective. *Journal of Law and Medical Ethics, 24,* 301.

Portenoy, R.K. & Payne, R. (1997). Acute and chronic pain. In J.H. Lowinson, P. Ruiz & R.B. Millman (Eds.), *Comprehensive Textbook of Substance Abuse* (3rd ed.) (pp. 563–590). Baltimore, MD: Williams & Wilkins.

Porter, J. & Jick, H. (1980). Addiction is rare in patients treated with narcotics. *New England Journal of Medicine, 302,* 123.

Radnitz, C.L., Broderick, C.P., Perez-Strumolo, L., Tirch, D.D., Festa, J., Schlein, I.S., Walczak, S., Willard, J., Lillian, L.B. & Binks, M. (1996). The prevalence of psychiatric disorders in veterans with spinal cord injury: A controlled comparison. *The Journal of Nervous and Mental Disease, 184,* 431–433.

Rasmussen, G. & DeBoer, R. (1980). Alcohol and drug use among clients at a residential vocational rehabilitation facility. *Alcohol Health Research World, 5,* 48–56.

Ravelshoot, C.H. (1996). Attributions of purpose and meaningful activity following spinal cord injury. *SCI Psychosocial Process, 9,* 135–136.

Roots, J. (1999). *The Politics of Visual Language: Deafness, Language Choice and Political Socialization.* Ottawa: The Canadian Association of the Deaf.

Rosenblum, A., Joseph, H., Fong, C., Kipnis, S., Cleland, C. & Portenoy, R.K. (2003). Prevalence and characteristics of chronic pain among chemically dependent patients in methadone maintenance and residential treatment facilities. *Journal of the American Medical Association, 289,* 2370–2378.

SARDI. (2003). The Substance Abuse Resources and Disability Issues SARDI Program. Available: www.med.wright.edu/citar/sardi/index.html.

Schug, S.A, Zech, D., Grond, S., Jung, H., Meuser, T. & Stobbe, B. (1992). A long-term survey of morphine in cancer pain patients. *Journal of Pain Symptom Management, 7,* 259–266.

Senate Special Committee on Illegal Drugs. (2002). *Cannabis: Our Position for a Canadian Public Policy: Report of the Senate Special Committee on Illegal Drugs.* Ottawa: Canadian Senate. Available: www.parl.gc.ca/english/senate/com-e/lega-e/04evb-e.htm.

Shakespeare, T. (1994). *Cultural Representations of Disabled People: Dustbins for Disavowal? Disability and Society.* London: Cassell.

Statistics Canada. (2001). *Participation and Activity Limitation Survey: A Profile of Disability in Canada.* Available: www.statcan.ca/Daily/English/021203/d021203a.htm.

Stewart, T.D. (1988). Psychiatric diagnosis and treatment following spinal cord injury. *Psychosomatics, 29,* 214–220.

Talmadge, J. (2003, March). Highlights from the 13th Annual Meeting of the American Association for Addiction Psychiatry, December 12–15, 2002, Las Vegas, NV: Conference Report. *Medscape Psychiatry & Mental Health, 8.* Available: www.medscape.com.

Trieschmann, R. (1980). *Spinal Cord Injuries: Psychological, Social and Vocational Adjustment.* New York: Pergamon Press.

Von Roenn, J.H., Cleeland, C.S., Gonin, R., Hatfield, A.K. & Pandya, K.J. (1993). Physician attitudes and practice in cancer pain management: A survey from the Eastern Cooperative Oncology Group. *Annals of Internal Medicine, 119,* 121–126.

Walker, K. (1996). *Harm Reduction and the Prevention of Alcohol-Related Problems following Spinal Cord Injury.* Las Vegas, NE: American Association of Spinal Cord Injury, Annual Symposium.

Walker, K. (1997). *The Concept of "Harm Reduction" As a Central Principle in the Development of Policies and Protocols to Address Alcohol and Drug Problems.* Unpublished manuscript. Toronto: Lyndhurst Hospital.

Waller, P.F., Blow, F.C., Maio, R.F., Singer, K., Hill, E.M. & Schaffer, N. (1997). Crash characteristics and injuries of victims impaired by alcohol versus illicit drugs. *Accident Analysis and Prevention, 29,* 817–827.

Ward, S.E., Goldberg, N., Miller-McCauley, V., Mueller, C., Nolan, A., Pawlik-Plank, D. et al. (1993). Patient-related barriers to management of cancer pain. *Pain, 52,* 319–324.

Watanabe, T.K., Zafonte, R.D. & Lairson, E.J. (1999). Traumatic brain injury associated with acute spinal cord injury: Risk factors, evaluation, and outcomes. *Topics in Spinal Cord Injury Rehabilitation, Dual Diagnosis: SCI-TBI, 5,* 83–90.

Weathermon, R. & Crabb, D.W. (1999). Alcohol and medication interactions. *Alcohol Research & Health, 23,* 40–51.

Weissman, D.E. & Haddox, J.D. (1989). Opioid pseudoaddiction: An iatrogenic syndrome. *Pain, 36,* 363–366.

West, M.D. (1995). Choice, self-determination and VR services: Systemic barriers for consumers with severe disabilities. *Journal of Vocational Rehabilitation, 5,* 281–290.

Westgren, N. & Levi, R. (1998). Quality of life and traumatic spinal cord injury. *Archives of Physical Medicine and Rehabilitation, 79,* 1433–1439.

Wilkinson, R.G. (1996). *Unhealthy Societies: The Afflictions of Inequality.* London, England: Routledge.

Winter, J.A. (2003). The development of the disability rights movement as a social problem solver. *Disability Studies Quarterly, 23,* 33-61. Available: www.cds.hawaii.edu/dsq.

World Health Organization. (1980). *International Classification of Impairments, Disease, and Handicaps: A Manual for Classification Relating to the Consequence of Disease.* Geneva, Switzerland: World Health Organization.

World Health Organization. (1990). *Cancer Pain Relief and Palliative Care: Report of a WHO Expert Committee.* Geneva, Switzerland: World Health Organization.

World Health Organization. (2000). *Global Status Report on Alcohol*. Geneva, Switzerland: World Health Organization.

World Health Organization. (2001). *International Classification of Functioning, Disability and Health*. Geneva, Switzerland: World Health Organization.

Wortman, C. & Cohen Silver, R. (2001). The myths of coping with loss revisited. In M.S. Stroebe, R.O. Hansson, W. Stroebe & H. Schut (Eds.), *Handbook of Bereavement Research: Consequences, Coping, and Care* (pp. 405–429). Washington, DC: American Psychological Association.

Wright, B.A. (1991). Labeling: The need for greater person-environment individuation. In C.R. Snyder & D.R. Forsyth (Eds.), *Handbook of Social and Clinical Psychology: The Health Perspective* (pp. 469–487). New York: Pergamon Press.

Zames Fleischer, D. & Zames, F. (2001). *The Disability Rights Movement: From Charity to Confrontation*. Philadelphia, PA.: Temple University Press.

WEB-BASED RESOURCES

CANADIAN DISABILITY LINKS
Canadian Abilities Foundation: www.enablelink.org/index.html.

Canadian Association of Independent Living Centres: www.cailc.ca.

Canadian Centre on Disability Studies. University of Manitoba: www.disabilitystudies.ca/.

Canadian Health Network: www.canadian-health-network.ca/1people_with_disabilities.html.

Council of Canadians with Disabilities (CCD): www.pcs.mb.ca/~ccd/.

Disability Studies Online Magazine: www.disabilitystudies.com/.

Disability WebLinks: http://www.disabilityweblinks.ca/.

Graduate Programme in Critical Disability Studies. York University, Toronto: www.yorku.ca/grads/cal/disa.htm.

Institute for Disability Studies Research and Education. Ryerson University, Toronto: www.ryerson.ca/ds/RBCInstitute.htm.

SUBSTANCE USE AND DISABILITIES
National Association on Alcohol, Drugs and Disability: www.naadd.org/.

Rehabilitation Research and Training Center on Drugs and Disability, School of Medicine, Wright State University, Dayton, Ohio: www.med.wright.edu/citar/sardi/index.html.

Chapter 15

Older Adults and Substance Use

JANE BARON, JENNIFER BARR, VIRGINIA CARVER AND MARGARET FLOWER

INTRODUCTION

Our population is aging and the proportion of older people in Canada has grown from one in 20 in 1921, to one in eight in 2001. It is estimated that by 2041, older adults will make up over 25 per cent of the population (Health Canada, 2001). As the population ages, those who work in substance use treatment will see a resulting increase in the number of older clients; service providers need then to prepare by becoming familiar with the issues that affect older adults, and the best practices to use in serving them.

Alcohol is the substance most commonly used by seniors (Health Canada, 1999). However, some illicit drug use has now been observed among those over 55, a trend that may increase as the "baby boomers" (those born between 1946 and 1966) who have had more experience with "recreational" drug use (Gurnack, 1997).

Historically, older adults have been under-represented in the substance use treatment system (Graham et al., 1997). Reasons include the under-identification of problems; co-occurring illness and disability, which can mask or exacerbate a substance use problem; and a general lack of sensitivity among service providers to the older person's differences and needs. On the part of older adults, there may be a particularly keen sense of stigma, which could be due to generational attitudes about who develops alcohol problems and why. Certainly, there has also been a lack of professional interest in this population, and an intrinsic reluctance to attend to their needs, perhaps reflecting overall negative social attitudes toward the elderly.

Fortunately, there is an increasing understanding of approaches that work well for older adults, particularly the need for specialized treatment. The principles of specialized treatment have been demonstrated by the success of Ontario programs such as Lifestyle Enrichment for Senior Adults (LESA), Community Outreach Programs in Addictions (COPA) and other Canadian programs. These principles include:

• a harm reduction and health enhancement philosophy, including a pragmatic and problem-solving orientation
• individual counselling in a setting in which the older person is most comfortable, often his or her own home
• group and recreational opportunities.

What is little known is the very positive prospect of success in treatment, particularly for the client who may have only recently developed the problem. In fact, older adults may fare better than their younger counterparts in treatment (Gurnack et al., 2002).

Older adults are a heterogeneous group. Compounding the disadvantage and stigma of "old age" are other diversity issues. Men are generally more likely to experience alcohol use problems and may need special support moving from work to retirement (Adlaf & Smart, 1995). Women with alcohol problems may feel an even greater sense of stigma than men with the same issues—this is especially true for older women who grew up at a time when public drinking was less acceptable for women.

Sexuality and sexual orientation can pose challenges to older adults placed in an institutional setting. Cultural and language barriers exist. There are considerable differences in the "young old" (those in their 60s and 70s) and the "old old" (those in their 80s and over). There are differences in living situations—residential or "retirement home," long-term care and independent community living. Each person presents a different set of challenges, strengths and special issues for those offering help.

Substance use professionals who wish to prepare themselves for the anticipated increase in the numbers of older clients will find education in gerontology—the interdisciplinary study of aging—extremely useful. This education gives the clinician an understanding of the normal process of aging, the distinct issues relevant to this time of life and changes in metabolism and physiology, all of which can impact on the use and effects of alcohol and other drugs. It also helps to develop counsellors' awareness and appreciation of the cognitive problems that can sometimes come with advancing age, and how depression, dementia and other mental health conditions may be manifested and are best addressed.

Counsellors who adopt a respectful, genuine and non-judgmental approach toward people entering this phase of life can help the client adopt positive attitudes toward aging. The purpose of this chapter is to encourage this process. It introduces several issues specific to the older adult, describes proven clinical approaches for treatment and offers a blueprint to communities for improving the older person's likelihood of being referred to and ultimately succeeding in a substance use treatment program.

SUBSTANCE USE AMONG OLDER ADULTS

Older adults are less likely than people in other age groups to drink, but are more likely to use prescription and over-the-counter medications, particularly central nervous system (CNS) depressants such as tranquilizers and sleeping pills. Illicit drug use in this age group is low; however, it may increase as the "boomer" population ages (Gurnack, 1997).

The 1998–1999 *National Population Health Survey* (Statistics Canada, 2000) polled older Canadians on their alcohol consumption, and found that it decreased with age. Regular drinking was reported by 55 per cent of those aged 55–64, 44 per cent of those aged 65–74, and 30 per cent of those aged 75 and over. Rates of abstention from alcohol increased with age, from eight per cent of those aged 55–64 to 20 per cent of those aged 75 and over. Overall, women were less likely than men to drink regularly and more likely to drink only occasionally, not at all or to be lifetime abstainers.

While, as a whole, older Canadians are less likely to consume alcohol as they age, those who do drink consume about the same amount each week as younger Canadians. The *National Population Health Survey* (Statistics Canada, 2000) found that the majority of older Canadian drinkers (approximately two-thirds) reported drinking six or fewer drinks a week, while an average of 10 per cent reported drinking 14 or more drinks a week, rates that are not dissimilar to those for younger age groups. Similar results have been found among older adults in the most recent survey of substance use among Ontario adults as well as previous national surveys (Adlaf & Ialomiteanu, 2002).

While older adults may drink about the same total amount each week as younger adults, they are more likely to drink daily rather than consuming larger quantities less frequently, as is common in younger adults. Spencer (2002) notes, "while the proportion of daily drinkers has been decreasing significantly in other age groups in Ontario over the past 24 years, the decrease in percentage is far less among older adults."

These trends are important because of the high percentage of older adults who regularly take prescribed or over-the-counter medications. Equally important, even small amounts of alcohol can be problematic in older adults because of the changes in metabolism and physiology. For example, older adults show a higher blood alcohol concentration than younger people after consuming an equal amount of alcohol (National Institute on Alcohol Abuse and Alcoholism, 1998).

Surveys indicate that older adults generally have fewer alcohol-related problems than younger adults (National Institute on Alcohol Abuse and Alcoholism, 1998). For example, a study using the Alcohol Use Disorders Identification Test (AUDIT) found that in Ontario, only five per cent of those aged 65 and older reported hazardous drinking, compared with 25 per cent of those aged 18–29 (Adlaf & Ialomiteanu, 2002). However, these low rates of reported problems may be misleading as they do not reflect the actual numbers of older adults whose drinking puts them at risk. As we know, lower levels of alcohol will have a more powerful effect on an older person.

Also, detection of alcohol problems is difficult because of the lack of common diagnostic criteria used in studies, the lack of applicability of some measurement tools and the general problem of under-recognition in this age group.

In contrast to the use of alcohol, use of prescribed and over-the-counter medication generally increases with age, with pain relievers and heart and blood medication among the drugs most commonly used by older adults (Adlaf & Smart, 1995; Bergob, 1994; Dufour et al., 1995). Other common medications include stomach remedies and laxatives, sleeping pills, cough and cold medication and herbal remedies.

Canada's 1994 *Alcohol and Other Drug Use Survey* (Health Canada, 1997) found that the percentage of Canadians reporting use of one or more prescribed psycho-active medications (pain medication, sleeping pills, tranquilizers, antidepressants or diet pills) was 27.4 per cent among those aged 65 years or older, compared with 18.5 per cent among those aged 15–24 years. Consistent with previous surveys, these differences were particularly marked for use of tranquilizers, sleeping pills and anti-depressants (Health Canada, 1997). Somewhat higher rates of medication use were found in a survey of older adults in one Ontario community in which 30 per cent of those surveyed reported use of one or more CNS depressant medications (Graham et al., 1995).

Use of CNS depressants has been associated with poorer health, more stress and lack of support from family and friends (Bergob, 1994; Graham et al., 1996). It is important to note that the use of antidepressants (as distinct from CNS depressants) among older adults is low compared with the rate of depression in this age group. Older adults are much less likely than younger adults to have mental health problems such as depression recognized and treated.

WHY SUBSTANCE USE MAY BE A PROBLEM FOR OLDER ADULTS

There are many reasons why people use substances inappropriately, and in some cases the reasons are different for older adults than for younger adults. Older people may experience significant physical and social changes associated with aging, although over 80 per cent of aging people lead productive, happy and active lives and do not experience debilitating conditions. If an older person does not have good coping strategies, or if those strategies no longer work, he or she may begin to rely on alcohol or other drugs to handle the stresses of aging. For some older adults with lifelong histories of chronic substance use problems, the alcohol and other drug use habits may be manifested in significant health problems, as well as ongoing personal crises, including the risk of homelessness.

As people age, their bodies change and they may become more sensitive to the effects of substances (Dufour, 1995; McKim & Mishara, 1987; Smith, 1995). These changes include a reduction in the amount of body water and lean body mass, and an increase in body fat, which may mean that water-soluble drugs (such as alcohol) are more concentrated, and drugs that are stored in the fat (such as benzodiazepines) stay in the body longer. At the same time, older people may experience a decline in kidney and liver functions, resulting in higher concentrations and slower elimination of some drugs from the body. Because women are generally smaller and have less body water and more fat than men, they are more vulnerable to the effects of substances. Counsellors need to be aware that this greater sensitivity to the effects of substances can result in problems such as overmedication, even with therapeutic doses. Overmedication, particularly in the case of CNS depressants, may result in difficulties with motor function (leading to falls and injuries), co-ordination problems, confusion and forgetfulness and, in extreme cases, death. In some cases, the types of prescriptions provided may cause an older person to unknowingly develop a dependence. When medication is prescribed by a physician, its use is perceived as appropriate by older adults and others around them. Particular care and concern must be given to long-term benzodiazepine use.

The variety of prescribed and over-the-counter medications used by older adults may have additive effects when used together. For instance, an older adult may be simultaneously using several drugs that depress the central nervous system. These might include alcohol, a prescribed sleeping medication and an over-the-counter painkiller containing codeine, such as 222s. Such use increases the risk of problems. Older adults should be particularly careful about driving, using machinery and negotiating unfamiliar ground when they are using alcohol or CNS depressant medications. In addition, older adults need to be aware that alcohol can react with many commonly used medications. Over 100 prescription and over-the-counter drugs can cause adverse reactions when used with alcohol, sometimes with serious medical consequences (Dufour, 1995).

Here are two examples of common situations:

Situation 1

Mrs. M. is 70 years old. She has high blood pressure, and her physician has prescribed an anti-hypertensive and a benzodiazepine as a mild sedative to help her sleep. She also frequently takes over-the-counter pain medication containing codeine to ease her tension headaches. She uses the maximum recommended daily dosage and occasionally exceeds it. She has not told her doctor about taking this over-the-counter drug. Several times a week she consumes two to four standard drinks in the course of an afternoon bridge game. The minor tranquilizer, codeine and alcohol have an additive effect, because they are all CNS depressants. She has experienced occasional dizziness, confusion and recent memory loss, and has also had several unexplained falls, most recently resulting in a fractured wrist.

Situation 2

Mr. H. is 63. His living situation has deteriorated to the extent that the volunteers from Meals-on-Wheels are concerned about his well-being. He reports a family history of alcohol problems and has a long history of heavy drinking, both socially and at work. Over the years, he has been jailed several times for impaired driving. Mr. H. also has had periods of abstinence of up to two years. In recent years, he drinks alone in his apartment. Mr. H. no longer works and has no social contacts or satisfying leisure pursuits. His poor health limits his activities. His drinking is apparently in response to his loneliness, depression and boredom.

According to Mr. H., he typically consumes two to three drinks a day when he is drinking. However, based on his appearance, mood and the empty bottles in his room, it is likely that he is under-reporting his consumption. When drinking, he tends to severely neglect himself (e.g., not eating). He also does not take adequate care of his apartment, which has led to complaints from his landlord.

IDENTIFICATION OF SUBSTANCE USE PROBLEMS

Identifying alcohol or other substance use problems in older adults can sometimes be challenging for a number of reasons: First, current standard measures or criteria for dependence or problem use may not be relevant for older people. Many of these are based on research on a younger population, and do not reflect greater sensitivity to substances with aging, or that the use of prescription medication is more common among older adults. To accurately assess problem substance use in older adults, it is important to look not only at the risk levels of substance use (e.g., number of drinks per drinking occasion), but also the reasons for use and the effects of the use on daily activities, health and coping abilities. Potential legal problems also need to be considered.

Second, older people may not report problems when asked about drinking or other drug use (Graham, 1986). Older adults sometimes fear such a discussion will result in their losing their independence; they may also be concerned with other substance use issues such as stigma.

Another problem is that it may be difficult to distinguish between a substance use problem and depression or dementia, because of similar indicators. However, health care professionals should be alert to the extent of alcohol or medication use if the client seems to be confused, depressed, has memory or other cognitive problems, has frequent falls or fractures, or is neglecting himself or herself or his or her environment. (Nonetheless, clinicians must always bear in mind that such problems could have other causes.)

Finally, identification of a problem may be hampered by the attitudes of those around the older person. Family, friends and even health and social service professionals may feel that it is a private matter and may not know how to react. There is a common myth that for the older adult, alcohol "is all they have" or "they have earned it" or "after all why bother now, they only have a few years left." Some may also feel that if a physician has prescribed a drug, its use must be appropriate. Caregivers greatly need improved training, education and awareness (both formal and informal) regarding substance use problems in older adults. Alcohol and other drug use is not usually pleasurable for older people—it often causes them distress, robbing them of their quality of life and undermining their independence. There are several common responses when family, friends or health care professionals suggest to the older person that his or her substance use is causing problems. The older person may deny there is a problem and challenge the person broaching the subject (e.g., "You don't understand what it's like for me" or "You're exaggerating"), or he or she may try to manipulate the relationship.

Two typologies, "early onset" and "late onset," are commonly used to describe substance use problems among older adults. These typologies are based on patterns of substance use and age of onset, and help increase identification, understanding of substance use problems in older adults and development of appropriate treatment. Early onset refers to alcohol or other drug problems that developed early in life and continued into old age (this category comprises about two-thirds of cases). Late onset refers to problems that developed later in life, often in reaction to stresses associated with aging, mainly losses or illnesses (about one-third of cases). A third typology, "intermittent," refers to substance use problems that occur periodically throughout adult life but that become more serious or consistent as a person ages.

SCREENING

Counsellors working with older adults should always take a careful history of all substances used by each client. Screening provides an opportunity to explore potential problem use and to decide whether a referral and/or a more in-depth assessment is required. This initial screening also provides an opportunity to educate the client on safe drinking levels, medication management and alternative ways of coping with stress, anxiety or sleep problems (e.g., relaxation techniques, exercise, non-chemical sleep aids and diet).

The following questions can be used to ask older adults about medication and alcohol use. If the client's response does not reflect the question, this may indicate either a cognitive problem or impairment from alcohol or other drugs, including medication.

This initial contact is crucial to successfully engaging the client. Equally, the most therapeutic intervention is to identify the problem from the client's perspective. Health care professionals must recognize that helping older clients requires a therapeutic alliance, and that the process of change does not necessarily begin with changing their substance use.

Medications
(Prescription, over-the-counter and health food supplements/
herbal remedies)

QUESTIONS

Can you tell me the names of medications you are taking?

What was [name or indicate the medication] prescribed for?

How long have you been taking these medications?

Do you take them regularly (at the recommended time)?

Do you skip days, or forget days?

Do you ever have difficulty remembering when to take your medication?

Do you take any other prescribed medications?

Do you ever take medication that belongs to someone else (e.g., a family member or friend)?

Do you ever share your medication with someone else?

Who is your family doctor?

Do you have a specialist?

Do you see any other doctors?

Which doctor knows all the medications you are taking?

Where do you keep your medication?

Do you sometimes put your medication in a different bottle from the one given to you by the doctor or the pharmacy?

How is that helpful for you?

Do you use other pills, vitamins or herbal remedies that you buy without needing a prescription?

Do you take this medication on the advice of a doctor?

Do you find your pharmacist helpful?

Which pharmacist do you use?

Do you ever drink alcohol while you are also taking medication without checking with a doctor?

WARNING SIGNS OF PROBLEMS WITH MEDICATION MANAGEMENT

• not knowing the purpose of the medication

• forgetting to take medication or getting confused about which medication is in the container

• not having one doctor who knows about all the medication the person is taking (including over-the-counter medication and medication prescribed by another doctor)

• using old medications on symptoms that seem similar to those the person had when the medication was prescribed.

WARNING SIGNS OF INAPPROPRIATE MEDICATION USE
• not taking medication as prescribed (taking more or less than prescribed)
• regularly taking over-the-counter medication without the advice of his or her doctor
• using medication (e.g., benzodiazepines to help sleep or for anxiety) regularly for several months or longer
• drinking alcohol while taking medication without checking with his or her doctor
• using medication that has been prescribed for someone else
• driving (or operating other machinery) while using depressant medications.

Alcohol

Make sure you and the client define a drink in the same way. Ask what size of glass he or she uses. A standard drink is 340 millilitres (12 ounces) of beer, 140 millilitres (5 ounces) of wine or 40 millilitres (1.5 ounces) of liquor.

QUESTIONS
Do you ever have a drink containing alcohol (e.g., beer, wine, hard liquor, cider, sherry, brandy, cooler or a liqueur)?
How often do you have a drink containing alcohol?
How many drinks containing alcohol do you have on a typical day when you are drinking?
Are there days or times of the week when you drink more than usual?
Do you ever drive (or operate other equipment) after having one or more drinks during the previous hour?

WARNING SIGNS OF INAPPROPRIATE ALCOHOL USE[1]
• drinking more than two standard drinks on any one day
• drinking more than nine standard drinks per week for women or 14 standard drinks per week for men
• drinking and driving or operating other machinery
• drinking while using medication when this is contraindicated.

1. These warning signs are adapted from low-risk drinking guidelines for healthy adults, developed in 1993 by the Addiction Research Foundation and the Canadian Centre on Substance Abuse. The U.S. National Institute on Alcohol Abuse and Alcoholism (NIAAA) recommends that older adults (defined by NIAAA as people older than 65) consume no more than one standard drink a day (NIAAA, 1998, p. 2).

ASSESSMENT

If a fuller assessment is appropriate, the context will help guide the process. What is the reason for the assessment? Who has requested it? Is the assessment at the client's home or the counsellor's office? Is the client a willing participant? Is he or she aware that the concern is substance use? Who is the clinician and what is his or her specialty—substance use or gerontology?

Agencies providing services to seniors need to connect with each other. Sharing skills and knowledge between service providers will greatly improve services and limit the possibility of misdiagnosis. It is important for counsellors to understand the differences between normal aging and problems in aging. For example, knowing the difference between memory problems and ordinary forgetfulness could change an assessment outcome.

The purpose of the in-depth assessment is to establish a trusting and therapeutic relationship. The desired outcome is that the older person will continue with the service offered. Whether the assessment is conducted by a substance use counsellor or by another health or social work practitioner, the following points should be considered.

- The assessment may require a number of contacts, rather than a structured, time-limited interview. An older person may find the process intrusive and/or tiring, though he or she may comply because the health care professional is perceived as being in a position of authority.
- The initial presenting problem, or in some cases a crisis, may have to be dealt with first. Often, this is not related to alcohol or other drug use, but to another health problem, a crisis in the family or a change in living situation (such as impending eviction). The counsellor should attend to the client's most immediate concern in order to engage the person in a process of change. The substance use issue is best introduced when the person is most receptive—often after the initial concern is attended to and a therapeutic and caring relationship has been developed.
- Older people need time to tell their stories and may not be willing or able to complete forms or other structured tests. In listening to these stories a skilled practitioner will gain much information that can be translated into a formal assessment. There will also be information that indicates a client's self-perception and coping abilities, and identifies areas that may require further investigation.
- For older people, the assessment should focus on areas such as sensory functioning, mobility, living environment and lifestyle, losses, diet, mental condition, physical health, social support, literacy and speech (each area is discussed in detail below). If information on some of these areas is already available from other involved health professionals, do not repeat a questioning process that may feel invasive or tiring for an older person.
- The level of functioning in these areas determines the older person's ability to make changes in his or her life. Someone who is in poor health, cannot get around, is living in unhealthy circumstances or is confused will not be able to deal with issues related to alcohol and other drug use until these immediate problems are addressed.

In contrast, the younger person who presents for treatment, once he or she has stopped drinking or using drugs, is more likely to be in good health and have the energy and motivation to develop a healthy lifestyle.

The following areas are important to assess with an older client:

- **Sensory function**: How well does the person hear or see (e.g., read labels on medication containers, books, newspapers)? This knowledge reflects the person's communication and comprehension. Has sense of taste been lost? This could result in loss of interest in diet.

- **Mobility**: Can the person move about inside and outside, walk without aids, bathe and dress independently, shop for himself or herself? Lack of self-care may be a physical problem, not a self-esteem indicator. Accessing transportation and interacting with the community indicate possibilities for socializing.

- **Living environment and lifestyle**: Is the person happy in his or her living situation? Have there been housing problems because of substance use? Can the person maintain his or her living environment? Are there fire hazards or sanitation problems? Is it close enough to stores, buses, etc.? Does the person go out? How often does he or she see other people? You may find referring to community services helpful with some of these issues, and that you are the conduit to other forms of help.

- **Diet**: What are the person's eating habits (e.g., does he or she eat alone)? Does the person have a good appetite and enjoy food? How is food prepared and stored? Does the client know the importance of good nutrition and its effect on his or her daily living? This is an excellent information-sharing opportunity.

- **Losses**: Has he or she lost family, friends, physical health (hearing, sight), a job or home? Grief and loss is a specialized field for which you may or may not have the skills and the agency mandate to provide. If not, who in your network of community services can help?

- **Mental health**: Is the person confused or having memory problems? Does he or she appear depressed or exhibit symptoms that might indicate a dementia? All these concerns may warrant a referral to a mental health specialist. Screening and assessment tools such as the Beck Depression Inventory (Beck et al., 1961) or Folstein's Mini Mental Status exam could prove valuable (Folstein et al., 1975). The Geriatric Depression Scale (GDS) is a commonly used tool for assessing depression in older adults. The GDS is available in English, French and other languages (van Marwijk et al., 1995). Those trained as substance use counsellors might add these and other tools to their assessment protocols to identify the early stages of an underlying depression or dementia. If during an interview a client seems to avoid the issue of mental health, the avoidance may not be due to alcohol or medication use—it could be a genuine indicator of an age-related mental illness.

When a client has developed alcohol-related dementia from chronic drinking, the counsellor will need to understand why the person may have trouble with executive functions (carrying out plans) or abstract thinking. The client may seem to be in denial or may be acting difficult—but it is possible that his or her brain is not functioning properly.

- **Physical health**: Ask about sleeping patterns, weight change, disabilities and illnesses, dizziness, vision, hearing, foot care, digestion/elimination and dental problems. Has there been a recent hospital admission? Has the person had recent surgery? Is there a physical problem that has not been addressed? Is the client in regular contact with a doctor?
- **Social support**: Is there contact with family and friends? How much contact does the client have with other people? Does the person have close support or only acquaintances? Knowing how the person's support has changed will help identify strategies to replace supports that are missing.
- **Alcohol and other drug use**: How often and how much does he or she drink alcohol? Has the pattern of drinking changed (increased, decreased, periods of abstinence)? Has drinking affected other areas of functioning? What medications (prescribed, over-the-counter, or herbal remedies) are being used? How often are they used? How long has the client used them? What purpose do the medications serve? Do they still have a place in the client's well-being? Has the person ever experienced withdrawal? How did he or she cope? Is the client afraid to stop using alcohol or other drugs? Who can help explain the process? What are the options in the community? Remember, signs and symptoms that may indicate a drug withdrawal in a younger person do not necessarily apply to an older person. For example, falls, tremors, memory problems and hallucinations may not be symptoms of withdrawal.
- **Abuse**: Physical, emotional, financial or other forms of abuse may need to be assessed. Drinking problems can affect self-determination, and the ability to assess personal risk can be a problem for both the victim and the perpetrator of the abuse.
- **Literacy and speech**: Does the client have reading or writing problems? Are the problems a result of limited education or loss of ability? Is English a second language? It is known that as memory problems develop, people tend to revert to their original language. Are there other issues that might limit the client's literacy or speech pattern, such as a stroke?
- **Culture**: Being sensitive to cultural diversity helps build trust. Cultural differences may, for example, make it very difficult to meet with a person individually, or may provide close familial support to be drawn on. Culture should be understood in the broadest sense: all of us are influenced by, for example, our beliefs, ethnicity, age, sexual orientation and religion.

This in-depth assessment will help both the client and the practitioner to determine the next steps for treatment.

REFERRAL

When referring a client to a substance use treatment program, it is crucial to know how the treatment program can meet the client's wants and needs. What is the philosophy of the treatment centre: abstinence or reduced use, a medical or biopsychosocial model? Does the client know how the treatment will proceed? Are the program's content, pace and delivery compatible with the client's abilities and needs?

For a number of other reasons, traditional substance use programs may not be appropriate for older people:

• Many older people do not consider their use of alcohol or other drugs to be a problem, which may prevent acceptance by substance use treatment programs that require clients to be motivated to stop using substances upon entry. In the initial stages of treatment, the client may only be willing or able to change the use of one substance.

• Abstinence from the problem substance prior to entering the program may be a prerequisite. Also, the program may not allow the use of some medications, particularly if they are mood altering.

• Many programs require clients to travel to or be in residence to participate. Some older persons are not ready or able to leave their homes because of physical limitations or emotional problems such as depression.

• The older person may be so socially isolated that being with strangers is overwhelming.

• There may be transportation or financial barriers.

• The kinds of issues discussed in many programs may not be relevant to the lives of older people and they may be uncomfortable participating in a group that requires them to talk about themselves. Also, they may have difficulty in following group interaction because of hearing or sight problems.

Older people benefit most from services geared to their special needs and life circumstances. Depending on the resources available in a community, referrals should be made to a clinician or program that is able to respond to alcohol or other drug problems within the older person's context. It is possible that a program that focuses on substance use problems may not meet all of the client's needs, so referrals to other agencies may be appropriate. The person making the referral may need to be involved in problem resolution, case management and advocacy to ensure a good transition to treatment.

TREATMENT

Substance use treatment for older adults ideally involves "outreach" activities. "Outreach" in this context means working with the client in his or her own home or neighbourhood, or in places where the person is most comfortable. "Outreach" can also mean psychologically reaching out to offer help in a way that accommodates the older person's needs. This means addressing the problems that are of most concern to the client and not having unrealistic expectations. In other words, it is advisable to adjust the program or efforts to help the client's situation, and not to expect the client to adjust his or her needs to the program or the help that is offered. A wide range of ages and stages of problem use are found in older people in treatment. Those whose substance use problems are early onset or late onset form two fairly distinct groups. They share some similarities in terms of the developmental tasks of aging, but also have different needs and require different treatment approaches.

Clients with early onset problems experience more widespread physical, psychological, social and spiritual losses. They often present for treatment with major problems such as poor health, chronic illness, mobility problems, loneliness, low self-esteem, poor coping mechanisms, isolation, depression and loss of meaning in life. These problems often create a sense of helplessness and hopelessness. A treatment approach that attends to these problems, as well as to the alcohol or other drug use, is most effective for this group.

In contrast, the client with late onset has usually experienced fewer overall losses. He or she may have developed a dependence on alcohol or other drugs through increased social drinking or in response to a crisis or stress. Important treatment approaches for this group include education about substance use, attention to the crisis, fostering healthy ways of dealing with distress and providing support.

For people whose substance use becomes problematic intermittently, treatment can be tailored to the individual and will depend on his or her symptoms. For instance, if the person has a past history of major losses as a result of alcohol use, treatment would be more reflective of that given to the early onset group. If the person has more recently developed an intermittent drinking pattern, this would indicate approaches similar to those for the late onset client. The following section describes the different approaches for early and late onset substance use problems.

Early Onset

People with early onset substance use problems usually come for treatment in the chronic stage. Those who still use addictive substances often use less and fewer times per week than younger people, or than they did when they were younger. This can mislead a client and others to believe that the severity of the problem has decreased, while in fact the person is still using at hazardous levels for his or her age and physical condition.

Clinicians may find that the client's income is spent on alcohol, that he or she is not eating properly, is neglecting self-care or is not paying the rent, which is risking eviction. It is helpful to know if the client with early onset problems has tried treatment before, what was and wasn't helpful, and the person's concerns and fears about trying treatment again.

Some older people may be abstinent for one reason or another when they enter treatment, often in response to some acute injury or illness associated with their substance use. However, with post-acute withdrawal effects it can take weeks or even months for confusion to clear, which will affect the pace of treatment and make it necessary to repeat information and to provide it in different formats. Many of the physical, psychological and social problems associated with long-term use will still be acute. These range from physical illnesses such as diabetes, arthritis, digestive disorders, heart disease, cancer and respiratory diseases (many drinkers are smokers) to the social and psychological problems of depression, isolation, loneliness and low self-esteem.

The person with early onset substance use problems may enter treatment in his or her 50s, but have problems usually associated with older people (e.g., chronic illness, isolation and multiple losses). Housing, financial constraints and inadequate social support are often problems. (Most specialized substance use programs for older adults accept clients aged 55 and older when they have the profile of an older person.)

These people often require a specialized intervention that responds to the person's physical, psychological, emotional and spiritual needs.

PHYSICAL NEEDS

Alcohol affects every system of the body. It adversely affects appetite and digestion, sleep patterns, and nerve, muscle and joint functioning. Poor nutrition, inadequate sleep and lack of exercise over many years weaken the person's physical condition and predispose him or her to chronic illnesses. Long-term alcohol use can cause or exacerbate diseases such as hypertension, diabetes and disorders of the digestive system.

Psychoactive substances can also harm the physical system, so it is important to be aware of the client's physical condition while also focusing on withdrawal from the drug. The older person may have to withdraw from alcohol and other substances under the supervision of a physician rather than in a non-medical detoxification setting. For older people, very slow tapering off from mood-altering medications is recommended, as it causes less distress and allows the person to plan for coping without the substance. It is invaluable to have the support of the doctor who has prescribed the medication and who can provide consultation and oversee other medical needs. If the doctor does not recognize the substance use as a problem, it may be necessary to find other solutions.

PSYCHOLOGICAL NEEDS

If the client has had drinking problems most of his or her adult life, they may have interfered with or prevented the completion of earlier tasks of development. Such tasks include developing one's life work, becoming productive in a job, developing intimacy with a partner and learning to be interdependent, becoming responsible to others in a family or similar situation and finding one's place in society.

Failure to fully develop one's potential, and losing many jobs as a result of substance use, lead to psychological problems associated with failure, insecurity and condemnation by family, friends and society. Poorly developed work habits and skills are accompanied by feelings of low self-esteem and inadequacy. In most cases, the older client will not be returning to the workforce and treatment should focus more on addressing the person's use of time; days without structure tend to be filled with drinking. Often, it is a treatment goal to help the person rediscover earlier skills and interests or develop new ones.

Over the years, as alcohol or other drug use became the main focus of life, the client may have failed to develop intimate relationships. The person may have used substances to deal with difficulty in developing relational skills. The result is poor social skills, inability to relate to others at a deep-feeling level, and loss of family and friends due to behaviour associated with alcohol and other drug use. Service providers may need to help the client move away from dwelling on past failures and toward recognizing his or her own strengths. Try to help the client focus on planning for future activities and successes, and respond to the client's immediate problems in the here and now.

Treatment that includes an opportunity to socialize and helps a person become comfortable in expressing his or her feelings will help to alleviate loneliness. Though many older people will initially prefer individual counselling, one goal of the counselling could be to help the person feel comfortable joining a group. A group can often be a key to developing new friendships and developing alternatives to drinking, and can provide a stepping stone to moving out into the wider community. At the same time, it is important to recognize that group work is not for everyone.

People with long-term substance use problems have usually not developed the ability to be interdependent—to be responsible to and for others, and to have others be responsible to and for them. This may present in various ways: not showing up for appointments, demanding behaviour or overdependence on the counsellor. The client may fluctuate between angry feelings of "I don't need anyone, leave me alone," to clinging to the counsellor. Approaches to take at this juncture are those that lead to strengthening the relationship, yet do not result in overdependence. The goal is to gradually broaden the base of support and to help the person interact with others in a give-and-take relationship.

SOCIAL NEEDS

Social isolation is a major problem for the client with early onset problems, and the physical and psychological limitations mentioned above affect the person's ability to form and maintain friendships. Compounding this is the loss of family and friends because of addictive behaviour.

Social isolation can be a problem for many older people as they lose the company of work colleagues, children who have left home and partners or other close friends who have died. For the person with early onset substance use problems, these changes often occur earlier in life and are more extensive than for others of a similar age. Friends and family have been replaced with "drinking friends" and places, and drinking friends may have died. The long-term effects of substance use may have decreased the ability to actively participate in relationships; communications are blurred. Energy for social activities may also decrease. Be aware that an underlying depression can also affect the person's ability to be an active participant.

Social isolation promotes feelings of loneliness and fear, as well as anxiety when with people. It must be attended to gradually in treatment, helping the person to rebuild those social skills— skills that are easily lost when they are not actively used. A relationship with one caring person is often a good place to start, followed by encouraging the client to gradually extend his or her circle of contacts.

SPIRITUAL NEEDS

The spiritual issues associated with long-term use of alcohol and other drugs usually concern the meaning of life and feelings of guilt and remorse. Freedom to talk about these issues is a necessary part of treatment. Understanding and accepting his or her addiction can help a person feel less guilty and accept the personal strengths that have allowed the person to survive the negative consequences of substance use.

Finally, it is important to consider the effect of society's attitude toward the person with a substance use problem. Frequently this attitude is pessimistic. Family and caregivers have observed many years of substance use, promises made and broken, efforts to stop using followed by even greater use. Attempts to control the drinking are often brief, and then the cycle begins again. The family reaches the end of its coping ability and moves away in an effort to reclaim its own health. Eventually, friends and colleagues look on from a distance and it is left to the professional caregiver to offer support and to try once again.

Without an understanding and acceptance of the chronic relapsing nature of the problem, even the health care professional may give up. If this happens, the client's feelings of hopelessness and helplessness are reflected by all those around him or her. Using creative interventions to engage a person with a chronic substance use problem in a process of change will break this impasse. It is essential to find areas of change that are important to the client and in which he or she feels some confidence for success. Often this is not initially in the area of substance use. However, as people become stronger—both physically and emotionally—and with support, they can change their use of alcohol and other drugs.

BEST APPROACHES

The best approaches (Graham et al., 1989; Health Canada, 2002; Hogstel, 1990; Kinney & Leaton, 1983; Kola et al., 1980; Olsen-Noll & Bosworth, 1989; Zimberg, 1978) to helping the person with an early onset substance use problem include:
- an individual approach focusing on areas for change that the client sees as both important and achievable (For example, a relationship with a counsellor can be the first step toward alleviating loneliness, to be followed later by other social activities; basic needs such as food and shelter can be addressed as well.)
- developing trust by helping the person with the problem that he or she identifies (This gives the clear message that help will be provided, and that it is not based on clients having to first "prove" themselves by addressing their biggest challenge, the substance use.)
- a supportive one-to-one relationship, which is non-confrontational and nurturing, recognizing the possible initial need for dependence
- outreach—working with the client in his or her own home, allowing for physical and emotional comfort; reaching out to offer help instead of waiting for the person to seek help

• group activities that offer support and social interaction with peers (These may take the form of a supportive counselling group, as well as recreational activities undertaken by the group.)
• a thorough knowledge and use of available health and social services in the community.

Late Onset

Late onset substance use problems often develop as a reaction to stresses of aging. The person usually enters treatment at a later age, commonly 65 to 75 or older, with fewer years of substance use problems and fewer associated losses. Thus, these clients present quite a different picture than those with early onset. Often they have lived a full life, having successfully managed a career and family. The person has developed skills and interests during the adult years, and family ties are more likely to be intact.

A late onset substance use problem can develop through two routes. Some people may have been social drinkers all their lives. After retirement, with more leisure time and drinking-related social activities, and fewer work-related constraints, drinking may escalate. Combined with increased physical sensitivity to the effects of alcohol and other drugs as people age, this is sufficient to initiate major health and possibly other problems related to substance use.

The other route is when an older person self-medicates with alcohol or other psychoactive drugs, or is prescribed psychoactive drugs to alleviate stress caused by physical ill health or loss of someone close.

Like early onset problems, late onset problems may affect many dimensions of people's lives—physical, psychological, social and spiritual. However, late onset problems may present somewhat differently.

In some ways, the person with late-onset difficulties resembles the younger person with a substance use problem. The person finds it hard to recognize and accept that he or she has crossed the line from social to harmful use. In addition, symptoms or problems associated with heavy alcohol or other drug use (e.g., confusion, disorientation, recent memory loss, tremors, inflammation of joints, gastritis, hypertension, depression, heart disease and sleep disturbances) are often erroneously accepted as normal signs of aging. Thus, the client, the family and professional caregivers may fail to identify the problem in its early stages.

The person with late onset problems is often dealing with a crisis. It is important to identify the stressor and attend to it along with the substance use problem. Crises in later years most often pertain to loss (e.g., loss of a life partner, friends, pets, health, independence, autonomy or status). As one client aptly described it after reading about the stages of grief in a magazine, "I am perpetually in several stages of grief at the same time. I never get out of it." Counsellors must be aware of the impact of multiple losses on the older person. These losses and the resulting grief are best responded to by interpersonal means rather than by using drugs (Harrison, 1987).

Feelings of acute fear, anger, sadness and anxiety often accompany the experience of loss. Cognitively, the person may fluctuate between preoccupation with the object of loss and denial of it. Careful listening with empathetic responses will allow the person to feel and express his or her grief safely.

Concurrent Disorders

Though there are no estimates of the prevalence of concurrent disorders in older people, professionals working with them know that the combination of mental illness and dependence on alcohol or other drugs is a major treatment challenge. Depression is particularly common, though it is often unclear whether the depression preceded or is the result of substance use. Older people who are depressed are three to four times more likely to have alcohol-related problems than are older people who are not depressed (Devanand, 2002). Between 15 and 30 per cent of those with major late-life depression have alcohol use problems (Devanand, 2002). Also, the extent of the depression may be unclear until the person is fully detoxified. Both situations need to be investigated and treated.

Family Issues

It is important to support families and those close to the person. Education, acknowledgment of the situation and validation of their attempts to help are essential. The next step is to ask if they are willing to remain supportive even after years of disenchantment. Introduce the concept of harm reduction, including how this approach will be presented to the client. It is important to acknowledge the difficulty the family may have with a harm reduction approach, when it is clear that abstinence from alcohol use or compliance with medications would resolve many of the client's problems. For family and friends, it may be inconceivable that the older person seems unable or unwilling to recognize the problems and take the necessary actions. But redefining the goal and focusing on the problems that the client identifies allows for change and brings the client hope. Care providers will benefit as they see movement in areas that the client has identified as problematic. Although a family may be looking for the "magic cure," small gains must be noted and appreciated, whether or not these involve reduced alcohol use or better medication compliance.

Developmental Tasks of Aging

Anyone working with older people should know the normal developmental tasks of aging. The major tasks are to
• successfully resolve one's life conflicts

• review and integrate one's past events with a personal value system that reflects the achievement of life satisfaction
• develop a life philosophy
• acquire wisdom (Birren & Renner, 1981).

Older people need to face their mortality and accept, understand and value their life as it has been lived. Success in achieving this personal integration is highly influenced by the successful completion of earlier developmental tasks. For the older client, attention to developmental tasks is a necessary part of treatment and recovery. It is particularly important to either resolve or accept life conflicts related to alcohol or other drug use. An understanding of the addiction process can help this process. Thus, education is an element of treatment. Reminiscing is another way older people sort through the events and meaning of their lives in order to understand and achieve self-acceptance. This process often involves expressing feelings and problem solving. The counsellor or other caregiver can facilitate this process of integration by:
• recognizing its importance
• lending support and validation through careful listening and affirmation of the person's life achievements
• helping clients understand traumatic issues, including those associated with the substance use problems
• helping them solve, where possible, remaining issues.

Support Groups

The gerontological literature recognizes the benefit of support groups in dealing with common age-related issues, such as specific health problems and bereavement. Support groups for older people with alcohol problems are a way to break isolation, rebuild social skills and provide education and mutual support. For some, support groups are critical in the success of substance use treatment. Support groups may focus on reducing the amount of drinking, or they may be abstinence-based. They tend to be a lifestyle support group, in contrast to therapeutic counselling. Older people stress that the importance of the support group is that it gives them a place to talk to others who understood what they are experiencing and provides a safe place for them to talk without feeling ashamed. They say they are helped by the non-judgmental attitude within the group. They emphasize that the support group helped them stay on track, and gave them a reason to get out of the house and a reason to remain sober.

Community Networks

Substance use counsellors need to involve others in supporting the older person with substance use problems, including family, friends and the network of community services. Substance use in older adults needs to be better understood by all caregivers, both formal and informal. Those most often in close contact with the older person have the greatest chance of noticing a problem and encouraging the person to get help. Often, the family member or service provider is aware of the substance use problem but does not know what to do or where to turn. Caregivers and the community need general education about substance use in the older adult, about the concepts of harm reduction and the stages of change, and especially to improve understanding that substance use problems are a health condition, rather than a moral failing. More knowledge in this area will help those who work with older adults to recognize problems and encourage more referrals for help.

An adequate response will require a comprehensive approach at a community level. Specialized community resources such as bereavement counselling, pain management, respite care and geriatric services (including assessment) are some of the key services that substance use counsellors should be familiar with and with which they should establish close working relationships. Counsellors should also advocate in all community services for policies that do not discriminate against those with substance use problems. Public and staff education efforts need to focus on alleviating stigma and expanding options for care and support for older people with substance use problems.

Inter-agency consultation and collaboration can increase workers' awareness and skills, which can in turn prevent problems and improve identification and referral. One of the authors experienced this in an Ontario community where an inter-agency committee worked together to provide staff training in substance use problems across several services. The result was increased referrals of older adults to substance use treatment.

In addition, more creative community responses need to be devised. One possibility is a partnership between a substance use service and a community support service. This could involve the substance use agency providing substance use education to interested staff and volunteers, together with ongoing consultation and support. The community support agency could then provide a variety of social and practical supports to older clients with substance use problems—including group and recreational activities, friendly visiting, telephone reassurance, driving services—in conjunction with the interventions provided by the substance use agency. Finally, as the older person needs increasing care, institutions need to be sensitive and avoid discriminating against those with continuing substance use problems. Retirement and nursing home facilities must recognize the ethical obligation to allow individuals to age with proper care in spite of a substance use problem, and should develop programs and facilities in response to that obligation. In Edmonton, the Safe Haven Program at Capital Care Norwood uses a harm reduction approach that offers a safe, non-judgmental environment where residents can buy, keep and consume alcohol in their own rooms.

CONCLUSION

Canadians are living longer as a result of the health, social and economic gains of the last century. Now it is time to turn the attention of science to maintaining and optimizing the life of the mind. As we age, we may be more susceptible to the effects of alcohol and other drugs, including medication. Since medication may be life-saving and health-giving, we must support people in using prescription, over-the-counter and herbal remedies in healthy and appropriate ways. Hopefully, in the future older adults with alcohol and other drug problems will receive more encouragement than they did in the past to seek treatment, and the treatment provided will be suitable and specific to the older person's needs.

REFERENCES

Adlaf, E.M. & Ialomiteanu, A. (2002). *CAMH Monitor eReport: Addiction and Mental Health Indicators among Ontario Adults in 2001, and Changes since 1977.* CAMH Research Document Series No. 12. Toronto: Centre for Addiction and Mental Health. Available: www.camh.net/research/population_life_course.html.

Adlaf, E. & Smart, R. (1995). Alcohol use, drug use and well-being in older adults in Toronto. *The International Journal of the Addictions, 30*(13 & 14), 1985–2016.

Beck, A.T., Ward, C.H., Mendelson, M., Mock, J. & Erbaugh, J. (1961). An inventory for measuring depression. *Archives of General Psychiatry, 4,* 561–571

Bergob, M. (1994). Drug use among senior Canadians. *Canadian Social Trends,* Summer 1994, 25–29. Statistics Canada Catalogue, 11-008E.

Birren, J.E. & Renner, V.J. (1981). Concepts and criteria of mental health and aging. *American Journal of Orthopsychiatry, 51.*

Devanand, D.P. (2002). Comorbid psychiatric disorders in late life depression. *Biological Psychiatry, 51*(3), 236–242.

Dufour, M.C. & Fuller, R. (1995). Alcohol in the elderly. *Annual Review of Medicine, 46,* 123–132.

Folstein, M.F., Folstein, S.E. & McHugh, P.R. (1975). "Minimental state." A practical method for grading the cognitive state of patients for the clinician. *Journal of Psychiatric Research, 12,* 189–98.

Graham, K. (1986). Identifying and measuring alcohol abuse among the elderly: Serious problems with existing instrumentation. *Journal of Alcohol Studies, 47*(4), 322–326.

Graham, K., Brett, P. & Baron, J. (1997). A harm reduction approach to treating older adults: The clients speak. In P.G. Erickson, D.M. Riley, Y.W. Cheung & P.A. O'Hare (Eds.), *Harm Reduction: A New Direction for Drug Policies and Programs* (pp. 429–452). Toronto: University of Toronto Press.

Graham, K., Carver, V. & Brett, P. (1996). Women aged 65 and over: Alcohol and drug use. In M. Adrian, C. Lundy & M. Eliany (Eds.), *Women's Use of Alcohol, Tobacco and Other Drugs in Canada* (pp. 82–103). Toronto: Addiction Research Foundation.

Graham, K., Clarke, D., Bois, C., Carver, V., Marshman, J., Brett, P. et al. (1995). Alcohol use, depressant medication use, and reasons for drinking among older people. Paper presented at the 1995 21st Annual Alcohol Epidemiology Symposium of the Kettil Bruun Society of Social and Epidemiological Research on Alcohol, Porto, Portugal.

Graham, K., Saunders, S., Flower, M.C., Birchmore Timney, C., White-Campbell, M. & Zeidman, A. (1989). Evaluation of the COPA Project: A description of client characteristics, interventions and outcomes. Unpublished draft report. Toronto: Addiction Research Foundation.

Gurnack, A.M. (1997). *Older Adults' Misuse of Alcohol, Medicines, and Other Drugs: Research and Practice Issues.* New York: Springer.

Gurnack, A.M., Atkinson, R. & Osgood, N.J. (Eds.). (2002). *Treating Alcohol and Drug Abuse in the Elderly.* New York: Springer.

Harrison, M.K. (1987). Loss, grief and adaptation. In D. Wasylenki (Ed.), *Psychogeriatrics: A Practical Handbook.* Toronto: Gage.

Health Canada. (1997). *Canada's Alcohol and Other Drugs Survey 1994. A Discussion of the Findings.* Cat. No. H39-338/1-1994E. Ottawa: Minister of Supply and Services.

Health Canada. (1999). *Best Practices—Substance Abuse Treatment and Rehabilitation.* Cat. No. H39-438/1999E. Ottawa: Minister of Public Works and Government Services.

Health Canada. (2001). Canada's seniors: A growing population. *Statistical Snapshots, Division of Aging and Seniors.* Available: www.hc-sc.gc.ca/seniors-aines/pubs/factoids/2001/pdf/no01_e.pdf.

Health Canada. (2002). *Best Practices—Treatment and Rehabilitation for Seniors with Substance Use Problems.* Cat. No. H46-2/03-295E. Ottawa: author.

Hogstel, M.O. (1990). *Geropsychiatric Nursing.* Toronto: C.V. Mosby.

Kinney, J. & Leaton, G. (1983). *The Elderly: Loosening the Grip.* Toronto: C.V. Mosby.

Kola, L.A., Kosberg, J.I. & Wegner-Burch, K. (1980). Perceptions of the treatment responsibilities for the alcoholic elderly client. *Social Work in Health Care, 6*(2), 69–76.

McKim, W.A. & Mishara, B.L. (1987). *Drugs and Aging.* Toronto: Butterworths.

National Institute on Alcohol Abuse and Alcoholism. (1998). *Alcohol Alert, 40.* Available: www.niaaa.hih.gov/publications/aa40.htm.

Olsen-Noll, C. & Bosworth, M. (1989). Alcohol abuse in the elderly. *American Family Physician, 39,* 173–179.

Spencer, C. (2002). *Alcohol and Seniors.* Available: www.agingincanada.ca.

Statistics Canada. (2000). *National Population Health Survey 1998–1999: Alcohol Consumption by Sex, Age Group and Level of Education.* Available: www.statcan.ca/english/Pgdb/health05a.htm.

van Marwijk, H.W., Wallace, P., de Bock, G.H., Hermans, J., Kaptein, A.A. & Mulder, J.D. (1995). Evaluation of the feasibility, reliability and diagnostic value of shortened versions of the geriatric depression scale. *British Journal of General Practice, 45*(393), 195–199.

Zimberg, S. (1978). Treatment of the elderly alcoholic in the community and in an institutional setting. *Addictive Diseases: An International Journal, 3*(3), 417–425.

RESOURCES

Action on Women's Research and Education. (1992). *Drug Wise: A Book for Older Women about Safe Drug Use.* Kingston, ON: Aware Press.

Action on Women's Research and Education. (1992). *Drug Wise: A Book about Safe Drug Use for Older Women Who Are Caregivers.* Kingston, ON: Aware Press.

Beresford, T. & Gomberg, E. (1996). *Alcohol and Aging.* New York: Oxford University Press.

Centre for Addiction and Mental Health. (1998). *Choosing to Change: A Client Centred Approach to Alcohol and Medication Use by Older Adults.* Toronto: author.

Graham, K., Saunders, S.J., Flower, M.C., Birchmore, T.C., White-Campbell, M. & Pietropaolo, A.Z. (1995). *Addictions Treatment for Older Adults: Evaluation of an Innovative Client-Centred Approach.* New York: Haworth Press.

Chapter 16

Working with Lesbian, Gay, Bisexual, Transsexual, Transgender, Two-Spirit, Intersex and Queer (LGBTTTIQ) People Who Have Substance Use Concerns

FARZANA DOCTOR

INTRODUCTION

Most clinicians who work in the substance use field receive little education and training to work with people from the lesbian, gay, bisexual, transgender, transsexual, two-spirit, intersex and queer (LGBTTTIQ) communities. As a result, LGBTTTIQ people have historically been underserved by substance use treatment agencies (Craft & Mulvey, 2001; Finlon, 2002). To increase clinicians' understanding, skill and competence in working with this diverse and marginalized population, this chapter offers information about the unique needs and concerns of LGBTTTIQ people who have substance use problems. (For definitions of relevant terms, check the glossary at the end of the chapter.)

PREVALENCE OF SUBSTANCE USE IN LGBTTTIQ COMMUNITIES

Hughes & Eliason (2002), leading researchers in this area, state that "writing a state of the science paper on substance use among lesbians, gay men, bisexual and transgender (LGBT) persons is a daunting task" (p. 263). They cite many reasons for this, including:
• lack of research on LGBT communities
• methodological problems in previous research, such as small and non-random samples
• inconsistent definitions of sexual orientation and substance use.

Further, bisexual, transgender and transsexual people are largely missing from research about substance use. Bisexuals are often either grouped with gays and lesbians, or excluded from analyses due to low numbers. Sell & Becker (2001) describe this lack of quality research as "one of the greatest threats to health" for the LGBTT-TIQ communities (p. 876). The following are summaries of the results of research studies that have been done on substance use among LGBTTTIQ people:

McKirnan & Peterson (1989) compared a large sample of Chicago gays and lesbians with an earlier study done of men and women from a general rural and urban population. They found that:
• Lesbians were less likely than heterosexual women (15 per cent vs. 35 per cent) to abstain from alcohol but were more likely to be moderate drinkers (76 per cent vs. 59 per cent). Lesbians and heterosexual women were shown to have similar rates of heavy drinking (nine per cent vs. seven per cent).
• Despite similar rates of heavy drinking, lesbians reported higher rates of alcohol-related problems (23 per cent vs. 8 per cent).
• Lesbians and gay men showed similar rates of marijuana and cocaine use.
• Gays and lesbians showed less age-related decline in alcohol and other drug use than is typical in the general population.
• Gay men were less likely than heterosexual men to abstain from alcohol (13 per cent vs. 23 per cent) and less likely to report heavy drinking (17 per cent vs. 21 per cent), but were more likely to report alcohol-related problems (23 per cent vs. 16 per cent).
• Gay men were more likely than heterosexual men to report lifetime use of marijuana and cocaine, but the two groups did not differ in how frequently they used these substances.
• Gay men and their heterosexual counterparts in the same age group reported different use of substances. For example, gay men over 35 were more likely to use cocaine frequently than heterosexual men in the same age group.
• 14 per cent of gay men reported using amyl nitrate (poppers) regularly and 7 per cent reported daily use.

Hughes et al. (1997), reporting from a study of lesbian and heterosexual women in Chicago, New York and Minneapolis-St. Paul, found that:
• Lesbians were more likely than heterosexual women (24 per cent vs. 17 per cent) to abstain from alcohol, a finding that contrasts with that of McKirnan & Peterson (1989).

- Most lesbians (73 per cent) and heterosexual women (82 per cent) reported light to moderate drinking (fewer than two drinks per day on average).
- Only three per cent of lesbians and one per cent of heterosexuals reported heavy drinking (more than two drinks per day on average).
- More lesbians (14 per cent) than heterosexual women (6 per cent) reported participation in 12-step programs.
- The incidence of an age-related decline in drinking, commonly found with heterosexual women, was lower among lesbians.

Hughes also found that alcohol use among lesbians may be declining. She believes this may be due to increased awareness of health and substance use issues, decrease in stigma for gays and lesbians, and changing norms in the gay and lesbian communities.

Aaron et al. (2001) compared the prevalence of smoking and alcohol use among lesbians and the general population of women and found that:

- More lesbians than general population women (35.5 per cent vs. 20.5 per cent) currently smoked.
- Fewer lesbians than general population women (42.5 per cent vs. 55.4 per cent) abstained from alcohol.
- More lesbians (4.7 per cent) indicated that they drank heavily than did women in the general group (1.1 per cent).

Mansergh et al. (2001), in a study of circuit parties (dance parties that can attract up to 20,000 mostly-gay men) in the San Francisco/Bay Area, found that 25 per cent of attendees reported having "overused" drugs, along with engaging in unprotected sex. Clements et al. (2001) studied male-to-female (MtF) and female-to-male (FtM) transgender people in San Francisco and found that lifetime use of intravenous drugs was prevalent among both MtF people (34 per cent) and FtM people (18 per cent).

Reback & Lombardi (1999) studied MtF people in West Hollywood, 35 per cent of whom were sex-trade workers, and found that:

- In the past month, 37 per cent reported drinking alcohol, 13 per cent reported marijuana use, 11 per cent reported crack use, 11 per cent reported methamphetamine use, 7 per cent reported cocaine use and 2 per cent reported heroin use.
- More of the sex-trade workers than the general MtF group reported methamphetamine use (21 per cent vs. 5 per cent) and crack use (25 per cent vs. 3 per cent).

Most writers explain the higher rates of substance use in LGBTTTIQ communities in relation to the experiences of marginalization and oppression LGBTTTIQ people face (Hughes & Eliason, 2002; Ghindia & Kola, 1996; Doctor, 2003). It is not being LGBTTTIQ but coping with oppression that may increase the risk of substance use. These experiences may also cause higher rates of mood and anxiety disorders, and thoughts and plans of suicide (Gilman et al., 2001).

Many writers also theorize that while the bar, rave and circuit party cultures in LGBTTTIQ communities are important because they provide safe places to socialize without fear of discrimination, these cultures also normalize substance use (Collins & Howard, 1997; Kauth et al., 2000).

ANTI-OPPRESSION FRAMEWORK AND CULTURAL COMPETENCE

An anti-oppression framework and cultural competence (understanding concepts of gender and sexual orientation and the unique issues that concern LGBTTTIQ communities, specifically societal oppression) is a requirement for working well with LGBTTTIQ people. For example, a recent survey of transgender people found that the expertise of a gender specialist is important to those who seek help for gender-related issues. Clinicians without updated information about transgender issues and communities were not as helpful to clients (Rachlin, 2002), and in fact, may do harm. Many LGBTTTIQ people may not access care due to fear of discrimination and being stigmatized (Clark et al., 2001).

It is not uncommon for LGBTTTIQ clients to face oppression in a social service environment (Coalition for Lesbian and Gay Rights in Ontario, 1997; Barbara, Chaim & Doctor, 2002). In 1976, after lobbying from gay organizations, psychologists and psychiatrists, the American Psychiatric Association (APA) removed the designation of homosexuality as a sexual deviation from the *Diagnostic and Statistical Manual of Mental Disorders (DSM)*. Though Gender Identity Disorder remains in the *DSM-IV*, some LGBTTTIQ organizations argue that the label pathologizes transgender, trans-sexual, gender diverse and gender variant people (Van Wormer et al., 2000), and are lobbying to have it removed. Clients of substance use treatment agencies have reported the following examples of oppression:

• A gay male client at a mainstream residential treatment centre is told not to speak about his sexual orientation because it is not relevant to his substance use, while other clients are encouraged to talk about their relationships and families.
• A preoperative transsexual woman (someone who cannot afford the very costly gender reassignment surgery not covered by her health plan) is asked to wear "masculine" clothing while she is in treatment.
• A lesbian is asked at intake if she is married. When she tells the intake worker that she has a partner, the intake worker asks, "What's his name?"
• A transgender woman is asked not to sit in the women's lounge of a treatment agency.

LGBTTTIQ people and communities also face societal oppression. "Homophobia," "biphobia" and "transphobia" are terms for overt and covert fear and hatred of gays and lesbians, bisexuals and transgender and transsexual people, respectively. Examples include derogatory jokes, name-calling, bashing, and pathologizing. Feinberg (2001, 897–898) provides an example of transphobia:

> Five years ago, while battling an undiagnosed case of bacterial endocarditis, I was refused care at a Jersey City emergency room. After the physician who examined me discovered that I am female bodied, he ordered me out of the emergency room despite the fact that my temperature was above 104°F (40°C). He said I had a fever "because you are a very troubled person". . . . Had I died from this illness, the real pathogen would have been bigotry.

"Heterosexism" refers to the systemic, or societal discrimination, encountered by gay, lesbian and bisexual people (it is assumed that heterosexuality is the normal and preferred sexual orientation). "Genderism" refers to the systemic discrimination encountered by transgender, transsexual and gender-nonconforming individuals (it is assumed that the binary construct of gender is preferred and normal). Some examples of heterosexism and genderism include the exclusion of LGBTTTIQ people from marriage and adoption rights, intake and application forms that do not include options other than "M" and "F" or "married" and "single," and lack of resources and services available to these communities.

"Heterosexual privilege" refers to the unearned and often invisible privileges afforded to those who do not challenge dominant sexual orientation norms. Examples include marriage rights and the ability to appear in public with one's partner without facing harassment. "Gender privilege" refers to the unearned and often invisible privileges afforded to those who do not challenge dominant gender norms. Examples include being able to use a public bathroom without being challenged by other patrons, and attending for medical care without facing scrutiny about one's gender identity. It is worthwhile to note that these privileges, while often invisible to those who receive them, are usually strikingly obvious to those who are not afforded them.

In a society that supports genderism and heterosexism, it can be difficult for us as clinicians to identify and change our own biases. However, we must recognize and challenge our homophobia, biphobia and transphobia to become more competent in this area. Clinicians must also learn more about their local LGBTTTIQ community; its specific needs, challenges, resources and strengths. To do this, they can:
• access print, electronic and visual media to expand awareness
• attend workshops and conferences on LGBTTTIQ issues
• encourage discussion with colleagues and members of local LGBTTTIQ communities.

LGBTTTIQ communities include people of different ages, races, classes, abilities, rural/urban locations, religions and politics. Though glossy gay magazines tend to depict the LGBTTTIQ community as homogeneous, white, male and affluent (Plumb, 2001), research suggests that gay men may earn less on average than their straight counterparts, and that transgender and transsexual people, as well as people of colour, tend to face the most employment-related discrimination. The "myth of affluence" ignores the diversity of LGBTTTIQ communities (Anastas, 2001). LGBTTTIQ clients who are poor, older, of colour or who have disabilities may face double or triple marginalization, and their experiences of being LGBTTTIQ cannot be separated from their other identities.

APPROPRIATE USE OF LANGUAGE

The use of appropriate language and terminology is important when working with members of LGBTTTIQ communities. Because words are often used to oppress marginalized groups, it is key that these groups name themselves rather than be labelled by others. For example, a word such as "homosexual," used to refer to people with same-gender desire, is rarely used by people to refer to themselves (most will prefer the terms "gay" or "lesbian"; Broido, 2000). Language issues can be confusing because sometimes terminology changes as a particular group gains strength and voice. For example, some LGBTTTIQ people have reclaimed words such as "queer," "fag" and "dyke" to proudly describe themselves. "Queer" is often used as an umbrella term for all LGBTTTIQ people. A person's decision about how or whether to label himself or herself may be connected to factors such as geographical location, degree of "outness" (openness about sexual orientation), political beliefs and the relative safety of his or her situation, age or culture (Hughes & Eliason, 2002; Stone, 1990; Savin-Williams, 1996; Liu & Chan, 1996). Further, each LGBTTTIQ community uses terminology differently, depending on its size and culture. Given the variety of labels and ways in which people may identify their gender and sexual orientation, it is wise to ask LGBTTTIQ clients how they prefer to be described and identified. This may include asking transgender, intersex, transsexual and two-spirit clients which gender pronoun(s) they wish you to use when referring to them (Pazos, 1999).

Gender Identity and Sexual Orientation

To better understand LGBTTTIQ clients, one must first understand key concepts and the meanings of "gender identity" and "sexual orientation."

"Gender identity" refers to how individuals identify and understand their core or innate sense of maleness or femaleness (Mallon, 1999). Society generally views gender as a binary construct, in which people are either male/masculine or female/feminine, with little tolerance for those who conform to neither. Manifestations of this binary construct are found in many cultural norms (e.g., our custom of asking whether a newborn is a boy or a girl). As a result, many transgender, transsexual and intersex people are often pathologized for their gender variance or diversity (Cooper, 1999; Raj, 2002), though some clients may accept a binary construct and reject a more fluid notion of gender. Some transsexuals, for example, who hope to live as the opposite gender, may view gender identity in a more traditional way (Raj, 2002).

An alternative to the binary construct of gender is to view identity as a continuum (Feinberg, 2001) that contemplates genders along a spectrum of gender expression, where particular expressions are not favoured or seen to be normal or abnormal.

This is a challenge for many of us. We are trained from a very young age to understand gender in a rigid, "either/or" way. In the English language, there are no gender pronouns for people who do not see themselves as "he" or "she."* But what if we were not to assume that a newborn's genitals would necessarily predict its gender identity? What if a parent said, "I can't wait to see what gender my child becomes"?

---

*Feinberg (1998) has coined the gender neutral pronouns *hir* (pronounced "here") and *sie* (pronounced "see") to replace "him"/"her" and "he"/"she."

"Sexual orientation" is a term for the emotional, physical, sexual and sometimes spiritual attractions a person has for others. This attraction may be experienced through fantasy, desire or behaviour and may or may not be acted upon. Sexual orientation is distinct from sexual behaviour; the former is a way of identifying attraction and the latter is a way of identifying what we *do*. For example, a person may be gay, but celibate. A woman may be in a long-term, monogamous relationship with another woman, but consider herself bisexual. Some individuals may not label their sexual orientation at all. As with gender identity, it can be useful to consider sexual orientation as a continuum, where sexuality is fluid and changeable over time (Broido, 2000).

Sexual orientation is distinct from gender identity, although the two are often confused. A transgender, transsexual, two-spirit person may identify as heterosexual, gay, lesbian, bisexual or polysexual. These two dimensions of identity overlap in crucial ways for many LGBTTTIQ people. It is often gender non-conformity that schoolyard bullies identify when they tease a child they perceive to be gay. Identifying where sexual orientation and gender identity intersect is important for many clients. For example, some lesbians identify as "butch," a gender expression that does not conform to gender norms of how women are supposed to look and act. These women, as they "come out" and begin to understand themselves, affirm both same-gender desire and non-conforming gender expression. A transsexual man who pre-transition identified as a lesbian may need, post-transition, to re-evaluate his sexual orientation. Partners of transitioning transsexual people may also face this re-evaluation process themselves in relation to their partner's gender transition.

UNIQUE ISSUES IN ASSESSMENT AND TREATMENT

LGBTTTIQ people with substance use concerns may share many of the same concerns as the general population. What makes LGBTTTIQ communities distinct is the effect of oppression and the different cultural norms in some of the communities. This section will outline both considerations.

Coming Out

Coming out is a process, not a destination. Various stage models exist for this process, and these have been both embraced for aiding in the understanding of a complex process, and criticized for being too simplistic. The Cass model is one such model, which identifies the stages of coming out, basically describing how at the beginning of the process, there is usually uncertainty or confusion around identity. The process traverses acceptance and pride, until finally the person coming out integrates his or her sexual orientation into his or her overall identity. A person may move back and forth through this process at different times, depending on the situation. Moving to a new neighbourhood, city, job or school may prompt a person to become more out or closeted, depending on the circumstances.

All LGBTTTIQ people go through this process of coming out; it is unique to each person and is ongoing. "Transitioning" is a term to describe the process transgender or transsexual people may go through as they begin to express a different gender identity. A transition process may involve a name change, or hormonal, aesthetic or surgical treatments. However, not all transgender or transsexual people wish to transition:

> While some transgendered individuals desire to "transition" from one sexed body to another by means of hormones, electrolysis and surgery, not all do and fewer still have the economic ability to do so. An increasing number of transgendered individuals are choosing to identify as neither male nor female and are claiming unique contours of sex and gender that offer new and unlimited possibilities. Understanding the nature of these possibilities requires a language that challenges cultural assumptions of sex and gender. The language and literature of transgendered existence is only now emerging as the transgendered community develops and we begin to think beyond the binary of male and female, man and woman, masculine and feminine. (Cooper, 1999, p. 112)

COMING OUT AND COMMUNITY

An important part of coming out is finding a community of other LGBTTTIQ people. Reynolds & Hanjorgiris (2000) write that for gay people, "Identification with the gay community has been found to promote understanding of, coping with, and ultimately accepting of a gay identity and behaviour" (p. 42).

Racialized minority LGBTTTIQ people face racism from both mainstream society and the LGBTTTIQ communities and homo/transphobia from their ethno-racial communities (Walters, Simoni & Horwath, 2001). For those who are negotiating identity development and are from more than one marginalized group, it is important to find communities that recognize and support the intersection of both identities (Duruz, 1999). For example, a Chinese lesbian may find she experiences affirmation for both "parts" of herself in an organization for Chinese lesbians and a deaf gay man facing ablism from LGBTTTIQ communities and homophobia from a deaf community may find support from a group for LGBTTTIQ people with hearing impairments. If such resources are not available, as is likely in rural areas and smaller centres, Web resources such as chat groups and e-mail distribution lists may be good alternatives.

DELAYING OR CHOOSING NOT TO COME OUT

It is uncertain whether healthy identity development for LGBTTTIQ people depends on being "out" to everyone they know, including family (Van Wormer et al., 2000). There are good reasons to avoid or delay coming out. For some adolescents, coming out while living with their families may mean abuse or a loss of support. The following is a description of the experience of transgendered youth:

If the child continues to express her/himself outside of the gender expectations into adolescence . . . the interventions become more swift and severe. . . . Parents or guardians take out their own discomfort with gender non-conformity on their child, resulting in strained relations and further isolation of the adolescent. . . . In the event of extreme and/or persistent gender non-conformity, or if youths disclose to their parents that they are transgender, the family may react with extreme behaviours in turn. Physical, emotional and verbal abuse may occur, or the youth might be thrown out of the home (Burgess, 1999, p. 42).

A young person in this situation might benefit from waiting until he or she is more independent before coming out to parents, and might first seek allies in his or her family and community to provide a support network.

Some people of colour may choose not to come out to their families for fear of losing an important support that affirms their ethno-racial identity (Fukuyama & Ferguson, 2000). Liu & Chan (1996), referring to the specific cultural context of Asian Americans, state that, "Because Asian Americans' individual identities are so tied to family identity, even if sexuality is not disclosed or openly discussed, the adult daughter or son may still feel very secure and cared for and may not be willing to risk jeopardizing this relationship by coming out." Racism within the larger society and also within LGBTTTIQ communities (Ridge et al., 1999) can make a connection with their family and their ethno-racial community even more important to LGBTTTIQ people of colour (Diaz et al., 2001; Kanuha, 1990).

Interestingly, recent studies suggest that there is greater acceptance from families of gay and lesbian people of colour than from families of white gay men and lesbians. Washington (2001) suggests that although the former do not necessarily celebrate their LGBTTTIQ children, fewer families of colour tend to disown their children in these circumstances.

Families and other loved ones of LGBTTTIQ people appear to go through a process themselves during which their attitudes and beliefs change as they gain more awareness about, and comfort with, their loved one's coming out. One model includes the following eight stages: repulsion, pity, denial, tolerance, acceptance, support, celebration and activism (Charania & Surani, 2002). Family members may need to come to terms with their loved one's changes and grieve for perceived losses. For example, some parents may worry that their newly out gay, lesbian or bisexual child will give not them grandchildren (even though LGBTTTIQ people can and often do have children). Families of transgender and transsexual people may also need time to adjust to new pronouns, names and expectations associated with their loved one's transition (Cooper, 1999).

THE CLINICIAN'S ROLE IN SUPPORTING THE COMING OUT PROCESS
Clinicians should encourage discussion of sexual orientation and gender identity to help their clients with the coming out process (Van Wormer et al., 2000). Without such discussion, many LGBTTTIQ clients may not disclose or question their identity

to a clinician (Reynolds & Hanjorgiris, 2000), which in turn may result in care that is not as relevant to them as it could be. To encourage disclosure, clinicians should be "intentionally inclusive," a term used to describe the explicit communication needed to help marginalized clients discuss taboo subjects. One way to be intentionally inclusive is to ask direct questions, in a non-judgmental way, about gender identity and sexual orientation issues. *Asking the Right Questions: Talking about Sexual Orientation and Gender Identity during Assessment for Drug and Alcohol Concerns* (Barbara et al., 2002) provides a guide for asking relevant questions. The Gay and Lesbian Medical Association has produced a similar helpful guide (GLMA, 2002a). Another way is to change agency forms and decor to be LGBTTTIQ inclusive. Unless a clinician is intentionally inclusive, clients may not come out or may feel that the clinician is judgmental or rejecting or will pathologize their LGBTTTIQ identity.

The clinician can help the client understand the process of coming out by emphasizing its ongoing, developmental nature, and that it is unique for each individual. Clients may not understand that it is normal to experience many different feelings during this time, including joy, fear, loss of heterosexual or gender privilege, awkwardness around other LGBTTTIQ people, freedom, and anger at societal oppression. On this last point, clinicians should help clients understand that the coming out process is not only a personal issue, but also one that is affected by community and societal oppression. A clinician can play an important role by advocating for a client within the social service agency, or when the client's family, school or community is involved (Reynolds & Hanjorgiris, 2000; Burgess, 1999). Clients may also need help with what Reynolds & Hanjorgiris (2000) call "the process of identity management" (p. 50), in which the clinician helps clients understand how their "identity intersects with and affects other aspects of their life such as career, relationships with family of origin, religion or faith, and coming out to others."

COMING OUT AND SUBSTANCE USE

There are many links between coming out and substance use. Most clients I have spoken with about identity development and substance use identify a connection between coming out, internalized oppression and substance use. For example, clients may increase their substance use to cope with feeling different, being closeted or fitting in with other LGBTTTIQ people, or to deal with internalized oppression, fear of rejection or discomfort in sexual situations. Some clients notice that stopping or reducing substance use makes them more conscious of identity issues. Other clients find that their substance use decreases as their identity becomes more integrated. Some clients notice no link between coming out and substance use and may instead connect their substance use to other stressors, such as childhood trauma.

Discrimination and Bashing

LGBTTTIQ people often encounter verbal assaults, violence and other forms of discrimination because they challenge dominant sexual orientation and gender norms (Swigonski, 2001). The harm caused by such encounters can manifest in hypervigilance, fear, lack of trust and decreased self-worth (Walters et al., 2001). However, despite the harm caused by discrimination, LGBTTTIQ people can also develop resilience and strength by living with adversity (Shernoff, 2002). Social activism can be an important strategy for a client who, by creating change, may better cope with oppression (Diaz et al., 2001; Jones, 2002). Counselling that acknowledges the existence of oppression and allows clients to explore its impact is also helpful.

A study of experiences of homophobia, racism and poverty among gay and bisexual Latino men in the United States found links among all three forms of oppression and suicidal thoughts. Most striking was the presence of suicidal ideation among those who "as a child heard that gays are not normal" (Diaz et al., 2001, p. 930). Some LGBTTTIQ people may use alcohol and other drugs to feel more empowered when enduring discrimination. For example, a lesbian client who, at work, encountered daily teasing, put-downs and threats about her lesbian identity would often cope by drinking before and after her shift. Another client with gender identity issues felt more confident in public in masculine clothing, and used amphetamines to make himself less aware of people's reactions to him.

Internalized Oppression

Internalized oppression refers to how people internalize negative messages, beliefs and myths about their identities (Chen-Hayes, 2003; Mascher, 2003). Internalized oppression can affect a person's self-esteem and health, which can result in increased substance use (Diaz et al., 2001; Cabaj, 2000; Hughes & Eliason, 2002). Addressing internalized oppression and teaching clients how to affirm their identity (or identities) may lead to more successful treatment (Craft & Mulvey, 2001).

• Internalization of oppression is a normal reaction to societal discrimination. Internalized homophobia, biphobia and transphobia may become apparent through a person's negative statements about, discomfort with or isolation from LGBTTTIQ communities.

• Clinicians, whether they belong to the LGBTTTIQ communities or not, need to be aware of their own heterosexism and genderism when working with clients. Given that oppression is prevalent in society, if a clinician does not have this self-awareness, negative beliefs about LGBTTTIQ people can be easily transferred to the client. This is particularly the case for LGBTTTIQ clinicians who may be seen as role models to clients who are coming out or transitioning.

RESOLVING INTERNALIZED OPPRESSION ISSUES
The clinician's role in helping a client resolve internalized oppression includes not colluding with it by gently challenging expressions of homophobia, biphobia and transphobia. For example, an effective response to a statement such as, "Lesbian relationships don't last," might be, "What do you mean when you say that? Is that your experience? Where did you learn that? Do you think that's true for all lesbians?"

A clinician can also disagree, or give examples of LGBTTTIQ people who contradict the client's expressed myth. Boyd & Whitman (2003) provide a list of questions that helps clinicians explore the causes of a client's internalized oppression, while Bowers (2003) suggests using a technique known as semihypnotic visualization to explore internalized negative beliefs.

INTERNALIZED OPPRESSION AND MULTIPLE MARGINALIZATION
A client who experiences multiple marginalization may have to integrate several aspects of his or her identity to effectively resolve his or her internalized oppression (Walters et al., 2001). There are ways to do this in therapy:
• Chen-Hayes (2003) suggests identifying and rating, with the client, the importance of multiple forms of identity (i.e., social class, citizenship status, disability status, gender) and present and past levels of internalized oppression connected to each.
• Addison & Brown (2003) provide a list of questions to help therapist and client explore dimensions of sexual orientation and ethnic identity.

Body Image

Body image and eating disorders are concerns for LGBTTTIQ people. Negative body image relates to substance use in different ways. Some substances, such as cocaine and crystal methamphetamine, can be used to lower appetite. Other substances can be used to help a person cope with negative perceptions about his or her appearance. It is useful to ask LGBTTTIQ clients to assess how, for them, community and societal pressures, substance use and body image intersect with each other (Barbara et al., 2002).

Some studies suggest that lesbian and bisexual women are less affected by negative body image than heterosexual women and gay men. Explanations for this include:
• an appreciation for larger body sizes
• less concern with appearance
• more satisfaction with their bodies (Kauth et al., 2000; Lakkis et al.,1999).
Yet lesbians, as women, remain affected by societal messages that emphasize the "relentless pursuit of thinness" (Szekely, 1988) and are likely internalize them to some degree.

Gay and bisexual men face greater body image challenges (Barbara, 2002; Kauth et al., 2000; Lakkis et al., 1999), because of both pressure to conform to the "ideal body" image prevalent in gay culture—that of a young, white, muscular, masculine male (Ayres, 1999)—and internalized homophobia (Pytluk, 2003). LGBTTTIQ people with disabilities may have additional trouble developing a positive self-image because of the stereotype that people with disabilities are asexual (Schneider, 2003).

Ayres (1999) describes his experience as a gay, Chinese man in Australia and how body image pressures have race and age dimensions:

[The gay bar] is an environment where being physically desirable is closely related to being socially desirable . . . as I became a participant in the gay world, I found myself increasingly influenced by the imagery which determined what was desirable. . . . There is no single Ideal Body. Advertisements are variously filled with blondes, brunettes, Latinos, chunky men, lean men. But the closer you look at what is considered "sexy," "hunky," "desirable," the more you realize that there is a limited range of parts which make up Ideal Bodies. The recurring themes are youth, masculinity and race . . . how can we as Asian men see ourselves as desirable? This is true not only for Asian men, but for all excluded categories: old men, fat men, short men, Aboriginal men (p. 91).

Research on transgendered and transsexual people and body image is scarce. For some transpeople, eating problems and poor body image may intersect with gender issues (Marone et al., 1998). I have worked, for example, with large-framed transsexual women who diet in an attempt to become smaller. But transpeople are not that different from non-transpeople when it comes to conforming with societal gender norms. Many women remove facial and body hair, and wear makeup (to appear more "feminine"), and men often work out to achieve a more "masculine" physique (Cooper, 1999).

Aging

Older LGBTTTIQ people are largely invisible to mainstream and LGBTTTIQ communities because of society's obsession with youth, and because it is often wrongly assumed that older people are non-sexual (Van Wormer et al., 2000). Penny Coleman's (2000) photodocumentary of older LGBTTTIQ people is an example of this group's efforts to become more visible. It includes an interview with "Gerry," an older lesbian, who describes the ageism in the lesbian community:

These days, Gerry spends much of her time alone. It's a little quieter than she would like. The last time she walked into a gay bar by herself was to meet some friends on her seventieth birthday. "The whole wall was lined with leather jacketed kids, and I heard somebody say, 'Geez, did you see what just walked in?'" Gerry got off a well-aimed rejoinder, but it stuck and it stopped her. . . . "But really, the only difference between me now and me thirty years ago is I ain't getting laid. Go find me another ninety-year old lesbian who wants to go to bed with me! That's my problem now." (pp. 4–5)

A report from a Canadian community centre serving LGBTTTIQ communities revealed that services for older adults, including LGBTTTIQ-positive housing, geriatric care and social activities, need great improvement. The report also suggested that LGBTTTIQ organizations include older LGBTTTIQ people in leadership roles and advocate efforts to change how the community views, recognizes and celebrates its elders (Harmer, 2000). When working with LGBTTTIQ older adults who have sub-stance use concerns, it is important to be aware of the issue of ageism and invisibility. Does it impact their ability to access appropriate services and supports? Do they iden-tify any impact on self-esteem? In what ways does substance use help them to cope with ageism and invisibility?

HIV/AIDS

Research into HIV/AIDS and its risk factors has focused mostly on men who have sex with men (MSM), a term that includes:
• gay or bisexual men
• men who may not identify as gay or bisexual but who engage in same-gender sex
• transgender and transsexual people (Hughes, 2002).

HIV/AIDS has an impact on both those infected and their loved ones (Kauth et al., 2000; Van Wormer et al., 2000). Highly active antiretroviral therapy (HAART) has decreased HIV/AIDS-related mortality, but is costly and the side-effects make it diffi-cult to maintain (Wolitski et al., 2001). The availability of these medications may also lead some MSM to believe that they can be less vigilant about safer-sex behaviour.

SAFE SEX AND SUBSTANCE USE

Studies with MSM have shown that substance use often precedes unsafe sex (Calzavara et al., 2003; Halkitis & Parsons, 2002). In a Washington, DC–based survey, 66 per cent of the men surveyed said that they had had sex while under the influence of alcohol or other drugs during the previous year, 58 per cent said they were more likely to engage in unprotected sex when drinking (District of Columbia Department of Health, 2002). The respondents also reported use of the following substances:
• alcohol (79 per cent)
• poppers (amyl nitrate) (39 per cent)
• marijuana (30 per cent)
• ecstasy (28 per cent).

Substance use also helps gay and bisexual men and transpeople cope with the loss, due to HIV/AIDS, of others in their social and support networks; it can also help people cope with an uncertain HIV status or with a new diagnosis (Halkitis & Parsons, 2002).

Substance use plays a role in HIV infection in transgender and transsexual people as well. Because HIV risk increases with sex work, the transgendered and transsexual people who do this work (due to limited job options and employment discrimination) are at greater risk (Clements-Nolle et al., 2001; Hughes & Eliason, 2002; Reback & Lombardi, 1999). Namaste (1999), in her study of female-to-male people in Quebec, found that many did not believe they were at risk for HIV/AIDS. However, she did find that in areas of Quebec where clean needles were not readily available (for the injection of hormones), there was a higher HIV rate in the female-to-male population.

My clinical experience has shown that lesbian and bisexual women report not being affected by HIV/AIDS other than discussing the impact of caring for or losing gay and bisexual male friends with the disease. There is a perception that lesbians are at a low risk for the disease because woman-to-woman contact has not shown conclusive risks of transmission. However, sexual orientation does not necessarily match with sexual behaviour; some lesbians and bisexual women have had or do have sex with men. Some may use injection drugs , which can also increase their risk (Kauth et al., 2000).

See Chapter 27 for further discussion of HIV/AIDS and other blood-borne diseases.

Family Issues

The role of the family is often different for LGBTTTIQ people than for heterosexual or gender-conforming people, and presents different issues.

Coping with estrangement, alienation and rejection from one's family of origin after coming out or transitioning can cause distress. Fear of rejection may cause some LGBTTTIQ people to avoid disclosure (Barbara, 2002). This may also be true when already "out" LGBTTTIQ people raised in adoptive families are reunited with their biological families.

Substance use may help one cope with this distress. From my clinical experience, some clients find that a visit (or even anticipation of a visit) with a homophobic, transphobic or biphobic family member who seems not to accept them can trigger substance use. Relapse-prevention planning and education about boundaries can help a client resist turning to substance use in these circumstances. Family therapy may also be appropriate (Anderson, 1996). If this is not possible, a "chosen family" (a close network of, for example, friends, ex-partners, lovers and some biological family members) may provide much-needed support to an LGBTTTIQ person (Siegel & Walker, 1996). Parents and Families of Lesbians and Gays (PFLAG) offers support to families coming to terms with loved ones' gender identity or sexual orientation, and has chapters all over North America. Though couple therapy is often not considered in traditional substance use treatment due to heterosexist bias (Anderson, 1996), such therapy can be appropriate as it addresses issues of trust, intimacy and support; it may also be useful for a couple where one or both partners are reducing or stopping substance use, or to investigate whether the substance use of one partner has influenced the other to use (Hughes & Eliason, 2002).

LGBTTTIQ people are also affected by issues involving children, including:
• having children and/or coming out to them (Van Wormer et al., 2000)
• beginning a relationship with someone with a child or children (Hollingsworth & Didelot, 2003)
• coping with societal discrimination toward LGBTTTIQ parents and their children (McLean, 2003).

The LGBT Parenting Network, created in 2002, provides a newsletter, activities and a Web site (http://familypride.uwo.ca) dedicated to these issues.

Sexuality

Substance use may help men and women feel less inhibited about same-gender sexual activity. Lesbians and bisexual women are more likely to use alcohol for this purpose, while gay and bisexual men are more likely to use drugs such as:
• methamphetamine (to increase sexual potency)
• amyl nitrate (poppers) (to prolong orgasm and relax the anal sphincter)
• Viagra® (to enhance sexual performance) (Hughes & Eliason, 2002).

Gay social venues such as community events, dances, bath houses, circuit parties, sex clubs and dance clubs, while providing havens from homophobia, normalize substance use. The link between sexuality and substance use in these venues is problematic because, as discussed above, there is a higher risk of unprotected sex. These are often also sexualized environments, where LGBTTTIQ people flirt, cruise or have sex (Barbara, 2002; Halkitis & Parsons, 2002).

LGBTTTIQ people in urban centres might have a range of other social venues available to them (e.g., sports, social, support, spiritual and hobby groups) and it is important to encourage clients to explore these alternatives (Cooper, 1999). But many clients choose to socialize at venues where substance use occurs; these venues are central to the LGBTTTIQ community, and their historical importance as the "first gay community centres" lives on. In this situation, the clinician can help the client develop a plan to avoid high-risk behaviours at these venues. This plan might include:
• learning and exercising refusal skills
• going with a "buddy"
• going late and leaving early to reduce exposure to triggers
• taking very little money to avoid impulsive substance use.

Some clients also use substances to relieve shyness or discomfort with their bodies (physical pain or poor body image), or to block intrusive traumatic imagery (related to past sexual abuse) during sex. A number of the lesbian clients I have worked with who had had past heterosexual relationships reported that they first used substances while having non-pleasurable heterosexual sex, hoping that this would improve the experience. They were later unable to break the habit when having pleasurable sex with women.

Intersex children, who often have scarred, insensitive or painful genitals as a result of intrusive surgeries, can have difficulty exploring their sexuality. Support groups, where intersex people can meet others with similar experience, can help (Cooper, 1999).

Like their gender-conforming queer counterparts, transgender and transsexual people (and their sexualities) have been portrayed as exotic, repulsive or immoral through pornography and the popular media (Cooper, 1999). For them, forging a healthy sex life requires examining and challenging internalized transphobia.

Clinicians, too, should consider the messages they have internalized about sexuality in general and LGBTTTIQ sexualities in particular. Most of us have personal beliefs about what types of sexual behaviour are "normal." These beliefs are socially constructed, and challenging them is necessary when working with the diversity of human sexuality. Ask yourself how you feel about non-monogamy or S/M (sadomasochism) or how you would react on seeing two men kissing on the street? Where did you learn these beliefs and how do you think they might affect your work with clients? Our beliefs about sexuality are likely a creation of our social norms, which in many cases (and not just in relation to sexuality) tend to marginalize those who do not fit within them.

See Chapter 24 for further discussion of sexuality and sexual issues.

CREATING LGBTTTIQ-POSITIVE SPACES AND SERVICES

In order to make a social service organization more welcoming to LGBTTTIQ clients, it is helpful to assess its overall sensitivity to LGBTTTIQ people. The organization should have:
• LGBTTTIQ-positive policies and procedures
• an environment that communicates LGBTTTIQ-related policies
• forms that are LGBTTTIQ-positive
• services (both generic and LGBTTTIQ-specific) that acknowledge the needs of LGBTTTIQ communities
• staff who are LGBTTTIQ-positive and trained in LGBTTTIQ issues, or who are out themselves
• community outreach activities
• LGBTTTIQ representation on program advisory committees and boards.
Each of these elements is discussed in more detail below.

Policies and Procedures

The organization's policies and procedures should:
• be sufficiently specific to and inclusive of LGBTTTIQ people
• stipulate how to address discrimination from staff and clients
• communicate to staff the expected code of conduct.

Physical Space

The office, group rooms, agency hallways and waiting areas can communicate to marginalized people that they are in a safe and sensitive environment. You can do this by:
• putting up posters that communicate anti-oppression and appreciation of diversity
• displaying in the waiting area pamphlets, magazines and newspapers from diverse communities
• installing unisex bathrooms in your organization (Gay and Lesbian Medical Association, 2002a).

LGBTTTIQ-POSITIVE FORMS

Heterosexist and genderist questions on intake forms (such as, "Are you married?" or those that limit gender to "M" and "F") communicate very quickly to LGBTTTIQ clients that they are not welcome. Ensure that your forms encourage clients to disclose their sexual orientation and gender identity. See Barbara et al. 2002 and Gay and Lesbian Medical Association (2002 b) for more information.

Services

LGBTTTIQ-SPECIFIC SERVICES

For some clients, LGBTTTIQ-specific services are more appropriate than generic services (Hicks, 2000). Group counselling can help LGBTTTIQ clients address life issues and transitions, behaviour change and the intersection of substance use with coming out, internalized oppression and other issues mentioned in this chapter. LGBTTTIQ-specific groups create an environment in which people feel safe addressing these issues (Debord & Perez, 2000). Without these specific services, clients attending generic programs might "closet" themselves; they might avoid discussing personal issues or lie about a same-gender partner.

SAFER GENERIC GROUPS

Clinicians can make their generic or mixed groups safer for all marginalized groups, including LGBTTTIQ clients, by being "intentionally inclusive." For example, during a first session when guidelines and group norms are discussed, the clinician can review some common differences between people (the group can generate a list through brainstorming or a pairs exercise) and remind clients that discriminatory remarks will not be tolerated. The facilitator might begin a group session on a specific topic by reminding clients that the discussion will include diverse experiences and opinions. A discussion about relationship issues, for example, could start with a reference to the variety of relationships that exist, including opposite-gender and same-gender relationships; this reference invites clients to raise issues and sets a group norm of openness to, and affirmation of, difference.

Clinicians should address and challenge discriminatory remarks as they arise during groups (Bush & Sainz, 2001). They can do this by:
• asking clients to clarify the meaning of statements
• reminding them of group guidelines
• asking group members to share their feelings about the statements being made.
A clinician who avoids or neglects to address discriminatory statements lowers the safety level of the group.

LGBTTTIQ-Positive, -Trained and Out Staff

To be effective and culturally competent, staff need anti-heterosexism and anti-genderism training as well as information about LGBTTTIQ communities. Such training may be facilitated by:
• asking (and paying) local LGBTTTIQ groups to help train your staff
• subscribing to journals and listservs that keep your staff up to date (see the list of references below for ideas)
• recruiting LGBTTTIQ staff to work at your organization, listening carefully to them and seeking their advice, and encouraging all staff to be LGBTTTIQ-positive
• being allies to LGBTTTIQ staff, making it safe for them to come out to other staff and clients; don't expect them to do all the work to make your organization LGBTTTIQ-positive
• ensuring that human resource forms and practices are not genderist and heterosexist (Clark et al., 2001).

Outreach

Consider in your outreach plan:
• where and how you advertise your services
• whether your flyers indicate that LGBTTTIQ people are welcome and that your services reflect their needs
• contacting LGBTTTIQ services and groups in your area by accessing a local paper, listserv or community bulletin board, or leaving flyers in bars or coffee shops
• participating in LGBTTTIQ community events, such as Pride Day.

LGBTTTIQ Representation

Without the participation of the communities, your other efforts, such as policy development, service provision and outreach, may not be successful (Feinberg, 2001). Make sure that you have LGBTTTIQ staff and community members involved in:
• hiring committees
• strategic planning
• other decision making.

SERVICES AND RESOURCES

In Canada, there are very limited LGBTTTIQ-specific services available to clients with substance use concerns, but here are some examples:

Rainbow Services (formerly the LesBiGay Service) is a service at the Centre for Addiction and Mental Health in Toronto, Ontario. It provides a full range of services for LGBTTTIQ clients with substance use concerns. Clients from outside Toronto are welcome.

Web site: www.camh.net/rainbow_services

The Robins Hill Aftercare Site of the Northern Regional Recovery Continuum in Sudbury, Ontario, offers outpatient life-skills groups for lesbians.

Web site: www.lakesidecentre.ca

In Vancouver, B.C., the Lesbian, Gay, Bisexual and Transgender Population Health Advisory Group recently held extensive community consultations on the issue of substance use problems in the LGBT communities, and drafted a report recommending the development of LGBT-sensitive and LGBT-specific services for the Vancouver-Richmond area (LGBT Health Association of B.C., 2003).

The Pride Institute and Alternatives are two private hospital-based programs that provide mental health and addiction services in a number of cities in the United States.

Web sites: www.pride-institute.com and www.alternativesinc.com

The BBCM Foundation organizes medical and other health care volunteer professionals to operate infirmaries at Canadian circuit parties that primarily serve gay men. It also produces educational materials about "party drugs" for circuit party patrons.

Web site: www.bbcm.org

The U.S. National Association of Gay and Lesbian Addiction Professionals (NALGAP) offers information and articles.

Web site: www.nalgap.org

Gay and Lesbian Alcoholics Anonymous, Narcotics Anonymous and Cocaine Anonymous groups exist in most large urban centres. The International Advisory Council for Homosexual Men and Women in Alcoholics Anonymous has a listing of gay and lesbian meetings worldwide.

Web site: www.iac.aa.org

The U.S. Substance Abuse and Mental Health Services Administration (SAMHSA) has information and downloadable guides specifically addressing LGBTTTIQ issues.

Web site: www.health.org

GLOSSARY

The discourse around LGBTTTIQ issues and the definitions in this glossary will change over time. Changes in thinking and attitudes toward sexual orientation and gender identity are continually taking place in society as a whole and within the LGBTTTIQ communities. These terms and definitions are not standardized and may be used differently by different people and in different regions.

Asexual: a word describing a person who is not sexually and/or romantically active, or not sexually and/or romantically attracted to other persons.

Autosexual: a word describing a person whose significant sexual involvement is with oneself or a person who prefers masturbation to sex with a partner.

Biphobia: irrational fear or dislike of bisexuals. Bisexuals may be stigmatized by heterosexuals, lesbians and gay men.

Bisexual: a word describing a person whose sexual orientation is directed toward men and women, though not necessarily at the same time.

Coming out: the process by which LGBTTTIQ people acknowledge and disclose their sexual orientation or gender identity, or in which transsexual or transgendered people acknowledge and disclose their gender identity, to themselves and others (See also "Transition"). Coming out is thought to be an ongoing process. People who are "closeted" or "in the closet" hide the fact that they are LGBTTTIQ. Some people "come out of the closet" in some situations (e.g., with other gay friends) and not in others (e.g., at work).

Crossdresser: a person who dresses in the clothing of the other sex for recreation, expression or art, or for erotic gratification. Formerly known as "transvestites." Crossdressers may be male or female, and can be straight, gay, lesbian or bisexual. Gay/bisexual male crossdressers may be "drag queens" or female impersonators; lesbian/bisexual female crossdressers may be "drag kings" or male impersonators.

Dyke: a word traditionally used as a derogatory term for lesbians. Other terms include lezzie, lesbo, butch, bull dyke and diesel dyke. Many women have reclaimed these words and use them proudly to describe their identity.

Fag: a word traditionally used as a derogatory term for gay men. Other terms include fruit, faggot, queen, fairy, pansy, sissy and homo. Many men have reclaimed these words and use them proudly to describe their identity.

Family of choice: the circle of friends, partners, companions and perhaps ex-partners with which many LGBTTTIQ people surround themselves. This group gives the support, validation and sense of belonging that is often unavailable from the person's family of origin.

Gay: a word to describe a person whose primary sexual orientation is to members of the same gender or who identifies as a member of the gay community. This word can refer to men and women, although many women prefer the term "lesbian."

Gender conforming: abiding by society's gender rules, e.g., a woman dressing, acting, relating to others and thinking of herself as feminine or as a woman.

Gender identity: a person's own identification of being male, female or intersex; masculine, feminine, transgendered or transsexual. Gender identity most often corresponds with one's anatomical gender, but sometimes people's gender identity doesn't directly correspond to their anatomy. Transgendered people use many terms to describe their gender identities, including: pre-op transsexual, post-op transsexual, non-op transsexual, transgenderist, crossdresser, transvestite, transgendered, two-spirit, intersex, hermaphrodite, fem male, gender blender, butch, manly woman, diesel dyke, sex radical, androgynist, female impersonator, male impersonator, drag king, drag queen, etc.

Genderqueer: this very recent term was coined by young people who experience a very fluid sense of both their gender identity and their sexual orientation, and who do not want to be constrained by absolute or static concepts. Instead, they prefer to be open to relocate themselves on the gender and sexual orientation continuums.

Gender role: the public expression of gender identity. Gender role includes everything people do to show the world they are male, female, androgynous or ambivalent. It includes sexual signals, dress, hairstyle and manner of walking. In society, gender roles are usually considered to be masculine for men and feminine for woman.

Gender transition: the period during which transsexual persons begin changing their appearance and bodies to match their internal identity.

Genderism: the belief that the binary construct of gender, in which there are only two genders (male and female), is the most normal, natural and preferred gender identity. This binary construct does not include or allow for people to be intersex, transgendered, transsexual or genderqueer.

Hate crimes: offences that are motivated by hatred against victims based on their actual or perceived race, colour, religion, national origin, ethnicity, gender, disability or sexual orientation.

Heterosexism: the assumption, expressed overtly and/or covertly, that all people are or should be heterosexual. Heterosexism excludes the needs, concerns and life experiences of lesbian, gay and bisexual people, while it gives advantages to heterosexual people. It is often a subtle form of oppression that reinforces silence and invisibility for lesbian, gay and bisexual people.

Heterosexual: term used to describe a person whose primary sexual orientation is to members of the opposite gender. Heterosexual people are often referred to as "straight."

Heterosexual privilege: the unrecognized and assumed privileges that people have if they are heterosexual. Examples of heterosexual privilege include: holding hands or kissing in public without fearing threat, not questioning the normalcy of your sexual orientation, raising children without fears of state intervention or worries that your children will experience discrimination because of your heterosexuality.

Homophobia: irrational fear, hatred, prejudice or negative attitudes toward homosexuality and people who are gay or lesbian. Homophobia can take overt and covert, as well as subtle and extreme, forms. Homophobia includes behaviours such as jokes, name-calling, exclusion, gay bashing, etc.

Homosexual: a term to describe a person whose primary sexual orientation is to members of the same gender. Most people prefer to not use this label, preferring to use other terms, such as gay or lesbian.

Internalized homophobia: fear and self-hatred of one's own sexual orientation that occurs for many lesbians and gay men as a result of heterosexism and homophobia. Once lesbians and gay men realize that they belong to a group of people that is often despised and rejected in our society, many internalize and incorporate this stigmatization, and fear or hate themselves.

Intersex: a person who has some mixture of male and female genetic and/or physical sex characteristics. Formerly called "hermaphrodites." Many intersex people consider themselves to be part of the trans community.

Lesbian: a female whose primary sexual orientation is to other women or who identifies as a member of the lesbian community.

LGBTTTIQ: a common acronym for lesbian, gay, bisexual, transsexual, transgendered, two-spirit, intersex and queer individuals/communities. This acronym may or may not be used in a particular community. For example, in some places, the acronym *LGBT* (for lesbian, gay, bisexual and transgendered/transsexual) may be more common.

MSM: refers to any man who has sex with a man, whether he identifies as gay, bisexual or heterosexual. This term highlights the distinction between sexual behaviour and sexual identity (i.e., sexual orientation). A person's sexual behaviour may manifest itself into a sexual identity, but the reverse is not always true; sexual orientation is not always reflective of sexual behaviour. For example, a man may call himself heterosexual, but may engage in sex with men in certain situations (e.g., prison, sex work).

Out or Out of the closet: varying degrees of being open about one's sexual orientation or gender identity.

Passing: describes transgendered or transsexual people's ability to be accepted as their preferred gender. The term refers primarily to acceptance by people the individual does not know, or who do not know that the individual is transgendered or transsexual. Typically, passing involves a mix of physical gender cues (e.g., clothing, hairstyle, voice), behaviour, manner and conduct when interacting with others. Passing can also refer to hiding one's sexual orientation, as in "passing for straight."

Polysexual: an orientation that does not limit affection, romance or sexual attraction to any one gender or sex, and that further recognizes there are more than just two sexes.

Queer: traditionally, a derogatory and offensive term for LGBTTTIQ people. Many LGBTTTIQ people have reclaimed this word and use it proudly to describe their identity. Some transsexual and transgendered people identify as queers; others do not.

Questioning: people who are questioning their gender identity or sexual orientation and who often choose to explore options.

Sexual behaviour: what people do sexually. Not necessarily congruent with sexual orientation and/or sexual identity.

Sexual identity: one's identification to self (and others) of one's sexual orientation. Not necessarily congruent with sexual orientation and/or sexual behaviour.

Sexual minorities: include people who identify as LGBTTTIQ.

Sexual orientation: a term for the emotional, physical, romantic, sexual and spiritual attraction, desire or affection for another person. Examples include heterosexuality, bisexuality and homosexuality.

Straight: a term often used to describe people who are heterosexual.

Transgendered: a person whose gender identity is different from his or her biological sex, regardless of the status of surgical and hormonal gender reassignment processes. Often used as an umbrella term to include transsexuals, transgenderists, transvestites (crossdressers), and two-spirit, intersex and transgendered people.

Transgenderist: someone who is in-between being a transsexual and a transgendered person on the gender continuum, and who often takes sex hormones, but does not want genital surgery. Transgenderists can be born male (formerly known as "she-males") or born females (once called a "he/shes"). The former sometimes obtain breast implants and/or have electrolysis.

Transition: the process (which for some people may also be referred to as the "gender reassignment process") whereby transsexual people change their appearance and bodies to match their internal (gender) identity, while living their lives full-time in their preferred gender role.

Transphobia: irrational fear or dislike of transsexual and transgendered people.

Transsensual: a term for a person who is primarily attracted to transgendered or transsexual people.

Transsexual: a term for a person who has an intense long-term experience of being the sex opposite to his or her birth-assigned sex and who typically pursues a medical and legal transformation to become the other sex. There are transmen (female-to-male transsexuals) and transwomen (male-to-female transsexuals). Transsexual people may undergo a number of procedures to bring their body and public identity in line with their self-image, including sex hormone therapy, electrolysis treatments, sex reassignment surgeries and legal changes of name and sex status.

Transvestite: see "Crossdresser."

Two-spirit: an English term coined to reflect specific cultural words used by First Nation and other indigenous peoples for those in their cultures who are gay or lesbian, are transgendered or transsexual, or have multiple gender identities. The term reflects an effort by First Nation and other indigenous communities to distinguish their concepts of gender and sexuality from those of Western LGBTTTIQ communities.

WSW: refers to any woman who has sex with a woman, whether she identifies as lesbian, bisexual or heterosexual. This term highlights the distinction between sexual behaviour and sexual identity (i.e., sexual orientation). For example, women who identify as lesbian can also have sex with men and not all WSW identify as lesbian or bisexual.

REFERENCES

Aaron, D.J. , Markovic, N., Danielson, M.E., Honnold, J.A., Janoky, J.E. & Schmist, N.J. (2001). Behavioural risk factors for disease and preventative health practices among lesbians. *American Journal of Public Health, 91*(6), 972–975.

Addison, S. & Brown, M. (2003). Who am I really? Understanding the intersections of sexual and ethnic identity. In J. Whitman & C. Boyd (Eds.), *The Therapist's Notebook for Lesbian, Gay and Bisexual Clients* (pp.179–182). New York: Haworth Clinical Practice Press.

Anastas, J.W. (2001). Economic rights, economic myths, and economic realities. *Journal of Gay and Lesbian Social Services, 13*(1/2), 99–116.

Anderson, S.C. (1996). Addressing heterosexist bias in the treatment of lesbian couples with chemical dependency. In J. Laird & R. Green (Eds.), *Lesbians and Gays in Couples and Families* (pp. 316–340). San Francisco: Jossey-Bass.

Ayres, T. (1999). China doll, the experience of being a gay Chinese Australian. *Journal of Homosexuality, 36*(3/4), 87–97.

Barbara, A.M. (2002). Substance Abuse Treatment with lesbian, gay and bisexual people: A qualitative study of service providers. *Journal of Gay and Lesbian Social Services, 14*(4), 11–17.

Barbara, A.M., Chaim, G. & Doctor, F. (2002). *Asking the Right Questions: Talking about Sexual Orientation and Gender Identity during Assessment for Drug and Alcohol Concerns.* Toronto: Centre for Addiction and Mental Health.

Bowers, R. (2003). Semihypnotic visualization: Treating internalized homophobia in sexual and gender minorities. In J. Whitman & C. Boyd (Eds.), *The Therapist's Notebook for Lesbian, Gay and Bisexual Clients* (pp. 20–24). New York: Haworth Clinical Practice Press.

Boyd. C. & Whitman, J. (2003). Who told me that? Challenging internalized homophobic messages. In J. Whitman & C. Boyd (Eds.), *The Therapist's Notebook for Lesbian, Gay and Bisexual Clients* (pp. 56–59). New York: Haworth Clinical Practice Press.

Broido, E.M. (2000). Constructing identity: The nature and meaning of lesbian, gay and bisexual identities. In R.M. Perez, K.A. Debord & K.J. Bieschke (Eds.), *Handbook of Counseling and Psychotherapy with Lesbian, Gay and Bisexual Clients* (pp. 13–34). Washington, DC: American Psychological Association.

Burgess, C. (1999). Internal and external stress factors associated with the identity development of transgendered youth. *Journal of Gay and Lesbian Social Services. 10*(3/4), 35–47.

Bush, I.R. & Sainz, A. (2001). Competencies at the intersection of difference, tolerance, and prevention of hate crimes. *Journal of Gay and Lesbian Social Services, 13*(1/2), 205–224.

Cabaj, R. (2000). Substance abuse, internalized homophobia, and gay men and lesbians: Psychodynamic issues and clinical implications. *Addictions in the Gay and Lesbian Community, Journal of Gay and Lesbian Psychotherapy, 3*, 5–24.

Calzavara, L., Burchell, A.N., Remis, R.S., Major, C., Corey, P., Myers, T. et al. (2003). Delayed application of condoms is a risk factor for Human Immuno-deficiency Virus infection among homosexual and bisexual men. *American Journal of Epidemiology, 157*(3), 210–217.

Cass, V.C. (1979). Homosexual identity development: A theoretical model. *Journal of Homosexuality, 4*, 219–235.

Charania, G. & Surani, T. (2002). *Rewriting the Script Discussion Guide.* Toronto: Equity Logistics.

Chen-Hayes, S. (2003). Challenging multiple oppressions with GLBT clients. In J. Whitman & C. Boyd (Eds.), *The Therapist's Notebook for Lesbian, Gay and Bisexual Clients* (pp. 20–24). New York: Haworth Clinical Practice Press.

Clark, M.E., Landers, S., Linde, R. & Sperber, J. (2001). The GLBT health access project: A state-funded effort to improve access to health care. *American Journal of Public Health, 91*(6), 895–896.

Clements-Nolle, K., Marx, R., Guzman, R. & Katz, M. (2001). HIV prevalence, risk behaviors, health care use, and mental health status of transgender persons: Implications for public health intervention. *American Journal of Public Health, 91*(6), 915–921.

Coalition for Lesbian and Gay Rights in Ontario/Project Affirmation. (1997). Systems failure: A report on the experiences of sexual minorities in Ontario's health-care and social-services system. Toronto: author.

Coleman, P. (2000). *Village Elders*. Chicago: University of Illinois Press.

Collins, B. & Howard, B. (1997). Working with lesbians and gay men. In S. Harrison & V. Carver (Eds.), *Alcohol & Drug Problems: A Practical Guide for Counsellors* (2nd ed., pp. 293–318). Toronto: Addiction Research Foundation.

Cooper, K. (1999). Practice with transgendered youth and their families. *Journal of Gay and Lesbian Social Services, 10*(3/4), 111–129.

Craft, E.M. & Mulvey, K.P. (2001). Addressing lesbian, gay, bisexual and transgender issues from the inside: One federal agency's approach. *American Journal of Public Health, 91*, 889–891.

Debord, K.A. & Perez, R.M. (2000). Group counseling theory and practice with lesbian, gay, and bisexual clients. In R.M. Perez, K.A. Debord & K.J. Bieschke (Eds.), *Handbook of Counseling and Psychotherapy with Lesbian, Gay and Bisexual Clients* (pp. 183–206). Washington, DC: American Psychological Association.

Diaz, R.M., Ayala, G., Bein, E., Henne, J. & Marin, B. (2001). The impact of homophobia, poverty, and racism on the mental health of gay and bisexual Latino men: Findings from 3 US cities. *American Journal of Public Health, 91*(6), 927–932.

District of Columbia Department of Health HIV/AIDS Administration & Whitman-Walker Clinic. (2002). *Men Who Have Sex with Men (MSM), Survey Results 2001*. Available: www.wwc.org/MSMStudy.

Doctor, F. (2003). Examining links between drug and alcohol use and experiences of homophobia/biphobia and coming out. In J. Whitman & C. Boyd (Eds.), *The Therapist's Notebook for Lesbian, Gay and Bisexual Clients* (pp. 262–267). New York: Haworth Clinical Practice Press.

Duruz, A. (1999). Sister outsider, or "just another thing I am": Intersections of cultural and sexual identities in Australia. *Journal of Homosexuality, 36*(3/4), 87–97.

Feinberg, L. (1996). *Transgender Warriors*. Boston: Beacon Press.

Feinberg, L. (1998). *Trans Liberation, Beyond Pink or Blue*. Boston: Beacon Press.

Feinberg. L. (2001). Trans health crisis: For us it's life or death. *American Journal of Public Health, 91*(6), 897–900.

Finlon, C. (2002). Health care for all lesbian, gay, bisexual and transgender populations. *Journal of Gay and Lesbian Social Services, 14*(3), 109–116.

Fukuyama, M.A. & Ferguson, A.D. (2000). Lesbian, gay and bisexual people of colour: Understanding cultural complexity and managing multiple oppressions. In R.M. Perez, K.A. Debord & K.J. Bieschke (Eds.), *Handbook of Counseling and Psychotherapy with Lesbian, Gay and Bisexual Clients* (pp. 81–106). Washington, DC: American Psychological Association.

Gay and Lesbian Medical Association. (2002a). *Creating a Safe Clinical Environment for Lesbian, Gay, Bisexual, Transgender and Intersex (LGBTI) Patients.* Available: www.glma.org.

Gay and Lesbian Medical Association. (2002b). *MSM: Clinician Guide to Incorporating Sexual Risk Assessment in Routine Visits.* Available: www.glma.org.

Ghindia, D.J. & Kola, L.A. (1996). Co-factors affecting substance abuse among homosexual men: An investigation within a midwestern gay community. *Drug and Alcohol Dependence, 41,* 167–177.

Gilman, G.E., Cochran, S.D., Mays, V.M., Hughes, M., Ostow, D. & Kessler, R.C. (2001). Risk of psychiatric disorders among individuals reporting same-sex sexual partners in the National Comorbidity Survey. *American Journal of Public Health, 91*(6), 933–939.

Halkitis, P.N. & Parsons, J.T. (2002). Recreational drug use and HIV risk sexual behaviour among men frequenting gay social venues. *Journal of Gay and Lesbian Social Services, 14*(4), 19–38.

Harmer, J. (2000). *Older Gay, Bisexual, Transgender, Transsexual Persons; Community Services Challenges and Opportunities for the 519 Community Centre and the GLBT Community, A Review.* Toronto: The 519 Community Centre. Available: www.the519.org.

Hicks, D. (2000). The importance of specialized treatment programs for lesbian and gay patients. *Journal of Gay and Lesbian Psychotherapy, 3,* 81–94.

Hollingsworth, L.A. & Didelot, M.J. (2003). Coming out of marriage: Developing an emerging gay, lesbian, or bisexual identity. In J. Whitman & C. Boyd (Eds.), *The Therapist's Notebook for Lesbian, Gay and Bisexual Clients* (pp. 50–55). New York: Haworth Clinical Practice Press.

Hughes, T.L. & Eliason, M. (2002). Substance use and abuse in lesbian, gay, bisexual and transgender populations. *Journal of Primary Prevention, 22*(3), 263–298.

Hughes, T.L. & Wilsnack, S.C. (1997). Use of alcohol among lesbians: Research and clinical implications. *American Journal of Orthopsychiatry, 67,* 20–36.

Jones, T. (2002). Characteristics of a group of lesbian and gay radical street activists. *Journal of Gay and Lesbian Social Services, 14*(4), 39–54.

Kanuha, V. (1990). Compounding the triple jeopardy: Battering in lesbian of colour relationships. In L.S. Brown & M.P. Root (Eds.), *Diversity and Complexity in Feminist Therapy* (pp. 169–184). New York: Harrington Park Press.

Kauth, M., Hartwig, M. & Kalichman, S. (2000). Health behaviour relevant to psychotherapy with lesbian, gay and bisexual clients. In R.M. Perez, K.A. Debord & K.J. Bieschke (Eds.), *Handbook of Counseling and Psychotherapy with Lesbian, Gay and Bisexual Clients* (pp. 435–456). Washington, DC: American Psychological Association.

Lakkis, J., Ricciardelli, L.A. & Williams, R.J. (1999). Role of sexual orientation and gender-related traits in disordered eating. *Sex Roles, 41*(1/2), 1–16.

LGBT Health Association of B.C. (2003). *LGBT Communities and Substance Use—What Health Has to Do with It! A Report on Consultations with LGBT Communities.* Available: www.vcn.bc.ca/vrhb/Whats_New.htm.

Liu, P. & Chan, C.S. (1996). Lesbian, gay and bisexual Asian Americans and their families. In J. Laird & R. Green (Eds.), *Lesbians and Gays in Couples and Families* (pp. 137–152). San Francisco: Jossey-Bass.

Mallon, G.P. (1999). Knowledge for practice with transgendered persons. *Journal of Gay and Lesbian Social Services, 10*(3/4), 1–17.

Mansergh, G., Colfa, G.N., Marks, G., Rader, M., Guzman, R. & Buchbinder, S. (2001). The Circuit Party Men's Health Survey: Findings and implications for gay and bisexual men. *American Journal of Public Health, 91*(6), 953–958.

Marone, P., Iacoella, S., Cecchini, M.G. & Ravenna, A.R. (1998). An experimental study of body image and perception in gender identity disorders. *International Journal of Transgenderism, 2*(3). Available: www.symposion.com/ijt/ijtc0501.html.

Mascher, J. (2003). Overcoming biphobia. In J. Whitman & C. Boyd (Eds.), *The Therapist's Notebook for Lesbian, Gay and Bisexual Clients* (pp. 78–83). New York: Haworth Clinical Practice Press.

McKirnan, D.J. & Peterson, P.L. (1989). Alcohol and drug use among homosexual men and women: Epidemiology and population characteristics. *Addictive Behaviours, 14*, 545–553.

McLean, Ron. (2003). Family care planning for gay, lesbian, bisexual and transgendered parents: Creating healthy living environments for adults and children. In J. Whitman & C. Boyd (Eds.), *The Therapist's Notebook for Lesbian, Gay and Bisexual Clients* (pp. 249–255). New York: Haworth Clinical Practice Press.

Namaste, V. (1999). HIV/AIDS and female to male transsexuals and transvestites: Results from a needs assessment in Quebec. *International Journal of Transgenderism, 3*(1+2). Available: www.symposion.com/ijt/hiv_risk/namaste.html.

Pazos, S. (1999). Practice with female-to male transgendered youth. *Journal of Gay and Lesbian Social Services, 10*(3/4), 65–82.

Plumb, M. (2001). Undercounts and overstatements: Will the IOM Report on lesbian health improve research? *American Journal of Public Health, 91*, 873–875.

Pytluk, S.D. (2003). Body as self: Resolving body image disturbances in gay men. In J. Whitman. & C. Boyd (Eds.), *The Therapist's Notebook for Lesbian, Gay and Bisexual Clients* (pp. 215–219). New York: Haworth Clinical Practice Press.

Rachlin, K. (2002). Transgender individuals' experiences of psychotherapy. *International Journal of Transgenderism. 6*(1). Available: www.symposion.com/ijt/ijtvo06no01_03.htm.

Raj, R. (2002). Towards a transpositive therapeutic model: Developing clinical sensitivity and cultural competence in the effective support of transsexual and transgendered clients. *International Journal of Transgenderism. 6*(2). Available: www.symposion.com/ijt/ijtvo06no02_04.htm.

Reback, C.J. & Lombardi, E.L. (1999). HIV risk behaviors of male-to-female transgenders in a community-based harm reduction program. *International Journal of Transgenderism, 3*(1+2). Available: www.symposion.com/ijt/hiv_risk/reback.htm.

Reynolds, A.L. & Hanjorgiris, W.F. (2000). Coming out: Lesbian, gay and bisexual identity development. In R.M. Perez, K.A. Debord & K.J. Bieschke (Eds.). *Handbook of Counseling and Psychotherapy with Lesbian, Gay and Bisexual Clients* (pp. 35–55). Washington, DC: American Psychological Association.

Ridge, D., Hee, A. & Minichiello, V. (1999). "Asian" men on the scene: Challenges to the "gay communities." *Journal of Homosexuality, 36*(3/4), 43–68.

Rothblum, E.D. (2000). Historical perspectives. In R.M. Perez, K.A. Debord & K.J. Bieschke (Eds.). *Handbook of Counseling and Psychotherapy with Lesbian, Gay and Bisexual Clients* (pp. 57–79). Washington, DC: American Psychological Association.

Savin-Williams, R.C. (1996). Self-labeling and disclosure among gay, lesbian and bisexual youths. In J. Laird & R. Green (Eds.) *Lesbians and Gays in Couples and Families* (pp. 153–183). San Francisco: Jossey-Bass.

Schneider, K. (2003). An alphabet of GLBT and disability issues. In J. Whitman & C. Boyd (Eds.), *The Therapist's Notebook for Lesbian, Gay and Bisexual Clients* (pp. 262–267). New York: Haworth Clinical Practice Press.

Sell, R.L. & Becker, J.B. (2001). Sexual orientation data collection and progress toward healthy people 2010. *American Journal of Public Health, 91*(6), 876–882.

Shernoff, M. (2002). Terrorist attacks in America: Impact on queer clients and clinicians. *Journal of Gay and Lesbian Social Services 14*(3), 95–102.

Siegel, S. & Walker, G. (1996). Connections: Conversations between a gay and straight therapist. In J. Laird & R. Green (Eds.), *Lesbians and Gays in Couples and Families* (pp. 316–340). San Francisco: Jossey-Bass.

Stone, S.D. & the Women's Survey Group. (1990). Lesbian life in a small centre: The case of St. John's. In S.D. Stone (Ed.), *Lesbians in Canada* (pp. 94–105). Toronto: Between the Lines.

Swigonski, M.E. (2001). Human rights, hate crimes and Hebrew-Christian Scripture. *Journal of Gay and Lesbian Social Services 13*(1/2), 33–46.

Szekely, E. (1988). *Never Too Thin*. Toronto: Women's Press.

Van Wormer, K., Wells, J. & Boes, M. (2000). *Social Work with Lesbians, Gays and Bisexuals*. Toronto: Allyn and Bacon.

Walters, K.L., Simoni, J.N. & Horwath, P.F. (2001). Sexual orientation bias experiences and service needs of gay, lesbian, bisexual, transgendered, and two-spirited American Indians. *Journal of Gay and Lesbian Social Services, 13*(1/2), 133–149.

Washington, P. (2001). Who gets to drink from the fountain of freedom?: Homophobia in communities of colour. *Journal of Gay and Lesbian Social Services, 13*(1/2), 1117–1131.

Wolitski, R.J., Valdiserri, R.O., Denning, P.H. & Levine, W.C. (2001). Are we headed for a resurgence of an HIV epidemic among men who have sex with men? *American Journal of Public Health, 91*, 883–888.

Chapter 17

Working with Youth

GLORIA CHAIM, JOANNE SHENFELD AND DENNIS LONG

WHAT DEFINES "YOUTH"?

Youth is a time of change and transition. The biological changes that take place starting in early adolescence are accompanied by cognitive and emotional changes. As
youth strive to discover who they are and redefine themselves in light of all of these
changes, they are more likely to experiment with various roles and ways of coping and
interacting, sometimes before they have self-regulation strategies to manage the
situations they encounter. As a result, they are more likely than people at other life
stages to engage in risk-taking behaviours. Prevalence of traffic accidents, homicides
and sexually transmitted infections is highest at this age. Youth are also more likely to
initiate substance use (Schulenberg et al., 2001).

Youth are clearly vulnerable. However, the factors that put them at risk are
the same factors that can create opportunity. Intervention at this time can be very
powerful, as behaviours are often transitional and not yet entrenched. For example,
youth experimenting with substances to control mood can benefit from learning
about and experimenting with alternative coping strategies.

This chapter provides an overview of engaging, assessing and treating youth with
substance use issues, and also concurrent substance use and mental health issues.
These issues are approached from a "harm reduction" perspective, which aims to
minimize the consequences of risk-taking behaviours. The chapter also includes
a section on working with street-involved youth. Although we assume that most practitioners come in contact and work with youth in traditional office-based settings, the
principles provided here may also be applied to outreach in less traditional settings,

including community centres, malls, video arcades, schools and on the street. Programs group youth in different ways, and may define youth as being aged, for example, 12–18, 14–21 or 16–24. In this chapter, youth ranging in age from 12–24 will be considered.

ENGAGING AND ASSESSING YOUTH

Working with Youth in Context

Substance use, its antecedents and its consequences are rooted in a biological, psychological, social, cultural and political context. To engage and assess youth, it is essential to work in a way that allows for each client's substance use problem to be understood within his or her unique context. As populations, particularly in urban areas, become increasingly diverse, the counsellor must learn to ask questions that go beyond standardized assessment instruments and structured interviews, and to understand that while these tools are important, they are limited in providing an understanding of the client's context.

The counsellor must be aware of his or her own biases, beliefs and values and how they interface with those of the client. Youth need to feel accepted and safe in order to trust enough to engage in the assessment and treatment process. Power is inherent in the counsellor's role, and this must also be considered. Open and honest sharing of what the counsellor knows, and genuine interest and curiosity about what he or she does not know, can help engage the client in a process of investigation and potential change.

Where Does Substance Use Fit In?

A certain amount of adolescent risk-taking can be viewed as normative and part of successfully negotiating the transition between adolescence and adulthood. Smoking, drinking and experimenting with other drugs are a way to test social and family limits, as well as personal boundaries. Ultimately the adolescent uses risk-taking or experimentation as a way to gain autonomy from parents, experiment with alternative identities and form a new adult identity. It is therefore important to assess and address these behaviours carefully, for while they may have minimal or transitory impact, they can also have tragic results.

Trends in Youth Drug Use

The *Ontario Student Drug Use Survey* (Adlaf & Paglia, 2003), a comprehensive survey of youth in junior high and high school conducted every two years, reports that "the escalating trend in drug use, which began in the early 1990s, has generally subsided." The most frequently used drugs remain alcohol, cannabis and tobacco. While 66 per cent of all students reported using alcohol in the past year, only 12 per cent reported drinking at least once per week. Thirty per cent of students reported use of cannabis in the past year, at an average of 16 times during the year. Cigarette use declined significantly from 1999, when 28 per cent reported use, to 19 per cent in 2003. Only cocaine showed an increase in use, from 3.4 per cent in 1999 to 4.8 per cent in 2003.

Risk Factors

Several risk factors are associated with substance use problems in youth. Simply being a male youth is a primary risk factor. More male youth become involved in problematic use than any other population group, and represent more than half of the total treatment population. Parental use, and a history of physical or sexual abuse, are also risk factors. The younger the age of first use, the more likely a youth is to go on to problematic use. Identity issues, self-esteem, socio-economic factors, family stress and poor coping skills are also risk factors (Health Canada, 2001).

Health Canada notes that "some involvement in alcohol, drugs and tobacco is statistically 'normative,' particularly in late adolescence," and "may not be predictive of long-term substance use problems" (2001, pp. 12). However, some youth may be particularly vulnerable; two populations who are most at risk are youth with mental health problems and those who are street involved. Later in the chapter, we will discuss mental health concerns commonly found in youth in substance use treatment. A section on street-involved youth appears at the end of the chapter.

Harm Reduction

Harm reduction has been described as "strategies focused on minimizing the consequences associated with drinking and other high risk behaviors" (Miller et al., 2001). The approach grew out of public efforts to tackle the spread of AIDS and HIV in the early 1980s, and includes needle exchange programs, education regarding safer drug use and other policy efforts to reduce use and associated harm (Miller et al., 2001). The harm reduction approach is one of the most important developments in substance use intervention in general, and especially for youth.

Harm reduction can mean several things when working with youth. Early intervention and education programs, focused on making healthy choices, self-management, behaviour rehearsal and other types of skills, can help youth understand the implications of substance use and provide alternatives. These programs have a realistic, accessible message, and place drug use along a continuum from occasional or experimental use to more serious or problematic use. As well, these programs encompass youth who may have already started using, and provide options for reducing use and making changes for those at higher risk for problem use (Miller et al., 2001).

For example, in recent years many youth-focused Internet resources have been designed to promote prevention and early intervention of drug use in youth. Some sites experiment with Web-based counselling. Skinner et al. (2001) provide an overview of these resources and challenge practitioners to be innovative and to make resources available to youth in places where they will be most likely to access them. Harm reduction strategies aimed at "club" drugs have focused on outreach and education about the dangers of use, and strategies to minimize risk—such as hydration and "buddy" systems at raves and other events.

For counsellors working with youth in a clinical or counselling setting, where problem use has already been identified, a harm reduction approach can mean several things. Youth often use several substances, and may be willing to set a goal for abstinence or reduction for one of the substances, but not for others. They may also be willing to look at change in certain areas of their lives, such as abstaining while at school or during the week. Once they have been able to experience success in an initial or harm-reducing goal, they may be more willing to go further in reducing use or even abstaining from use. Harm reduction is also a key strategy in working with street-involved youth, as we will discuss later in this chapter.

Harm reduction is an accepting, client-centred approach that fits in well with the "stages of change model" (described in Chapter 2). The motivational interviewing approach applies well to working with youth, as many of the youth who come to a clinical setting are in the pre-contemplative or contemplative stage, under pressure from school, parents or even a legal mandate. Setting goals that are appropriate to the client's stage of change and using a harm reduction approach can help keep youth in treatment. For clients in the early stages of change, an initial goal may simply be to engage them in dialogue about their use and to explore the possibility that such use may have negative consequences. Over time, as trust builds or the problem worsens, the youth may be willing to engage in further treatment and goal setting.

Youth who present for treatment in the early stages of change are often not willing to engage in any type of substance use goal at first. Another aspect of a harm reduction approach is to allow youth to define what areas outside substance use they are willing to address. Taking a holistic approach in engaging youth can help in establishing an alliance and working with them on a treatment contract regarding a goal that they define as important. For example, youth may be unhappy about the pressure they are receiving at school or at home regarding behaviour or other issues. They may be willing to receive help on ways to reduce this pressure, and may then be more open to seeing links between their use and other problematic areas.

Marlatt (1996) summarizes the harm reduction approach:

People's problems are best conceptualized within an integrative, holistic perspective that views drug use and/or high risk sexual behaviours as interdependent and reciprocally interactive components of one's life-style. . . . harm reduction can offer an attractive, low-threshold gateway to welcome anyone who is willing to "come as they are" (p. 788).

Harm reduction strategies can be part of an approach with youth at all stages along the substance use continuum.

TABLE 17-1

Substance Use Continuum

STAGE	DESCRIPTION	GOAL	COURSE OF ACTION
Non-use	Has never used a particular substance.	Prevent initiation of substance use	Reinforce Education & prevention Monitoring
Experimental use	Has tried a substance once or several times. Use is motivated by curiosity about the substance effect.	Enhance motivation for change Prevent further involvement in substance use Reverse involvement in substance use Reduce harm from substance use	Education & prevention Harm reduction Monitoring
Irregular use	Use is infrequent and irregular, usually confined to special occasions or when opportunities present themselves directly.	Prevent further involvement Reverse involvement	Education & prevention Monitoring
Regular use	Use has a predictable pattern, which may entail frequent or infrequent use. The user actively seeks to experience the substance effect, or to participate in the substance-using activities of the peer group. Usually feels in control of the substance use.	Prevent further involvement Reverse involvement Reduce harm from substance use	Education & prevention Harm reduction Monitoring Assessment

TABLE 17-1

Substance Use Continuum (cont'd)

STAGE	DESCRIPTION	GOAL	COURSE OF ACTION
Dependent use	Use is regular and predictable and usually frequent. The user experiences a physiological and/or psychological need for the substance. Feels out of control with use, and will continue to use despite adverse consequences.	Enhance motivation for change Reverse involvement Reduce harm from substance use	Harm reduction Assessment Treatment
Harmful use	Use has resulted in harmful consequences. Use has resulted in high-risk behaviours.	Enhance motivation for change Reverse involvement Reduce involvement Reduce harm	Harm reduction Assessment Treatment

Adapted from Centre for Addiction and Mental Health (2004).

Assessment

Historically, youth were assessed and treated using the same principles, tools and approaches that were used with adults. Although there is still much work to be done in understanding the unique needs of youth and developing effective youth-specific treatments, it is clear that the same patterns of use and behaviours do have different consequences and meanings in the lives of youth and adults, and many youth-specific tools have been developed over the past 20 years.

Assessments in settings that address issues related directly or indirectly to substance use generally cover the same standard categories, regardless of the age of the person. These categories include substance use history, family history, education, vocational/leisure activities, legal history and medical concerns. Over the years, the category of medical concerns has expanded to include mental health, often with a focus on trauma history. More recently, many settings have added questions about ethnicity, cultural identification and spirituality. In Ontario, addiction treatment agencies are required to gather minimal data on gambling and behaviours such as injection drug use and safer sexual practices (e.g., condom use). Some agencies ask questions designed to allow disclosure of gender identity and sexual orientation (Barbara et al., 2002). Depending on the perspective of the agency or the service provider and the needs of the client, there may be more emphasis or interest in certain areas.

Developmental Tasks of Youth

With youth, the response to each area of assessment needs to be viewed through the lens of "developmental tasks" or the concept of "age-appropriate" behaviour. This age/stage-focused lens lets the counsellor see how a treatment plan for a youth may need to differ from one for an adult with the same presenting concerns. While specific questions may be included in the assessment to elicit this information, counsellors need to be aware of normative developmental tasks and expectations.

Schulenberg and colleagues (2001) offer a "developmental-contextual frame-work" that emphasizes "stability and change occurring as a function of the dynamic interaction between individuals and their contexts" (p. 19). They summarize the developmental transitions and opportunities of adolescence as:
• puberty
• cognitive development
• emotional development: increased self-regulation
• affiliation transitions: changes in relationships with parents, peers, romantic partners
• achievement transitions: school and work changes
• identity transitions: changes in self-definition.

Certain factors can help youth navigate this life stage. Some of them may naturally be part of the context that youth encounter; others may be facilitated by parents, teachers or treatment providers. These factors include:
• opportunity to develop coping strategies and life skills
• minimal transitions (school changes, moves)
• balance between nurturing and monitoring by parents and schools, and opportunity to seek independence and self-expression
• developmentally appropriate challenges and experiences
• social networks that discourage risky behaviour.

Despite stereotypes, jokes and lore to the contrary, most youth navigate the stage between adolescence and adulthood without undue conflict and upheaval. Rather, they experiment, develop skills, use the challenges of this period of transition as opportunities, and are able to take on adult roles and responsibilities in a successful manner.

Strength-Based/Holistic Assessment

When assessing youth, a holistic approach provides a complete picture and is most helpful. Traditional assessments seek to highlight and categorize problems as presenting and/or underlying. A holistic approach includes a strength-based assessment, which highlights strengths, skills and personal assets. Strength-based assessments help counsellors to identify protective factors and to build a hopeful view, even if there are a number of risk factors present. This approach helps to engage young clients.

Motivational, solution-focused and narrative strategies also help to engage young clients, to build positive expectancies, hope and strength, and to move them in a positive direction (Breslin et al., 1999). These strategies acknowledge young people's need to experiment and learn from experience, and allow them to perform their developmental tasks at their own pace.

Any behaviour, including substance use, can have an impact on many aspects of one's life, and vice versa. Information about behaviours can be gathered through informal discussions, by following standardized interview formats and question-naires, and by using tools designed and validated for assessing youth. Collateral information from family members or other significant people in the young person's life can be useful for treatment planning (Smith & Chaim, 2000). In Ontario, each agency in the addiction treatment system that serves youth currently uses three standardized tools: the Drug History Questionnaire, the Adverse Consequences Questionnaire and the BASIS 32. In addition, agencies may also have their own assessment questionnaires and structured or informal interviews.

The following issues of adolescence should be considered when assessing the various areas of a young person's life in relation to substance use concerns. It is important to be clear about what one is looking for in each focus area and to understand how the areas fit together and interact.

Assessment Focus Areas

SUBSTANCE USE HISTORY

As with adults, a thorough drug use history is necessary for problem identification and treatment planning. Although alcohol use is prohibited by law under certain ages (usually between 19 and 21, depending on the jurisdiction) and substances that are commonly used by adolescents (such as cannabis, club drugs and cocaine) are illegal, some level of use by most adolescents is to be expected. It is helpful to place adoles-cent substance use along a continuum from non-use to dependent use, as described in Table 17-1. Although "harmful use" is listed at the end of the continuum, keep in mind that harmful use can occur at any point in the continuum, other than non-use, depending on individual circumstances and context. Assessing the potential and actual harm related to use is essential.

Most youth substance use falls within the experimental and recreational cate-gories. Youth who are between the ages of 16 and 21 are most likely to use in this man-ner, and may be more likely to binge at parties and on weekends. Polysubstance use is common. Youth who use substances may try whatever ones are available, often using several different substances at once or a variety of substances at different times. They tend to experience fewer withdrawal symptoms than adults or to tolerate them more comfortably, and as a result may develop tolerance to substances over a shorter time.

Earlier onset, under age 15, may be more likely to be seen in youth where there is a family history of substance dependence, or substance dependence and comorbid mental health problems. These youth may tend to seek out peers who are known to engage in risky behaviours and will likely demonstrate problems in many other areas of their lives, usually most evident in school performance, peer relationships and family functioning. Onset under the age of 18, coupled with regular or dependent patterns of use, usually interferes with successful completion of developmental tasks, and the stage of adolescence is prolonged. When onset is over the age of 18, the person may be considered an adult for both assessment and treatment purposes, depending on how far along he or she may be in the completion of developmental tasks, and where he or she would best fit (particularly if group treatment is being considered).

Legal, social and family limits and expectations shift through the period of adolescence, so that the context and meaning of the behaviour changes. Drinking can be seen by the adolescent as a rebellious behaviour at 15, whereas at 19 or 20 it is seen as a right and norm of adulthood. Of course, specific ethnocultural or religious group norms will create different contexts, limits and expectations.

FAMILY

The importance of assessing substance use issues in the context of the family is becoming increasingly well understood, as is the importance of involving the family in the assessment and treatment process. Information about substance use by other family members helps one to understand the context of the youth's use. Problematic use in the family may mean that the youth is at more risk, and will be a factor in deciding the best treatment approach. Including family members in the assessment process also gives a broader picture of the youth's use and functioning, and opens the door to family counselling as a treatment option.

PEER RELATIONSHIPS

The peer group can exert a powerful influence on adolescents. During adolescence, youth often experiment with belonging to different groups. Youth who are involved with problematic substance use are often isolated or involved with peers who are using. It can be very helpful to identify positive peer experiences and opportunities for the youth to experience and develop new relationships. Youth from diverse backgrounds and cultures, youth who are new to a community and youth with special needs may require particular assistance in developing peer relationship skills, and in identifying peer groups that will be accepting and will provide opportunities for growth. Including supportive and concerned peers in the treatment process can also be helpful. Some youth are more likely to engage in a change process if at least one of their peers is involved along with them. Encouraging peer involvement in the change process can help facilitate lasting change.

GENDER IDENTITY/SEXUAL ORIENTATION

Lesbian, gay, bisexual and transgender (LGBT) youth face unique challenges as they go through adolescence, in addition to the challenges faced by all youth. Many youth realize their identity and orientation by early adolescence but, because of pervasive stigma and discrimination, lack the opportunities to explore them fully or express them openly. Adolescence is a time when conformity to the peer group is highly valued. LGBT youth in many areas often have difficulty finding a peer group, and as a result may feel isolated and that they are "defective." The process of identity formation and consolidation may therefore be delayed. They may use substances as a coping strategy. These youth need acceptance, validation and an opportunity to disclose and explore their personal questions and concerns in a safe environment (Barbara et al., 2002; Hershberger & d'Augelli, 2000).

EDUCATION

School attendance is the primary requirement and expectation for young people. As a result, the impact of substance use is often reflected in school behaviour, academic performance and/or peer and authority interactions at school. Performance in this area is often seen as a barometer of adolescent functioning. Strengths in this area can be a protective factor and anticipated rewards in school can be an incentive for some adolescents to consider change.

VOCATION

Adolescents make a transition from school as "work" to paid employment as "work." Some use volunteer and other "practice" opportunities to prepare for the transition. Some work while attending school and gradually make the shift. Success in this transition can be a marker for successful entry into adulthood. Inherent in this area are many societal challenges, such as availability of employment opportunities, and personal challenges, such as job-skill acquisition, which can be further exacerbated by— or can trigger—substance use.

LEISURE/RECREATION

Involvement in leisure and recreational activities allows youth to take risks and experiment with different roles and peer groups, and to optimize individual aptitudes, interests and strengths. Leisure and recreational pursuits are often voluntary and are focused on a particular skill or interest. This is a very important area to focus on in an assessment, as it can help identify strengths, individual styles and how young people see themselves in the world. This information can be used to generate non-threatening discussion, which helps to facilitate the person's engagement with the therapist and the treatment process.

FINANCIAL SITUATION

Generally, it is expected that parents have a financial responsibility for their children until age 16–18. This expectation is extremely variable, and is often dependent on social, cultural and family norms, values, expectations and possibilities.

GAMBLING

As the proliferation and acceptance of gambling have increased, so has the number of youth who gamble. Parents and professionals may be concerned about behaviours that co-occur with gambling, such as substance use, lying and stealing, but they are generally not concerned about gambling itself, seeing it as a harmless recreational activity. However, youth who gamble are at increased risk of suicidal ideation, depression and other mental health problems, as well as substance dependence (Derevensky & Gupta, 2000). Youth gamble primarily for enjoyment, excitement and distraction or to escape from negative feelings and problems, rather than for money. Some studies report that over 80 per cent of youth gamble, with over 35 per cent gambling at least once per week. The prevalence is higher among males than females (Derevensky & Gupta, 2000). Gambling is a risk-taking activity, and is particularly attractive to youth. However, their vulnerability and inexperience put them at higher risk than adults of developing gambling-related problems.

HIGH-RISK BEHAVIOURS

Risk-taking is part of adolescence. It is important to explore the type of risk-taking behaviours that youth are involved in, particularly in relation to sexual behaviour and drug use. Unsafe practices, such as unprotected sex and needle sharing, increase the risk of sexually transmitted infections, including HIV/AIDS, and the risk of unwanted pregnancies and physical and/or emotional trauma. Youth require opportunities to acquire knowledge and skills in order to make informed and responsible decisions.

LEGAL HISTORY

Some youth test limits, take risks and experiment with various roles, behaviours and peer groups through involvement in illegal activity. Substance use and/or co-occurring mental health concerns can trigger or exacerbate this behaviour. Youth generally do not view underage use of alcohol or use of illicit substances as "illegal." It is important for them to understand the meaning, context and consequences of their substance use and other illicit behaviours.

ACCOMMODATION

It is the responsibility of parents to provide safe and suitable housing for their children until the age of 16; nonetheless, many youth are marginally housed or homeless. Youth may live in the home of one or both parents or the extended family, with friends, in group homes, in foster homes, in shelters or on the street. To be able to accomplish the developmental tasks of adolescence, young people need accommodation that is safe, both physically and emotionally. Suitable accommodation can be broadly defined, depending on the youth, and needs to be assessed in terms of the type of accommodation, and who shares the accommodation with the youth.

PHYSICAL HEALTH

The assessment of physical health is crucial when assessing substance use concerns. Substances may be used to deal with physical discomfort related to growth and hormonal changes. Medical problems such as seizure disorders may trigger substance use as a self-management strategy, or alternatively may be triggered by substance use. It is important to assess the pattern and sequence of problems. Medical emergencies such as a diabetic coma may be mistaken as substance overdose.

MENTAL HEALTH

Adolescence can be a turbulent period, and it is often difficult to determine whether certain presentations are "normal" adolescent behaviour, or are the result of a mental health problem or of substance use. As adolescence is also the time of onset of a number of mental health disorders, many of which can trigger or be triggered by substance use, this is an essential area to assess when a young person presents with a substance use concern. It is also essential to assess for suicidality. Substance use and mental health disorders have been associated with increased suicidality and completion of suicide (Hershberger & d'Augelli, 2000). Suicide rates among adolescents have quadrupled over the last 50 years, and suicide represents 12 per cent of youth mortality (Connor, 2002). The mental health concerns most commonly seen in youth in substance use treatment will be explored in further detail later in the chapter.

ETHNICITY/CULTURAL IDENTIFICATION

It is important to understand how youth see themselves with respect to culture, and what values, beliefs, assumptions and traditions may be aligned with their cultural identification. It is also important to understand how this identification relates to that of the youth's family, peer group and the dominant culture in their milieu. Culture may be looked at in relation to ethnicity, race, age, gender, sexual orientation and ability. A person's relationship to culture, and his or her situation within a culture or sub-culture, is complex and evolving.

SPIRITUALITY

Adolescence is a time to experiment with various values and belief systems, and ways of expressing those beliefs. Many people use this time as an opportunity to "try on" practices that differ in some ways from those of their parents. They may gravitate to unconventional practices that upset their families or religious leaders. As with other areas, it is important to understand how the adolescent views himself or herself in religious or spiritual terms, and what strengths may be accessible in this area to facilitate the development of a healthy lifestyle. There may be rites of passage related to certain cultural, religious and ethnic groups that can be important in facilitating movement through this stage of life.

Common Concurrent Mental Health Concerns

In the past, youth who presented for substance use treatment were often not assessed for mental health problems, and such problems were often left undiagnosed and untreated. Substance use and mental health problems were seen as separate problems to be treated in separate specialized treatment settings. If both concerns were identified, substance use and mental health treatment providers were often in conflict as to which concern should be treated first. As a result, clients were often sent back and forth between facilities as symptoms of one or the other became manifest. Over time, both types of problems were exacerbated, or one would appear to resolve as the other became more prominent.

Recent studies show that youth in treatment for substance use disorders often also have mental health disorders (cited in Kandel et al., 1999). Conduct disorder was particularly prevalent, but mood, anxiety and other disruptive behaviour disorders were also found. Substance use may also be linked with major mental illnesses, such as schizophrenia.

When Kandel et al. (1999) compared adolescents who had substance use disorders (SUDs) with those who did not, they found that psychiatric disorders were three times more common in those with SUDs. When youth and adults with SUDs were compared, psychiatric disorders were found more often in youth. Some studies have tried to determine which disorder is precedent or causal, but none have been conclusive. Some studies suggest that depression precedes SUDs in females, whereas in males, conduct and anxiety disorders precede SUDs, and SUDs precede depression. Some evidence shows that prepubertal onset of psychiatric disorders is followed by onset of SUDs in adolescence (Kessler, 1996).

While the causality and links between substance use and psychiatric disorders may not be fully understood, the evidence points to a need for a comprehensive approach to concurrent substance use and mental health problems. Youth is a time of crucial developmental transitions, risks and opportunities, and issues affecting development, such as mental health and substance use problems, must be identified and addressed. To accomplish this, treatment providers in both fields must be able to identify issues and, when they cannot provide all the interventions required, to make appropriate and timely referrals. Depending on the problems identified, interventions may be sequential or concurrent.

Many mental health disorders remain undiagnosed in youth, or may be complicated by concurrent substance use. The following discussion outlines the characteristics of the mental health disorders most commonly seen in youth in substance use treatment settings. The intention is to briefly provide a sense of how these disorders may present, and is not to be seen as a diagnostic or comprehensive description. Also included here are descriptions of acquired brain injury, fetal alcohol spectrum disorder and learning disabilities. These often co-occur with substance use and/or other mental health disorders, and are often overlooked.

ATTENTION-DEFICIT/HYPERACTIVITY DISORDER

The most common features of attention-deficit/hyperactivity disorder (ADHD) include:
• distractibility
• impulsivity
• hyperactivity

A key diagnostic feature is that these behaviours must appear before the age of seven, and continue for at least six months. They must create a significant problem in at least two areas, such as school, home, work or social life. These criteria set ADHD apart from the "normal" distractibility and impulsive behaviour of adolescence. Another cue may be the knowledge that another family member has ADHD. Evidence suggests that ADHD runs in families (Jaksa, 1998).

As with all disorders, the exact nature and severity of ADHD symptoms varies. Approximately one-third of people with ADHD are not hyperactive. This means that ADHD can be difficult to diagnose, and is often undiagnosed. Over half the adolescents with ADHD self-medicate with stimulants or depressants, depending on which symptom they are seeking to modify (National Center, 2000). This puts them at high risk of developing a substance use dependence.

Other disorders or behaviours such as substance use, conduct disorder, learning disabilities and fetal alcohol spectrum disorder, may have similar symptoms and are often misdiagnosed as ADHD. They may also coexist with ADHD (Booth, 1998).

CONDUCT DISORDER
Conduct disorder is a disorder of childhood and adolescence that involves:
• long-standing behaviour problems such as defiance and impulsivity
• antisocial behaviours such as vandalism, fire-setting, bullying and fighting
• substance use
• criminal activity
• a lack of concern for others.

In order to warrant this diagnosis, the behaviours must be extreme, exceeding those of adolescent rebellion or role experimentation. If the problem substance use began before the symptoms appeared, they are likely sequelae of substance use and may resolve once substance use stops. Conduct disorder often co-occurs with ADHD, and the two together carry a major risk for alcohol and/or other drug dependence.

DEPRESSION AND BIPOLAR DISORDER
The U.S. National Institute of Mental Health (NIMH) (2000) reports that over eight per cent of adolescents in the United States have depressive disorders, such as major depressive disorder (unipolar depression), dysthymic disorder (chronic, mild depression) and bipolar disorder (manic depression). Young women are twice as likely as young men to develop depression.

The diagnostic criteria for depression are the same for youth as for adults; however, it can be much more difficult to diagnose depression in youth, as they may have difficulty articulating their feelings. Features of depression in youth may include:
• "bad" behaviour, such as irritable or angry outbursts
• complaints of physical ailments such as headaches, stomach aches or tiredness
• complaints of boredom or lack of interest in activities
• social isolation
• poor performance at school.

Use of substances to alleviate negative feelings is common. At the same time, use or withdrawal from certain substances may induce depression.

Regardless of suspected or confirmed diagnosis, all young clients should be assessed for suicidality. NIMH (2000) reports that in 1997 suicide was the third leading cause of death in 10- to 24-year-olds. Among adolescents diagnosed with a major depressive disorder, for example, as many as seven per cent may commit suicide in the young adult years. Those who have attempted suicide "unsuccessfully" in the past should be monitored especially carefully, as research has shown that between 10 and 14 per cent eventually die in a subsequent suicide attempt (Hershberger & d'Augelli, 2000).

Twenty to 40 per cent of adolescents with major depression develop bipolar disorder within five years of the onset of a depression (NIMH, 2000). Bipolar disorder is generally manifested differently at different stages of development. When the illness develops in early adolescence, a common presentation:
• includes continuous, rapid-cycling, irritable states
• often co-occurs with ADHD or conduct disorder.

Later adolescent onset is less often associated with ADHD or conduct disorder, and is characterized by:
• a first sudden manic episode, followed by relatively stable periods between episodes
• manic symptoms that may include extreme irritability or elation, increased energy, distractibility, "hypersexuality" and risk-taking.

SOCIAL ANXIETY DISORDER

There are a number of anxiety disorders that can affect people of all ages. Social anxiety disorder (SAD) is one of the most common, and has been found to affect up to 13 per cent of the U.S. population in their lifetime. The mean age of onset is 15.5 years (Kashdan & Herbert, 2001). SAD is commonly seen in substance use treatment settings for youth. Characteristics include:
• intense fears of embarrassment, humiliation and being judged in a negative manner by others
• debilitating fears in social and school or work situations.

Self-medication with substances may alleviate symptoms, allowing those with SAD to appear to be more functional when using. However, the perceived effects may decrease as tolerance develops, and the symptoms may be exacerbated by substance use. SAD may be mistaken for shyness and social skill deficits that are common to the adolescent stage of development.

POST-TRAUMATIC STRESS DISORDER

Depending on the population and the study methodology, research shows that 66 to 99 per cent of people in substance use treatment report that they were physically, sexually or emotionally abused during childhood (Swan, 1998). Women were two to three times more likely than men to have post-traumatic stress disorder (PTSD; Najavits, 1999). Characteristics of PTSD include:
• flashbacks
• difficulty regulating emotions.

To fully understand the meaning and function of the substance use, it is important to identify the existence of trauma history. Youth with flashbacks and difficulty with emotion regulation need to learn alternative coping strategies to manage these symptoms. Trauma treatment requires specialized training and skill. For more information on helping clients with a history of trauma, see Chapter 18.

FETAL ALCOHOL SPECTRUM DISORDER

Fetal alcohol spectrum disorder (FASD) is a spectrum of neurological, behavioural and cognitive deficits that interfere with growth, learning and socialization, and that are caused by maternal alcohol use during pregnancy. Characteristics of FASD may mimic those of other disorders, and include:

• poor organizational skills
• poor concentration, attention and memory
• poor judgment and problem-solving skills
• socially inappropriate behaviours
• poor impulse control.

These behaviours may be manifest for different reasons and the treatment may differ. People with FASD generally don't learn from experience, so the most effective intervention is often to structure the environment for them in such a way that their inappropriate or maladaptive behaviour is incompatible with the structure.

For further discussion of FASD, see Chapter 22.

ACQUIRED BRAIN INJURY

Although acquired brain injury (ABI) is not a mental health disorder per se, many of its manifestations, like those of FASD, may mimic other psychiatric disorders or be antecedent or consequent to substance use problems. ABI is caused by an injury to the brain, which may be the result of a trauma such as a fall or of medical conditions such as a tumour, infection or anorexia. Like FASD, manifestations of ABI include:

• poor organizational skills
• poor concentration, attention and memory
• poor judgment and problem-solving skills
• socially inappropriate behaviours
• poor impulse control.

As with FASD, the "symptoms" are often not known to be a result of brain injury and may be misdiagnosed and treated ineffectively. A further complication is that it is not uncommon for people with ABI to also have a psychiatric or substance use disorder (Cochrane et al., 2000).

LEARNING DISABILITIES

Learning disabilities are caused by a "condition of the brain" that affects a person's ability to take in, process or express information. Some experts believe that one-third to two-thirds of children with learning disabilities in special education classes have been affected by prenatal exposure to alcohol or other drugs (National Center, 2000).

Studies have shown that a high proportion of people in substance use treatment programs have learning disabilities, ranging from 40 per cent of those in outpatient programs to 60 per cent of those in residential programs (National Center, 2000).

Adolescents with learning disabilities are twice as likely as others to also have a diagnosis of ADHD. The characteristics of adolescents with learning disabilities are also risk factors for substance use. These include:

• low self-esteem
• academic difficulties
• loneliness
• depression
• a desire for social acceptance.

As with the other disorders described here, learning disabilities may not be diagnosed, or may be diagnosed but inadequately addressed, resulting in exacerbation of these characteristics and the inherent risks.

SCHIZOPHRENIA

First episode of schizophrenia usually occurs between the ages of 16 and 25. This disease distorts the senses and is characterized by personality change and bizarre behaviour. Some of the early symptoms may be confused with signs or symptoms of substance use or other disorders, and may include:

• withdrawal from social activities, interactions and interests
• personality change
• thought disorder
• perceptual changes
• deterioration of personal hygiene
• extreme preoccupation with religion or with the occult
• inability to express emotion or inappropriate expression of emotion
• peculiar use of words or odd language structures.

These symptoms and others may be triggered by substance use; or youth may use to deal with the symptoms, which often are extremely distressing, both to the person experiencing the symptoms and to significant others (British Columbia Schizophrenia Society, 2001).

TREATMENT

The two main foci of youth treatment are the individual and the family. Waldron et al. (2001) note that family treatment is particularly effective when used in conjunction with individualized cognitive behaviour therapy. Below we discuss different options for an individual approach, and also family treatment. The discussion is followed by a case example.

Treatment for Youth: An Overview of Approaches

"Meeting youth where they're at" is the hallmark of client-centred work with youth. Approaches that use various levels of coercion have their proponents, but these approaches are not currently considered to be best practice (Health Canada, 2001). The motivational strategies used in a holistic and harm reduction approach to engagement and assessment are also used to reach out to youth in best practice treatment approaches.

A key principle of treatment matching must be to consider and recommend the "least intensive, least intrusive" treatments that the provider can expect to be effective. This is particularly important with youth because, during this formative stage of life, it is important not to pathologize by "over-treating," but to overemphasize strengths and help young people to regain balance so that they can move on with their life tasks. Youth-specific programs need to provide a youth-friendly and safe environment. Features that help to retain youth in treatment include a harm reduction philosophy, a flexible, open-ended approach, a holistic perspective and cultural appropriateness (Health Canada, 2001).

The continuum of treatment offers a range of options. These options vary in intensity and modality (i.e., they may be individual or group-based). Following is a brief description of the major treatment options.

WITHDRAWAL MANAGEMENT

Withdrawal management services are rarely available for youth, and when they are, they are rarely youth-specific. When they are available, they can be useful in extreme situations, such as when the youth is homeless or when other severe psychosocial factors are present. Issues of emotional and physical safety must be considered, particularly for younger adolescents, if only adult facilities are available. Withdrawal in a supervised setting is particularly useful for youth with suspected or confirmed concurrent mental health disorders, as a period of abstinence is often necessary for an accurate diagnosis to be made and for appropriate medication management to be determined. Youth with concurrent disorders often find it especially difficult to withdraw or maintain abstinence on their own, as their symptoms may be more distressing and difficult to cope with when they are abstinent.

RESIDENTIAL PROGRAMS

Residential programs allow youth to "take a break" from their using environment, and can be particularly helpful when the situation is extreme. Programs that are youth-specific are the most appropriate, and can incorporate leisure activities, as well as alternative therapies such as art and music therapy, to provide a holistic approach.

DAY TREATMENT

Day treatment allows youth to benefit from the more intensive aspects of a residential program, while remaining at home or in a community residence. Day programs can provide long-term support and allow youth to transition to less intense involvement more gradually. These programs may incorporate academic programming, vocational training, leisure and recreation, in addition to drug treatment.

OUTPATIENT TREATMENT

Outpatient treatment serves the majority of youth seeking substance use counselling. The continuum of outpatient treatment includes supportive counselling and the provision of information and resources, offered in informal settings through drop-in groups. These options are particularly useful for young people who are ambivalent about treatment, or are chaotic or disorganized due to their life situation, substance use pattern and/or mental health status. Youth can access these treatment options easily, and can use them as stand-alone interventions or in conjunction with more formal treatment for additional support. Case management can also be an important resource or bridge for youth who are ambivalent about treatment, or who need immediate assistance with basic needs before engaging in in-depth counselling. Outpatient treatment is usually a more formal arrangement, consisting of regular appointments with a counsellor or therapist in a youth mental health or substance use treatment setting. Studies have shown that, on average, youth attend only four sessions before leaving counselling, and that youth respond well to treatment that is motivationally based, emphasizing "non-confrontation, self-reliance and personal choice" (Breslin et al., 1999).

Outpatient treatment can be offered in group or individual format. Group treatment is an effective choice for many youth, as it offers a sense of belonging, and encourages youth to find the balance between conformity and individual expression, and to experiment with roles and skills. However, for youth with sensitive issues to address, or with anxiety or other social concerns, group treatment may not be optimal. Flexibility and a range of options are key in this area (Health Canada, 2001).

One outpatient program specifically for youth is "First Contact," which was developed over several years at the Addiction Research Foundation (now the Centre for Addiction and Mental Health) in Ontario. The program consists of four structured sessions, which incorporate specific motivational exercises, self-monitoring and alternatives to use. The sessions can be delivered in individual or group format. The focus is on goal setting and harm reduction. The program can be used to engage clients in further treatment and commitment to reduction of use or, for more reluctant clients, it can be used as a stand-alone program to build motivation and identify risk. The program has been in use for a number of years, and research has shown that two-thirds of clients who participate report a significant reduction in days of use (Breslin et al., 1999). Recent developments include the use of First Contact in school settings, and adaptation for clients with concurrent mental health issues.

ALTERNATIVE AND COMPLEMENTARY THERAPIES

Alternative and complementary therapies can be an important part of individualized treatment, particularly with diverse populations. What may be alternative or complementary in one setting or with one population group may be the accepted, expected or primary approach in others. This is particularly true of culture- or religion-based approaches, such as the healing circles and sweats often used by traditional Aboriginal healers.

Stress management, art therapy, nutrition, massage and recreation therapies are often integrated into comprehensive treatment programs as adjuncts to more traditional "talk" therapies. As we have discussed, the diagnosis and treatment of adolescents is extremely complex. There is a high rate of concurrent emotional, physical and learning problems. Each person processes information and makes changes in a unique way. Alternative and complementary therapies and approaches provide options for tapping into unique strengths, thereby optimizing the possibility for matching approaches to client needs, learning and personal styles.

After-care is generally a less prominent part of youth treatment programs, likely due to the high dropout rate and preference for briefer treatment among youth (Breslin et al., 1999). A more successful type of secondary or follow-up treatment with youth takes a flexible, non-traditional approach, which emphasizes skill development or other specific areas of focus.

FAMILY TREATMENT

Family treatment for youth is supported by strong evidence that "the engagement of even one family member is considered critical," and can improve treatment retention and outcome (Health Canada, 2001). Developmentally, youth may still be expected to be involved and residing with their families of origin. As cited above, family stress and parental substance use are risk factors for problematic use by youth.

Many youth do not live in traditional two-parent families; they may reside with one parent, with step-parents, with extended families or alone. Some youth, such as street-involved youth or those in the care of child welfare agencies, are disenfranchised from their families. It is not surprising that many therapists consider that "changing family interactions and improving relationship functioning is key to reducing adolescents' involvement with alcohol and other drugs" (Waldron et al., 2001). Prior to involving "the family," it is important to understand how a particular youth defines family. Some youth may bring a peer, relative or even a professional such as a case manager into counselling as a "supportive family member," rather than a member of their family of origin.

Not all youth or families are willing to engage in intensive family counselling. However, research shows that less intensive programs can also be effective in boosting a youth's treatment outcome (Boudreau et al., 1998). Programs geared to family members may include treatment orientation, psychoeducation on substance use, and support groups.

Many youth are unwilling or unable to have their family members participate in their counselling, even minimally. However, addressing family issues is often a necessary and critical part of youth counselling. Szapoznik et al. (1986) describe a method of "one person family therapy" with adolescents, in which principles of family therapy are used individually to effect change in the family unit. This is consistent with systems theory, which holds that change in any part of the system will have an effect on the system as a whole. This method is described as being useful when the family is unwilling to attend treatment, the youth is unwilling to involve them, or the youth is in a residential setting apart from the family.

Case Example

The following case example illustrates how several different interventions can be used to engage a young client and his family, and to provide assessment and treatment. The example shows that a broad, holistic view allows consideration of family, personal and mental health issues. The treatment plan is responsive, and incorporates the recommendations of the assessor, the psychiatrist and the client.

> Jesse, 17, has been using drugs since the age of 15, including ecstasy, methamphetamines, cannabis and alcohol. He recently dropped out of high school due to his heavy drug use. Jesse's mother, Linda, has been upset and concerned about Jesse's drug use, but did not take any action until after Jesse passed out at a rave and was taken to the emergency room. Jesse was reluctant to attend an assessment on his own, but agreed to come in for a treatment consultation with his mother.
>
> The purpose of the first session was to engage Jesse in the treatment process through an exploration of the presenting problem, and to provide information about the treatment process. Initially, most of the information was provided by Linda. The therapist made an effort to engage Jesse around his own concerns and what he saw as problematic. Linda stated that her approach to parenting Jesse emphasized independence, and the right to make his own choices. Linda saw herself as a support rather than an authority. For the last 10 years, Linda had been a single parent to Jesse. After Jesse's parents divorced, Jesse's father remarried and moved out of the area, and was only peripherally involved with Jesse until he moved back two years ago. At this time Jesse began to see his father, stepmother and stepsister more regularly. His father's parenting and family lifestyle were very different, and Jesse had trouble adjusting to the rigid structure and expectations when he visited. In particular, he reported ongoing conflict with his stepmother over his drug use and risky behaviour. When Linda recounted the family history, Jesse became tearful around the conflict with his stepmother, blaming his stepmother for causing a rift between him and his father, and saying he wished things were better between them.
>
> As the session continued, Jesse identified that he had been frightened "waking up in the emergency room," and not knowing how he got there. With the therapist's help, he was able to link this event to his drug use, and

agreed that further exploration could be helpful. At the end of the session, Jesse agreed to return for an assessment on his own.

Jesse arrived late for the assessment, but soon became engaged in the process. He chose a substance use goal to stop his use of "club drugs," as he saw that they put him at risk of harm. He also chose to continue using cannabis and alcohol, although he was willing to consider a goal of working toward reduced use. Other goals included returning to school and improving his relationship with his father and his family. Use of a psychiatric screening tool indicated possible depression. The therapist's treatment recommendation included a return to school by engaging in an intensive substance use day-treatment school program. In addition, family treatment and a psychiatric assessment were recommended.

Jesse was reluctant to commit to an intensive program, but agreed to a treatment plan that included a four-session outpatient group intervention, family counselling with his father and stepmother, and a psychiatric assessment. To ensure that there would be no contraindications to this treatment plan due to mental health issues, the psychiatric assessment was the first step.

The psychiatric assessment confirmed that Jesse was depressed. It was recommended that he follow through with the treatment plan and that efforts be made during the brief intervention to engage him in a longer-term, more structured program. This would address his concurrent substance use and mental health concern, and would provide structure and an opportunity to monitor and prevent exacerbation of his depression.

While he was attending the outpatient group, family sessions were initiated. In the presence of the therapist, Jesse called his father to inform him that he had started substance use treatment and would like his support. He asked him to speak to the therapist, who then invited him and his family to an initial session. As with the initial consultation with Jesse and his mother, the primary purpose of this session was to engage the family and develop a treatment plan. The focus of the family sessions was to increase regular positive interactions between Jesse and his father, stepmother and stepsister. In the sessions, their anger, frustration and resulting inflexibility were reframed by the therapist as concern. As Jesse began to accept that his family really did care about him, he was more open to discussing and negotiating expectations regarding his behaviour. Jesse started spending weekends at his father's home regularly. He reported feeling understood by the family as he began to see the limits they set, such as curfew and not allowing substance use in the home, as a way for him to get control over his life, remain safe and work toward his goals. This process occurred over eight sessions. During that time, two additional sessions were held with Jesse's mother to keep her engaged and supportive of Jesse as he made changes, and to ensure that she would accept Jesse's growing relationship with his father.

Jesse completed the four group treatment sessions, which gave him the opportunity to become comfortable participating in the group, to further define his goals, and to realize that a more intensive program would give him the time and structure to achieve his goals. He enrolled in the day-treatment school program. His commitment to the program fluctuated and was characterized by occasional poorly explained lates and absences. Outside of program time, he continued to use drugs in excess of the goals he had set for himself, which put him in situations he later regretted. However, he remained engaged in treatment, and overall, continued to progress towards his goals. Some of his struggle with follow-through was attributed to his depression. He received concurrent psychotherapy to address this issue.

STREET-INVOLVED YOUTH

Street-involved youth are often seen in Canadian cities, but few people understand who they are or what their lives are like. Compounding this, only two studies (Smart et al., 1990, 1992) have investigated this population in the Canadian context. In this section, we draw on what these studies have told us, and also on the personal experience of one of the authors and other staff of an agency that provides harm reduction and substance use treatment outreach to street-involved youth in Toronto.

A Profile of Street-Involved Youth

The term "street-involved youth" is preferred to "street kids," which has fallen out of favour, primarily because it has often been used in a derogatory way. "Street-involved youth" is more exact in that it includes all those who are involved in street activities such as "hanging out," prostitution, panhandling and petty crime. While some of these youth are truly homeless, many have some sort of accommodation, albeit inadequate and transient. Their circumstances are the result of having run away— or having been "thrown away"—from their families of origin.

There appear to be three kinds of street-involved youth. The first, "runaway kids," most often run from home several times before leaving permanently. Some begin leaving as young as age 10, but most are between the ages of 11 and 15. Few come from intact families, most have been physically abused and many (more females than males) have been sexually abused (Smart et al., 1990, 1992). The second kind, referred to as "throwaway youth," are young people who have been forced out of their families of origin, either through the application of "tough love" principles or by parental choice (i.e., due to not being wanted in a reconstituted family, or to family breakdown or other reasons). Case workers indicate that these youth are older (15–16) when they begin life on the street. The third kind are those who are on the street intermittently. Sometimes called "curbsiders," these are youth who have varying degrees of unsatisfactory home environments, but still spend some time there, appearing on the street mostly on weekends and evenings (Lowery et al., 1996).

Many street-involved youth are frequently depressed. Not surprisingly, the incidence of attempted suicide, at 43 per cent, is high. The incidence of other psychiatric illness is more difficult to determine. Smart and colleagues (1992) reported a high incidence of "psychotic" thoughts, although without a full examination, which was not possible, this was not a reliable indicator of psychiatric illness.

Paradoxically, Smart and colleagues (1990, 1992) also found that those youth who identified themselves as street people, as most did, showed a high level of self- esteem and less frequent episodes of depression. Despite their self-esteem, street life is not conducive to stable mental health, and street-involved youth have higher than average mental health needs.

The studies of these youth tell us little about their physical health status. However, anecdotal information from workers tells us that factors such as injection drug use and poor hygiene, nutrition, health care and shelter put street-involved youth at risk of traumatic injury, and of infections such as HIV/AIDS, tuberculosis and hepatitis A, B and C. In the general street population, hepatitis C has become endemic, with infection rates, as reported by Toronto public health case workers, in excess of 80 per cent. Although two studies of hepatitis C in Canada (cited in Zou et al., 2001) indicate that infection rates are relatively low among street-involved youth (4 per cent and 12.6 per cent), these youth are clearly vulnerable, and their exposure to the infectious diseases found in the general street population must be watched closely.

The studies by Smart and colleagues (1990, 1992) indicate that street-involved youth use alcohol and other drugs heavily. Ninety-five per cent indicated that they drank, at least on occasion (compared with 59 per cent of the general youth population); six per cent reported that they drank daily (compared with one per cent of the general youth population); and over 30 per cent reported that they drank heavily (five or more drinks at a time, five or more times in the last four weeks). Other drug use was also pervasive; over 80 per cent reported daily drug use. As noted earlier, drug use among all youth increased throughout the 1990s (Adlaf & Paglia, 2001; Metro Toronto Research Group, 1999). Anecdotal evidence indicates concomitant increases among the street-involved population. Predictably, street-involved youth report high levels of alcohol and other drug problems, with about one-third reporting an alcohol problem and the same number reporting other drug problems. There is also significant overlap, with about one-quarter reporting both alcohol and other drug problems (Smart et al., 1990, 1992).

In summary, the picture of street-involved youth that emerges is of a group that has either chosen or been forced into a lifestyle that is difficult, dangerous and stressful. The incidence of depression among these youth is high. Indications also point to an elevated rate of more serious mental health problems, and of infection and physical injury. These are people who have significant problems meeting their financial and shelter needs. Nonetheless, they have great pride in their identity as street-involved youth, and gain self-esteem from their ability to manage their lives and maintain themselves on the street.

Services for Street-Involved Youth

Providing service to street-involved youth requires an approach that reduces potential harm to their health and safety, respects their self-image and provides for their needs. This includes giving these youth the opportunity to enter structured treatment programs or to establish themselves in stable living situations off the street.

The first priority is harm reduction—especially if youth are not prepared to alter their living situation or drug use. A harm reduction approach accepts that drug use will continue, that it cannot immediately be eliminated, and that street-involved youth regard drug use as part of the street culture. For these youth, drug use is an environmental or normalizing factor, rather than an aberrant behaviour. Many street-involved youth also point out that drug use helps them to deal with the stress and other emotional challenges of their lifestyle. Attempting to "cure" them of drug use would be futile, as it would likely be seen as an attempt to impose "straight" values. Street-involved youth need harm reduction services: needle exchange, condom distribution, safe injection education and on-the-street crisis intervention.

Some street-involved youth do identify their drug use as a problem. However, drug use is so integrated into the lifestyle of street-involved youth that it is difficult, if not impossible, to address only the problem of drug use, even when identified as a separate issue.

Most street-involved youth struggle with a multiplicity of problems and have for many reasons learned to distrust adults, particularly those in positions of authority, or who profess to be "on their side." To build trust with street-involved youth, the following principles must be adopted.

OUTREACH

To reach street-involved youth, workers must take their services and go out to meet these youth anywhere they are likely to be found. One approach is to operate a mobile service out of a van. This can be effective, but is limited to areas where street-involved youth are concentrated, such as downtown Toronto. A van may also separate workers from their clients and be intimidating. Workers who approach youth on foot on the street are less intimidating and more likely to connect with youth and the street culture. Workers need this connection in order to develop sensitivity and understanding of the social structure of the street, and to develop the etiquette of approaching someone on the street.

Settings such as youth centres, pool halls and video arcades are also key places to provide outreach. Another is juvenile detention centres. Many of these youth become involved in the legal system. When they do, having access to workers they know from the street is essential, as it provides continuity of care at a time of high stress and anxiety.

When providing outreach services to street-involved youth, care must be taken to find the appropriate time of day. For example, youth working in the sex trade would not welcome outreach during their working hours—usually the late evening. Such youth may be more receptive to contact in the late afternoon or early evening. Similarly, youth who panhandle may be more approachable after rush hour.

Workers who distribute cards with their cell phone numbers and hours of availability make it easier for street-involved youth to call them and arrange meetings of mutual convenience (including times when the worker is out of his or her office). This approach is particularly effective when a quick response is needed, such as in providing needle exchange or other harm reduction services.

PROVISION OF IMMEDIATE NEEDS

The immediate needs of street-involved youth are generally quite basic: money, food and shelter, in roughly that order, followed by clothing and employment (Smart et al., 1990, 1992). Since it's difficult for anyone to relate on a meaningful level when he or she is hungry, cold and has no place to sleep, workers must first help their clients to meet these needs. Beyond these basics, most need condoms, and many need clean needles. They may also need health care. Youth on the street seldom receive regular health care, and often find their reception in formal health care facilities less than accepting. Workers need to help youth connect to sympathetic and accessible health care.

Along with these basic physical needs, street-involved youth may also need emotional support and empathy. Often street-involved youth report that they have access to support from their own social links. They may be resistant, at least initially, to help from outsiders. To know what's really going on, and to be accepted as trustworthy, workers must spend the time and effort to connect to the youth and the street culture.

TRUST

Street-involved youth often have difficulty trusting others, particularly adults. The credibility of a worker or service is far more important than the ability to "walk the walk and talk the talk" of street culture. The communications system on the street is efficient. Any hint that a worker or a service has betrayed a client's trust, broken confidentiality or, even worse, co-operated with the police or other authorities, will damage or destroy the effectiveness of that worker or service.

INFORMALITY

Services for street-involved youth must be, and must appear to be, informal. Rules and procedures should be minimal, and staff dress and the physical environment (where relevant) should be designed to increase the comfort level of clients. Staff should wear, for example, jeans and sneakers, avoiding suits on one extreme and "street" attire, such as piercings and "goth" clothes, on the other.

RESPECT

Everyone wants respect, and these youth are no different. Agency policies, structures and culture must reflect and reinforce their respect for street-involved youth. One way to do this is to avoid labelling. As noted, most street-involved youth do not like to be labelled by others as "street kids," even though they may self-identify with this term. Workers and agencies should avoid using labels in their description of clients, and their services. Workers should also avoid trying to act (or talk) like a street person if they are not one. It is more respectful to be yourself and speak plainly.

CONSISTENCY

Street-involved youth live in a transient world. Few things are constant in their lives, and they expect that all relationships will be brief and temporary. Once a relationship with a street-involved youth has been established, workers and programs must make a deliberate and concentrated effort to maintain contact. The office-based model—"If you don't come, you lack motivation, and we will move to the next client on the waiting list"—is neither helpful nor effective with this population. If a worker or agency fails to maintain contact, it replicates youth's street experience and reinforces their view that adults and professionals are not trustworthy or committed to them.

Developing and maintaining a supportive, respectful and enduring relationship with a client requires skill, perseverance, patience and time. Most street-involved youth find it difficult to trust, and behave in ways designed to test the relationship.

With street-involved youth, the case management model works to ensure contact with clients is maintained throughout clients' involvement with other agencies and programs. Case management is key to ensuring progress is made, and to responding effectively to setbacks.

Although the primary goal of working with street-involved youth is harm reduction, the ultimate goal is to move youth into a more stable (although not necessarily abstinent) life off the street. Some youth are able to achieve this on their own or with the help of the outreach worker. However, most require services such as vocational training, supportive housing, addiction treatment or mental health treatment. Preparing street-involved youth for these services is a key role for outreach workers.

When promoting the option of treatment for clients receiving harm reduction services, outreach workers must be cautious. Treatment failure is common in this population, and workers must be prepared to re-engage with clients who return to the street. After an unsuccessful attempt at treatment, the client may feel failure, shame or anger. If the worker was seen as promoting the treatment, attempts to reconnect and provide further service may be inhibited.

Smart and colleagues reported that few street-involved youth seek out addiction treatment, and that those who do seek it out do not find most programs helpful (1990, 1992). Street-involved youth often find integration into structured programs difficult. Notably, clients seem to prefer residential programs, which shows that a stable environment and housing is one of the key needs of these clients. More traditional programs such as AA were rated extremely low. At this time, most residential services only provide an abstinence model of treatment.

Most treatment programs are not designed to meet the needs of street-involved youth. Outpatient services that do not provide for the housing and other needs of these clients, or are not prepared to work closely with services that do, will not be successful. Day programs with too high a "threshold," requiring complete and immediate abstinence and perfect attendance, will likewise fail. Residential services must be youth-focused, and provide a community that is supportive of the needs of street-involved clients, including their ongoing housing needs.

The factors that lead youth into a street-involved life are not the same as those that keep them there. Factors making it difficult for youth to leave the street include a severe lack of appropriate housing that will accept them, a socio-political climate that is increasingly punitive rather than rehabilitative, and government funding policies that make it difficult for agencies to provide the services that these clients need. In Ontario in recent years, street-level services have been severely reduced, and new lower welfare rates and more stringent rules have made it almost impossible for a youth to survive on a welfare cheque alone.

Innovative programs hold some promise, but most have closed as a result of funding restrictions. One program used former street-involved youth as peer counsellors to deliver services to youth who are currently street involved. Other innovative approaches to serving these youth are desperately needed.

CONCLUSION

Flexibility, a broad perspective and a holistic approach are among the most important aspects of treatment when working with youth. A harm reduction framework helps to reach youth "where they are" and facilitates the change process by allowing clients goal choice in all areas of their lives including, for example, non-abstinent goals. Acceptance and a non-judgmental attitude are inherent in this approach and are essential to working with youth. Understanding developmental tasks and challenges that are part of adolescence is necessary in order to assess and identify individual strengths and challenges. A comprehensive assessment that encompasses many areas of psychosocial functioning and development is important for treatment planning, and can provide other opportunities to engage youth in goal setting and to build motivation for change. Reaching out to the family and peers and, where possible, including them in the treatment and recovery process, can be very powerful in helping youth to identify and build on their strengths.

Youth with substance use disorders frequently have concurrent mental health problems (and vice versa), including conduct disorder and mood, anxiety and disruptive behaviour disorders. For many years, these two fields have operated in isolation. However, it is now recognized that providers in both systems must be trained to identify both types of problem and their associated issues, and that they must ensure that young people receive comprehensive care, either within the same program or through referrals as part of an integrated treatment plan.

The problem of street-involved youth will not just disappear, and shows every indication of getting worse. They are a population that has been poorly studied and about whom we are just beginning to build adequate data. However, what we do know raises serious concern. These are young people who are experiencing a complex mix of problems. They have adopted a difficult and challenging lifestyle that provides them with an identity and self-esteem, but that is also severely damaging and dangerous. Providing services to these youth requires approaches that are respectful, sensitive and responsive to their immediate needs. While some innovative models have been and are being developed, both the youth and the services that work with them are facing serious challenges from our changing fiscal and social environment.

REFERENCES

Adlaf, E.M. & Paglia, A. (2003). *Drug Use among Ontario Students: Findings from the Ontario Student Drug Use Survey (1977–2003)*. Toronto: Centre for Addiction and Mental Health.

Barbara, A., Chaim, G. & Doctor, F. (2002). *Asking the Right Questions: Talking about Sexual Orientation and Gender Identity during Assessment for Drug and Alcohol Concerns*. Toronto: Centre for Addiction and Mental Health.

Booth, R.C. (1998). *Basic Information about Attention Deficit Disorders*. Pottstown, PA: Attention Deficit Disorder Association (ADDA). Available: www.add.org/content/abc/basic.htm.

Boudreau, R., Chaim, G., Pearlman, S., Shenfeld, J. & Skinner, W. (1998). *Working with Couples and Families: Skills for Addiction Workers, Trainer's Guide*. Toronto: Addiction Research Foundation.

Breslin, F.C., Kathy, S.J., Tupker, E. & Pearlman, S. (1999). *First Contact: A Brief Treatment for Young Substance Users*. Toronto: Centre for Addiction and Mental Health.

British Columbia Schizophrenia Society. (2001). *Schizophrenia: Youth's Greatest Disabler*. Available: www.mentalhealth.com/book/p40-sc02.html.

Centre for Addiction and Mental Health. (2004). *Youth & Drugs & Mental Health: A Primer for Professionals*. Toronto: author.

Chaim, G. & Shenfeld, J. (In press). Concurrent disorders: A framework for working with couples and families. In W. Skinner, J.C. Negrete & P. Smith (Eds.), *Treating Addiction and Mental Health Problems Concurrently: A Practical Guide for Helpers*. Toronto: Centre for Addiction and Mental Health.

Cochrane, J., Goering, P., Durbin, J., Butterill, D., Dumas, J. & Wasylenki, D. (2000). Tertiary mental health services: II. Subpopulations and best practices for service delivery. *Canadian Journal of Psychiatry, 45*, 185–190.

Connor, D.F. (2002). *Aggression and Antisocial Behaviour in Children and Adolescents: Research and Treatment*. New York: Guilford Press.

Erickson G.E. (1995). Harm reduction: What it is and is not. *Drug and Alcohol Review, 14*, 283–285.

Derevensky, J.L. & Gupta, R. (2000). Youth gambling: A clinical and research perspective. *eGambling: The Electronic Journal of Gambling Issues, 2*. Available: www.camh.net/egambling/issue2/feature.

Health Canada. (2001). *Best Practices: Treatment and Rehabilitation for Youth with Substance Use Problems*. Ottawa: Health Canada.

Hershberger, S.L. & d'Augelli, R. (2000). Issues in counseling lesbian, gay, and bisexual adolescents. In R.M. Perez, K.A. DeBord & K.J. Bieschke (Eds.), *Handbook of Counseling and Psychotherapy with Lesbian, Gay and Bisexual Clients* (pp. 225–247). Washington, DC: American Psychological Association.

Jaksa, P. (1998). Fact sheet on attention deficit/hyperactivity disorder (ADHD/ADD). Pottstown, PA: Attention Deficit Disorder Association (ADDA). Available: www.add.org/content/abc/factsheet.htm.

Kandel, D.B., Johnson, J.G., Bird, H.R., Weissman, M.M., Goodman, S.H., Lahey, B.B. et al. (1999). Psychiatric comorbidity among adolescents with substance use disorders: Findings from the MECA study. *Journal of the American Academy of Child and Adolescent Psychiatry, 38*(6), 693–699.

Kashdan, T.B. & Herbert, J.D. (2001) Social Anxiety Disorder in childhood and adolescence: Current status and future directions. *Clinical Child and Family Psychology Review, 4*(1), 37–61.

Kessler, R.C. et al. (1996). The twelve month prevalence and correlates of serious mental illness. In R.W. Manderscheid & M.A. Schnerschein (Eds.), *Mental Health, United States* (pp. 59–70). Washington, DC: U.S. Government Printing Office.

Lowery, G., Lee, T. & Ward, J. (1996). *A Situational Analysis of Services to Concurrent Disorder Street Youth in Metropolitan Toronto*. Ottawa: Health Canada.

Lubman, D.I. & Sundram, S. (2003). Substance misuse in patients with schizophrenia: A primary care guide. *The Medical Journal of Australia, 178*(9, Supplement 5 May), S71–S75.

Marlatt, G.A. (1996). Harm reduction: Come as you are. *Addictive Behaviors, 21*(6), 779–788.

Metro Toronto Research Group on Drug Use. (1999). *Drug Use in Metropolitan Toronto*. Toronto: author.

Miller, E.T., Turner, A.P. & Marlatt, G.A. (2001). The harm reduction approach to the secondary prevention of alcohol problems in adolescents and young adults: Considerations across a developmental spectrum. In P.M. Monti, S.M. Colby & T.A. O'Leary (Eds.), *Adolescents, Alcohol, and Substance Abuse: Reaching Teens through Brief Interventions* (pp. 58–79). New York: Guilford Press.

Najavits, L.M., Weiss, R.D. & Shaw, S.R. (1999) A clinical profile of women with PTSD and substance dependence. *Psychology of Addictive Behaviors. 13*, 98–104.

National Institute of Mental Health (2000). *Depression in Children and Adolescents: A Fact Sheet for Physicians*. NIH Publication No. 00-4744. Bethesda, MD: author. Available: www.nimh.nih.gov/publicat/depchildresfact.cfm.

Schulenberg, J., Maggs, J.L., Steinman, K.J. & Zucker, R.A (2001). Development matters: Taking the long view on substance abuse etiology and intervention during adolescence. In P.M. Monti, S.M. Colby & T.A. O'Leary (Eds.), *Adolescents, Alcohol, and Substance Abuse: Reaching Teens through Brief Interventions* (pp. 19–57). New York: Guilford Press.

Skinner, H., Maley, O., Smith, L., Chirrey, S. & Morrison, M. (2001). New frontiers: Using the Internet to engage teens in substance abuse prevention and treatment. In P.M. Monti, S.M. Colby & T.A. O'Leary (Eds.), *Adolescents, Alcohol, and Substance Abuse: Reaching Teens through Brief Interventions* (pp. 297–320). New York: Guilford Press.

Smart, R.G., Adlaf, E.M., Porterfield, K.M. & Canale, M.C. (1990). *Drugs, Youth and the Street*. Toronto: Addiction Research Foundation.

Smart, R.G., Adlaf, E.M., Walsh, G.W. & Zdanowicz, Y.M. (1992). *Drifting and Doing: Changes in Drug Use among Toronto Street Youth, 1990–1992*. Toronto: Addiction Research Foundation.

Smith, G.T. &. Anderson, K.G. (2001). Personality and learning factors combine to create risk for adolescent problem drinking: A model and suggestions for intervention. In P.M. Monti, S.M. Colby & T.A. O'Leary (Eds.), *Adolescents, Alcohol, and Substance Abuse: Reaching Teens through Brief Interventions* (pp. 109–144). New York: Guilford Press.

Smith, P. & Chaim, G. (2000). Adolescent substance use and the family. In B. Brands (Ed.), *Management of Alcohol, Tobacco and other Drug Problems: A Physician's Manual* (pp. 371–386). Toronto: Centre for Addiction and Mental Health.

Swan, N. (1998). Exploring the role of child abuse in later drug abuse: Researchers face broad gaps in information. *NIDA Notes, 13*(2).

Szapocznik, J., Kurtines, W.M., Foote, F., Perez-Vidal, A. & Hervis, O. (1986). Conjoint versus one-person family therapy: Further evidence for the effectiveness of conducting family therapy through one person with drug-abusing adolescents. *Journal of Consulting and Clinical Psychology, 54*(3), 395–397.

The National Center on Addiction and Substance Abuse at Columbia University (CASA). (2000). *Substance Abuse and Learning Disabilities: Peas in a Pod or Apples and Oranges*. New York: author.

Waldron, H., Brody, J.L. & Slesnick, N. (2001). Integrative behavioral and family therapy for adolescent substance abuse. In P.M. Monti, S.M. Colby & T.A. O'Leary (Eds.), *Adolescents, Alcohol, and Substance Abuse: Reaching Teens through Brief Interventions* (pp. 216–243). New York: Guilford Press.

Zou, S., Tepper, M. & Giullivi, A. (2001, September). Hepatitis C in Canada. *Canada Communicable Disease Report*, Volume 27S3. Available: www.hc-sc.gc.ca/pphb-dgspsp/hcai-iamss/bbp-pts/pub_e.html#hepc.

Chapter 18

Trauma and Substance Use

MICHAEL GITBERG AND LUCY VAN WYK

The focus of this chapter is on trauma survivors, a complex and unique group of clients who are frequently seen in substance use treatment services. Here, we will identify the prevalence of trauma among people with substance use problems, describe the effects of interpersonal violence and trauma, and discuss the links between trauma and substance use problems. We will examine the impact on service providers of working with trauma survivors and the relational aspects of treatment, including the identification of specific challenges at various stages in the recovery process for both the client and the therapist. Throughout the chapter we use a case study to illustrate the considerations and strategies in working with a trauma survivor in a substance use treatment setting.

In our experience of working with both male and female trauma survivors, we have found that the basic framework for therapy with men and women is more alike than different. This experience is reflected in the chapter. However, as more research is done in this area, the differences may become better known.

> Judy, a substance use counsellor, is confused and sometimes angry with her client, Sandy. At their last meeting, Judy and Sandy worked together to develop a strategy to help Sandy with her triggers to use alcohol. Sandy had stated her intention to stop drinking and appeared motivated to follow through, but this week she relapsed. When Judy suggested they discuss why the relapse strategies did not work for her, Sandy had no memory of these plans and became angry. She stated that Judy was trying to trick her just as her last counsellor had done. She added that she felt she could not trust Judy.

Judy had noticed in the past that Sandy often seemed "spacey" and had difficulty following her train of thought. Judy had thought this was due to Sandy's continued alcohol use. Now, Judy is frustrated and questions Sandy's motivation to stop drinking and follow through with the treatment plan.

In Judy's clinical setting, the philosophy of treatment is to first address substance use issues and then to deal with other concerns. Sandy had disclosed a history of childhood sexual abuse, but said that she was not affected by these experiences any more. However, Sandy also reported that when she reduced her use of alcohol, she often had vivid dreams and memories of being abused as a child and woke up feeling frightened. Judy is aware that Sandy previously had periods of about three months of abstinence and then relapsed as memories of abuse emerged.

Judy's confusion is understandable given the complex presentations of people with both substance use problems and trauma histories. Should Judy conclude that Sandy could not remember their plans for relapse strategies because she had been in an alcohol-induced blackout when the plans were made? Or was Sandy unable to remember their plans because she was experiencing a trauma-related dissociative episode and was "not present" at that time?

PREVALENCE OF TRAUMA AND OF CO-OCCURRING TRAUMA AND SUBSTANCE USE PROBLEMS

Clinical literature has established clear links between substance use problems and a history of trauma. Among those receiving treatment for substance use, the prevalence of trauma history ranges between 25 per cent and 66 per cent (Najavits et al., 1997). In some substance use treatment populations as many as 90 per cent of the clients report trauma histories (Brown et al., 1999). Among those seeking help for substance use problems, women report past abuse much more frequently than men. In fact, most women in substance use treatment programs report physical and sexual abuse over their lifetime and about one-quarter have received a diagnosis of post-traumatic stress disorder (PTSD). For men, the physical abuse is more common than sexual abuse, while women report a higher level of sexual victimization and more abuse that was both physical and sexual (Ouimette et al., 2000).

A comprehensive population health survey in Ontario found that up to 38 per cent of the general population report childhood physical or sexual abuse. (MacMillan et al., 1997). Chu (1998) reports on the results of the U.S. National Comorbidity Study, which surveyed a sample of adults in the general population. In this study the estimated lifetime exposure to severe traumatic events was 61 per cent in men and

51 per cent in women. The trauma in men that was most likely to result in PTSD included rape, combat exposure, and childhood neglect and childhood physical abuse. Women were more likely than men to develop stress symptoms following rape, sexual molestation and physical attack, being threatened with a weapon or childhood physical abuse. Although men were more likely than women to be exposed to traumatic conditions, women were twice as likely to develop symptoms of PTSD (10 per cent versus five per cent). This difference may be related to the fact that women are 13 times more likely than men to be raped or sexually molested (Chu, 1998).

Knowledge of Trauma

While there has long been awareness that traumatic experiences have a powerful impact on a person's life, the study of trauma has only recently received concentrated attention and research. Van der Kolk et al. (1996) wrote, "Psychiatry itself has periodically suffered from marked amnesias in which well-established knowledge has been abruptly forgotten, and the psychological impact of overwhelming experiences has been ascribed to constitutional or intrapsychic factors alone" (p. 47).

Much of the early knowledge of the impact of traumatic events came from those treating war veterans and concentration camp survivors who were exhibiting powerful and distressing symptoms. Amazingly, between 1895 and 1974, the study of trauma focused almost exclusively on its effect on white males. This focus expanded in the early 1970s when the women's movement began to address violence against women and children.

The thrust to address the impact of trauma came from those who suffered its effects, such as Vietnam veterans, and from people working with women and children who were victims of violence. Counsellors working with assaulted women observed their clients experiencing terrifying flashbacks and nightmares, and noted that their symptoms resembled the traumatic neuroses of war. Research investigating the effects of family violence, including wife assault and the sexual and physical abuse of children, began to document and verify the subsequent devastating effects of trauma on people's lives.

Effects of Trauma

People who have been abused may later experience great difficulty in coping with the day-to-day demands of living and in establishing successful interpersonal and intimate relationships. Abuse survivors often struggle with high levels of fear, distrust, anxiety, depression, suicidal ideation, self-harm, low self-esteem and dissociative symptoms. They are frequent consumers of health care and mental health care services to address their multiple problems, and many receive multiple psychiatric diagnoses.

Clients with a trauma history often have a complex array of symptoms. Some clients report intrusive experiences, such as memories of the traumatic episode, distressing dreams or reliving the experience as though it were happening in the present (flashbacks). Others report the avoidance of feelings and appear to lack access to their emotions. They may appear emotionally numb or detached from their feelings and actively use distractions to avoid experiencing feelings, especially as they relate to the traumatic experience. Additional symptoms may be hypervigilance (such as having a sense of a dangerous presence), hyperarousal, irritability and exaggerated startle response. Many report great difficulty concentrating. Often clients shift rapidly from a state of emotional constriction to one of hyperarousal and have difficulty moderating their emotional states.

For trauma survivors, substances can, in the short term, be very effective in modulating their extremes of mood. For example, those who present with a flat affect may use cocaine and other stimulants to increase their level of energy and concentration and to decrease their sense of emotional numbness. Others may use depressants such as alcohol, heroin and benzodiazepines to decrease their physical, emotional and cognitive states of hyperarousal. These substances may temporarily help to decrease their anxiety and pervasive perception of danger.

In a study of almost 25,000 people seeking treatment for their substance use problems, a history of abuse was associated with higher levels of such problems (Ouimette et al., 2000). Abuse was also related to increased problems in other areas of their lives—such as social relations, family, employment and legal problems—and with greater psychiatric problems and comorbid diagnoses—including depression, anxiety, post-traumatic stress symptoms, phobias and personality disorders. Definitive conclusions are not established regarding the relationship between gender and subsequent development of specific psychological problems.

Defining Trauma

Common to definitions of trauma is the understanding that trauma is the result of overwhelming experience(s). These may be experiences of war, natural disaster, accident or crime; of physical, sexual or emotional abuse; or of neglect. Herman (1992) describes psychological trauma as an "affliction of the powerless. At the moment of trauma, the victim is rendered helpless by overwhelming force. Traumatic events overwhelm the ordinary systems of care that give people a sense of control, connection and meaning" (p. 33).

Evans & Sullivan (1995) define abuse from an interpersonal perspective and state that it is "the experience of highly stressful events inflicted by another person that is beyond the individual's capacity to cope and that impairs the individual's sense of well-being" (p. 33).

The majority of people who experience a traumatic event are able to integrate the experience and move ahead with their lives. However, some people are unable to move on, and despite the passage of time, "begin to develop the specific patterns of avoidance and hyperarousal that are associated with PTSD. What distinguishes people who develop PTSD from people who are merely temporarily stressed is that they start organizing their lives around the trauma (van der Kolk & McFarlane, 1996, p. 6.)

Research focusing on biological and physiological responses to traumatic events has led to the understanding that traumatic memory is stored differently than ordinary memories (van der Kolk, 1996b). In contrast to ordinary, explicit memory, which is semantic, symbolic and integrated in the person's schemas of meaning, traumatic memory consists of images, feeling states and behaviours that are highly state-dependent and do not change over time. Ogden & Minton (2000) describe how traumatized people are unable to process and assimilate their cognitive, emotional and physical reactions to the traumatic event, and thus are unable to fully integrate the experience of the event into their subsequent development.

Many trauma survivors are treated in psychiatric settings and their presenting problems are formulated using the *Diagnostic and Statistical Manual of Mental Disorders (DSM-IV)*. The *DSM-IV* refers explicitly to trauma only when it describes PTSD. The criteria used to assign a diagnosis of PTSD are grouped around three areas of symptoms: intrusive re-experiencing, avoidance and numbing, and increased arousal. Brett (1996) suggests that there are some disadvantages to the *DSM-IV* diagnostic approach. She states that the focus on one post-traumatic syndrome can hinder the exploration of alternative forms or variations of traumatic reactions and symptoms. She cautions that it misses the complexity of the effects that trauma has on the personality. Brett notes that

> the restriction of the diagnosis to its most essential features can result in two types of clinical errors: either a clinician may miss the posttraumatic stress disorder diagnosis (PTSD) because associated features are most prominent or the associated features may be overlooked because of the presence of the PTSD (Brett, 1996, p. 125).

Herman (1992) developed a diagnosis formulation that includes the associated features of PTSD and the complex effects of trauma on the development of personality. Her formulation, complex post-traumatic stress disorder (not included in the *DSM-IV*), describes the following criteria:

1. A history of subjection to totalitarian control over a prolonged period (months to years). Examples include hostages, prisoners of war, concentration camp survivors and survivors of some religious cults. Examples also include those subjected to totalitarian systems in sexual and domestic life, including survivors of domestic battering, childhood physical or sexual abuse and organized sexual exploitation.

2. Alterations in affect regulation, including persistent dysphoria, chronic suicidal preoccupation, self-injury, explosive or extremely inhibited anger, compulsive or extremely inhibited sexuality.

3. Alterations in consciousness, including amnesia or hyper-amnesia for traumatic events, transient dissociative episodes, depersonalization/ derealization, reliving experiences, either in the form of intrusive posttraumatic stress disorder symptoms or in the form of ruminative preoccupation.

4. Alterations in self perception, including sense of helplessness or paralysis of initiative, shame, guilt, and self blame, sense of defilement or stigma, sense of complete difference from others (may include sense of special-ness, utter aloneness, belief no other person can understand, or non-human identity).

5. Alterations in perception of perpetrator, including preoccupation with relationship with perpetrator (includes preoccupation with revenge), unrealistic attribution of total power to perpetrator (caution: victim's assessment of power realities may be more realistic than clini-cian's), idealization or paradoxical gratitude, sense of special or super-natural relationship, acceptance of belief system or rationalizations of perpetrator.

6. Alterations in relations with others, including isolation and withdrawal, disruption in intimate relationships, repeated search for rescuer (may alternate with isolation and withdrawal), persistent distrust, repeated failures of self-protection.

7. Alterations in systems of meaning: loss of sustaining faith, sense of hope-lessness and despair (p. 121).

Clients may not have access to memories of the abuse or may only have access to partial memories, making their symptoms puzzling to them and to the therapist. Terr (1994) distinguishes between two types of trauma to assist in understanding why individual responses to trauma vary. Type I trauma is the result of a single traumatic event while Type II trauma is the result of repeated traumatization. Rothschild (2000) suggests the addition of a further subclassification to distinguish between, first, people with multiple traumas that overwhelmed their previously developed internal resources, and second, those with multiple traumas who have unstable backgrounds and did not develop sufficient internal resources. This distinction helps the develop-ment of a treatment plan. Those who have sufficient internal resources to draw upon can generally work directly on processing the traumatic experiences. The therapeutic relationship tends to be less intense because developmental issues are not in the fore-ground. Clients who lack internal resources must first be assisted in the building of these resources, prior to addressing traumatic experiences more directly. In this case, the therapeutic relationship is often more intense, complex and of longer duration.

> From the time she was born, both of Sandy's parents were dependent on alcohol. Along with her eight siblings, Sandy witnessed her father assaulting her mother on many occasions. Often there was not enough food in the house, and because the rent was not paid, her family moved frequently. At times Sandy's mother left home without telling anyone where she was. Sandy's eldest brother was most often the target of her father's rage when he was drunk.

> When Sandy was about five years old, her father began entering her bed-room at night when she was asleep. Initially, he fondled her sexually, and by the time she was eight he was having intercourse with her. She was told to keep their relationship a secret and she became her father's favourite child. Sandy found that if she focused on the wallpaper pattern of a little duck, she could pretend the abuse was not happening, and she did not feel the pain. Several times she tried telling her mother, but was told that she was an evil girl to be making up such terrible stories about her father. When Sandy was 10 she ran away from home and was placed in the first of many foster homes, where she continued to experience abuse. One of the older foster children introduced Sandy to alcohol and she immediately liked the way it helped her feel less afraid and anxious, especially around older men. By the time she was 17 she was living on the street, using a variety of sub-stances and vulnerable to exploitation by men who promised her protec-tion, usually in exchange for sexual favours.

STAGES OF RECOVERY

Traditionally there has been a tension between sequential and integrated models of treatment. In the sequential model, the client is treated for one condition, usually sub-stance use problems, before the trauma is addressed. The integrated approach com-bines the treatment of trauma and substance use problems. The rationale for a sequential treatment model is the belief that addressing issues related to the trauma in early recovery from substance use problems can precipitate relapse. Najavits (2002) makes a case for an integrated approach to treatment, stating that it is recommended by clinicians and researchers who have found that it is more likely to succeed, is more cost-effective and is more sensitive to client needs. Such an integrated approach advocates for the development of skills in early recovery to mitigate trauma-related symptoms, and thereby decreases the risk of relapse.

Initially the treatment focus for both substance use problems and trauma must be to identify problems, develop plans for safety and skill building, and develop the therapeutic relationship. Counsellors must be attuned to the possibility in any setting that both issues may be present and therefore require careful assessment, while accepting that full disclosure of either issue seldom occurs at the outset.

Widely accepted in the treatment of trauma is the model proposed by Herman (1992), in which recovery is broadly described in three stages: safety, remembrance and mourning, and reconnection. Herman cautions that a conceptualization of stages should not be taken literally and reminds therapists that "they are an attempt to impose simplicity and order upon a process that is inherently turbulent and complex" (p. 155).

In the first stage, seeking safety, the primary therapeutic tasks are:
• the identification of problem areas, including traumatic symptoms and substance use problems
• the development of coping skills
• stabilization
• the establishment of supports and resources.

Additional tasks include restoring routines and patterns of living, such as sleep and eating, and beginning to exercise control of self-destructive behaviours. Some clients may need medication for symptoms of depression, anxiety and traumatic hyperarousal at this stage of recovery. Because some of these medications have addictive properties they must be prescribed with caution and monitored with care. Their use can present a challenge for clients who have relied on substance use for emotional regulation. Clients with a history of substance use problems may seek to use prescribed substances to compensate for the loss of alcohol and other drugs. These clients will require additional support as they seek ways to regain control of their lives.

There is great similarity between recovery from substance use problems and recovery from trauma, particularly in the first stage. Many of the very concrete strategies long employed in substance use treatment (Prochaska et al., 1994) help clients achieve safety, develop skills and understand the motivational shifts that accompany the change process. The treatment of trauma, like that of substance use problems, requires an understanding of the ways in which the issue impacts all aspects of a person's life.

As clients achieve a sense of safety and control in their lives, they become ready to engage in the second stage: the work of remembering and mourning. This work includes finding ways to put the trauma into words or telling the story of and mourning their many losses. Usually this story unfolds as a fragmented and non-sequential narrative, making it difficult for the therapist to understand. Often the story is told devoid of feelings, which may make it difficult for the therapist to respond empathically and remain attuned, reinforcing the client's belief that his or her story is not significant or that the therapist does not care. The story may also unfold through re-enactments of the traumatic experience, an increase in self-harm behaviours or an escalation of substance use, as the client struggles to both remember and forget the traumatic events. The therapist's task is to carefully attend to the story and collect the narrative fragments and dissociated experiences into a whole story. The therapist acts as an ally and compassionate witness who helps the survivor to name and endure the previously unbearable traumatic memories, mourn the many losses and integrate the fragmented aspects of his or her self.

After working through remembrance and mourning, trauma survivors face the task of reclaiming their lives, finding meaning and orienting themselves toward the future. At this third and final stage the client is ready to re-engage with life, establish friendships and participate more actively in the world. Because clients are now no longer responding defensively and reactively, it becomes possible for them to take control of their lives and have a sense of accomplishment and achievement. Preoccupation with the past is greatly diminished, as is the pervasive belief that one is a damaged person. Clients may at various points revisit aspects of earlier stages of recovery, especially as they negotiate challenging moments in their lives, and may re-engage in treatment to address these challenges.

ASSESSMENT AND DISCLOSURE

Many counsellors in substance use treatment settings have little or no training or experience in dealing with trauma and/or mental health disorders, and as a result they may not assess for trauma or understand the importance of addressing trauma in a substance use treatment program. Clients typically report that they have never been asked about a history of trauma. Conversely, in other clinical settings, substance use issues are frequently overlooked, and counsellors have no training or experience in dealing with these concerns. The result in each case is that clients are poorly served and treatment progress is compromised.

Symptoms similar to those observed in people with a history of trauma may also be present in those who are using substances or are in withdrawal. This can be confusing for the clinician. Initially it may be difficult to accurately assess clients who continue to use substances. A period of abstinence is recommended in order to distinguish substance-related symptoms from the effects of trauma.

Clients are well served when counsellors understand that people may present with both substance use and trauma issues, regardless of the treatment setting. Clients should be told at the outset that there will be an exploration of a wide range of potential concerns commonly seen in clients in this setting. This preparation helps clients who present for substance use treatment to recognize and understand that people with substance use problems frequently also have trauma issues, and that they are not alone. In other counselling settings this approach reassures clients that substance use issues are understood and that they may safely disclose their use of alcohol and other drugs. Clients should be alerted that some of the questions may be difficult to answer, and that they always may choose whether or not to answer a specific question; they can also choose the amount of detail to provide and to end this exploration at any time. It is essential that this assessment be conducted with great sensitivity and that care be taken to provide containment—that is, the client should be taught the skills of emotional self-regulation—so as to avoid inappropriate overdisclosure in the context of the brief assessment relationship. It is often necessary to teach grounding skills early on so that the assessment process is not itself destabilizing for the client. Grounding techniques are self-soothing strategies to contain intense emotions and impulses, such as cravings for alcohol and other drugs, self-harm, anger or sadness. Grounding helps clients gain a sense of control and safety as they disclose painful experiences.

Clients almost always have powerful reactions to disclosing past abuse. Many abuse survivors have been forbidden by the perpetrator to tell anyone about the abuse or have been threatened with further harm if they disclose. Many report that they are too ashamed to talk about it and are afraid of being blamed for the abuse. They may believe that when they are seeking substance use treatment it is not relevant to speak about trauma. And, as noted earlier, many clients are not yet able to tell their story as a coherent narrative; instead, the story unfolds over time in a fragmented and nonlinear fashion.

Herman (1992) cautions that

> though the single most common therapeutic error is avoidance of the traumatic material, probably the second most common error is premature or precipitate engagement in exploratory work, without sufficient attention to the tasks of establishing safety and securing a therapeutic alliance (p. 172).

This care is particularly important in helping avoid the risk of relapse when working with clients with co-occurring substance use and trauma problems.

The following questions are examples of how to approach the subject of past traumas gradually and sensitively. The questions begin with quite general areas of exploration and move into more detailed inquiry as the client becomes more comfortable with the assessment and the counsellor.

• Can you tell me about your childhood?
• Were there situations in your childhood that made you uncomfortable?
• Were you ever asked to do something that made you feel uncomfortable or ashamed?
• Are there parts of your childhood that you can't remember? If yes, which time periods?
• Do you ever have very bad dreams or nightmares?
• Do you have strange body sensations, intrusive thoughts or images that you can't explain?
• Do you sometimes feel that you have lost time or can't remember periods of time? If so, does this happen only when you use substances excessively or also at other times?
• Do you have a sense that you have no feelings or feel numb?

• Do you avoid specific situations or people who remind you of the past?
• Were you ever physically/emotionally/sexually abused?

If the client discloses abuse, the following questions may help the counsellor move into seeking more detail about the abuse.

• Were you able to tell anyone about this? If not, why not? If so, were you believed and what happened?
• Did you receive treatment? (Explore further about the nature of the treatment and whether or not the client found it helpful.)
• Have you ever used substances to deal with thoughts or feelings related to the abuse?

> At Sandy's assessment interview, Judy asked about trauma issues. Sandy reported that there were significant conflicts in her home while she was growing up, such as her father's explosive temper, but did not identify clear memories of abuse. She spoke about these experiences in a detached way and did not provide further details. She said they had little bearing on her substance use.

Sandy's assessment experience highlights a situation in which a client has little access to traumatic memories and does not view them as relevant to her substance use problems and recovery. Yet other clients present quite differently. Some may have access to many memories and want to address the trauma issues without dealing with the substance use. Others may recognize that they have been using substances to mediate the effects of the traumatic experiences. Assessment questions may produce severe anxiety and other emotional and somatic reactions. To gauge clients' responses to the exploration of trauma, it is useful to explore changes in mood, sleeping patterns, increased substance use, memory gaps and intrusive memories in subsequent sessions. For many people the act of revealing past trauma is very powerful, particularly if this is the first time they have disclosed their traumatic experiences. This material must be handled with great sensitivity and care so that clients feel understood, validated and respected. Common fears are that they will not be believed, their experiences will be minimized or they will be judged as being responsible for the abuse. Shame and guilt are powerful emotions that accompany discussion of these issues.

Just as clients are fearful for many reasons to disclose their traumatic experiences, counsellors are often fearful of asking about abuse. Some counsellors may believe that substance use is a problem all of its own, and that exploring other issues is not advisable. Others find that they avoid asking about abuse because they are not confident of their ability to handle the answers that may emerge or their ability to handle their own emotional responses. As discussed earlier, counsellors must have skills to support, contain and validate clients who risk making disclosures, including the ability to teach grounding strategies.

It is important to keep assessing the client's stability, resources and capacity to tolerate the difficult aspects of the next stages of therapeutic work. In the past, the client has dissociated the traumatic experiences, either intrapsychically or through the use of substances. Associating the intolerable aspects of the past can be retraumatiz-ing unless provisions are made for increasing tolerance for the memories.

Sandy continued to meet with Judy over a five-year period. She became increasingly able to recall and integrate memories of the abusive experi-ences while mastering skills of containment. The episodes of self-harm and substance use, which formerly accompanied emerging memories, became less frequent and severe. For a period of time midway through the treatment process Sandy found herself inexplicably using substances again. When this episode was fully explored, she realized that it occurred at a time when a new memory was surfacing. At times, her memories came in clusters that overwhelmed her capacity to function and attend to her present life needs. At this time, her drinking became a very serious problem again, and Sandy accepted a referral to a residential substance use treat-ment program, which helped her to regain stability.

Later in her treatment, Sandy's anger became directed primarily at her mother and it threatened their current relationship. This represented a painful change for Sandy, as it meant viewing her mother in a less idealistic way. Despite her mother's frequent abandonment of the family, Sandy had maintained a belief that her mother had provided her with love and nur-turing, and that her mother was another helpless victim of her father's violence. There were long periods when Sandy felt overcome by despair, and lost hope that her life could be anything but a disaster. When she fully realized the extent of the past abuse, she had difficulty viewing herself as any-thing other than a damaged victim. During this period, it was critical that Judy remained predictable and that their relationship was secure. As her trust increased, Sandy was able to maintain her goal of abstinence from alcohol and other drugs and remain in therapy, though she often struggled with urges to withdraw from therapy. Sandy also used the support of her self-help group and stable friends to help her maintain sobriety and resist temptations to use substances.

When Sandy had achieved stability and tolerance for exploring of memo-ries, Judy referred her to a group for abuse survivors. Sandy successfully used the group to further gain support, address her issues of shame and recognize that she was not alone in dealing with recovery from substance use and trauma. In the group, Sandy processed her overwhelming anger toward her father. She decided that she would not exclude him from her life, but that she would limit their relationship in specific ways. Sandy gained clarity about her own needs and gradually lost most of her fear and distrust of men. She was able to recognize when her reactions to men were based on past negative experiences rather than the reality of the present situation. As her periods of stability increased, Sandy became hopeful and began to envision a future for herself in which the past no longer controlled her, and she became confident that she had the resources to cope with life's stresses.

RELATIONAL ASPECTS OF TREATMENT

Counsellors in substance use treatment settings frequently struggle with the ways in which clients present. Often the therapeutic alliance is fragile, and the therapeutic relationship may be volatile or significantly more intense than is generally encountered in other settings. Clients may have frequent crises, commit self-harm or threaten self-harm or suicide, have erratic attendance and relapse to substance use. Counter-transference reactions are common and clients may be perceived as "crazy, lazy or bad" by others and by themselves. They may be perceived to be lacking a commitment to their recovery.

People who have survived trauma bring to all their relationships, including the therapeutic one, assumptions that are based on their previous significant relationships. The therapeutic relationship becomes the theatre in which unresolved relational aspects of the person's abuse are re-enacted. It is no surprise then that trauma survivors, particularly those with histories of early childhood physical and sexual abuse, are among the most challenging clients to work with. Even the most competent therapist may get frustrated and confused by a client's inability to trust, unrealistic expectations of the therapist, patterns of self-harm and substance use, explosive rage or persistent patterns of victimization.

The therapist brings to the relationship expectations based on training, personal experience and the desire to be an effective helper. Therapists also bring their own responses to the dynamics the client is presenting, which include their unresolved and unconscious issues. It is common for the therapist to experience very powerful emotions, such as feeling immobilized or attacked, becoming enraged or being over-gratified by the client. Therapists may find themselves struggling with intense feelings that may be in conflict with their training, personal values and beliefs. For example, a therapist who believes that any feelings of anger toward a client are wrong will be reluctant to accept this feeling. Inattention to the counsellor's emotional responses to the client has the potential to create breaches in the therapeutic relationship, possibly leading to premature abandonment of therapy by the therapist or client.

It is often assumed that the therapist should not be of the same gender as the client's abuser, because of the presence of trauma transference. While the gender of the therapist may initially provoke powerful transference responses from clients, no research has yet shown that it affects treatment outcome. In our view, gender-based transference is only one of many relational configurations that will manifest in the course of treatment.

Chu (1988) describes relational treatment dynamics as therapeutic impasses and identifies several traps for therapists, including control, denial, projection, idealization and motivation. He notes that therapists commonly fall into the trap of assuming the presence of trust from the client. However, a reasonable level of trust often takes several months to develop and a normal level of trust usually exists when the treatment nears the end. While trauma survivors desperately wish to trust, they nonetheless fully expect betrayal and in the course of treatment will repeatedly test therapists' trustworthiness. In response to clients' resistance to trusting, their overwhelming neediness and constant pleas for reassurance, therapists may feel the urge to withdraw. This withdrawal may recapitulate the client's earlier experiences of neglect. Chu invites therapists to view the therapeutic relationship as a dynamic interpersonal arena in which both parties participate and have an impact on each other. In clinical practice, moving closer to the client rather than becoming more distant often has the effect of reducing crises in the treatment. Considering that one aspect of childhood abuse and neglect is unpredictability and a severe lack of appropriate boundaries, one of the important therapeutic tasks is the establishment and maintenance of clear, predictable boundaries. While the placement of a particular boundary may vary from therapist to therapist, clarity about established boundaries and adherence to them help establish trust and stability in the client.

> At the outset of their therapeutic relationship, Sandy continually expressed mistrust of Judy and her belief that Judy would probably leave and not be available. Despite Judy's efforts to reassure her, Sandy continued to express these doubts and questioned Judy about her personal life, stating that if she knew more about Judy she would be better able to trust her. After this dynamic became a dominant theme for several weeks, Judy began to be frustrated and feel that her personal space was being invaded. She began to resent Sandy, and she found these feelings uncomfortable. As a result she became distant. For example, she did not return Sandy's phone calls as quickly as she had done in the past. Judy then noticed that Sandy became more anxious, pressed for more information and threatened that if Judy did not comply that she would likely relapse.

Davies & Frawley (1994) approach the discussion from a relational psychoanalytic perspective. They argue that the therapist must be willing to work with the powerful and rapidly shifting relational paradigms of transference and countertransference commonly found in the treatment of trauma clients. They insist that unless all combinations and permutations of relational roles are experienced and worked through, the treatment will not be complete. Because clients are often unconscious of relational roles, it is the therapist's task to gradually increase their awareness. An example given by Davies and Frawley is one they name "The Sadistic Abuser and the Helpless Impotently Enraged Victim" paradigm. The client's role in this enactment is that of the abuser who presents the therapist with graphic descriptions and visible signs of self-harm, such as cutting or burning. The clinician may feel shocked or paralyzed by the intense rage or violence inherent in these acts and may feel frightened or helpless, thus enacting the victim's responses. "There is often a sense of patients' saying 'take this. Don't think that you can really have an impact on me because in the end I will do exactly what I want (Davies & Frawley, 1994, p. 173).'" Other commonly seen dual roles enacted in treatment include "The Unseeing Uninvolved Parent and the Unseen Neglected Child," "The Idealized Rescuer and the Entitled Child" and "The Seducer and the Seduced."

"To study psychological trauma is to come face to face both with human vulnerability in the natural world and with the capacity for evil in human nature. To study psychological trauma means bearing witness to horrible events" (Herman, 1992, p. 7). Working with survivors of interpersonal trauma forces counsellors to face the extent of human degradation. These experiences have the potential to overwhelm a therapist's worldview, belief systems and coping capacity. There may be times when a therapist views the world only through the eyes of his or her victimized clients. This phenomenon is known as vicarious traumatization (Pearlman & Saakvitne, 1995). In order to address this issue, therapists need to access clinical supervision, seek ongoing peer support and attend to their own self-care needs. Since trauma survivors are such a large proportion of those who seek help for substance use problems, it is vital that treatment programs understand the links between trauma and substance use, and support their staff with education, training and supervision regarding these concurrent issues.

GROUP AND INDIVIDUAL TREATMENT

Treatment settings vary tremendously in the kinds of services they offer clients. Most substance use treatment settings are group-based and provide little opportunity for individual therapy. Ideally, trauma clients require a combination of individual and group therapy. In all cases the decision regarding treatment must be made collaboratively with the client, and the rationale for each modality explained so that clients know what to expect.

Individual counselling offers clients a secure environment in which to explore issues related to substance use and trauma. Many clients respond well to the flexibility and individuality of therapy tailored to their specific needs at any given moment. Because the issues are complex and often presented in a fragmented way, individual work allows greater ease in following the thread of the story as it unfolds. The session belongs to the client alone, making it possible to explore themes in greater depth and complexity. There are some clients who find this individual attentiveness overwhelming and find that a group helps to defuse this intensity. For these clients the fear of being noticed is so great that it makes the intensity of individual work unbearable, and they may better tolerate the scattered attention they receive in a group. Other clients find that they are overwhelmed or triggered by listening to the experiences of others in a group setting.

Group work has the benefit of decreasing the isolation many trauma survivors experience. Groups provide social support and help clients to develop interpersonal skills, which are often lacking for people with a history of trauma. In addition, groups create a larger matrix of coping strategies, knowledge and other resources than is available in individual work. Peer feedback is, in some instances, more acceptable than the feedback of an authority figure such as the therapist. This is especially true for clients who feel a great deal of shame and keep their substance use a secret, which parallels their keeping the abuse a secret. Many clients observe that therapists can be naive about substance use and that group members are often more astute at detecting defensive strategies and unacknowledged substance use in one another. One of the most potent benefits of groups for trauma survivors is a decrease in isolation and shame, two common themes in recovery.

Referrals to groups should match the client's stage of recovery. When clients are addressing issues of safety and containment, the preferred group is time limited, structured and supportive, and teaches concrete skills in grounding and safety. The focus is on each member rather than on the group's dynamics. As clients progress and are ready to begin dealing more directly with traumatic experiences, group work that emphasizes the development of insight and trust and addresses member-to-member interactions is recommended. Members attend to each other's stories and explore the effects of trauma on their lives. Generally speaking, these groups are of greater duration and intensity. Finally, when clients are ready, they can move to long-term, open-ended groups in which they work at a variety of difficulties in a less structured, free-flowing format. They complete the work of integrating the fragmented aspects of themselves, and shift away from defining themselves as victims to a position of wholeness and strength. In general, the higher the level of the client's functioning, ego strength and anxiety tolerance, the more feasible it is to offer a long-term, insight-oriented group.

Mixed-gender treatment programs and groups are often especially difficult for women who have been abused by men, and are therefore generally not advised. Although research is limited, some data is emerging that women-only treatment programs are more beneficial for women (Ouimette et al., 2000). In the later stages of treatment, mixed-gender groups can be tremendously beneficial in helping clients reintegrate into society.

COMMUNITY SUPPORTS

As a general rule, trauma survivors are encouraged to seek a variety of supports to help them with their recovery. Inevitably they encounter conflicting ideologies in the treatment of trauma and of substance use problems. The role of the therapist is to help clients navigate the discrepancies between the various approaches. At times a case conference is required to ensure that service providers are working together in the client's best interest.

Many clients successfully use mutual aid programs, such as Alcoholics Anonymous. Especially in the early stages of recovery, clients can benefit from peer support, replacing their friends who support their substance use problems and decreasing their isolation. The stable structure of the self-help program helps create structure in the person's previously unstable life.

MEDICATION

Several kinds of medication can be used to treat the symptoms that result from traumatic experiences. Very few of these, however, have been systematically researched to verify their effectiveness specifically for trauma symptoms (Davidson & Van der Kolk, 1996a). Many clients find that medication helps them manage their overwhelming emotions, intrusive memories and anxiety. Medications may also be prescribed to clients to decrease depression and numbing, to reduce generalized hyperarousal, to manage psychotic or dissociative symptoms and to reduce impulsive aggression against themselves or others. Clients with concurrent mental health and substance use problems present a special challenge. They may become dependent on medications and may also continue to use alcohol and other drugs without disclosing this use. If prescribed indiscriminately, medications can hinder a client's ability to recognize and regulate his or her emotions, which becomes counterproductive to the therapy. The counsellor should have a good collaborative relationship with the prescribing physician to ensure that the client is receiving the best possible care.

BEYOND TALK THERAPY

It is true that at the core of our traumatized and neglected patients' disorganization is the problem that they can not analyze what is going on when they reexperience the physical sensations of past trauma, but that these sensations just produce intense emotions without being able to modulate them, then our therapy needs to consist of helping people to stay in their bodies and to understand these bodily sensations. And that is certainly not something that any of the traditional psychotherapies, which we have all been taught, help people to do very well (van der Kolk, 1998, cited in Rothschild, 2000, p. 15.)

An approach that incorporates work with the somatic aspects of trauma is described by Ogden & Minton (2000). Here the body, rather than cognition or emotion, is the primary entry point in processing trauma. Sensorimotor psychotherapy directly treats the effects of trauma on the body, which in turn facilitates emotional and cognitive processing. The client is helped to develop awareness of, and skills to regulate, the extreme fluctuations of arousal, which often lead to dissociation. Through interactive therapist-client work, clients develop awareness of their inner body sensations and processes, and develop resources for self-regulation. A wide range of somatic interventions is employed, including the teaching of body awareness and sensation, movement awareness and education, and working with alignment, posture and breath. Sensorimotor psychotherapy was developed as an adjunct to traditional talk therapies and the techniques can be easily integrated into other approaches.

Other non-verbal therapies that can be used as an adjunct are music therapy and art therapy, mindfulness-based meditation and eye movement desensitization and reprocessing (EMDR). EMDR (Shapiro & Forrest, 1997) is a recently developed treatment in which the client is asked to hold in mind a disturbing image, an associated negative cognition and bodily sensations associated with a traumatic memory. At the same time, the client is asked to focus on an external stimulus such as therapist-directed lateral eye movements, hand tapping or auditory tones. Variations of the procedure are repeated until distressing aspects of the traumatic memory are reduced and more adaptive cognitions emerge regarding the trauma. Similar procedures are used to install alternative positive cognitions, coping strategies and adaptive behaviours.

CONCLUSION

The link between trauma and the later development of substance use problems has become more widely understood, and is evident from the large numbers of people seeking help for these dual concerns. In substance use treatment programs, more women than men are dealing with these concurrent issues. The ways that people are affected by traumatic events vary tremendously; the presentation of trauma in treatment settings is complex and confounding, and profoundly impacts those who work with trauma issues. No single treatment approach is successful in addressing the complex needs of people with concurrent trauma histories and substance use problems; a combination of treatment strategies is recommended. Research and clinical experience suggest that it is advisable to address trauma and substance use problems concurrently. The initial focus is to stabilize substance use and trauma symptoms at the same time. Because part of the traumatic experience is the violation of trust, and many trauma survivors come from families in which they have been abused or neglected, trust in the therapeutic relationship is a focal point. Treatment can be described as progressing through several stages, from stabilization to remembering and mourning and finally to reconnection and integration. Evidence is emerging that traumatic experiences affect the body, and the use of somatic approaches to address these bodily effects is progressing.

REFERENCES

Brett, E.A. (1996). The classification of posttraumatic stress disorder. In B.A. van der Kolk, A.C. McFarlane & L. Weisaeth (Eds.), *Traumatic Stress: The Effects of Overwhelming Experience on Mind, Body, and Society*. New York: Guilford Press.

Brown, P.J., Stout, R.L. & Mueller, T. (1999). Substance use disorder and post traumatic stress disorder comorbidity: Addiction and psychiatric treatment rates. *Psychology of Addictive Behaviors, 13*, 115–122.

Chu, J.A. (1988). Ten traps for therapists in the treatment of trauma survivors. *Dissociation, 1*(4), 24–32.

Chu, J.A. (1998). *Rebuilding Shattered Lives: Treating Complex Post-traumatic and Dissociative Disorders*. New York: John Wiley.

Davidson, J.R.T. & van der Kolk, B.A. (1996). The psychopharmacological treatment of posttraumatic stress disorder. In B.A. van der Kolk, A.C. McFarlane & L. Weisaeth (Eds.), *Traumatic Stress: The Effects of Overwhelming Experience on Mind, Body, and Society*. New York: Guilford Press.

Davies, J.M. & Frawley, M.G. (1994). *Treating the Adult Survivor of Childhood Sexual Abuse*. New York: Basic Books.

Evans, K. & Sullivan, J.M. (1995). *Treating Addicted Survivors of Trauma*. New York: Guilford Press.

Herman, J.L. (1992). *Trauma and Recovery*. New York: Basic Books.

MacMillan, H.L., Fleming, J.E., Trocme, N., Boyle, M.H., Wong, M., Racine, Y.A. et al. (1997). Prevalence of child physical and sexual abuse in the community. *Journal of the American Medical Association, 278*(2).

Najavits, L.M., Weiss, R.D. & Shaw, S.R. (1997). The link between substance abuse and posttraumatic stress disorder in women: A research review. *American Journal on Addictions, 6*, 273–283.

Najavits, L.M. (2002). *Seeking Safety: A Treatment Manual for PTSD and Substance Abuse*. New York: Guilford Press.

Ogden, P. & Minton, K. (2000). Sensorimotor psychotherapy: One method for processing traumatic memory. *Traumatology, 6*(3).

Ouimette, P.C., Kimmerling, R., Shaw, J. & Moos, R.H. (2000). Physical and sexual abuse among women and men with substance use disorders. *Alcoholism Treatment Quarterly, 18*(3), 7–17.

Pearlman, L.A. & Saakvitne, K.W. (1995). *Trauma and the Therapist: Countertransference and Vicarious Traumatization in Psychotherapy with Incest Survivors*. New York: W.W. Norton.

Prochaska, J.O., Norcross, J.C. & DiClemente, C.C. (1994). *Changing for Good.* New York: William Morrow.

Rothschild, B. (2000). *The Body Remembers: The Psychophysiology of Trauma and Trauma Treatment.* New York: W.W. Norton.

Shapiro, F. & Forrest, M.S. (1997). *EMDR: The Breakthrough Therapy for Overcoming Anxiety, Stress, and Trauma.* New York: Basic Books.

Terr, L. (1994). *Unchained Memories.* New York: Basic Books.

van der Kolk, B.A. (1996a). The body keeps the score: Approaches to the psychobiology of posttraumatic stress disorder. In B.A. van der Kolk, A.C. McFarlane & L. Weisaeth (Eds.). *Traumatic Stress: The Effects of Overwhelming Experience on Mind, Body, and Society.* New York: Guilford Press.

van der Kolk, B.A. (1996b). Trauma and memory. In B.A. van der Kolk, A.C. McFarlane & L. Weisaeth (Eds.), *Traumatic Stress: The Effects of Overwhelming Experience on Mind, Body, and Society.* New York: Guilford Press.

van der Kolk, B.A. & McFarlane, A.C. (1996). The black hole of trauma. In B.A. van der Kolk, A.C. McFarlane & L. Weisaeth (Eds.), *Traumatic Stress: The Effects of Overwhelming Experience on Mind, Body, and Society.* New York: Guilford Press.

Chapter 19

Counselling Newcomers to Canada

SHIRLEY SMITH AND BERYL TSANG

INTRODUCTION

Canada has always been a multi-ethnic, multilingual and multiracial society, but it has become even more so in the last five years. According to the 2001 Census, "The proportion of Canada's population who were born outside the country has reached its highest level in 70 years" (Statistics Canada, 2003).

The majority of newcomers (58 per cent) are from Asia and the Middle East; 20 per cent are from Europe, 11 per cent are from the Caribbean and Central and South America, and eight per cent are from Africa (Statistics Canada, 2003).

Seventy-three per cent of these newcomers live in the three largest urban centres (Toronto, Vancouver and Montreal). Addiction services and related mental health services in these cities have had to respond to the large numbers of newcomers by providing services that are culturally sensitive. While the numbers of newcomers living in smaller communities are lower, research shows that they too need culturally sensitive services (Immigrant and Visible Minority Women of Saskatchewan, 2002).

The goal of this chapter is to help addiction service providers across the country meet the needs of the 200-plus newcomer communities in Canada (Building Bridges, Breaking Barriers Access Project, 2003). We will provide an overview of the experience of people who are new to Canada, including the context of immigration, the settlement process and a discussion of trauma and its impact on health, particularly in terms of substance use. We define culture, ethnicity and race, and consider how the difference in the meaning of these three terms may affect communication when counselling newcomers. We discuss the substance use patterns and problems of those who are new to Canada, and the barriers they face in accessing addiction and mental health services. We also examine counselling and communication strategies and the roles counsellors may need to assume when working with newcomers, and give information on using an interpreter and other community resources.

WHO ARE THE NEWCOMERS?

Aboriginal communities might consider anyone who is not First Nations or Inuit to be a "newcomer." However, in this chapter, the term includes:

- immigrants who leave their homes to resettle in Canada. Of these, most come to be with family members who are already established here, or to search for better employment or educational opportunities. Sometimes second-generation Canadians whose parents did not fully "settle" in Canada consider themselves immigrants.
- refugees fleeing a "well-founded fear of being persecuted," in need of protection due to risk of life or risk of cruel and unusual treatment or punishment, and/or in need of protection from torture (this includes women fleeing gender-based persecution) (Office of the High Commissioner for Human Rights, 1951).
- workers (such as live-in caregivers) who come to Canada to work and eventually settle as immigrants
- people who live and work in Canada illegally
- people who come to Canada on visitor and student visas and stay after their visas expire, or who stay in Canada after marrying Canadian citizens.

UNDERSTANDING NEWCOMERS

To better understand clients who are new to Canada, counsellors need to understand the context in which immigration takes place, how the settlement process affects people and how newcomers' experiences of trauma, oppression and discrimination affect their health and help-seeking behaviours.

Context

For many years, immigration to Canada has been based primarily on the needs of the Canadian labour market. Most immigrants are selected on the basis of skills and knowledge that are needed in certain sectors. Between 1880 and 1920 Asian immigrants were imported to build the railways and work in the mines and in other labour-intensive occupations. Once the need for cheap labour ended, new immigration measures were put in place to create different categories of immigrants. With a booming economy that saw Canadian workers advancing to better-paid jobs, labour shortages occurred in low-skilled and semi-skilled occupations. In time, Canadian immigration policies came to focus on acquiring cheap labour from the newly decolonized nations of Asia, Africa and the Caribbean to work in sectors that the average Canadian citizen avoided. For example, black women from the English-speaking Caribbean filled the shortages in domestic services. There was also a need for professionals in the areas of education and medicine. Doctors, nurses, teachers and administrators were recruited to fill these shortages.

Most of today's immigrants to Canada come with savings, professional or skilled trade credentials and dreams of a better life for themselves and their families. Contrary to what some believe, they do not come to take advantage of the system, get welfare or cause trouble.

Despite their qualifications, the majority of immigrants face multiple barriers to employment in their fields (Canadian Task Force on Mental Health Issues, 1988). In Ontario, for example, foreign-trained teachers find the process of getting their credentials recognized lengthy and difficult, even though the province is short of teachers. It is often difficult for newcomers to find work in their field because they don't know anyone, don't have the right connections or don't have any Canadian experience. As a result, they are forced to work in marginal or menial positions that Canadians do not want. Here they work long hours, are paid less than they would earn in their field, and paid less than Canadians doing the same menial jobs, and may have to put up with racism in the workplace (as well as in the wider society).

Other newcomers arrive in Canada as refugees. Canada's refugee protection procedures are based on its international obligations as a member of the United Nations and its constitutional beliefs in a just and fair society. The goals of the 2002 *Immigration and Refugee Protection Act* include ensuring that:
• immigration and refugee protection remain a source of strength for Canada both socially and economically
• fairness and respect are promoted
• systems and processes are streamlined and efficient.

Most refugees who come to Canada have suffered at the hands of oppressive political regimes. Historically we think, for example, of the Asian Ugandans expelled by Idi Amin in the 1970s, the Hungarians who fled Communism in the 1950s, or the Russian Jews who fled pogroms earlier in the 20th century. Refugees may have been prisoners of conscience or victims of torture as a result of their opposition to oppressive regimes. Some refugees who come to Canada were arrested or detained in their home countries simply because they were in the wrong place at the wrong time. Some have witnessed the disappearance of family, friends or associates. Almost all have experienced or witnessed some form of traumatic event.

Most of the world's refugees are women and children. The majority of women who seek asylum in Canada are fleeing gender-based oppression such as sexual violence, domestic violence or sex slavery (African Canadian Coalition against Racism, 2002).

The health of many newcomers is impacted by experiences of trauma before they come to Canada and, after they arrive, by discrimination and racism, individual acts of rejection and an inability to find work in their area of training. To understand the health and human service needs of newcomers, we look at how the settlement process affects them and how their needs change over time.

The Settlement Process

The settlement process varies broadly and is shaped by the person's:
• abilities
• age
• class
• education
• race
• ethnicity
• religion
• gender
• sexual orientation
• occupational group
• existing links to communities in Canada
• reasons for moving.

For example, the experience of a young woman of colour from China who is sponsored by her husband differs vastly from that of a middle-aged white man from South Africa who comes on his own. The young woman has her husband and may also have extended family already living in Canada who can help her navigate Canadian society and find language classes, work or school. Because he speaks English, the South African man does not need language classes, but without the support of family or friends he may find the process of orienting to Canadian society daunting. If he does not have a job waiting (as is often the case) he may find the job search frustrating, especially if he was employed before immigrating and had not had to look for work in some time. The young woman is more likely to be the victim of overt racism. If she is, she may find this difficult to deal with, having spent her childhood in a homogeneous society. The white male is not likely to experience racism, but since he comes from a highly racialized society he may become anxious when he witnesses racism directed at others.

With refugees, other factors also play a role, for example:
• Did they arrive alone or in a group?
• Are they still waiting for a decision on their refugee claims?
• Have they spent time in refugee camps?
• Have they survived torture?

Newcomers settle at different rates, and experience the process of settlement at different levels of intensity. However, the following outline provides a general guide and will familiarize substance use counsellors with newcomers' experiences at various stages of the settlement process, and point out needs particular to each stage. Note that if the health and human service needs of newcomers are not met in the earlier stages of settlement, the resources required to meet their needs later will usually be greater. Some members of newcomer communities may not complete the settlement process due to systemic barriers, such as language and discrimination. Their children and sometimes even their grandchildren may continue to experience the settlement process.

FROM ARRIVAL TO SIX MONTHS AFTER ARRIVAL

Before moving to Canada, many people have conflicting feelings, such as expectations of happiness and success in their new home, but sadness about leaving friends and family behind. Almost all feel stress over the logistics of moving. Once they arrive, some newcomers have an initial sense of being on holiday, with a delight and fascination with their new home. Others may have culture shock, including a sense of displacement, a lack of context for understanding Canada and a lack of desire to get to know it. They may avoid and criticize things unique to their new country. Almost all experience both stress and excitement. Refugees may feel relief at escaping persecution or fear, but at the same time feel disoriented and confused (e.g., excited and happy but also preoccupied with safety).

This time is usually focused on basic things such as:
• creating a new home
• looking for work
• accessing schools and health care
• getting professional or vocational accreditation.

For some, learning English or French is important. Most newcomers experience a change in socioeconomic status. Some people find support and community through contact with others from the same background, while others connect with neighbours or colleagues at school or work.

Needs

Newcomers who access substance use services in this initial stage of settlement may also need:
• help in meeting their basic physical needs (e.g., work, shelter, food, clothing, transportation)
• information on professional or vocational accreditation or skills development
• language training
• legal advice or assistance through legal aid
• orientation to basic health and human services (e.g., hospitals, health centres, senior or youth groups)
• orientation to religious institutions, lifestyles, educational facilities, food shopping and child care
• recreational opportunities
• help in accessing financial institutions, or setting up a business
• information on cultural resources such as libraries, music programs or social clubs
• interpreter services, if they do not speak English or French.

Most refugees should have (but rarely receive) an assessment of pre-arrival experience (e.g., time spent in a refugee camp, family and friends left behind, experiences with violence or torture) to determine the type and scope of services they may need. They may also need help in determining if they need mental health services to help them deal with trauma.

FROM SIX MONTHS TO THREE YEARS AFTER ARRIVAL

During this period, some newcomers may feel they are on a "honeymoon." They remember the reasons why they came to Canada, and are happy for the move. But newcomers may also feel anxiety over separation from what is familiar, fear of further change and a sense of isolation. They may mourn the loss of their old life, lose self-esteem and feel that no one is interested in them, their country of origin or their life experiences. People who are new to Canada may experience a sense of disillusionment or embarrassment at not being able to achieve their goals or meet expectations. They may suppress anger and frustration over their perceived inability to cope in a new environment. For some, the initial reasons for the move may become unclear.

During this period, newcomers often want to achieve or contribute something in their new country. Some may want to sponsor family members to come to Canada and may encourage friends to emigrate. Most realize that a major shift has occurred in their lives and that they will need to continue to grow, change and adapt.

By now, some newcomers will have developed positive mechanisms for adapting to life in Canada (e.g., making new friends, getting involved with community or heritage groups), while others may have developed less useful mechanisms for coping with change (e.g., withdrawal from friends and family, problem substance use, idealization of their former home).

During this period, family roles may change in ways that reinforce the family structure (e.g., parents and children pull together to get a business off the ground), or in ways that undermine it (e.g., parents and children become "experts" on different things).

As refugees begin to experience safety, they may feel anxious about their separation from their home country. They may also feel guilty about leaving friends and family behind, and being safe when others at home may still be in danger. They are likely to have ongoing fears about their safety and well-being, and to fear further change. Some refugees become depressed. They may also feel extreme disappointment or anger over the indifference of Canada and Canadians to the events and economic or political situation in their home country. Often they do not express their feelings about this indifference.

Needs

Newcomers who come in contact with substance use services at this time may also need:
• to be reminded to recognize achievements in their life in their home country, such as professional credentials, life experiences and awards, and to be given information on how to draw on and apply these former achievements to their life in Canada
• help to identify and express unsettling thoughts and emotions
• validation of their experiences, including their experiences of loss

- help to find or create a peer/support group, and information on self-care and supporting family members
- encouragement to get involved in new challenges and activities
- help to realistically assess skills, resources and knowledge (e.g., they are not unqualified to work in Canada just because they got a rejection letter when they applied for a job)
- practical help and information to sponsor family members to come to Canada.

FROM THREE YEARS TO FIVE YEARS AFTER ARRIVAL

By now, most newcomers feel a permanent sense of disconnection from their old life. They realize they have shifted values, practices and norms. They feel a sense of resolution about the move, and feel identification and familiarity with their new home.

However, those who have not achieved what they had hoped, and feel frustrated about it, may be uncertain about themselves, their families and their future. Their resolve to stay may be weakened, and they may question their reasons for leaving their home country. Some desire to go back to visit, to make sure that leaving was the right thing to do.

Most newcomers pursue permanent connections to their new home (e.g., developing long-term career plans and plans for their children, getting involved in the community, establishing peer groups). Some, though, may continue to develop negative coping mechanisms and others may make connections while retaining some unproductive ways of coping.

Needs

Newcomers who access substance use services at this time may also need:

- help in connecting themselves and their families to communities, and in establishing goals and objectives
- continuing help in having their former achievements such as professional work, life experiences and awards recognized; in assessing their own skills, resources and knowledge; finding new challenges and activities; identifying unsettling thoughts and emotions and learning to express thoughts and emotions.

Trauma

Many newcomers, especially refugees, experience post-traumatic stress disorder (PTSD). PTSD may occur when a person has experienced or witnessed a traumatic event that was out of his or her control, and that involved physical harm, threat of harm or psychological distress. PTSD is a common co-occurring disorder in people with substance use problems.

Substance use counsellors working with refugee clients must be aware of the signs and symptoms of PTSD, such as:

- social isolation and withdrawal
- chronic fears

- depression
- overly dependent behaviour
- self-medication
- sleep disturbance
- physical complaints
- intrusive memories or flashbacks
- difficulty starting and maintaining meaningful relationships
- not knowing who to trust.

PTSD can lead to increased anxiety, to health problems such as cardiac and gastrointestinal pains, to difficulty coping with life and to suicide. People with both PTSD and substance use problems are in general at risk, but newcomers are even more so because of the additional daily stressors related to resettlement.

Women with PTSD and substance use problems have often experienced sexual and/or physical abuse and emotional neglect, and men tend to have experienced sexual and/or criminal victimization or war crimes (Marsella et al., 1996). Two themes emerge from these co-occurring disorders: secrecy and loss of control. Secrecy, because the newcomer feels ashamed and wants to keep his or her substance use and PTSD problems hidden; and loss of control, because the person feels powerless against the effects of the two disorders.

Newcomers with co-occurring substance use and PTSD are often aware that something is wrong, but because they lack trust and confidence in others, they may be afraid to reach out to mainstream health services. They are further prevented from accessing mainstream services by fears of being misunderstood (or not being understood because of language), of being labelled, of societal stigma, and of racism and other forms of discrimination.

The recommended approach for newcomers with concurrent substance use problems and PTSD integrates the treatment of the two disorders, and also takes into account the beliefs and behaviours of the newcomer client's culture (Marsella et al., 1996).

For more information on treating co-occurring trauma and substance use problems, please see Chapter 18.

Understanding Culture, Ethnicity and Race

People draw their identity from a number of different sources, such as ability, age, class, education, family relationships, gender/sexuality, geographic origins, language, peer groups, physical appearance/size, religion and spirituality. It is particularly helpful to understand how newcomer clients identify themselves in terms of their culture, ethnicity and race. Here is how we define these terms:

Culture is the totality of the beliefs, ideas, knowledge, myths, norms, practices and values of a group of people who share a common set of experiences (e.g., corporate culture, feminist culture, police culture). Everyone has a culture or set of cultures. Culture can change over a person's lifetime and people can belong to more than one culture at a time. Sometimes this can produce an internal conflict. For example, a lawyer who belongs to a lawyer culture but who is also a social activist and belongs to an activist culture may sometimes disagree with the laws he or she has to work within.

Ethnicity refers to a historical experience, place of origin or settlement process that is shared by a group of people (e.g., Acadians, Ashkenazic Jews, Kurds, Scots). Some indicators of ethnicity are a common culture, language, religion or spirituality.

Everyone has an ethnicity. Ethnicity may be hyphenated to reflect the experience of a particular historical or social context (e.g., Irish-Americans). Some people are of mixed ethnicities but identify with only one of them, while others identify with all their ethnicities.

Race is a social construction that classifies people according to what they look like (e.g., colour of skin, shape of eyes, texture of hair). It has led to the creation of ideologies and institutions that divide people along racial lines. Within these divisions, people of some races have been advanced and/or privileged based on the perceived attributes of their race, while others have been demoted or denigrated based on the perceived deficits of their race (Lee, 1985).

Newcomer communities, like other communities, are dynamic and diverse. Some members of a particular community may interpret their values, practices and beliefs narrowly, punitively and regressively, while others interpret the same values, practices and beliefs broadly, positively and progressively. Counsellors should consult and work with members of different communities to learn and identify what their needs are in terms of substance use services and related mental health services. Counsellors also need to recognize that while all people are different, sometimes that difference matters and sometimes it does not. Be aware of cultural, ethnic and racial differences. With each client, explore these differences and whether they are relevant. The following list points to common areas of difference, and gives questions to consider.

COMMON AREAS OF CULTURAL, ETHNIC AND RACIAL DIFFERENCE THAT CAN LEAD TO MISCOMMUNICATION

- **Attitudes toward feelings and emotions**: How acceptable is it to have feelings and express them? What feelings can or cannot be expressed (e.g., anger, joy)? How are they expressed?
- **Body language, personal distance and use of touch**: Is it acceptable, for example, to bow, break bread, make eye contact, greet, place chairs in a certain way or shake hands?
- **Forming relationships**: What period of time is considered appropriate to develop rapport, make friends or discuss a personal issue?
- **Gender roles and sexual orientation**: What roles do men and women play? Are they equitable? How are men and women expected to relate to each other? How are gays and lesbians viewed? What is the relationship of gays and lesbians to the larger social group?
- **Age, family and social group**: What privileges or limits do people have at certain ages? Why? What is the role of the family? Who has what responsibilities within the family? How do family members interact with each other? How do they interact

with the larger social group? What is the role of the social group? What are the components of the group? How are group members expected to relate to one another?

- **Personal and social boundaries**: What rules define what is private and what is public? What rules govern what may or may not be discussed, and with whom and in what context issues may be discussed? For example, sexuality may be openly discussed with members of both sexes within a family, but not with members of the same sex outside the family.
- **Values**: What things are valued (e.g., education, material goods, money, relationships, success at work)? To what extent are they valued? For example, is a PhD considered the ultimate accomplishment? If yes, why? Is it because a group has been marginalized that its members feel the need to have their children succeed?
- **Time**: What kind of time keeping is valued (e.g., punctuality, flexibility)?
- **Language, including intonation, and use of humour and metaphors**: Why are certain tones stressed? Why is something funny? Why are certain words or descriptions chosen? Why are certain images or references used?

SUBSTANCE USE PATTERNS IN DIFFERENT COMMUNITIES

Being aware of substance choices and patterns can be helpful when counselling newcomers.

People in different communities, newcomer or not, use alcohol and other drugs in various ways. For example, they may use drugs:
- recreationally (e.g., chewing khat, a vegetable with stimulant effects, after a dinner with friends)
- as part of a religious ceremony (e.g., drinking wine during communion)
- as a performance enhancer (e.g., chewing coca leaves to improve speed while hiking)
- as medicine (e.g., a hot toddy to treat a cold)
- to celebrate (e.g., giving a toast at a wedding)
- as part of an everyday meal (e.g., a glass of beer with dinner).

Different communities attach different meanings and rationales to substance use. In some groups, and especially in some newcomer groups, for example, "doctor knows best." If a doctor prescribes a medication such as a benzodiazepine, it is considered important to follow the doctor's orders. In other groups, cannabis is regarded as a holy substance intended for use during spiritual reflection.

Along with these meanings, there are rules, both spoken and unspoken, that govern substance use, including:
- who may consume what substances (e.g., men, women, youth, elderly people)
- when substances may be consumed (e.g., with lunch, after work, on weekends, during holidays)
- where substances may be consumed (e.g., at home, in a bar, at a social club, outdoors, indoors)

• why they are consumed (e.g., for relaxation, as a stress reliever, as a thirst quencher)
• how/with whom they are consumed (e.g., alone, with family, with friends).

These rules also indicate the effects that substances can be expected to have (e.g., it is acceptable to be happy and relaxed when drinking beer) and the penalties (e.g., being cut off) for showing unacceptable behaviours (e.g., being disorderly in a public place). Using certain substances may have cachet, whereas others carry stigma (e.g., drinking fine wine is sophisticated, but using heroin is unacceptable).

Substance Use Patterns in Newcomer Youth

The ways in which youth respond to the immigrant or refugee experience may affect their substance use patterns and help-seeking behaviours. They may:
• identify with the dominant group in the community in which they live (e.g., if they tend to drink socially with members of the larger community, they may not want addiction services that are specific to their newcomer communities)
• identify exclusively with their own community and not the larger community (e.g., "I'm not Canadian, so I'm not going to do what they do. I am not going to parties, I am not going to smoke. I don't need those services because I don't have those problems.")
• synthesize the values, practices and beliefs of both the community they come from and the community in which they live, and navigate between the different communities (e.g., "In my community it's okay for kids to have wine with their families but in Canada it's not. I'll still have some wine with my parents and, though my parents don't approve, I'll also have beers with my friends.")
• universalize experiences between their community and the larger community (e.g., "In our community everyone smokes a joint once in a while, just like everyone in your community takes pills of some sort, so it's no big deal.")
• become a "bridge" between members of their community (e.g., parents, peers) and the larger community (e.g., identify that a friend has a substance use problem and help that friend to seek help) (Crohn, 1994).

SUBSTANCE USE PROBLEMS IN NEWCOMERS

The reasons why a newcomer might develop a substance use problem are often the same as those for a member of a more established community. Contributing factors might include peer pressure, trauma, stress, social isolation, poverty, family breakdown, socializing or changes in employment or economic status. With newcomers however, the behaviours and experiences may be different. For them, social isolation may not mean living alone or being forgotten by family members, but instead may mean living in a newcomer community with few services and little contact with the larger Canadian society. Newcomers may experience poverty and unexpected changes in employment or economic status brought on by immigration.

Barriers to Accessing Services

Members of newcomer communities face significant barriers to accessing substance use and related mental health services. These include but are not limited to:
• shame and guilt about substance use (not knowing that a substance use problem is a health issue, not a moral issue)
• not wanting to be a burden on the health care system
• not knowing what services are available or what to expect from different services
• a lack of accurate information about substance use in the person's own language and from the perspective of his or her community
• a lack of community-specific prevention and treatment programs
• feeling responsible for "keeping it together" in the face of the upheaval caused by immigration
• a fear of ostracism from the community if the person discloses or discusses a substance use problem
• a fear that one's past experiences will not be believed or validated
• a fear of being seen as being a "bad" new Canadian or labelled a "bad export"
• a fear of losing a refugee claim because of a substance use problem
• a fear of being deported because of a substance use problem
• concerns about racism, stereotyping or discrimination against the person's community if he or she comes forward to seek help for a substance use problem.
    Some newcomers face additional barriers in seeking help. For example, it is not unusual for women who are newcomers to:
• be dependent on their partners to access services on their behalf, because they cannot speak the language
• have partners who are unable or unwilling to facilitate their access to services, causing further delay
• experience and tolerate physical and sexual abuse from partners who may use culture or religion to justify abusive behaviour
• feel guilt about seeking help, because they believe they should just be grateful for what they have in Canada (Crohn, 1994).

ROLES AND RESPONSIBILITIES IN COUNSELLING NEWCOMERS

When working with newcomers, substance use counsellors often need to take on roles that may not have been part of their work or training. Some counsellors may be unable or unwilling to play some or all of these additional roles due to agency mandate, professional ethics and boundaries, and service limitations. They may also be uncomfortable playing more than one role, because of a lack of appropriate professional training and experience. The counsellor may fear that he or she may do more harm than good to the client by taking on additional roles. If this is the case, the counsellor should link the client with others who can fulfil the necessary roles.

The following case study illustrates the many roles substance use counsellors may need to adopt when working with people from newcomer communities.

> Francesca is a Portuguese-speaking woman from Angola. A single mother, she left Angola during the war hoping to find safety. After spending three years in a refugee camp, she came to Canada with her daughter. Since arriving here two years ago, she has had problems finding an affordable apartment and is still living in transitional housing. Residents on her street frequently tell her and other refugees to go home; to stop getting a free ride in Canada. Francesca was a nurse in Angola and hopes to get her credentials recognized, but knows she does not have enough English to take the exams. Her daughter is struggling at school—the teacher is very supportive but Francesca does not understand the education system here and is frustrated that she cannot help her daughter with homework. She has difficulty sleeping at night and feels increasingly fearful and anxious during the day. Her family doctor prescribes Valium® and, after taking it for eight months, Francesca knows she is becoming dependent. She knows that she needs help but does not know where to go or what to expect when she gets there. Her family doctor refers her to a substance use service provider in a family counselling centre.

The counsellor who works with Francesca may see himself or herself as a therapist, with the job of helping Francesca to stop using Valium.

However, the counsellor also may have to adopt other roles, such as:
• a *shock absorber* who can help Francesca deal with the disparity between her expectations of life in Canada and the reality of that life
• a *detective* who can help her find clues in her past that may explain her fear and anxiety (e.g., witnessing war or experiencing torture)
• a *confidante* who talks with her about her past and links it to her present
• an *advocate* who can intervene on her behalf with housing providers
• a *transformer* who can help her see that while she is safer in Canada than in Angola, her substance use may prevent her from *feeling* safe
• a *motivator* who encourages her to study English as a second language so she can resume her career as a nurse
• a *guide* who can help her understand Canadian society, for example, the Canadian education system
• a *facilitator* who can help her make sense of the settlement process and the things she needs to do get her credentials recognized, as well as to respond to the anti-refugee hostilities she experiences
• a *cheerleader* who supports Francesca and shares her happiness when her daughter's marks improve (Galway 1991).

Francesca may also want the counsellor to assume roles that are not appropriate, such as those of:

• an *expert* who tells her what's best for her
• a *fixer* who solves her problems
• a *parent* who takes care of her
• a *rescuer* who saves her from herself and the world.

The counsellor needs to make Francesca aware that it is his or her job to empower her, not to undermine her by making her more dependent.

The substance use counsellor must also be aware of the power balance in the counsellor/client relationship and should consider the following questions:

• Is the counsellor a member of the dominant group (e.g., a white, middle-class, educated man)?
• Is the counsellor aware of the privileges of being a member of the dominant group?
• Does the counsellor consciously or unconsciously make Francesca feel grateful for the services provided?

Counselling Strategies for Working with Newcomers

When working with newcomer clients, it is important to be flexible and to re-interpret existing counselling strategies to meet clients' needs.

For example, an important strategy of cognitive behaviour therapy is that the client be the one to identify the need to make change. However, in some newcomer communities, that need may already have been identified by a family member who has encouraged the client to seek help. This same family member may accompany the client to appointments. Rather than assume that the client is not making change for himself or herself, the counsellor should enlist the family member as an ally and view him or her as enhancing the client's ability to move toward change. This family member can also become, at a later stage, a key player in helping the client develop relapse prevention strategies.

As well as re-interpreting existing counselling strategies, the counsellor should work to incorporate new approaches and models, including:

• education
• cultural enrichment/empowerment
• family counselling.

EDUCATION

An educational approach, focusing on prevention and early intervention, is based on the belief that people who know the health effects of substances will be less likely to use them in harmful ways. The counsellor explains in a non-judgmental way how substance use may affect well-being, and explains that use is a health issue, not a moral one.

CULTURAL ENRICHMENT/EMPOWERMENT

Newcomers who identify with positive aspects of their community, and have well-developed social networks in their community, may be less likely to have substance use issues. Taking this approach, the counsellor helps clients:

• identify aspects of their community that give them strength and support
• develop a strong community/self-image to rebuild their self-confidence
• share their strengths—for example, their experience, skills and wisdom—with the larger community.

The counsellor also encourages clients to tap into community resources that may help prevent, intervene in and treat substance use problems (e.g., discussing with a traditional healer factors that can contribute to substance use; participating in mind-body work such as yoga or Tai Chi to maintain or restore health; using acupuncture to ease withdrawal symptoms).

FAMILY COUNSELLING

Some newcomer communities have well-developed family structures and place great importance on the family. In these communities, the counsellor can look beyond helping the client identify situations where substance use problems arise. The counsellor can work with the client's family to examine both how family members may unintentionally contribute to the problems (e.g., by placing unreasonable expectations on the person) and how they can support the client's efforts to address the problems (e.g., by developing strategies to change the family dynamics). Counsellors should be aware that "family" can mean different things in different cultures, and may include extended family as well as close friends.

Case Management

Changing one's substance use is easier if basic needs are met. These include food, shelter and, for many newcomers, access to language training. Substance use counsellors should identify the client's needs and, if they are not being met, he or she should connect the client with services that can help. When referring clients, counsellors should prescreen services to ensure that they are appropriate. For example, when referring a Tamil-speaking woman with a background of abuse, counsellors should look for a service that provides addiction counselling in the woman's language, and that will also explore issues related to her abuse.

Newcomer clients may also need to be oriented to the types of services available, and coached on articulating their needs when they meet service providers. For example, a client looking for housing should know to say, in effect, "I am looking for housing that I can afford. I would like to know if there is a worker who may be able to help me look for such a place" (Grace, 1989).

CHECKLIST FOR EFFECTIVE COMMUNICATION

Providing services to newcomers may seem difficult at first. You may be concerned that you can't fully understand clients' needs because you are unaware of their experiences. You may worry about inadvertently offending them because you are unaware of their norms, values and practices. You may worry about not being able to provide them with adequate or appropriate services because you are of a different background. Your task, however, won't be difficult if you follow this basic checklist.

1. Remember that everyone has cultural, ethnic and racial assumptions and biases. Be aware of your own and try to put them on hold.

2. Remember that different people have different ways of expressing themselves.

3. Be patient; expect and anticipate different forms of self-expression and self-presentation. If in doubt, observe how clients interact with you and follow their lead.

4. Think about how you express yourself. How do you make others feel comfortable or safe? How might you inadvertently confuse or alienate others?

5. Learn to actively listen when the client speaks. Take all comments and concerns seriously, even if they have no apparent relationship to the issue at hand. Try to hear what the client is saying. Be sure to check your interpretation of what he or she says or doesn't say in a concerned or validating manner (for example, use phrases such as, "So you believe that you need. . . ."; "Your concern is. . . ."; "I understand that. . . ."; "You feel that. . . ."; "What can I do to make you more comfortable?"). Allow the client to correct you.

6. Learn to hear what the client is not saying; observe body language; be sensitive to silences—the client may be absorbing information or reflecting.

7. When communicating any sort of information, ask yourself:
   • Can the person hear me properly?
   • Am I using any words the person may not understand, such as jargon or colloquialisms?
   • Am I using gestures or body language that may make the person uncomfortable?
   • How familiar am I with his or her day-to-day life?
   • How well does the person understand English or French?
   • How familiar is he or she with the issues we are discussing?
   • How much can the person remember at once?
   • Is the person too shy or nervous to ask questions?

8. If possible, ask clients to explain their values, practices and norms.

9. If there is a language barrier, do not be afraid to use innovative means to communicate with clients (e.g., draw, refer to pictures in magazines, use props).

10. If difficulties arise, stop the situation or conversation for a few minutes and rest.

11. Remember that providing services to clients from diverse communities will become easier with practice.

12. Put yourself in the client's place: remember that you could be the one who is "different" and needing service (Sue et al., 1992).

Using an Interpreter

When working with newcomer clients you may need to provide service through an interpreter. In some cases you may be able to use a professional cultural interpreter who is specially trained to work with health and human service providers, or you may work with a settlement counsellor or community worker. These interpreters are usually familiar with the client's experiences and have a general knowledge of the services you offer.

In some cases a member of the client's family will act as an interpreter, or the newcomer may bring a religious or spiritual leader from his or her community—such as an imam, monk or priest—to speak on his or her behalf. These volunteer interpreters may be very familiar with the client's experiences, but not necessarily with your social context or your service models. In cases where the interpreter lacks knowledge of your services, make every effort ahead of time to explain the agency's service model in order to ensure the appropriate match for the client.

Sometimes addiction service providers may ask a multilingual staff member to act as a "lay interpreter." While this is acceptable in a crisis, it is not recommended on an ongoing basis unless that staff member understands the roles and responsibilities of an interpreter, has some basic interpreting skills and is comfortable with the role.

Remember that interpreters can also be facilitators, helping clients understand how your service can assist them. They can also help you understand what clients need, and why.

Community Resources

Services for newcomers are often fragmented due to lack of co-ordination, funding and communication, and are often strained by the ongoing arrival and settlement of newcomers. Being familiar with the resources for newcomers in your community will help you provide clients with comprehensive care. Listings for community resources can be found in service directories, phone books, community newspapers and information centres. Listed below are some types of services you may consider exploring. Also look for programming within these services that targets specific newcomer populations, such as women, youth and seniors.

• **Settlement services** provide support, language training, information, family and individual counselling, and general assistance during the settlement process.
• **Ethno-specific agencies** meet the social service needs of a particular community. Some serve large populations, and may be established and well resourced with large staffs; others serve smaller populations, have limited staff and resources, and depend on volunteers.
• **Multi-ethnic agencies** are specifically geared to meet the social service needs of several communities. Some may exclusively serve groups with a common geographic origin, language or race (e.g., a community health centre that serves the Asian-Canadian community) while others may serve as many populations as possible.

- **Literacy and English- or French-as-a-second-language services** provide language classes to newcomers, and are also meeting places where information can be exchanged and friendships made.
- **Training and development centres** provide life skills and professional training for unemployed or underemployed people, many of whom are members of newcomer communities.
- **Multi-service legal clinics** provide legal services, and often help clients obtain workers' compensation, social assistance benefits and housing.
- **Community information centres** serve as clearinghouses for community-based agencies, providing information about available services.
- **Interfaith groups and spiritual communities** provide a variety of social services to members of their faith and of other faith communities. Many are involved in refugee settlement work and social justice issues.
- **Cultural interpreter programs** facilitate understanding and provide linguistic and cultural translation between clients who do not speak English or French and their English- or French-speaking service providers.
- **Host programs** match "old" and "new" Canadians for an exchange of friendship and support.
- **Advocacy and education organizations** educate society about the social, political and economic issues that immigrants, refugees, in-settlement populations and minority groups face. They also advocate for social changes that will create more equity for these groups (Galway, 1991).

Guidelines to Facilitate Understanding between Counsellors and Newcomers

Addiction service providers have found the following guidelines helpful:
- Understand what creates a client's identity, including family of origin, geographic roots, religious and spiritual beliefs, socioeconomic status and lived experiences.
- Understand your own identity and your attitudes toward others.
- Understand the power and privilege that you bring to the counselling relationship.
- Make information about substance use problems and services available in the languages of the newcomer communities you serve.
- Learn the different beliefs, values and attitudes that different newcomer communities have toward substance use.
- When counselling, involve the client's beliefs, values and attitudes.
- Involve family and community members in counselling clients.
- Evaluate and revise how you work with newcomer clients on a regular basis.

CONCLUSION

This chapter provides substance use counsellors with some practical ways to work with newcomer communities. It is, however, only a guide—a starting point. Addiction counsellors must be open and willing to work with newcomers and to learn, grow and gain confidence from these experiences. Organizations must support counsellors in these efforts by changing their culture to be more inclusive. This can be achieved through training and education, the recruitment of diverse board members, staff and volunteers, and the development of partnerships and programs within different newcomer communities.

REFERENCES

African Canadian Coalition against Racism (ACCAR). (2002). *Challenging Anti-Black Racism in Canada*. Toronto: author.

Building Bridges, Breaking Barriers Access Project. (2003). *Internal Assessment Report*. Toronto: Canadian Heritage and Centre for Addiction and Mental Health.

Canadian Task Force on Mental Health Issues Affecting Immigrants and Refugees in Canada. (1988). *After the Door Has Opened: Mental Health Issues Affecting Immigrants and Refugees in Canada—A Report*. Ottawa: Health Canada.

Crohn, J. (1994). *Mixed Matches*. Berkeley: University of California Press.

Galway, J. (1991). *Immigrant Settlement Counselling*. Toronto: Ontario Council of Agencies Serving Immigrants.

Grace, C.A. (1989). Practical considerations for program professionals working with African American communities. In M.A. Orlandi (Ed.), *Cultural Competence for Evaluators: A Guide for Alcohol and Other Drug Abuse Prevention Practitioners Working with Ethnic/Racial Communities* (pp. 54–74). Rockville, MD: U.S. Department of Health and Human Services.

Immigrant and Visible Minority Women of Saskatchewan. (2002). *Post Traumatic Stress Disorder: The Lived Experiences of Immigrant, Refugee and Visible Minority Women*. Regina, SK: author.

Lee, E. (1985). *Letters to Marcia: A Teacher's Guide to Anti-Racist Education*. Toronto: Cross-Cultural Communications Centre.

Marsella, A.J., Friedman, M.J., Gerrity, E.T. & Scurfield, R.M. (Eds.). (1996). *Ethnocultural Aspects of Posttraumatic Stress Disorder: Issues, Research and Clinical Applications*. Washington, DC: American Psychological Association.

Office of the High Commissioner for Human Rights, United Nations. (1951). *Convention Relating to the status on Refugees*. Geneva: author. Available: www.unhchr.ch/html/menu3/b/o_c_ref.htm.

Statistics Canada. (2003, January 21). *The Daily*. Available: www.statcan.ca/Daily/English/030121/d030121a.htm.

Sue, D.W., Arrendondo, P. & McDavis, R.J. (1992). Multicultural counseling competencies and standards: A call to the profession. *Journal of Counseling and Development, 7*(March/April), 477–486.

Chapter 20

Addiction and Aboriginal Healing

PETER MENZIES

INTRODUCTION

There is growing evidence that problem substance use among Aboriginal people is symptomatic of broader systemic issues. This evidence suggests that the colonization of Aboriginal people has resulted in personal, familial and community trauma, and that substance use may be one manifestation of this trauma.

Aboriginal people and some mainstream service agencies are addressing these issues by implementing holistic treatment strategies. These efforts build on indigenous healing methods and help both the individual and the community to sustain long-term health. Culturally congruent service delivery requires the counsellor's commitment to develop an understanding of a client's cultural history, values, beliefs and norms, and to join him or her in a change process. This process may involve engaging other community members, including Elders, in the healing process. Healing thus becomes not just an individual process, but a community development effort.

PREVALENCE OF SUBSTANCE USE AND MENTAL HEALTH ISSUES AMONG ABORIGINAL PEOPLE

The increasing need for Aboriginal addiction and mental health support services is evidenced by the following facts:
• The rate of suicide among First Nations people is 2.1 times that of the general Canadian population (Health Canada, 2003).

- A 1999 health survey of First Nations and Inuit people found that poisoning and accidents accounted for 40 per cent of the deaths of First Nations males (Health Canada, 2003).
- Alcohol-related deaths are 43.7 per 100,000 for Aboriginal people, compared with 23.6 per 100,000 for the general population (Canadian Medical Association, 1994).
- Aboriginal youth are two to six times more at risk for alcohol-related problems than non-Aboriginal youth (Health Canada, 1999).
- Of the 1,500 Aboriginal people receiving substance use treatment annually, the majority receive it for use of alcohol, narcotics or hallucinogens (in order of use, from highest to lowest use; Scott, 1994).
- Evidence of high levels of depression, accompanied by failure to achieve, has been identified among children in many Aboriginal communities (Canadian Medical Association, 1994).
- Service providers report a large number of Aboriginals with concurrent disorders, whom the system is not serving well (Metro Toronto District Health Council, 1996).
- It is estimated that more than 25 per cent of people without shelter living on the streets of Toronto are Aboriginal (Metro Toronto District Health Council Native Steering Committee, 1996).
- A recent study of Downtown Eastside Vancouver found that the community's residents had the worst health status in Canada, with Aboriginal residents at the greatest risk for disease (Adilman & Kliewer, 2000).

HISTORY OF ABORIGINAL PEOPLE IN CANADA

Identity

The term "Aboriginal" generally refers to the original inhabitants of North America and their descendants. However, while most people or communities define themselves as belonging to a particular ethnic group based on place of birth or residence, language, cultural practices and beliefs, the definition of "Aboriginal" has largely been imposed by statute.

Prior to European contact, Aboriginals had (and still have) ethnically diverse languages, cultural practices and belief systems. However, European settlers found it easier to identify them as a single ethnic group—a person was either Indian or white. Frideres (1998) notes that understanding who was "Aboriginal" was based on both biological and cultural factors, including:

- who their birth parents were
- where they lived
- their language

- their mode of dress
- their patterns of behaviour
- their belief system.

STATUTORY DESIGNATIONS

Status and Non-status Indians

The *Indian Act* of 1876 codified the above factors, designating as "status" Indians those whom the federal government recognized as having treaty rights, and as "non-status" Indians those who did not. These designations ignored members of "mixed race" and disenfranchised women with non-Aboriginal husbands (Mawhiney, 1994).[1] The *Indian Act* continues to apply these "status" and "non-status" designations, consequently limiting which members of the community can "enjoy" benefits provided under the Act. Restoule (2000) observes that "(t)his definition has had a profound impact not only in how we are understood by non-Aboriginal people, but also in how we have come to understand ourselves" (p. 106).

Metis

"Metis" is another designation under the *Indian Act*. It refers to people of mixed Aboriginal and European descent. Historically, only Metis who lived on reserves could claim Indian status, and then only if the reserve agreed (Frideres, 1998). The federal government relinquished responsibility to the provinces for all other Metis people. As a result, many Metis formed their own distinct communities and developed political and economic institutions reflecting their distinct heritage (Frideres, 1998). Metis people's place of residence and cultural practices distinguish them from non-status Indians, and recognition of Metis status continues to be treated differentially across Canada's provinces and territories.

Inuit

Inuit people (historically referred to as "Eskimo") form the fourth group of Canada's Aboriginal people. Although they are referred to collectively as "Inuit," language, cultural practices and belief systems are distinct within many Inuit communities. Though after 1867 the Inuit were placed under federal jurisdiction, they continue to be distinct from those defined as "Indian" under the *Indian Act*.

Increasingly, Canada's Aboriginal people are asserting their right to identify membership from within their own communities rather than allowing membership to be imposed. This includes removing what has become pejorative nomenclature, such as "Indian," from the community's vocabulary. In 1985 Bill C31 was passed, removing the sexual discrimination inherent in the *Indian Act* and allowing for the repatriation of women who had married non-Aboriginal men, enfranchised Aboriginal people, as well as their descendants. As this new millennium unfolds, Aboriginal people are increasingly renewing ties with their families of origin and developing links to their historical roots.

IDENTITY AND CURRENT POPULATION DATA

Evidence that more and more Aboriginal people are identifying with their heritage is found in significant trends in Canada's population data. According to the 2001 census data, more than 1.3 million people identified their ancestry as linked to the Aboriginal peoples of Canada. Just under 1 million people claimed Aboriginal identity, a 22 per cent increase from the previous census data (See Table 20-1).

TABLE 20-1

Reporting Aboriginal Ancestry and Aboriginal Identity, Canada: 1996–2001

	1996	2001	% GROWTH
Total: Aboriginal ancestry	1,101,960	1,319,980	19.8
Total: Aboriginal identity	799,010	976,305	22.2
North American Indian	529,040	608,850	15.1
Metis	204,115	292,310	43.2
Inuit	40,220	45,070	12.1
Multiple and other Aboriginal responses	25,640	30,080	17.3

Source: Statistics Canada (2003).

As Canada's fastest-growing group, the Aboriginal population's median age is 13 years less than that of the rest of Canadians (see Table 20-2). This is due to a higher birth rate and lower life expectancy for Aboriginal adults.

TABLE 20-2

Reporting Aboriginal Identity by Age Groups, Canada: 1996–2001

	1996		2001	
	NUMBER	%	NUMBER	%
Total	799,101	100	976,305	100.0
0–14 years	280,420	35.1	323,960	33.2
15–24 years	143,795	18.0	169,065	17.3
25–64 years	346,485	43.4	443,600	45.4
65 years and over	28,310	3.5	39,680	4.1

Source: Statistics Canada (2003).

While the percentage of people reporting Aboriginal ancestry grows, the number of people who can speak an Aboriginal language is falling. In 2001, only 24 per cent of Aboriginal people said they could speak an Aboriginal language, a decline of 5 per cent from 1996. This decline may be explained in part by settlement patterns.

In 2001, 49 per cent of the Aboriginal population reported living in urban areas (up from 47 per cent in 1996) while the number of Aboriginal people living on First Nations reserves dropped to 31 per cent from 33 per cent. The trend in migration to urban centres is detailed below.

TABLE 20-3

Aboriginal People Living in Major Metropolitan Census Areas, 1951–2001

CMA	1951	1961	1971[1]	1981	1991[2]	1996[3]	2001
Halifax	–	–	–	–	1,185	2,115	–
Montreal	296	507	3,215	14,450	6,775	9,965	11,085
Ottawa-Hull	–	–	–	4,370	6,915	11,605	13,485
Toronto	805	1,196	2,990	13,495	14,205	16,095	20,300
Winnipeg	210	1,082	4,940	16,575	35,150	45,750	55,755
Regina	160	539	2,860	6,575	11,020	13,605	15,685
Saskatoon	48	207	1,070	4,350	11,920	16,160	20,275
Calgary	62	335	2,265	7,310	14,075	15,195	21,915
Edmonton	616	995	4,260	13,750	29,235	32,825	40,930
Vancouver	239	530	3,000	16,080	25,030	31,140	36,860

Notes:

1 Data do not include Inuit population.

2 Includes individuals who identified with an Aboriginal group in the Aboriginal Peoples Survey.

3 Does not include enumeration of Kanesatake or Kahnawake reserves within the Montreal CMA.

Sources: Statistics Canada (1981,1993, 1998a, 2003); Information Canada (1974); Long & Dickason (1996).

It is estimated that by 2016, Canada's urban Aboriginal population will total almost half a million people (Statistics Canada, 1998b). The Aboriginal profile within urban centres is distinct from that on reserves. Consider the following:

• Aboriginal people are much younger than the general population, with one out of three Aboriginal people under 15 years of age (Statistics Canada, 1998b).

• Single-parent families constitute nearly half of all migrants from First Nations reserves to Canada's urban centres (Royal Commission on Aboriginal Peoples (RCAP) [3], 1996).

• Young teenagers represent 35 per cent of the total number of people leaving reserves to settle in urban centres (RCAP [3], 1996).

Social conditions on reserves (i.e., limited housing, limited employment and educational opportunities, and limited access to health care and social services) are generally cited as the main stimulus for people leaving the reserves (RCAP, [4], 1993).

Historical Relationships in Aboriginal Communities

The social conditions described above exist as a result of the historical relationship between Aboriginal people and the federal government. Prior to European contact, Aboriginal people lived together in clans or communities across North America. Ample evidence exists to substantiate the importance of the extended family in sustaining traditional Aboriginal life (Red Horse, 1980); survival required that each member, including children, make a contribution to the well-being of the family.

Young children were cared for by older community members while their parents were hunting, farming or preparing meals (van de Sande, 1995). Children were encouraged through storytelling and experience to respect the natural world around them. Older people helped young parents develop appropriate techniques to help children fulfil their own role in the community (Horesji & Pablo, 1993). Women were highly regarded for their role in bringing new life into the community; they also participated in community decision making (Bull, 1991).

Decisions regarding the community were reached by consensus rather than through a central power base. The person with the most knowledge or experience was sought out to address particular issues. Older community members had a special place of honour. As oral teachings were the primary instrument in the transmission of knowledge and information to other members, Elders had a vital role in the community as the "keepers" of this knowledge. These roles and values were designed to promote harmony in the extended family and the community (Horesji & Pablo, 1993).

European Migration and Aboriginal Communities

In the 1500s these natural systems of support were challenged by European missionaries and traders, who introduced new values into the communities and undermined their balanced relations. The roles of women, children and Elders were challenged, and Aboriginal men were encouraged to assume a dominant role, regardless of experience, skill or knowledge (Bull, 1991).

In the early 1800s the elimination of the buffalo by Europeans created widespread famine in Western Canada. Epidemics compounded by severe droughts led to the deaths of thousands of Aboriginal people (Bull, 1991). Traditional life was threatened by the elimination of the economic and social structures that had existed for thousands of years (Good Tracks, 1973). The strategic partnerships that had evolved between Aboriginal communities and the French and English military during the period preceding the War of 1812 were no longer required. As the British prepared for the expansion of Western settlement, they relocated Aboriginal people from fertile lands to other, more remote areas. Furniss (1991) suggests that:

> Indian-European relations shifted from ones of strategic partnership to ones of direct, open competition for land and resources. Indians now were viewed as obstacles to the country's development. In regions of intense Indian-white conflicts over land, settlers began to generate racist discourses and calls for government assistance in suppressing the Indian populations (p. 19).

To aid the expansion of settlement, British policy focused on efforts to "civilize the native peoples of the Empire" (Scott-Brown, 1987).

In the 1900s industrialization spread across Europe, changing economic and social systems and concepts of family life. As European migration increased across Canada, many Aboriginal traditions were forcefully challenged through government policies and Christian practices (Cross, 1986). Aboriginal culture was seen as barbaric (Palmer & Cooke, 1996). Proulx & Perrault (2000) summarize the decline of community life:

> The cohesive aspects of Aboriginal life diminished as traditional customs and spirituality were forbidden. The collectives of family and community, and the sense of relationship with all people and all of nature were disrupted. The Elders' place in the community was negated through restrictions on cultural teachings. The extended family and sense of community was de-emphasized, while a focus on the nuclear family and individualism was accentuated. European ideas of superiority of humans over all other living things were promoted (p. 16).

Over this time, the Canadian government introduced policies to address the "Indian problem." Specifically, the *Indian Act*, the residential school system and child welfare legislation fulfilled a role in promoting the assimilation of Aboriginal people into Canadian society.

THE *INDIAN ACT*

The *Indian Act* of 1876 ("the Act") established the federal government as the "guardian" of Aboriginal people. When first introduced, the Act established a power relationship between the government and Aboriginal people, setting out:

• where Aboriginal people could live
• what traditional ceremonies they could practise
• what support they would receive from government agencies
• how they could interact with others outside of the community (Mawhiney, 1994).

The Act created a hierarchy of decision-making authorities within these artificial settlements (reserves) that did not reflect traditional values and practices. The Act essentially became a "legislative straightjacket" (RCAP [1], 1996) controlling the daily lives of Aboriginal people.

In 1951 the federal government amended the Act to allow provincial social service agencies to act on behalf of the federal government. These amendments allowed for "buck passing" of jurisdictional responsibility for programs and services to Aboriginal people (RCAP, 1993); federal and provincial governments passed responsibility for social programming back and forth, often to the detriment of those who relied on these programs, especially Aboriginal people living off-reserve and in urban communities. In response to calls from women's rights groups and Aboriginal leaders, the *Constitution Act* of 1982 introduced changes that entrenched existing Aboriginal rights and granted equality to Aboriginal women (Krosenbrink-Gelissen, 1998).

RESIDENTIAL SCHOOLS

The Act has allowed for the institutionalization of Aboriginal people in a manner unrivalled in Canadian history. Recognizing the importance of education in the transmission of social values, the government used institutions, including the Church, to force widespread social change on Aboriginal communities. Between 1840 and 1983, it is estimated that over one million Aboriginal children were placed in the residential school system (United Church of Canada, 1994). Over 100,000 residential school survivors currently live in Canada (Assembly of First Nations, 1994). The Assembly of First Nations chronicled the role of residential schools in relation to changing government policy concerning Aboriginal people. They found that the government used the schools, over time, for three different purposes: assimilation, segregation and integration.

Assimilation (1840–1910)

In 1842, the Bagot Commission (a group led by Charles Bagot and appointed by the federal government to study and make recommendations about the reserves) reported that conditions on reserves in Upper Canada could be improved only if Aboriginal people acquired "industry and knowledge" (Hodgson, 1990). The Commission recommended the introduction of a European education system to help prepare young Aboriginals for jobs in the industrial sector. Premised on the assumption that Aboriginal people needed to unlearn their "savage ways" and join the "civilized life" (Hodgson, 1990), various Christian churches established schools in Aboriginal communities with funding from the federal government. Aboriginal children on reserves were indoctrinated into Christianity, forced to speak only English or French and taught subjects that had no relevance to their traditional way of life. Corporal punishment was widely used to enforce rules and reshape behaviour.

Federal Indian agents, designated by the *Indian Act* to make decisions on behalf of Aboriginal people living on reserves (Ing, 1991), used their authority to remove children as young as three years old from the care of their families (RCAP, [1], 1996). In 1879, the Davin Report recommended establishing boarding schools to further remove children from their home communities and isolate them from the "damaging" influence of their parents and older family members. According to the Royal Commission on Aboriginal Peoples (1996), the creation of residential boarding schools for Aboriginal children helped the Canadian government implement its plans to assimilate Aboriginal people into the new society:

> Marching out from the schools, the children, effectively re-socialized, imbued with the values of European culture, would be the vanguard of a magnificent metamorphosis: the "savage" was to be made "civilized," made fit to take up the privileges and responsibilities of citizenship (RCAP, [1] 1996, 335).

By 1892 the federal government was providing significant funding to various religious groups to run these schools. Reports of overcrowding, tuberculosis, lack of cleanliness and poor sanitation were common, as were high death rates. Bagot's desire to create institutions that prepared Aboriginal children for industry took on a new light when the children were forced to grow produce not only for themselves, but also for the institutions to sell. Without adequate capital funding, buildings were constructed of substandard materials; meagre maintenance budgets did not allow for adequate heating and ventilation in some facilities. Having the children do much of the required labour reduced operating costs (RCAP, [1], 1996).

In 1907 the Bryce Report detailed the appalling conditions at the schools. The high rates of death—up to 40 per cent in one B.C. school—reflected the poor conditions at many facilities (RCAP, [1], 1996). Miller (1987) indicates not only that the schools failed to provide proper nutrition and care for the children, but that few were able to attain the level of education required for children to find success in mainstream Canadian society.

While residential schools may not have helped Aboriginal children achieve academic success, they were effective instruments of colonization. Because they were forced to communicate only in English or French, the children quickly lost the ability to speak their native language. Spiritual rituals practised for thousands of years were forbidden and replaced by rituals propagated by missionaries, who considered Aboriginals "pagans." Traditional teaching methods, including oral history and modelling by older members of the community, were replaced by a curriculum that emphasized reading, writing and arithmetic, skills of little value to children returning to communities that relied on knowledge of the land for survival. Traditional Aboriginal values emphasizing community sharing and respect for the natural environment were replaced by values emphasizing personal achievement, domination and control. Unable to practise their own culture or to connect to the culture imposed on them, Aboriginal children found themselves not belonging to any culture: "More and more Indians who had been through the residential schooling experience found themselves caught between two ways of life, comfortable in neither and not always welcome in either" (Miller, 1987; p. 8). Community and family bonds weakened and in many cases were severed, as children returned to homes that felt foreign to them.

Segregation (1910–1951)

By the turn of the 20th century, increased immigration into Canada reduced the need for skilled workers (Assembly of First Nations, 1994) and the rationale for the schools shifted from assimilation (ensuring Aboriginal people could provide low-wage labour) to an indifference that resulted in segregation. The schools during this time were so negligent toward Aboriginals that students had no skills on graduating and had no choice but to return to their home communities (Assembly of First Nations, 1994).

In the 1920s Aboriginal people realized the significant impact that residential schools had on family life and community well-being. High death rates in the schools continued; and according to Grant (1996), were five times higher than the rates for children attending non-Aboriginal schools. Many children who survived felt that they no longer belonged to their birth communities and did not return home (Miller, 1987). When parents attempted to prevent their children from attending residential schools, the federal government made attendance compulsory for Aboriginal children between six and 18 (Claes & Clifton, 1997). Threatening withdrawal of food rations and financial support from non-compliant reserves, officials used their authority to remove children from their home communities, sometimes without their parents' knowledge (Miller, 1987). In 1931 there were just over 755 children in residential schools, but by the 1940s attendance had increased to more than 8,000 children (York, 1989).

During this time, Aboriginal children did not receive the same level of education as non-Aboriginal children; few were educated beyond a Grade-8 level. Most of the day was spent on physical labour and religious instruction. Teachers were often not qualified or lacked the knowledge required by the government curriculum (United Church of Canada, 1994). With such inadequate education, "graduates" could not find employment in mainstream society and were forced to return to their home communities.

Integration (1950s)

In the late 1940s, for economic reasons, the federal government decided that some responsibilities for Aboriginal people (including education and child welfare) should be transferred to the provinces. The *Indian Act* was amended accordingly.

Haig-Brown (1988) suggests that this marked a turning point in federal Aboriginal policy, which resulted in enforced assimilation through the integration of children in the public school system. In the 1950s, Aboriginal children were permitted to attend secular schools near their reserves. Barman et al. (1996) add that "The federal goal became immediate Indian integration—to its critics, cultural assimilation in a new guise—into the dominant society through education" (p. 13).

Political wrangling regarding funding of social programs had a significant impact on Aboriginal families. Instead of dealing with one authority, Aboriginal families faced the scrutiny of two levels of government, and had difficulty accessing benefits. By 1966, approximately 75 per cent of Aboriginal children in residential schools were considered to be from "unfit" homes (Johnston, 1983). These children were referred to welfare or corrections services (RCAP, [1], 1996; Grant, 1996). According to Claes et al. (1997) "by the 1950s, residential schools were being used to serve substantial child welfare and social development purposes as well as educational functions" (p. 15).

The federal government continued to fund residential schools in rural or remote communities. However, staffing of these schools was transferred to secular administration, and teachers became government employees (Assembly of First Nations, 1994). In 1969, the federal government withdrew from its partnership with the churches in residential schools. The last residential school in Canada—in New Christie near Tofino, B.C.—closed in 1983 (Claes et al., 1997).

CHILD WELFARE

With the integration of Aboriginal children into the public school system, child welfare became the new instrument of government assimilation policies in the '50s and '60s. Many studies indicate a disproportionate number of Aboriginal children taken into care by child welfare authorities (Sanders, 1978; Hepworth, 1980), with other studies identifying how the child welfare system decimated Aboriginal communities across Canada (Johnston, 1983).

From 1951 until the late 1960s, the federal government argued with the provinces over financial responsibility for Aboriginals who lived off-reserve. As a result, these Aboriginal families were unable to secure social benefits, including welfare and housing. The interim agreement struck between the two levels of government provided that the needs of Aboriginal children would be met only if the government staff involved reported a life-or-death situation (Timpson, 1990).

No preventative measures were implemented to minimize the impact of this funding vacuum, and families faced a plethora of social issues without resources. In response, the government adopted a crisis intervention approach to child welfare. Johnston (1983) introduced the phrase "the '60s scoop" to identify the overwhelming number of Aboriginal children permanently removed from their homes and communities during this period and placed in foster care or made Crown wards (Andres, 1981; Johnston, 1983; Richard, 1989; Timpson, 1990).

Kimmelman's (1984) inquiry into adoptions and placement of Manitoba's First Nations and Metis children validated Johnston's findings, confirming Aboriginal people's claims that their communities were being destroyed by a child welfare system operating under the guise of providing for the "best interests" of the children. More recent studies by Kendrick (1990) and Warry (1991) provide disturbing evidence that a high proportion of Aboriginal children continue to be apprehended by child welfare authorities. The 1996 Royal Commission on Aboriginal Peoples concluded that the percentage of First Nations children in care is six times that of the general population. To compound this situation, the Commission found that placement of children in non-Aboriginal foster care homes has been as high as 90 per cent in some provinces (RCAP, [3], 1996). Children sent for adoption to the United States and Europe felt even more intense isolation from family and from their Aboriginal identity (Bagley et al., 1993). Lederman (1999) observes:

Children's Aid Societies perpetuated the same belief as residential schools: that a well-meaning white, cultural institution was better than a Native child's family and community. Many, perhaps even most, of the child welfare workers were compassionate and well-intentioned. But, however well-meaning Children's Aid Society intrusions may have been, they further continued the traumatization of Native people and likely compounded it (p. 64).

By 1969, widespread demonstrations and co-ordinated efforts by Aboriginal groups prevented further federal devolution of responsibilities for Aboriginal programs and services to the provinces and territories, as proposed in the federal government's White Paper (Timpson, 1990). However, by that time the child welfare system was well established as a new instrument of colonization (Armitage, 1993; Hudson, 1981).

THE LEGACY OF COLONIALISM: SUBSTANCE USE AND MENTAL HEALTH PROBLEMS IN ABORIGINAL COMMUNITIES

As instruments of colonization, the *Indian Act*, residential school and child welfare systems left many Aboriginal people without the resources required to build healthy communities (Deiter, 1999).

Child welfare studies describe the long-term effects of removing Aboriginal children from their birth family and placing them in non-Aboriginal homes (Couchi & Nabigon, 1994; Frideres, 1998; Locust, 1999). Warry (1991) reported that as these children matured, they became "apples": racially "red," or Aboriginal, on the outside, but culturally "white" on the inside. Locust (1999) used the term "split feathers" to describe the long-term psychological problems of these children. Gagne (1998) proposes that colonialism has been the "seed of trauma" for many First Nations communities and has left a legacy of dependency for many individuals and communities.

As adults, former residential school students and child welfare system survivors have demonstrated rates of problem substance use, anxiety disorders, depression, suicide and low self-esteem that are significantly higher than those of the general population (Beisner & Attneave, 1982; Gagne, 1998; Hodgson, 1990; Mussell, Nicholls & Adler, 1991). In its study of issues related to the delivery of mental health services to Native Americans in Washington State, the Swinomish Mental Health Project (1991) found that even "healthy" people may experience a "sense of personal doom" that prevents them from fully actualizing themselves:

The sense of personal doom is far more than a passive acceptance of nega-tive life circumstances. It is a powerful self image with an almost mythic dimension: certain Indian people feel personally destined to a life of tragedy, failure and early death (p. 54).

It is important to understand how the loss of connection to culture and the erosion of communities have contributed to the higher rates of substance use among Aboriginal people. McCormick (2000) notes that "[f]or many Aboriginal people, consumption of alcohol has been their attempt to deal with the state of powerlessness and hopelessness that has arisen due to the devastation of traditional cultural values" (p. 27).

Intergenerational Trauma

While post-traumatic stress and associated disorders usually focus on the direct or individual impact, recent studies on Aboriginal communities note that trauma has affected more than one generation within families and communities (Braveheart-Jordan & De Bruyn, 1995; Lederman, 1999; Phillips, 1999; Waldram, 1997). In a review of morbidity factors in Aboriginal communities, Waldram (1997) notes that "[t]he current state of affairs can be clearly linked to the traumatic effects of colonialism, including geographic and economic marginalization, and attempts at forced assimilation" (p. 184).

The removal of children from the home for long periods of time diminished opportunities for the intergenerational transmission of family values, parenting knowledge and community behaviour (Payukotayno, 1988; van de Sande, 1995). Grant (1996) suggested that without appropriate parenting models, many Aboriginal parents lacked the necessary knowledge to raise their own children, and instead introduced them to dysfunctional models of behaviour (Brant, 1990; van de Sande, 1995). The legacy of residential schools includes parenting models based on punishment, abuse, coercion and control (Hudson, 1981; Proulx & Perrault, 2000).

As a result, Napier (2000) concluded, "the bonds between many hundreds of Aboriginal children and their families and nations were bent and broken, with disastrous results" (p. 3). Hodgson (1990) summarized the cumulative impact across generations:

> If you subject one generation to that kind of parenting and they become adults and have children, those children become subjected to that treatment and then you subject a third generation to a residential school system the same as the first two generations. You have a whole society affected by isolation, loneliness, sadness, anger, hopelessness and pain (p. 17).

Phillips (1999) summarizes the intergenerational impact of trauma:

> If we do not deal with our trauma, we inadvertently hand it down to the next generation. We often take out our pain and hurt on those we love the

most—which is ourselves, and those closest to us—our family and friends. So, intergenerational trauma is trauma that is passed down behaviourally to the next generation: if we're angry and act angry all the time to others, our kids will think that's normal and do the same. If we ignore each other and deprive each other of love and affection in our relationships, our kids see and feel that deprivation of love and might think it's normal (p. 6).

Gagne (1998) identified the residential school experience as a key component within the cycle of trauma experienced by Aboriginal people. In a discussion of the socio-logical causes of intergenerational trauma among First Nations people, Gagne (1998) concluded that the effect of the residential school experience has been felt beyond the generation that attended the school: "At least two subsequent generations were also 'lost.' The children of these students became victims of abuse as their parents became abusers because of the residential school experience" (p. 363).

Both mainstream and Aboriginal health practitioners are challenging the *Diagnostic and Statistical Manual (DSM)* diagnosis of post-traumatic stress disorder (Waldram, in press), which ignores the role of culture and intergenerational or com-munity trauma and does not connect a person's experience to broader, systemic conditions that perpetuate and exacerbate it. Waldram (in press) suggests that "Approaching trauma through *DSM* by and large precludes a meaningful discussion of culture, and virtually excludes notions of history and collective, community or cultural trauma" (p. 41). Root (1992) suggests that racism and discrimination compound the impact of direct or personal trauma by allowing for the oppression of a community. This "insidious trauma" becomes "normalized" to the point that the group does not realize that social conditions continue to oppress them. Rather than being focused on a singular event that makes the individual feel unsafe, this insidious trauma leads to a view that the world is an unsafe place for a whole group of people (Root, 1992). Dutton (1998) adds that this "matrix of traumatic experiences . . . may shape the lived experience of a person within a given cultural group" (p. 1.).

Kirmayer et al. (2000) concur that the focus on individual trauma does not ade-quately reflect the Aboriginal experience. The authors suggest:

> The emphasis on narrating personal trauma in contemporary psycho-therapy is problematic because many forms of violence against Aboriginal people are structural or implicit and so may remain hidden in individual accounts. . . . Individual events are part of larger historical formations that have profound effects for both individuals and communities (Kirmayer et al., 2000, p. 613).

Duran & Duran (1995) concur with this assessment in their study of Native Americans in the United States. Critical of the focus on the individual diagnosis, they note that "the diagnostic process never takes a historical perspective" (p. 52). The authors advance the argument that many Native Americans are suffering from inter-generational post-traumatic stress disorders:

Many of the problems facing Native American people today—such as alcoholism, child abuse, suicide, and domestic violence—have become part of the Native American heritage due to the long decades of forced assimilation and genocidal practices implemented by the federal government (Duran & Duran , 1995, p. 35).

Kirmayer et al. (2000) present similar arguments in their review of a range of mental health studies of Aboriginal communities across Canada. They conclude that:

Individual events are part of a larger historical formation that has profound effects for both individuals and communities—effects that are harder to describe. These damaging events were not encoded as declarative knowledge but rather "inscribed'" on the body or else built into ongoing social relations, roles, practices and institutions (p. 613).

TOWARD AN ABORIGINAL MODEL FOR HEALTH CARE SERVICE DELIVERY

Historical social policies have impacted multiple generations of Aboriginal people. The severing of family ties has left a legacy of traumatized people who may be unable to function in mainstream society. Left dependent on social institutions, many Aboriginal people are unable to address their individual needs. Increasingly, both Aboriginal researchers and critical social scientists advance the need for culturally congruent service delivery based on local values and culture. They suggest that to strengthen communities in distress, Western methods of mental health practice must recognize and validate the value of traditional methods of healing. Duran et al. (1998) concur with this approach, noting that "Until traditional Indigenous therapies are implemented and considered legitimate, there will be a struggle, and sadly, the suffering of historical legacy and ongoing trauma will continue" (p. 349).

Cultural differences between Aboriginal people and the majority culture in North America have been well documented (see Red Horse, 1980; Morrissette et al., 1993; Johnston, 1983; Cross, 1986; Horejsi & Pablo, 1993). (A summary of these differences is included in Appendix A.) Aboriginal values necessitate a holistic approach to health care service delivery. Because the physical, mental, emotional and spiritual elements of health of the individual, family and community are interwoven and interdependent, "wellness" can be achieved only when all four elements of personal health are balanced.

Cultural Competence

Braveheart-Jordan & De Bruyn (1995) discuss the need for cultural competence in working with women in Aboriginal communities across North America. Their work has demonstrated that effective therapeutic relationships require knowledge of the history and values of a community. The counsellor must not only understand the nuances of a person's cultural background, but must also actively explore the client's cultural community—both with the client, and by approaching members of the community.

To work effectively in Aboriginal communities it is important to find out how closely individuals, families or communities identify with Aboriginal values. Morrissette et al. (1993) have developed a practical framework for working with Aboriginal people; they suggest asking clients to identify themselves on a cultural continuum that describes their cultural awareness in relation to three terms: "traditional," "neo-traditional" and "non-traditional."

Traditional Aboriginal people closely regard the teachings of Elders and acknowledge a strong interdependency between people and the earth or nature. A referral to an Elder or other traditional expert may help with personal development of these clients. Counsellors can also help by facilitating access to traditional healing methods such as the pipe ceremony, storytelling, traditional medicines, sweat lodge ceremonies, vision quests, shaking tent ceremonies and teaching circles.

Neo-traditional Aboriginal people identify with a blend of traditional spirituality and practices that reflect the dominant society and Christian beliefs. Support may be provided through a blend of traditional teachings and selected methods from conventional theories related to substance use counselling. The role of the counsellor is to facilitate the person's healing and recognize his or her need to become a more "balanced" community member.

Non-traditional Aboriginal people have adopted most of the norms and practices of the dominant society. They may experience ambivalence as a result of internal conflict between dominant values and exposure to Aboriginal values, and may feel culturally alienated as they do not fit into either the dominant society or Aboriginal society. The client may need the counsellor's help to discover his or her culture and heritage. This may also involve work with an Elder. However, it is important to note that some Aboriginal people may not identify a role for their culture in the treatment process. The treatment choice rests with the client.

Traditional Healing Strategies

The use of traditional healing strategies is gaining increased recognition in mainstream health care and social service settings. Waldram (1997) notes that Aboriginal people are regaining control of the healing process in mainstream treatment facilities through the use of the medicine wheel (to guide the process), sweat lodge ceremonies, healing circles and sweet grass ceremonies. Healing centres, such as Poundmaker's

Lodge in Alberta, affirm the value of Aboriginal people controlling their own healing processes.

ROLE OF ELDERS
Increasingly, Elders and traditional healers are recognized for their critical role as part of the treatment team; their place in the community means that their participation sanctions the healing process (Cross, 1986). The traditional role of Elders is returning as communities recognize that Elders' knowledge and experience support and enhance community activities.

COMMUNITY EMPOWERMENT
Duck et al. (1997), in their work with abuse in Aboriginal communities in northern Manitoba, recognize the need for a community-based approach to healing in Aboriginal communities. They have entrenched their work in community empowerment: "A key aspect of healing communities is the recapturing of community values: rebuilding the family, respecting the wisdom of the elders in sharing essential teachings, allowing women and children to voice their opinions, and recreating a strong nation" (p. 2).

THE MEDICINE WHEEL
The medicine wheel represents traditional theology, philosophy and psychology for Aboriginal people (Morrisseau, 1998), and is based on a world view that believes that the spiritual, mental, physical and social aspects of life are inseparably connected and continuously interacting (Swinomish, 1991). By understanding the meaning of four directions of the medicine wheel (East, South, West and North), the counsellor is better able to understand Aboriginal culture and to develop an effective way of working with these communities. (See Appendix B for a more detailed description of one way to use the medicine wheel.)

Integrating Aboriginal and Non-Aboriginal Practices

The blending of traditional healing and Western assessment and treatment processes is gaining increased recognition in mainstream institutions, such as the Centre for Addiction and Mental Health in Ontario. This agency's Aboriginal Services link Western assessment and treatment therapies for a range of substance use and mental health concerns with traditional healing strategies. The services are provided under the guidance of a community advisory committee, which consists of Aboriginal agencies, and non-Aboriginal services that have many Aboriginal clients. A team of therapists, a psychologist and an Elder visit both mainstream and Aboriginal agencies, helping to link Aboriginal people to services in the community and at the Centre, including healing circles, talking circles, one-to-one support from the Elder, and the use of sweat lodge ceremonies in a treatment module. In addition, the team works with the Centre's staff by sharing information about traditional healing strategies and cultural norms and values, as well as developing culturally congruent assessment and treatment skills. The team also works in partnership with First Nations communities and community agencies, by offering training and support to front-line staff in the area of addiction and mental health services. Centre staff receive training from community members in the area of traditional healing strategies and approaches to Aboriginal healing.

CONCLUSION

In order to effectively meet the needs of Aboriginal people requiring substance use and/or mental health services, the counsellor and the health care agency must understand the Aboriginal world view. History has played a critical role in the experiences of Aboriginal people; intergenerational trauma as a result of public policies related to the *Indian Act*, residential school system and child welfare authority has left a legacy of individual, family and community distress. Assessment and treatment strategies must be based on this knowledge and provide choices to Aboriginal people around their own healing processes. These indigenous processes must form the root of the healing strategy, and cannot be employed simply as an adjunct to Western healing methods.

APPENDIX A

TABLE 20-4

Cultural Value Conflict Areas

MAINSTREAM	ABORIGINAL
Family The individual is perceived as a separate entity. Individual responsibility is considered important. Decision making must involve the person affected as much as possible. Family is usually defined as biological parents and their offspring (nuclear family).	The individual is perceived in the context of his or her family. Involvement and dependence on family is encouraged. Decision making must involve the older, respected members of the family. Family consists of biological parents, their children, grandparents, aunts and uncles (extended family). A child's cousins may be viewed as his or her sisters and brothers.
Acceptance of Others People relate to others in terms of their roles (e.g., their job). People do not need to like or agree with someone to use his or her services (e.g., student and teacher). Assertiveness, directness, eye contact and a firm handshake are signs of a confident, trustworthy person.	Native people usually relate to other people in terms of the whole person. Individuals tend to accept or reject others completely and have difficulty working with those they have rejected. Directness and assertiveness are offensive. In interpersonal relations, a person must be patient, humble, quiet and respectful, especially toward older people.
Social Relations Differences in status and rank are noted and stressed. Communication follows predictable, formal steps to make others feel comfortable.	Differences in status are minimized to make others feel comfortable. An informal style of communicating is used to make others feel comfortable.
Relationship to Nature Humankind is rational and can construct machines and develop techniques to solve problems.	Nature guides and rules humanity. Humans must be accepting of such things as disease and suffering. Nature is the Creator. Nature is us. Nature is everything.
Time Time is perceived in terms of the clock (e.g., supper is at 5:00 p.m.). Time moves quickly from past to present to future; one must keep up with time and use it to change and master one's environment.	Time is perceived in terms of the right time to do something (e.g., supper is when you eat.) Time moves slowly; man must integrate himself with the environment and adapt to it rather than change it.

TABLE 20-4

Cultural Value Conflict Areas (cont'd)

MAINSTREAM	ABORIGINAL
Children Some children are "planned" while others may be viewed as an "accident" or unwanted. Children belong to the biological parents, who take primary responsibility for their care. Young adults are expected to leave home and become independent. Corporal punishment is often used in an attempt to control a child's behaviour. Shaming and teasing are commonly used to control a child.	All children are gifts from the Creator and valued, regardless of the circumstances of their birth. Children are members of the community, and all members are responsible for them. Adult children feel little pressure to leave home and establish an independent household. Children learn through direction and instruction. Children learn through modelling and observation.
Elderly People Because elderly people are no longer economically productive, they are not highly valued.	Elders are held in high esteem and often asked for advice and guidance. They are expected to be wise and understanding.
Non-interference Giving advice, exerting influence and providing direction are important roles for individuals as they mature. A person receiving advice is expected to accept it in good grace.	People are allowed to explore their environment and make decisions without direction and interference. Any interference is perceived as rude, bad behaviour. Power or dominance over another is not acceptable.
Competition Competition between people or groups is seen as healthy and good for the person's development, as well as for society.	Non-competition is valued as it avoids intra-group rivalry, prevents "showing off," and promotes the family, clan or tribe over the individual.
Sharing Acquiring material goods is a sign of success and power. The status of a person or family is enhanced in the community by the accumulation of goods and wealth.	Sharing with others is a sign of honour and respect for the person and the group. Survival of the family, clan and tribe is promoted. No individual is better off or more powerful than others in the group.
Language Patterns Speech is loud and fast with frequent interruptions. Responses to others are quick, using direct eye contact. Verbal skills are highly valued.	Speech is slow and soft with few interjections. Responses to others are delayed with very little eye contact. Non-verbal communication is highly regarded.

TABLE 20-4

Cultural Value Conflict Areas (cont'd)

MAINSTREAM	ABORIGINAL
Self A person learns to control himself or herself through trial and error. Aggressive use of self and competition with others are strengths. Value is placed on controlling the environment and other people, as well as one's own behaviour.	A person participates only when certain of ability. People allow others to go first to learn from them. Individual privacy and non-interference are highly regarded.

Adapted from Horejsi, C. & Pablo, J. (1993), Brant, C. (1990) & Sander, P. (1987).

APPENDIX B

The Medicine Wheel as a Counselling Tool*

The medicine wheel represents traditional theology, philosophy and psychology for Aboriginal people, and presents a way of understanding and assessing the progress of the therapeutic relationship from a cultural perspective. The path suggested by the four directions can help identify tasks or strategies the counsellor can use with the client. The wheel must be used in conjunction with the core values as a guide to action and in relating to other people.

THE EAST DOOR

The East door is the beginning of change or an opportunity for individual or community renewal. According to traditional teachings, the East door brings illumination and provides an opportunity to see more clearly. It is in the East that a person develops self-reliance and a sense of what needs to be done. There is an emphasis on meeting physical needs in order to build strength. Additional traditional healing methods and teachings, such as sweat lodges and fasting, may be required. These spiritual activities help the individual and the community work through issues, and identify a path to move toward the next door.

---

*Based on Coggins, K. (1990), Cross, T. (1986), Morrisseau, C. (1998), Morrissette, V. (1992), & Native Council of Canada (1990).

THE SOUTH DOOR

The South door is important as it provides an opportunity for unlearning as well as learning. For Aboriginal people, or those who do not share the world view of the dominant culture, it is an opportunity to develop an understanding of how they have been oppressed or limited. People learn from each other, share ideas and feelings, and reflect on their understanding of a shared vision; it is an opportunity to develop and nurture relationships. This door symbolizes time, patience and relationships. Personal realities and attitudes may shift as individuals become part of a collective; people may gain new insight and knowledge by reviewing previously held beliefs and ideals. For Aboriginal people, it is an opportunity to understand the impact of history, colonization and oppression; the South door encourages growth, change and the understanding of identity.

THE WEST DOOR

This door presents a time for meditation, reflection and development of inner strength before the process turns external. Before a person moves forward, the person (or family or community) must confront the issues that prevent him or her from meeting his or her goals. It is a time of healing and an opportunity to regain balance and harmony. This opportunity for introspection requires that the counsellor support the individual, family or community as they attempt to regain balance in their lives and respect for themselves.

THE NORTH DOOR

This is the door of wisdom, where an individual analyses, imagines, understands, organizes, synthesizes, predicts, calculates and interprets hidden meanings. At the North door, action plans are devised and caring behaviours are emphasized; social action, economic development, devising appropriate political structures and spiritual support can be explored. The existing network of Aboriginal social agencies and community members can be brought together to develop strategies for problem solving, with Elders facilitating the individual and group process of healing.

ENDNOTES

1. In 1985, Bill C31 amended the *Indian Act* to allow women with non-Aboriginal husbands and their children access to benefits, with the consent of the band. It also restored the rights of those who had been considered "enfranchised" through post-secondary education, employment or participation in a federal election.
2. Accurate data on the size of the Aboriginal population are difficult to ascertain because many Aboriginal people do not participate in the census. Those living off-reserve are difficult to identify: since only a minority speaks solely an Aboriginal language, measures of ethnocultural background (such as mother tongue) do not

apply to many Aboriginal people. Migration to and from reserves and urban centres makes it difficult to ascertain population sizes in urban areas (Kendall,1989). The 1996 data were based on a question asking specifically about Aboriginal origin rather than ethnic origin, as in the 1991 census.

REFERENCES

Adilman, S. & Kliewer, G. (2000). Pain and wasting on Main and Hastings: A perspective from the Vancouver Native Health Society Medical Clinic. *B.C. Medical Journal, 42*(9), 422–425.

Andres, R. (1981). The apprehension of Native children. *Ontario Indian, 46*, 32–37.

Armitage, A. (1993). Family and child welfare in First Nation communities. In B. Wharf (Ed.), *Rethinking Child Welfare in Canada*. Toronto: McClelland & Stewart.

Assembly of First Nations. (1994). *Breaking the Silence*. Ottawa: Assembly of First Nations.

Bagley, C., Young, Y. & Scully, A. (1993). *International and Transracial Adoptions: A Mental Health Perspective*. Aldershot-Brookfield: Avebury Press.

Barman, J., Hebert, Y. & McCaskill, D. (1986). The legacy of the past: An overview. In J. Barman, Y. Hebert. & D. McCaskill (Eds.), *Indian Education in Canada: Volume 1*. Vancouver: UBC Press.

Beisner, M. & Attneave, C. (1982). Mental disorders among Native American children: Rates and risk periods for entering treatment. *The American Journal of Psychiatry, 139*(2), 193–198.

Brant, C. (1990). Native ethics and rules of behaviour. *Canadian Journal of Psychiatry, 35*(3), 534–539.

Brant, C. (1993). Suicide in Canadian Aboriginal peoples: Causes and prevention. In *Royal Commission on Aboriginal Peoples. The Path to Healing*. Ottawa: Ministry of Supply and Services, Canada.

Braveheart-Jordan, M. & De Bruyn, L. (1995). So she may walk in balance: Integrating the impact of historical trauma in the treatment of Native American Indian women. In J. Adelman & G. Enguidanos (Eds.), *Racism in the Lives of Women: Testimony, Theory and Guides to Ethnoracist Practice*. New York: Haworth Press.

Bull, L.R. (1991). Indian residential schooling: The native perspective. *Canadian Journal of Native Education, 18*, 1–63.

Canadian Medical Association. (1994). *Bridging the Gap: Promoting Health and Healing for Aboriginal Peoples in Canada*. Ottawa: Author.

Claes, R. & Clifton, D. (1997). Needs and expectations for redress of victims of abuse at Native residential schools. *Law Commission of Canada*. Available: www.lcc.gc.ca/en/themes/mr/ica/sage/index.html.

Coggins, K. (1990). *Alternative Pathways to Healing*. Deerfield Beach: Health Communications.

Couchi, C. & Nabigon, H. (1994). A path towards reclaiming birth culture. In F. Shroff (Ed.), *The New Midwifery*. Toronto: LPC Inbook.

Cross, T. (1986). Drawing on cultural tradition in Indian child welfare practice. *Social Casework, 67*(5), 283–289.

Deiter, C. (1999). *From Our Mothers' Arms: The Intergenerational Impact of Residential Schools in Saskatchewan.* Toronto: Plenum Press.

Duck, J., Ironstar, V. & Ricks, F. (1997). Healing and the community. *Journal of Child and Youth Care, 11*(3), 1–13.

Duran, E. & Duran, B. (1995). *Native American Postcolonial Psychology.* New York: State University of New York Press.

Duran, E., Duran, B., Yellow Horse Brave Heart, M. & Yellow Horse-Davis, S. (1998). Healing the American Indian soul wound. In Y. Danieli (Ed.), *International Handbook of Multigenerational Legacies of Trauma.* New York: Plenum Press.

Dutton, M. (1998). Cultural issues in trauma treatment. *Centering 3*(2), 1–2. Available: www.thecenteratpiw.com.

Frideres, J. (1998). *Aboriginal Peoples in Canada: Contemporary Conflicts.* Toronto: Prentice Hall, Allyn & Bacon Canada.

Furniss, E. (1991). *A Conspiracy of Silence: The Care of Native Students at St. Joseph's Residential School.* Williams Lake: Cariboo Tribal Council.

Gagne, M. (1998). The role of dependency and colonialism in generating trauma in First Nations citizens. In Y. Danieli (Ed.), *International Handbook of Multigenerational Legacies of Trauma* (pp. 355–372). New York: Plenum Press.

Good Tracks, J.G. (1973). Native American non-interference. *Social Work, 18*(11), 30–34.

Grant, A. (1996). *No End of Grief: Indian Residential Schools in Canada.* Winnipeg: Pemmican Publications.

Haig-Brown, C. (1988). *Resistance and Renewal: Surviving the Indian Residential School.* Vancouver: Tillacum Library.

Health Canada. (November 1999). *A Second Diagnostic on the Health of First Nations and Inuit People in Canada.* Ottawa: Ministry of Supply and Services.

Health Canada. (March 2003). *A Statistical Profile on the Health of First Nations in Canada.* Ottawa: Ministry of Supply and Services.

Hepworth, P. (1980). *Foster Care and Adoption in Canada.* Ottawa: The Canadian Council on Social Development.

Hodgson, M. (1990). *Impact of Residential Schools and Other Root Causes of Poor Mental Health.* Edmonton: Nechi Institute on Alcohol and Drug Education.

Horejsi, C. & Pablo, J. (1993). Traditional Native American cultures and contemporary U.S. society: A comparison. *Human Services in the Rural Environment, 16*(3), 24–27.

Hudson, P. & McKenzie, B. (1981). Child welfare and Native people: The extension of colonialism. *The Social Worker, 49*(2), 63–88.

Indian and Northern Affairs Canada. (2002). *Economic Development in Ontario's First Nations Communities.* Ottawa: Minister of Public Works and Government Services Canada.

Information Canada. (1974). *Perspective Canada: A Compendium of Social Statistics.* Ottawa: Minister of Industry.

Ing, N.R. (1991). Effects of residential schooling on Native parenting. *Canadian Journal of Native Education, 18*, 65–118.

Johnston, P. (1983). *Native Children and the Child Welfare System.* Ottawa: Canadian Council on Social Development.

Kendrick, M. (1990). *Nobody's Children: The Foster Care Crisis in Canada.* Toronto: Macmillan.

Kimmelman, J. (1984). *Report on the Adoption of Native Children.* Winnipeg: Government of Manitoba.

Kirmayer, L., Brass, G. & Tait, C. (2000). The mental health of Aboriginal peoples: Transformations of identity and community. *Canadian Journal of Psychiatry, 45*(7), 607–616.

Krosenbrink-Gelissen, L. (1998). The Native Women's Association of Canada. In Frideres, J.S. (Ed.), *Native People in Canada* (pp. 299–325). Toronto: Prentice-Hall.

Lederman, J. (1999). Trauma and healing in Aboriginal families and communities. *Native Social Work Journal, 2*(1), 59–90.

Locust, C. (1999). Split feathers: Adult American Indians who were placed in non-Indian families as children. *Pathways, 14*(1), 1–5.

Long, D. & Dickason, O.P. (1996). *Visions of the Heart: Canadian Aboriginal Issues.* Toronto: Harcourt Brace.

Mawhiney, A. (1994). *Towards Aboriginal Self-Government: Relations between Status Indian Peoples and the Government of Canada 1969–1984.* New York: Garland Publishing.

McCormick, R. (2000). Aboriginal traditions in the treatment of substance abuse. *Canadian Journal of Counselling, 34*(1), 25–32

Metropolitan Toronto District Health Council Native Steering Committee. (1996). *Aboriginal Community Consultation.* Toronto: author.

Miller, J. (1987). The irony of residential schooling. *Canadian Journal of Native Education, 14*(2), 3–11.

Morrisseau, C. (1998). *Into the Daylight: A Wholistic Approach to Healing.* Toronto: University of Toronto Press.

Morrissette, V., McKenzie, B. & Morrissette, L. (1993). Towards an Aboriginal model of social work practice. *Canadian Social Work Review, 10*(1), 91–108.

Mussell, W., Nicholls, W. & Adler, M. (1991). *Making Meaning of Mental Health Challenge in First Nations.* Chiliwack, BC: Saltshan Institute Society.

Napier, D. (2000, May). Sins of the fathers. *Anglican Journal.* Available: www.anglicanjournal.com /126/rs/.

Native Council of Canada. (1990). *Native Child Care: The Circle of Care.* Ottawa: The Native Council of Canada.

Palmer, S. & Cooke, W. (1996). Understanding and counting racism with First Nations children in out-of-home care. *Child Welfare, 75*(6), 709–725.

Payukotayno, J. & Hudson Bay Family Services & Tikinagan Child and Family Services. (1988, August). *As Long as the Sun Shines: From Generation to Generation.* Author.

Phillips, G. (1999, November). *How We Heal.* Paper presented at the 1999 meeting of the National Stolen Generations Conference, Gold Coast. Available: www.visions.ab.ca.

Proulx, J. & Perrault, S. (2000). *No Place for Violence: Canadian Aboriginal Alternatives.* Halifax: Fernwood Publishing and RESOLVE.

Red Horse, J.G. (1980). American Indian elders: Unifiers of families. *Social Casework, 61*, 490–493.

Restoule, J.P. (2000). Aboriginal identity: The need for historical and contextual perspectives. *Canadian Journal of Native Education, 24*(2), 102–113.

Richard, K. (1989). Ken Richard fights racism with child welfare. *Metropolis, 2*(11), 3–4.

Root, M. (1992). Reconstructing the impact of trauma on personality. In Brown, L. & Ballou, M. (Eds.), *Personality and Psychopathology: Feminist Reprisals.* New York: Guilford Press.

Royal Commission on Aboriginal Peoples. (1993). *Aboriginal Peoples in Urban Centres: Report of the National Round Table on Aboriginal Urban Issues.* Ottawa: Minister of Supply and Services Canada.

Royal Commission on Aboriginal Peoples. (1996). Volume 1: *Looking Forward, Looking Back.* Ottawa: Minister of Supply and Services Canada.

Royal Commission on Aboriginal Peoples. (1996). Volume 3: *Gathering Strength.* Ottawa: Minister of Supply and Services Canada.

Royal Commission on Aboriginal Peoples. (1996). Volume 4: *Perspectives and Realities.* Ottawa: Minister of Supply and Services Canada.

Sander, P. (1987). Value conflicts. *Journal of Multicultural Counseling and Development* (1).

Sanders, D. (1978). *Admittance Restricted.* Ottawa: Canadian Council on Children and Youth.

Scott, K. (1994). Substance use among Indigenous Canadians. In D. McKenzie (Ed.), *Research Issues: Substance Use among Indigenous Canadians.* Ottawa: Canadian Centre on Substance Abuse.

Scott-Brown, J. (1987). The short life at St. Dunstan's Calgary Indian Industrial School, 1896–1907. *Canadian Journal of Native Education, 14*(1), 41–49.

Statistics Canada. (1981). DIAND customized data. Ottawa: Minister of Industry.

Statistics Canada. (1993). *Census and Aboriginal Peoples Survey,* cat. no. 94-327. Ottawa: Minister of Industry.

Statistics Canada. (1998a). 1996 Census: Total population by Aboriginal group. Ottawa: Minister of Industry.

Statistics Canada. (1998b, January 13). *The Daily.* Ottawa: author.

Statistics Canada. (2003, January). 2001 Census: Analysis Series. *Aboriginal Peoples of Canada: A Demographic Profile.* Ottawa: Minister of Industry.

Swinomish Tribal Mental Health Project. (1991). *A Gathering of Wisdoms: Tribal Mental Health; A Cultural Perspective.* LaConner, WA: Swinomish Tribal Community.

Timpson, J.B. (1990). Indian and Native special status in Ontario's child welfare legislation. *Canadian Social Work Review, 7*, 49–68.

United Church of Canada. (1994). *Residential Schools.* Toronto: author.

van de Sande, Adje. (1995). Native and mainstream parenting programs. *Native Studies Review, 10*(1), 1–20.

Waldram, J. (1997). The Aboriginal peoples of Canada. In I. Al-Issa & M. Tousignant (Eds.), *Ethnicity, Immigration and Psychopathology.* New York: Plenum Press.

Waldram, James B. (In press). History, culture and trauma: Aboriginal peoples and PTSD. In A. Rummens, M. Beiser, & S. Noh (Eds). *Immigration, Cultural Diversity and Health.* Toronto: University of Toronto Press.

Warry, W. (1991). Ontario's first people: Native children. In L. Johnson, & D. Barnhort (Eds.), *Children, Families and Public Policy in the '90s.* Toronto: Thompson Educational Publishing.

York, G. (1989). *Dispossessed: Life and Death in Native Canada.* Toronto: Little Brown.

Chapter 21

Substance Use Problems and the Family

RICHARD J. BOUDREAU

INTRODUCTION

This brief chapter outlines a framework or process for involving the family in the treatment of substance use problems. It is more about the "why" than the "how" of family treatment. The recommended reading list at the end of the chapter provides various resources that elaborate upon such topics as assessment instruments and treatment approaches, as well as the research evidence in support of couple and family work.

The chapter presents a systematic consideration of the questions, issues and principles that guide the decision to involve the family in treatment, followed by an extended case example illustrating this process.

While the chapter may primarily reflect the perspective of a more traditional family, the principles, strategies and approaches described here can and are being applied to the broadest diversity of contemporary families with alcohol or other drug problems.

WHY INVOLVE THE FAMILY?

There is still a widespread view, even among counsellors, that substance use problems primarily affect the individual. It may be recognized that others around the person are affected, but not necessarily that they may play a role in the development of or maintenance of the problem or, more importantly, could be vital to its resolution. Such views persist despite growing evidence that the family is a key factor in substance use intervention. Although the role family members play varies in each situation, involving them in treatment has been shown by research to contribute to a better outcome.

A basic tenet of family counselling is that whatever happens to one member of the family affects all the others and, similarly, the response of other members can impact the original member. This fundamental principle of family work holds true not only in terms of a family's deficits, but also, more significantly, in relation to its strengths. It is an assumption of this chapter that any work involving the family at any level should address and build upon family strengths while recognizing, in many cases, notable deficits.

The family represents a primary setting where problems of substance use are manifested. It also presents a context where these problems are either successfully dealt with or inadvertently reinforced and perpetuated. For this reason, any treatment intervention that neglects the importance of the family, at the very least, misses out on potent treatment strategies or, at worst, works against itself by ignoring factors that often contribute to relapse. Most substance use counsellors can likely recall having successfully intervened with a person only to have that client relapse upon return to an unchanged family environment.

Counsellors working with couples and families facing substance use problems recognize that treatment goals and objectives can encompass a broad range of possibilities. The objective of involving the family is to improve outcomes for both the person with a substance use problem and the family. Most people interpret this to mean that the family works things out and stays together, but while this, admittedly, is the preferred outcome, it is not necessarily always the best or only "good" result. Sometimes in the process of therapy, the family recognizes that their treatment goal must be for them to separate, hopefully in a healthy way. This might include couples separating or children (including adult children) becoming more independent, rather than estranged, from their families.

WHAT IT MEANS TO INVOLVE FAMILIES

Treatment Options

Generic and addiction-specific social services often advertise that they see, work with or counsel families. What do these services involve?

Working with families can involve an array of services ranging from basic orientation to long-term, in-depth family therapy. The family might merely be oriented to the program in which the family member with the substance use problem is enrolled, they might embark upon a carefully developed regimen of family therapy or their involvement might fall somewhere in between, depending on assessed family needs and available resources. Table 21-1 below outlines four categories of family involvement with suggested levels of intervention and related objectives. It should be noted that these are broad categories with numerous possible varieties within each.

TABLE 21-1

Categories of Family Involvement

TYPES OF FAMILY INVOLVEMENT	LEVEL OF INTERVENTION	OBJECTIVES
Family orientation	Introducing the family to the philosophy and approaches of the service	To orient the family about the program the identified client is embarking upon, and to enlist family support
Family education/ support group	Involving couples and families in family life education and social support with special reference to substance use issues (may/may not include identified client)	To support family members and inform them about family dynamics as they relate to substance use problems (Goal may/may not include recruitment of identified client into treatment.)
Family counselling	Contracting with the family for interventions aimed at resolving specifically identified problems	To bring about resolution of problematic issues identified by family members and related to the substance use
Family therapy	Contracting with the family for interventions aimed at chronic and systemic family dysfunction	To bring about change to elusive and intractable areas of systemic family dysfunction related to the problematic substance use

In addition to the services outlined above, which would typically be offered in family and social services agencies, family issues are also addressed by a growing array of mutual aid groups such as Al-Anon, Children of Alcoholics (COA) groups and Parents against Drugs (PAD). Many agencies that work primarily from an individual perspective collaborate with such groups when addressing family issues during therapy. It is a mistake to assume that because a service is not set up to do formal family counselling or therapy, it should not undertake any family work. The evidence indicates that important and effective changes can be brought about through simple but well-developed educational programs, especially with families presenting early-stage problems related to alcohol and other drugs.

Issues in Determining Treatment

It is important when working with families to determine early on whether the substance use problem lies with the parent(s) or with one (or more) of the children. Many families have substance use issues in both generations. In which generation the problem lies has important bearing on the following questions:

- Should the focus of the family work be primarily on couple or parental matters?
- Which of the family members most significantly need to be involved in the sessions?
- If there are substance use issues in both generations, should they be addressed separately or together?

Decisions around such matters vary greatly from family to family. Where there are substance use problems in both generations, the key factors to consider are:

- the counsellor's experience and ability to deal with both generations
- the advantages and disadvantages of engaging with each generation consecutively or concurrently
- the advantages and disadvantages of each generation's being seen by separate counsellors working collaboratively.

The unique circumstances of each case will help determine the best approach.

THE ROLE OF ASSESSMENT

A comprehensive assessment determines the nature and extent of family intervention required in conjunction with or separate from substance use–specific interventions. This will vary significantly depending on the situation, and may be indicated by answers to the following questions:

- What is the history and extent of the substance use problems? Are they early-stage or long-standing? Is there evidence that the family organizes around problematic substance use?
- Does the assessment suggest the substance use is inextricably tied in with other couple/family dysfunction? Are other, possibly more serious, family problems being displaced upon the client identified with problematic use?
- Should the substance use be brought under control before couple or family work is initiated?
- Will all the work be done in one facility, or will the family work be referred to another service?

Who Should Work with Families?

Once an assessment has established that family work is needed and what the nature and level of that work might be, it must be decided who will do the work. A major consideration in determining this is the service mandate of the initial contact. Does the range of services provide for family counselling, or is its mandate restricted to assessment/referral, primary care, withdrawal management or individual treatment?

If family work is within the general mandate of the service, a further consideration is the staff's ability to carry out the level of family intervention required. The skills of individual staff need to be clearly assessed. In addition, the combined resources of the agency to carry out family work should be explored, including:

- whether the agency's service hours accommodate the school and work schedules of family members

- determining agency attitudes and philosophies regarding family dynamics as they relate to substance use
- whether opportunities exist for collaborative work between staff, which can be critical in family work.

Such factors are important not only in terms of client care, but also in the on-going assessment of staff and agency development needs in the treatment of alcohol and other drug problems.

If a referral outside the agency of initial contact is needed, the referring agency requires up-to-date knowledge of family resources available in the community. This represents a pivotal juncture in the treatment process for a number of reasons. It is at this point that a worker or agency must assume primary care responsibilities for the client and his or her family, so that continuity of care and linkages between agencies can be co-ordinated and maintained. Also at this point, decisions need to be made about the division of roles and responsibilities:

- Will the interventions related to the substance use problems and family work be done concurrently or successively?
- Will the work be done by one or more agencies?
- Will the work be done by one or more workers?

How these co-ordinating, referring and follow-up functions are carried out determines to a great extent whether the clients and their families remain and progress in treatment. Without effective co-ordination, usually assumed by a primary care worker, clients can easily become entangled and lost within even fairly simple treatment systems. There is still a great deal of debate about the optimum timing of family work in the treatment of substance use problems, including whether the work should occur while the substance use issues are being addressed or begun only once the use of substances is under control. Many important factors enter into this debate, including:

- the extent and duration of the substance use and related problems
- the level of deterioration in the couple/family relationships due to the substance use
- the possible presence of family violence associated with the problematic use of alcohol and other drugs
- the willingness of the partner or other family members to be involved before the substance use problem has been brought under control
- whether the client has chosen abstinence or reduced use as a treatment goal, and the acceptability of a non-abstinent goal to family members.

Again, these issues can be clarified only through a comprehensive assessment. In addition, to protect families seeking service from the burden of inter-agency debate, collaborating agencies should ideally have clarity and understanding about any differences in their philosophies and policies regarding family work.

How to Work with the Family

A detailed presentation of all the various approaches to family counselling and family therapy in the treatment of alcohol and other drug problems is beyond the scope of this chapter. This information is readily available in many related resources (see Recommended Reading at the end of the chapter). It is important, however, for addiction counsellors to have some working knowledge of the major models of family treatment, broadly identified as structural, strategic, behavioural, solution-focused and multi-generational. Such knowledge allows the counsellor to make more informed decisions about the level of family work required and which approach may be most compatible with a family. For example, if a family appears to respond well to concrete contractual assignments, it might do better with a behavioural model of family therapy. A multi-generational/Bowenian model might seem a more appropriate choice where problematic substance use in a family has a clear multi-generational history and influence. Table 21-2 highlights five major models of family treatment, their underlying theories and main objectives.

TABLE 21-2

Major Models of Family Treatment

MODEL	UNDERLYING THEORY	FOCUS OF INTERVENTION
Structural	Theory of family relations in terms of proximity/distance and designated boundaries	Restructuring of interactions between family members
Strategic	Problem-solving theory	Resolving problems through assignment of therapeutic tasks, directives and prescriptions
Behavioural	Social learning theory	Modification of family behaviour through contracted changes in behaviour of individual members
Solution-focused	Expectation of change theory	Helping the family to focus on exceptions to the problem behaviour
Multi-generational/ Bowenian	Inter-generational dynamics theory	Resolution of individual member's role within the extended family system

The models and approaches outlined in Table 21-2 are those most often presented in connection with the family treatment of substance use problems. However, practitioners of newer models such as narrative and integrative family therapy are also reporting success in applying these models to alcohol and other drug problems. Currently, the general direction in family treatment is to apply the approach, or mix of approaches, that best addresses the identified problem and optimally meets the needs of the family.

Regardless of what level of family intervention is indicated, or what modality of family work is finally adopted, three fundamental elements have been found to enhance and contribute to the effectiveness of family treatment.

The first is the importance of identifying and promoting family strengths. Most families present with a diminished sense of their abilities and strengths because of their failure to resolve the identified problem(s) on their own. No family is left devoid of all strengths or skills no matter how intense or chronic the problem at hand may be. It is incumbent upon the effective family worker to help identify these family resources, no matter how compromised they may be under the circumstances, and develop strategies and interventions that build upon them. For example, a family may retain good problem-solving skills in other areas of family life, such as money management or the upkeep of the home, but be unable to bring these skills to bear on problems that may result from the use of alcohol and/or other drugs. An important dimension of family work in such a case would be to reinforce these skills, and enable the family to apply them to problems associated with substance use.

Closely related to the question of building upon family strengths is the importance of mobilizing the family members to do their own problem solving. In the final analysis, the most effective and elegant family treatment is one where the family members hardly recognize the counsellor had any part in resolving the problem(s).

Finally, most of the literature on family interventions encourages a team approach. Even very basic work with families can become complex and challenging to an individual therapist working in isolation. A team approach—which might be as minimal as regular consultation with colleagues, or as elaborate as direct observation using highly technical feedback equipment—provides many benefits, including a range of insights into complex family dynamics, support to the worker, enriched resources for the family, ongoing monitoring of treatment effectiveness of the therapist and the agency, and a continuous atmosphere of learning and development for the team members.

FAMILY INVOLVEMENT CHECKLIST

In summary, when deciding whether or how to include the family in therapy related to alcohol and other drug problems, counsellors should consider the following:
• Is the identified client in the parenting or offspring generation? Are there substance use problems in both generations?
• Is the substance use problem of recent origin or long-standing?
• Is there evidence that the family is organized around problematic substance use? Are there indications that other family problems or dysfunctions are displaced onto the person with alcohol or other drug problems?
• What level of family involvement is needed? Will a strategy of family support and education be adequate, or will a more structured regimen of family treatment be required?
• Given the characteristics of the identified client and other family members, what model or approach of family treatment (e.g., structural, strategic, behavioural, solution-focused, inter-generational) is most appropriate?
• Who will undertake the family work? Will it be done by the worker/agency of initial contact? Or will it be referred to a specialized worker/agency?

• If referred, who will assume the role and responsibility of ensuring the family becomes effectively engaged, and proper linkages are maintained between involved agencies from assessment through to follow-up?

• Are the specific strategies of family treatment based on identified areas of family strengths? Are strategies planned to empower the family to identify and resolve its own problem(s)? Is the family work organized to make the best use of the competencies, experience and support of the entire treatment team?

Case Study

The Smith family consists of the parents, George and Ruth, who are in their mid-40s, and their daughters, Paula, in Grade 11 at a local high school, and Jane, in university in another city. George had worked as a successful assistant sales manager at a mid-size corporation until his position was eliminated a year and a half ago. Since then, he and a colleague have started a sales consulting firm with some success, as well as a number of stressful start-up problems. Ruth works part-time off and on doing secretarial/bookkeeping work, and also some volunteer work.

Until recently, Paula had been outgoing, popular, reliable and an above-average student. In the past few months, her marks dropped suddenly and considerably. She was often absent from school without explanation and had a new peer group. At home she was often sullen and had angry outbursts. In the past, she had always come home at the agreed-upon time, but now she came much later, usually going directly to her room to avoid discussing why she was late. On two occasions she returned home talkative but unfocused, with slurred speech. Her family and teachers suspected drug use, which Paula strongly denied. At her parents' urging, Paula agreed to see their family physician. An appointment was made, but not kept.

A number of phone calls relating to unexplained missed classes were exchanged between Paula's school and parents. In brief meetings with the guidance counsellor, Paula expressed feelings of resentment toward her father and anger toward her mother, but refused to elaborate or become further engaged. The guidance counsellor consulted with a school board social worker who advised that Paula be referred to the local youth services centre for an assessment. Paula's parents were contacted by the guidance counsellor and agreed with the plan. Paula agreed reluctantly and only on the condition that her parents not be involved.

Paula had visited the youth services centre for a social studies project a year earlier and had been impressed with the staff, which probably facilitated the referral process. Within the first few sessions with the counsellor it became clear that Paula had become increasingly anxious over the past year or more with the situation at home. Her sister had left for university; her father, whom she had always felt close to, was often away for several days at a time with his new business, and her mother, also preoccupied and stressed about some of the same issues, was perceived by Paula to be often emotionally unavailable (attributed in one offhand reference to "mother's drinking").

Within a few sessions, trust was established, and Paula began to talk about her drug use and her new friends. She reported that she used drugs "fairly frequently," mostly alcohol and marijuana, and that "it helps me forget and feel better." Paula agreed to have her parents join her for the fourth session with her counsellor. At this appointment, they were also joined by an experienced family therapist from the same centre.

In the family session, the isolation felt by each family member over the past year surfaced. George reported that he felt he had let the family down in his role as provider; Ruth stated she was frustrated that her part-time work was no longer fulfilling and did not maintain the family at their accustomed financial level; Paula reported that she felt abandoned and, in a vague way, somehow responsible for what was happening to her parents. By the end of the session, each agreed that hearing what the others were feeling helped, and they contracted to structure time to do things together, such as family meals and outings, as they used to do.

Paula and her counsellor agreed to a treatment plan of a few more sessions, focusing primarily on alternatives to drug use in dealing with issues at school and at home. Paula's parents agreed to meet with the family counsellor on their own for one or two sessions to discuss what effects the events of the last couple of years had had on their relationship. The two counsellors planned to check in with one another at regular staff conferences.

As counselling progressed, Paula's school reported that her absenteeism decreased, and her academic performance improved. Paula's parents also reported positive changes at home. Although Paula continued to test the boundaries for greater independence from her parents, this was coupled with ongoing significant family involvement.

Paula's parents worked through the implications of their new financial situation with the help of a financial adviser, whom they were referred to by the family therapist. The financial adviser helped them to adjust their family budget and re-distribute some investments to better manage their present difficulties. The therapist also referred Ruth to a "women and work" support group to help her resolve her frustration with her career.

Ruth and George attended two couples sessions with the family therapist, but it was between sessions that a breakthrough occurred. Through the support group, Ruth had come to a decision to become qualified to work as a real estate agent—an undertaking she had started but stopped due to family demands, but could pursue now that the children were older. She was able to articulate her intent clearly to George. At the following session, she reported, "It's a measure of how isolated we've become that I was afraid George would not support me in my decision. I wasted so much gin and tonic and psychic energy worrying. And then, when we finally got around to discussing it, he was so terrifically supportive."

Ruth elaborated that prior to beginning these sessions, she had noticed a change in her drinking pattern—from the occasional drink when out to dinner with George or friends, to almost daily consumption, particularly in the evening while watching television by herself. She felt she was now returning to her previous pattern of the occasional social drink, especially now that she was exploring training in real estate work. She did however agree to self-monitor her intake of alcohol until the next session to ascertain more accurately her current consumption and pattern of use.

Based on the positive feedback from school and parents, Paula and her counsellor agreed to terminate her work with the youth services centre. Paula was invited to contact the centre again, if needed.

At a final family session, about a month after Paula's last individual session, Paula, George and Ruth presented as busy with their individual pursuits. George reported some success with his business, but was still not feeling firmly established. Ruth was enthusiastic about the real estate course she had enrolled in and was pleased with a part-time placement that held some promise in terms of future employment. In reporting on school, Paula made reference to looking into community colleges and social services programs as she prepared to graduate from high school in another year.

Although each was occupied with his or her own separate interests, the sense was that they were also aware of and interested in what was happening to each other, and in maintaining the gains they had made in the last few months. Toward the end of the session, Ruth produced the results of her self-monitoring and proudly indicated that her use of alcohol was back to occasional and limited rather than daily use.

Summary Observations

The Smith family received help early in the development of problems around family interactions and substance use. The problems were largely situational and stress-related. The family was able to benefit from relatively short-term treatment because of early intervention, the basic soundness of the family, and their individual and collective strengths.

One would expect such a family to benefit from counselling approaches that included strategies borrowing primarily from the behavioural, structural and solution-focused models of intervention. They were also able to benefit from good linkages between school and the youth service, as well as collaboration between staff within the same service.

CONCLUSION

Many factors determine the outcome of working with a family with problems related to alcohol and other drug use. They include matters that relate directly to the family, such as extent and history of substance use problems, other identified problems, basic soundness of the family structure and individual and collective strengths and skills. Other key factors external to the family include availability of family services and resources within the community, as well as effective linkages between services. Success in couple and family work is greatly influenced by the delicate timing, balancing and interplay between these important components of familial and social systems.

RECOMMENDED READING

The following references are provided to enable further exploration of the subject. The brief notations indicate the technical level and comprehensiveness of the individual items.

Boudreau, R. (1982). Alcohol abuse and the family system. *Canada's Mental Health, 30,* 17–18. (Brief overview of alcohol abuse from a family systems perspective.)

Kaufman, E. & Kaufmann, P. (Eds.). (1992). *Family Therapy of Drug and Alcohol Abuse.* Toronto: Allyn & Bacon. (An important collection of chapters on key topics by various leaders in the field.)

Meyers, R. & Miller, W. (Eds.). (2001). *A Community Reinforcement Approach to Addiction Treatment.* Cambridge, U.K.: Cambridge University Press. (Presents a broad spectrum of evidence-based applications of community reinforcement strategies including family support.)

Nicols, M. & Schwartz, R. (2001). *Family Therapy: Concepts and Methods.* Toronto: Allyn & Bacon. (Comprehensive review of the history, concepts, models and practice of family therapy.)

O'Farrell, T. (Ed.). (1993). *Treating Alcohol Problems: Marital and Family Interventions.* New York: Guilford Press. (This collection of chapters by numerous clinical researchers details various marital/family interventions.)

Pearlman, S. (1988). Systems theory and alcoholism. In D. Chaudron & D. Wilkinson (Eds.), *Theories on Alcoholism.* Toronto: Addiction Research Foundation. (An inclusive, detailed analysis of the topic.)

Roberts, L. & McCrady, B. (2003). *Alcohol Problems in Intimate Relationships: Identification and Intervention. A Guide for Marriage and Family Therapists.* NIH Publication No. 03-5284. Rockville, MD: NIAAA. (A detailed and well-presented guide to the application of couples and family treatment to alcohol problems.)

Sprenkle, D. (Ed.). (2003). *Effectiveness Research in Marriage and Family Therapy.* Alexandria, VA: American Association for Marriage and Family Therapy. (A comprehensive review of the research evidence about the effectiveness of marriage and family therapy, including its application to alcohol and other drug problems.)

Steinglass, P. (1987). *The Alcoholic Family.* New York: Basic Books. (A detailed analysis of important research questions related to the topic.)

Todd, T. & Selekman, M. (Eds.). (1991). *Family Therapy Approaches with Adolescent Substance Abusers.* Toronto: Allyn & Bacon. (Important presentation of diverse approaches by a number of prominent practitioners who work with this special population.)

Wagner, E. & Waldron, H. (2001). *Innovations in Adolescent Substance Abuse Interventions.* New York: Pergamon Press. (Presents a comprehensive array of contemporary approaches including family treatment of adolescent substance abuse.)

Chapter 22

Effects of Parental Alcohol Use on Children's Development

JULIANNE CONRY

INTRODUCTION

Since the 1950s, it has been recognized that children's development can be affected by parental substance use. The most comprehensive information concerns the effects of parental alcohol use on children. Evidence of developmental problems related to parental use of other substances is not well established.

A range of psychological problems has been found in the "children of alcoholics" (COAs): over dependence, low self-esteem, social withdrawal and even suicide. Externalizing behaviours such as lying, stealing and delinquency have been found. School problems, learning disabilities and neuropsychological deficits have also been reported. The belief that these are inevitable outcomes has been, perhaps, reinforced through the emergence of support organizations such as Children of Alcoholics and Adult Children of Alcoholics, which began in the United States and Canada in the 1980s. (The term "children of alcoholics" is widely used in research and clinical practice. Although the term "alcoholic" may be perceived as labelling or pejorative by some, we use it here to reflect the terminology of the research cited.)

Yet, remarkable coping skills and resilience have also been documented for some children of alcoholics. In fact, some writers believe that most children of alcoholics do not have lifelong problems and that the research has focused too heavily on the "casualties" of parental alcoholism. This may be why there is now some research on what makes some children more resilient than others when faced with disrupted family life.

Most of the research has focused on the psychosocial problems of children of alcoholic fathers. This is likely because more males than females are in treatment for alcohol problems; males, therefore, are more often identified for research studies. Cooper (1991) reported that between 1970 and 1984, women represented only eight per cent of subjects in alcoholism studies. In the 1980s, women made up only 20 per cent of the clients in treatment. But those in treatment may be people with more severe problems, or people for whom the economic consequences of drinking are more serious. Most people with alcohol problems are not in treatment.

Conclusions from these studies typically refer to "children from alcoholic homes," but often do not specify which parent has an alcohol problem. The absence of this distinction raises a number of questions. Which parent is alcoholic? Does the child live with both parents, or just one? Is a step-parent involved? From both treatment/intervention and research perspectives, these are extremely important questions. Also relevant is the stage of the child's development at which the parent began to drink problematically, and the pattern of use. In 1973, Jones and his colleagues coined the term "fetal alcohol syndrome" (FAS), when they published a landmark study describing a pattern of physical and behavioural abnormalities and cognitive delay among children born to alcoholic mothers (Jones & Smith, 1973; Jones et al., 1973). Since then, thousands of articles have been published on the subject in the areas of basic science (animal research), human studies, and clinical and anecdotal observations. Thus for children of alcoholic women who drank during pregnancy, problem alcohol use has both environmental and biological consequences.

Fetal alcohol syndrome came to wider public attention in 1989, with the publication of Michael Dorris's *The Broken Cord*, the true story of a single parent raising a developmentally delayed child who struggled to learn even simple concepts. The father sought to understand why and eventually learned that his son had FAS. Following publication of his book, Dorris was inundated with heart-wrenching letters from parents who realized that he had also described their children (Dorris, 1989).

With research that has accumulated since 1973, we are only now learning about adults who were born with FAS. FAS has lifelong neurological effects; those who have it are prone to various psychosocial problems, including being at risk for substance use problems themselves. Counsellors are faced with diverse challenges when working with clients who have been prenatally exposed to alcohol.

This chapter will introduce the counsellor to the lifespan implications for the child whose parents currently use alcohol problematically, and for the child who was exposed to alcohol in the womb. It will also discuss treatment implications for women who use alcohol during pregnancy.

CHILDREN OF ALCOHOLICS

Prevalence of Parental Alcohol Use

Many children grow up in a home in which one or both parents are alcoholic. With prevalence rates of alcoholism for men at about five to nine per cent and for women at about two per cent, it could be estimated that one child in eight has an alcoholic parent (MacDonald & Blume, 1986). Recent research has focused on the cognitive and personality characteristics of these children. The interest evolved as a result of finding familial patterns of alcoholism, implying the possibility of genetic predisposition. The research sought to determine whether the children shared unique characteristics that might be used to predict alcoholism in adulthood. It has been difficult, if not impossible, to separate the effects of environmental factors from those of biological factors that may make the child prone to various learning and behavioural problems.

Problems Co-existing with Alcohol Use

PSYCHOLOGICAL PROBLEMS

Many psychological problems can co-exist with alcoholism, including personality disorders, anxiety disorders and depression (Sher, 1997). These factors may be as important as alcoholism in predicting the effects on children. For example, alcoholism plus antisocial personality disorder (ASPD) in parents was associated with increased risk of oppositional defiant disorder in their children (Kuperman et al., 1999). Family conflict plus ASPD exacerbated disruptive behaviour by the time of school entrance and was associated with poorer school achievement (Loukas et al., 2003; Poon et al., 2000).

HOME ENVIRONMENT

The home environments of alcoholics have been characterized by disorganization, poverty, violence and abuse or neglect of the children (Lund & Landesman-Dwyer, 1979; Nylander, 1960; Tarter et al., 1984; Woodside, 1983). In a study of parental problem drinking and children's adjustment, parent-child conflict was the most significant mediator between drinking and externalizing problems in the children, and maternal depression was the most significant mediator between drinking and internalizing problems (El-Sheikh & Flanagan, 2001). As adults, COAs remembered their childhoods as chaotic and unpredictable—with inconsistent care, behavioural expectations and discipline (Beletis & Brown, 1981). The children's situations were often complicated by poverty and its associated problems. However, additional stressors such as divorce, parents' psychopathology, parental criminality and perinatal birth complications make it more difficult to attribute the child outcomes primarily to the environmental circumstances that characterize parental alcoholism (West & Prinz, 1987).

Effects on the Child

BEHAVIOURAL PROBLEMS

When children are selected for research on other problems, an association with alcoholism is often present. For example, among children diagnosed with "socialized aggression," there was a high prevalence of parental alcoholism (Stewart et al., 1980). In one longitudinal study of sons of alcoholic fathers, teachers rated these children significantly higher on impulsive-restless behaviours (Knop et al., 1985); but the link to hyperactivity is inconclusive—that is, among the hyperactive group, the prevalence of alcoholism in fathers is not significantly high (Morrison, 1980). Aggression and hyperactivity are not always separated in research definitions or in assessment of individual cases. The association is more striking between parental alcoholism and conduct problems (West & Prinz, 1987). When Danish COAs were compared with a reference population through the Child Behavior Checklist (CBCL), almost half these children functioned as well as the average of the controls, which demonstrates the heterogeneity among these children (Christensen & Bilenberg, 2000).

Personality traits associated with impulsivity and disinhibition (such as sensation seeking and aggressiveness) are most associated with children of alcoholics (Sher, 1997). Children of alcoholic mothers often have attention-deficit/hyperactivity disorder as well as other behavioural problems, but these results are counfounded by the effects of prenatal exposure to alcohol, since FAS is also known to produce these problems (Steinhausen et al., 1982). If a child has a difficult temperament, he or she may be at increased risk for behaviour problems if he or she is raised in an alcoholic family (Jansen et al., 1995).

PERFORMANCE IN SCHOOL

In a number of studies of children's intellectual functioning and achievement in school, the scores of COAs were generally lower than those of their counterparts from families without alcohol problems. Particularly in this area, investigation of maternal alcoholism, and the child's known (or unknown) prenatal exposure to alcohol, confound the generalizations. The early Seattle studies of FAS conducted by Streissguth and colleagues found significantly lower IQ scores for children of alcoholic mothers (Streissguth, 1976; Streissguth et al., 1979). Gabrielli & Mednick (1983) also found lower IQ scores, but this time none of the mothers had a known diagnosis of alcohol dependence, although some drinking during pregnancy may have occurred. More recent studies of COAs have been careful to consider the factor of prenatal alcohol exposure.

Resilience

HOME ENVIRONMENT
The home environment plays a role in mitigating the effects of parental alcoholism on children. Children who had an alcoholic parent—but who came from homes where the parents were well educated and held "white-collar" jobs and earned average or above-average incomes—were compared with children from homes where there were no alcohol problems. On cognitive and personality measures, the first group of children achieved test results that placed them below their controls, but still within the normal range (Bennett et al., 1988). Where children had an alcoholic father, but were otherwise in positive circumstances, they were no more likely than the controls to be truant or to drop out of school. Unfortunately, alcoholism in the family is more likely to be associated with disadvantaged circumstances (Robins et al., 1978).

PATTERN OF PARENTAL ALCOHOLISM AND RECOVERY
The history of parental alcoholism is also important. In one study, the children of recovered alcoholics showed no cognitive or personality scores outside the normal range (Whipple & Noble, 1991). Adolescent children of a recovered alcoholic father did not differ from controls on self-esteem and locus of control. It seems that having fathers who had recovered from alcoholism affected the quality of their lives, but not how they felt about themselves. They could rate their lives as happy compared with children whose fathers' drinking problem continued. Both groups who had alcoholic fathers were more positive than controls about alcoholics and were less damning of any personality fault or weakness. They were also more positive about the alcoholic's chances of recovery (Callan & Jackson, 1986). However, some children of parents who had relapsed to alcoholism responded with anxiety, depression and nightmares. (Moos & Billings, 1982). These findings suggest that the pattern of alcoholism and recovery has important effects on the children.

In reviewing the research on COAs, West & Prinz (1987) conclude that neither all nor a majority of such children are inevitably doomed. In particular, where differences have been found between these children and those from families with no alcohol problems, the overall differences are small and there is considerable overlap between the two groups. Sher (1997) cautions that "popular portrayals of COAs are clearly overgeneralizations and have the potential to be harmful" (p. 253). Clearly, longitudinal and better-controlled studies are needed.

OTHER FACTORS
In 1955, all children born on the Hawaiian island of Kauai became the subjects of a 32-year longitudinal study (Werner, 1992). A subset of that cohort (n = 49) was children of alcoholic parents. In 38 cases, the alcoholic parent was the father, in six cases the mother and in five cases both parents were problem drinkers. The children's lives were complicated by chronic poverty, little educational stimulation in the home,

family discord and divorce. A few suffered moderate to severe prenatal or perinatal trauma. By age 18, in spite of the adversity, 59 per cent had not developed any learning or behavioural problems; they did well in school, at work and in their social lives. This group of resilient children was compared with the group that had developed serious coping problems by adolescence. Three-quarters of the resilient group were females; two-thirds of those with problems were male. Only one of the resilient children had a mother who was alcoholic, while the children of the fathers who drank were divided between the resilient and problem groups.

What were the qualities of the caregiving environment or characteristics of the child that made a difference? In the earlier analyses, it was noted that the resilient children had received a great deal of attention from their primary caregivers during the first year of life, with no prolonged separations; there were also no additional births or parental conflict during the first two years (i.e., fewer stressful events during the first two years of life). The temperaments of the resilient group were described as "cuddly and affectionate," which tends to elicit positive attention. Conversely, the children who later developed problems were already delayed in intellectual and social-emotional development by age two, and this continued throughout school. Average intelligence, communication skills and achievement orientation were associated with a better outcome in the resilient group. A responsible, caring attitude, positive self-concept, a more internal locus of control and belief in self-help also characterized the resilient group (Werner, 1986).

The final follow-up occurred when the cohort reached age 32. It was apparent that, in the absence of serious damage to the central nervous system, the effects of perinatal stress diminished over time, with the outcome more dependent on the caregiving environment. Four characteristics were identified that distinguished the members of the resilient group:

1. Temperamental characteristics that helped them elicit positive responses from various caring persons
2. Skills and values that led to efficient uses of their abilities; faith that the odds could be overcome; realistic educational and vocational plans and regular household responsibilities
3. Caregiving styles of parents that reflected competence and fostered self-esteem in the children, mother's level of education, and rules and structure in the households
4. Supportive adults who fostered trust and acted as gatekeepers for the future. Some of these were "surrogate" parents such as grandparents, elder mentors, youth leaders or members of church groups.

Furthermore, for those in the resilient group, there was the opening of opportunities at major life transitions—for example, from high school to workplace. This tended to deflect the sometimes pathological trajectory of a significant proportion of high-risk children on to the path of normal adulthood. Particularly important was the availability of adult education and vocational training, which fostered responsibility and self-esteem (Werner, 1992).

Werner's findings are supported by other researchers, such as Rutter (1990), who are interested in protective mechanisms in vulnerable children. Werner notes that her own and others' research have shown that if a parent is incapacitated or unavailable, another person in the child's life can play an enabling role. Werner stresses the urgency of establishing interventions for these vulnerable children, but concludes her study with a message of hope because of the children who have succeeded against the odds.

FETAL ALCOHOL SYNDROME (FAS) AND OTHER ALCOHOL-RELATED CONDITIONS

Society has long known that drinking alcohol during pregnancy can have adverse effects on the developing fetus. In a biblical reference an angel appeared to Samson's mother and said, "Behold, thou shalt conceive and bear a son, and now drink no wine or strong drink" (Judges 13:3-4). During the gin epidemic in England, a Hogarth engraving from the mid-1700s entitled "Gin Lane" portrays a drunken woman with her child falling from her arms. Computerized enhancement of the child's features suggests FAS. In Pickwick Papers, Charles Dickens suggests that maternal drinking affected his character, Betsy Martin: "widow, one child and one eye, but knows her mother drank bottled stout, and shouldn't wonder if that caused it."

It wasn't until the thalidomide tragedy of the 1960s, however, that contemporary medicine recognized that drugs, toxins and infections cross the placenta and may harm the developing fetus. Articles published in France by Lamache (1967) and Lemoine et al. (1968), and in the United States by Jones et al. (1973), first documented what is now a recognizable and unique pattern of features caused by prenatal exposure to alcohol: retarded physical growth, altered facial characteristics (dysmorphology) and brain dysfunction. In the late 1970s, the first cases of FAS in Canada were reported to the Health Protection Branch, National Health and Welfare.

Many adults diagnosed with FAS today were born at a time when physicians were not aware that drinking during pregnancy is harmful. Women were not warned to avoid alcohol when pregnant—in fact they were told that drinking was okay; women who did drink (believing that alcohol was not harmful) while avoiding prescription and other drugs to protect their unborn babies tell some heartbreaking stories.

Prevalence of FAS

Worldwide estimates of the incidence of FAS vary depending on location and methodologies. The IOM (Stratton et al., 1996) estimated 0.6 to 3 cases out of 1,000 births worldwide. May & Gossage (2001) estimated 0.5 to 2 cases out of 1,000 of FAS and 10 out of 1,000, in the United States, for the full spectrum of diseases related to prenatal drinking. At present, while there are no statistics available for Canada, it is estimated that in some communities as many as one in five children may be affected (Robinson et al., 1987). FAS and its related conditions are underdiagnosed due to lack of recognition and lack of diagnostic clinics. Statistics for 1998 to 1999 show that 14.5 per cent of women report alcohol use during pregnancy (Human Resources Development Canada and Health Canada, 2002).

Diagnosis and Effects of FAS

Diagnosis of full FAS may be made in a case where there is documented significant prenatal exposure to alcohol, where the child shows the classic characteristic features in three areas:

1. Prenatal and/or postnatal growth delay (height and/or weight below the tenth percentile);
2. Central nervous system involvement (conditions such as head circumference below the third percentile, intellectual impairment, learning disabilities, attention-deficit/hyperactivity disorder or other neurological abnormalities); and
3. Characteristic facial features (short palpebral fissures [eye slits], flat midface, long/indistinct philtrum (the groove between the nose and upper lip) and thin upper lip.

Figure 22-1 depicts the "discriminating features" of FAS—those features that form the "gestalt" of FAS, and "associated features"—other characteristics that are frequently present with FAS.

FIGURE 22-1

Facies in Fetal Alcohol Syndrome in the Young Child

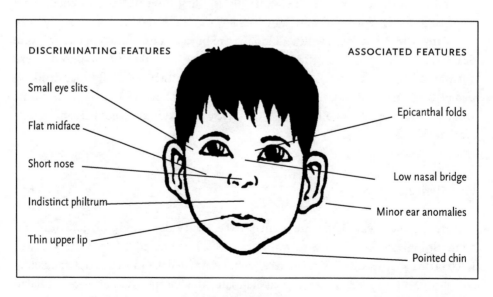

Source: Streissguth & Little, 1994.

When not all of the physical criteria for full FAS were present and there was known, documented and significant prenatal exposure to alcohol, an alcohol-related diagnosis of fetal alcohol effects (FAE) was made (Sokol & Clarren, 1989).* Recent follow-up research has found that FAE is not a "milder" form of FAS; while the physical features are often more subtle, the neurological deficits may be just as devastating. Adolescents and adults diagnosed with FAE are often at greater risk than those with FAS of having problems with adaptive functioning ("life skills") (Streissguth et al., 1996). For both FAS and FAE, there is a continuum of effects that depends on the amount of alcohol consumed, the timing of the drinking and other metabolic and genetic factors.

In 1996, the U.S. Congress mandated the Institute of Medicine (IOM) to review what was known and unknown about FAS. The IOM brought together a committee of American and Canadian FAS experts. Among the issues debated were diagnostic criteria and terminology. One recommendation arising from the study was that the term "fetal alcohol effects" be replaced by the terms "partial FAS" (pFAS) and "alcohol-related neurodevelopmental disorder" (ARND), depending on which features are present (Stratton et al., 1996). The IOM criteria remain the gold standard for diagnosis. A new umbrella term, fetal alcohol spectrum disorder (FASD), encompasses the range of effects found with prenatal alcohol exposure, but is not a diagnosis.

PHYSICAL APPEARANCE

FAS and other alcohol-related conditions such as pFAS and ARND are medical diagnoses made by a physician trained to recognize birth defects. There are other medical conditions with presentations similar to those of FAS, and these conditions must be distinguished. Some are chromosomal disorders that have behavioural profiles similar to that of FAS, such as Fragile X and Turner's syndrome. Other conditions produce a similar physical appearance such as Williams syndrome, fetal hydantoin syndrome (caused by the anticonvulsant drug Dilantin®), maternal phenylketonuria (PKU) and fetal toluene syndrome (caused by glue sniffing). Also, FAS may occur with other disorders such as autism, Tourette's disorder or attention deficit/hyperactivity disorder (ADHD).

A diagnosis of FAS may be hard to make; in an infant because of difficulty detecting brain dysfunction, and in an adolescent or adult due to changing facial features and catch-up growth. As with some other syndromes, the physical features become less detectable as the child develops. While some individuals with full FAS remain small, others grow to within the normal range of height. Girls, especially, tend to gain weight during adolescence. The characteristic facial features also change: the bone structure of the midface may become coarse, the philtrum may reappear and extensive orthodontia may alter the earlier appearance of the maxillary (jaw) area, though the eye slits (palpebral fissures) and head circumference tend to remain disproportionately small. To make a correct diagnosis of FAS in an adult, a review of childhood photographs is often required. More importantly, most people affected by prenatal

---

*In this chapter where research studies are cited, the terminology used by their authors is used.

alcohol exposure show neither remarkable facial features nor significant growth delay, but only brain dysfunction; these people would be diagnosed with pFAS or ARND.

BEHAVIOURAL AND LEARNING DIFFICULTIES

A youth's or adult's behavioural or learning difficulties may be a first indication that he or she is affected by prenatal alcohol exposure. In the early published descriptions of FAS, as in other newly discovered syndromes, the most extreme cases were the first described, with about half of those with FAS measuring IQ below the cut-off for "mental disability" (less than 70). Fetal alcohol syndrome is considered one of the three leading known causes of mental disability (the causes of most mental disabilities are unknown). A continuum of effects is now recognized among those with prenatal alcohol exposure. Dr. Ann Streissguth and her colleagues began their longitudinal study in 1992 when FAS and FAE were the only diagnostic categories. (When their studies are cited, "FAS/FAE" is used, though, as discussed above, "FAE" now includes those with a diagnosis of partial FAS and ARND.) In a recent follow-up study (Streissguth et al., 1996), the average IQ of people with FAS was 79 ("slow learner" range), and 90 ("average" range) for people with FAE. Only 27 per cent of those with FAS and only nine per cent of those with FAE had IQs below 70. With IQs ranging well into the average or above, FASD is better described as a disorder associated with learning disabilities, rather than mental disability. School-aged children often have difficulty learning basic subjects—reading, spelling and math—with math usually being the hardest to master. The underlying processes that contribute to a student's learning disabilities include problems with:
• language
• memory
• forming abstractions
• attention (Conry, 1990; 1996).

Young children with FASD usually show some degree of language delay or disability. Their understanding of single words is better than their understanding of connected language, and their ability to express themselves is weaker still (Asante et al., 2003). As they grow older, they often become adept at "cocktail chatter"—lots of words with little real meaning. At this superficial level, they seem competent, but on closer examination, it is apparent that they are easily confused by the normal pace and complexity of day-to-day language. For example, they do not understand sarcasm and may take jokes personally; problems processing information can occur at any level, including:
• receiving the information accurately (as the speaker intends)
• interpreting it (understanding)
• remembering it correctly
• acting on it.

PROBLEMS WITH MEMORY

People with FASD often have significant problems with memory. The most significant deficit is in working memory, which is the ability to hold information in mind while

performing some action on it (e.g., repeating sequences of numbers backwards). Concepts learned one day are forgotten the next. People with FASD may recall details from long ago, but cannot remember if they have had lunch. They have particular difficulty recalling sequences, such as the events in a story; while the information may be there, it cannot be retrieved without prompting. These people may be accused of lying because their attempt to fill in memory gaps results in confabulation (the involuntary production of a "logical" but false memory). In this regard, people with FASD are similar to those with other types of known brain dysfunction, such as traumatic brain injury or Alzheimer's disease. The ability to think abstractly and to reason means being able to:
• consider possibilities in the future
• make connections
• generalize from experience
• anticipate consequences.

People with FASD have difficulty thinking abstractly. They are often very concrete in their thinking; they cannot take a perspective different from their own experience, and can deal only with the present. As well as not being good at reasoning (thinking things through) they often act on impulse. This behaviour is common among those with attention-deficit/hyperactivity disorder and makes matters worse. In fact, attention-deficit/hyperactivity disorder affected approximately 60 per cent of the Seattle sample of FAS/FAE school-aged population (Streissguth et al., 1996). Impulsive behaviour got them into trouble and distractibility caused classroom problems. Most of the children with FAS/FAE had disrupted school experiences punctuated by suspensions or expulsions; many eventually dropped out. Nevertheless, a significant number completed high school, usually on modified programs, and attended post-secondary upgrading or training programs.

ADAPTIVE BEHAVIOUR

"Adaptive behaviour" refers to the degree and efficiency with which a person meets "the standards of personal independence and social responsibility of his age or cultural group" (Grossman, 1977). Included in adaptive behaviour are functional life skills such as self-care and daily living skills, "common-sense" judgment in interacting with the environment, and "appropriate" social skills. For those prenatally affected by alcohol, there is little correlation between adaptive skills level and IQ level, or diagnosis of FAS versus FAE. Higher IQ does not necessarily improve the prognosis for successful independent living in adulthood (Streissguth et al., 1996).

HYGIENE AND PERSONAL ROUTINES

People with FASD have difficulty establishing routines of basic hygiene and dressing appropriately. Household activities such as cooking can be a problem because of failure to keep track of the food during cooking or forgetting to turn off the stove. Mothers with FASD have their own challenges. They may not plan ahead to purchase baby items; or may be unable to properly prepare infant formula, forgetting to refrigerate the milk or clean the bottles.

HANDLING MONEY

Handling money creates problems for those with FASD. People with FASD may not understand the value of items (giving away valuable items or paying too much), or may squander money by spending it impulsively or giving it away. They are then unable to account for large sums of money they have spent. They are frequently too trusting of people; credit card debt and cell phone bills become overwhelming. Over 80 per cent of adults with FAS/FAE are so inept with money that they are unable to pay for basics such as rent, utilities and food (Streissguth et al., 1996).

CONCEPT OF TIME

By adolescence, most people with FASD have learned to tell time, although this skill is often late to develop. Having a concept of time—such as judging the difference between five minutes and five hours—is more problematic, and recalling a sequence of events (what happened when and in what order) is confusing. Some people with FASD don't recognize the importance that society places on being on time, which leads to complacency about getting to appointments, work and school. They may start out for appointments on time, but become distracted and never arrive; the urgency of a minor need (e.g., to do the laundry) may overwhelm the importance of keeping a doctor's appointment. In some cases, people with FASD are overly literal or overly rigid concerning matters of time, so directives such as "come home right away" or "come around 11 o'clock" are too vague and are misunderstood.

SOCIAL INTERACTION

Individuals with FASD often have social learning disabilities. The ability to read social cues, to understand others' feelings and to respond in socially appropriate ways is immature. In this regard, the youths or young adults are "egocentric," unable to take the perspective of another, and are viewed by peers as strange or different and are often rejected. Youths with FASD desperately want to be accepted, but they go about it in the wrong way. They are often manipulated, set up and easily led into situations that are troublesome or dangerous. They lack the ability to discriminate between friends and strangers, and are frequently victimized.

EMPLOYMENT

Problems getting and keeping a job were common in 79 per cent of those with FAS/FAE over age 21 (Streissguth et al., 1996). They appear to lack initiative or the ability to follow through even when job opportunities are provided. Often they would report losing their jobs without understanding why. The true reasons include:
• poor understanding of their job
• a lack of judgment
• being too easily frustrated or angered
• being unreliable
• friction with a supervisor
• other social difficulties at work.

When these situations repeatedly fail to work out, those trying to help often give up in frustration.

An additional problem of day-to-day living for the adult with FASD is not knowing how to access various social services such as disability or welfare benefits, medical services or counselling. The fact that they are told about such services does not ensure their ability to utilize them.

Adults with FASD and Substance Use Problems

Alcohol and other drug problems are common among both males and females with FASD. This may be due to a genetic predisposition and also because their life experiences put them at risk for substance use problems. In the Seattle study of people with FAS/FAE (Streissguth et al., 1996), approximately 30 per cent of those between the ages of 12 and 20 had alcohol problems, as did over 40 per cent in the 21 to 51 age group. About 20 per cent of the younger group had problems with other illicit drugs, rising to 30 per cent in the older group. Alcohol is the "gateway" drug: about 65 per cent who had abused alcohol later abused street drugs. For the vast majority, the onset of alcohol problems occurred at a young age—between 12 and 20—and 70 per cent had had their first alcohol treatment before age 21. Problems with alcohol and other drugs are more prevalent for those with a diagnosis of FAE than with a diagnosis of FAS. Reasons for abstinence among those who did not have alcohol problems included a lack of access to alcohol or a family that did not drink. However, nearly as frequently, alcohol problems within the family were also given as a reason for not drinking.

In a recent follow-up study, it was found that a mother's heavy prenatal alcohol use tripled her offspring's chance of having drinking-related problems at age 21. The study found no difference in the reported amount of drinking by those whose mothers drank heavily in pregnancy compared with those whose mothers had not. Rather, the difference was in how the two groups handled alcohol: those born to heavy-drinking mothers were three times more likely to show symptoms of alcohol dependence, including:
• blackouts
• hangovers
• being physically sick
• staggering
• unclear thinking (Baer et al., 2003).

It is likely that as a counsellor you will work with clients with FASD that has not yet been diagnosed. When difficulties arise in working with the client—the usual approaches aren't working and expectations of the client are not being met—it is time to consider a possible medical reason for the problem, such as FASD.

UNIQUE ISSUES IN TREATMENT

Chapter 23 addresses the cognitive deficits that can be directly caused by excessive alcohol consumption. For the client in alcohol and other drug treatment, these deficits might be interpreted as denial or a psychological defence. Reduced memory and poor ability to learn new information have been well documented during at least the first month of abstinence. The implication is that treatment modalities that rely on information processing or insight may be ineffective with clients who have a reduced ability to reason abstractly. For clients with FASD, these are the same cognitive deficits they have always had, but undoubtedly worsened due to alcohol and other drug problems.

When working with a client with FASD, counsellors are often frustrated by the apparent lack of carry-over from session to session. When the client is asked about thoughts or feelings, the response is often "I don't know." He or she is unable to think abstractly or about present or future events, but may be able to "parrot" back what he or she has been told. The client can "talk the talk" but not "walk the walk." The client's reasoning and the connections he or she makes don't make sense to the counsellor and the client may have difficulty staying on track. The client may present with a flat or even surly affect, make little eye contact or walk away mid-session for no apparent reason. One day the client may be resentful, angry and even abusive, but the next day present as though nothing had happened. The client doesn't know why people are angry with him or her because for the client, it's a brand new day, a clean slate. Missing appointments should not necessarily be interpreted as lack of motivation. The counsellor should try not to take such behaviour personally; the counsellor has little if anything to do with the client's actions.

In the Seattle studies, the FAS/FAE group were found to be at particularly high risk for additional mental health problems. The most frequent problem described for younger children and adolescents is attention problems (60 per cent). By adolescence and early adulthood, serious problems with depression and suicide threats or attempts emerge in 40 to 50 per cent of those with FAS/FAE (Streissguth et al., 1996).

No single approach to alcohol and other drug treatment has been found to be effective for those with FASD who have substance use problems. The key is recognizing the cognitive limitations and attempting to work in a concrete fashion, relying on repetition. Due to the underlying cause of this syndrome, those with FASD are likely to reside in environments where alcohol use is endemic. This is a very difficult barrier to successful treatment.

Is it worthwhile to seek a diagnosis of FASD? Where a counsellor suspects that an adult client may have FASD, a diagnosis can help both the counsellor and the client understand the implications. A diagnosis is not just a label; it can also lead to a blueprint for intervention planning. The diagnosis may allow the person to access certain benefits or services. If the client with FASD is a woman who is drinking, she is at considerable risk of having children with FASD. There is an opportunity to intervene to reduce the prevalence of alcohol-related birth defects in the next generation.

COUNSELLING WOMEN WHO DRINK DURING PREGNANCY

When FAS was first recognized in the early 1970s, the prospects for preventing FASD in children seemed straightforward. FAS is a preventable birth defect: if the pregnant woman does not drink, she will not have an affected child. However, those working in the addiction field recognize that FASD is a complex problem surrounded by issues of the root causes of problem alcohol use, attitudes toward women drinking (in particular, pregnant women who drink) and basic community education about the effects of alcohol use during pregnancy. Women do not drink to harm their babies. In addition, their pregnancies are often unplanned and they drink when they do not know that they are pregnant. That FASD is preventable is a double-edged sword. On the one hand, there is optimism that one of the leading known causes of mental and other disabilities can be eliminated. But on the other hand, that optimism prompts harsh criticism of women who, for whatever reason, cannot stop drinking. It is presumed, simply, that the woman knows better and could stop drinking if she wanted to. This is a dubious presumption.

In Health Canada's 2001 report on best practices for treatment of women with substance use problems, key experts identified the following barriers to treatment as specific to pregnant and parenting women:
• fear of losing their children
• lack of specialized child care and support services for children
• stigma attached to mothers misusing substances
• internal feelings of fear, guilt, grief and shame
• lack of specific programming for pregnant women.

Aboriginal and ethno-cultural minority women experience additional barriers related to culture, values and approaches. Stigmatization is expressed by the very health and social services personnel that pregnant women must access (Finkelstein, 1994). Comprehensive treatment models, including "harm reduction," are considered "best practice," but their effectiveness has not been adequately evaluated (Finkelstein, 1993) and certainly not in terms of preventing alcohol-related birth defects.

Recognizing and treating the mental health issues of pregnant women is critical to successfully reducing or eliminating alcohol use. In their study of 80 mothers of FASD children, Astley et al. (2000) found that only three did not have a mental health disorder. On average they experienced five mental health disorders. The most prevalent of these are:
• post-traumatic stress
• depression
• phobias
• antisocial personality
• anxiety.

Sexual and/or physical abuse had been experienced by 95 per cent of these women, while 98.8 per cent experienced emotional abuse as children and 86.3 per cent as adults. Very few had access to appropriate services for these problems at the time of their pregnancy (Astley et al., 2000).

According to Finkelstein (1993), "programs that provide comprehensive and coordinated treatment are better able to draw pregnant women into care as well as provide more effective treatment" (p. 1275). An active case manager is considered to be critical to effective treatment. One of the most successful prevention programs, pioneered in Seattle, is known as the "Birth to 3 Program." After giving birth to a child exposed to alcohol and other drugs, mothers received intensive support from a caseworker who advocated for them and helped them access services until the child was three years old. The results have been impressive, including:
• fewer subsequent children born exposed to alcohol and other drugs
• reduced placement in foster care
• less dependence on welfare (Ernst et al., 1999; Grant et al., 1999).

This program is now being replicated in communities in Canada.

Assessing Alcohol Use during Pregnancy

Even today some physicians conducting prenatal visits may not ask a pregnant woman about her drinking habits, and many women have not heard warnings about drinking during pregnancy. In a study conducted by Armstrong (personal communication) in British Columbia, physicians agreed to include a structured set of questions about alcohol use in their usual prenatal interviews.

The study identified a large proportion of women who were likely drinking enough to harm their infants. Yet at the study's conclusion, very few doctors said they would continue to use the questions in their regular practice, believing they lack training or knowledge in this area. Some were also worried that such questions might offend the women and that they wouldn't come back.

The questionnaire used in Armstrong's study is known as the T-ACE (Sokol, 1988; Sokol et al., 1989), the structure of which is shown below. Using the T-ACE questionnaire with pregnant women, the study found that:
• 51.7 per cent drank alcohol at some point during their pregnancy
• 36.4 per cent fell in the medium-risk category for alcohol use during pregnancy
• 14.2 per cent fell in the high-risk category.

TABLE 22-1

T-ACE Questions to Identify Risk Drinkers

Tolerance	How many drinks does it take to make you feel "high"—feel the effects?	Three drinks or more = 2 points
Annoyed	Have people annoyed you by criticizing your drinking?	Yes = 1 point
Cut down	Have you felt you ought to cut down on your drinking?	Yes = 1 point
Eye-opener	Have you ever had an "eye-opener"—a drink first thing in the morning to steady your nerves or get rid of a hangover?	Yes = 1 point
Total:	A total score of 2 points or more indicates a risk drinker.	

Source: Sokol, 1988.

As a group, the women had additional risk characteristics including single parenthood, poverty and premature birth of their babies. Since the time of this study, the T-ACE questions have been printed on the prenatal form, however, only 0.1 per cent of physicians ask these questions.

A recent Canada-wide survey (Clarke et al., 2003) assessed the attitudes and practices of 5000 health care professionals towards alcohol consumption by pregnant women. The professionals included psychiatrists, pediatricians, obstetricians, family physicians and midwives. While 93.6 per cent of survey respondents reported asking all pregnant women if they are currently drinking alcohol, only 62.3 per cent used a standard tool to screen for alcohol use; 64.9 per cent indicated they "always" discuss adverse effects of alcohol use with pregnant women who report moderate alcohol use, but only just over half (52.9 per cent) "always" referred to treatment women who report binge drinking during pregnancy. Only 54.2 per cent of respondents felt prepared to care for pregnant women in the area of alcohol abuse or dependence. There is clearly a need to build greater awareness and skills among these key health professionals. In Health Canada's *Canadian Perinatal Health Report* for the years 1996–1997, 16.6 per cent of children under the age of three had mothers who reported drinking alcohol during pregnancy (Health Canada, 2000).

The treatment of such women is a priority, requiring close community cooperation among physicians, pregnancy outreach programs and substance use counsellors.

Effects of Alcohol and Frequency of Use

Alcohol has a teratogenic effect during the first three months of pregnancy, affecting the proper formation of the body organs and brain. In the latter six months of pregnancy, alcohol has a toxic effect on physical growth and brain development. FASD is more likely to occur with continuous drinking or heavy consumption of alcohol during pregnancy. Binge drinking is especially harmful. Children born to mothers who have an average of one to two drinks per day or who may occasionally have up to five or more drinks at a time are at increased risk for learning disabilities and other cognitive and behavioural problems (Health Canada, 1996). In one study, binge drinking appeared to be more prevalent among younger women (Gladstone et al., 1997). However, the U.S. Centers for Disease Control reported that among pregnant women who reported any alcohol use, the binge and frequent drinkers were more likely to be over 30 years old (Sidhu & Floyd, 2002). Between 1991 and 1999 the rate of any alcohol use had declined slightly among the U.S. pregnant women who were interviewed, but binge (2.7 per cent) and frequent drinking (3.3 per cent) had not. 12.7 per cent reported use some time during their pregnancies. As unplanned pregnancies are common, it is worrisome that among the non-pregnant women, binge rates were 12.3 per cent. Also, older women appear less likely to reduce their alcohol use once they find out they are pregnant, suggesting a greater degree of alcohol dependence (Ebrahim et al., 1999). Comparable data are not available for Canada.

Effects of Health Promotion and Media on Pregnant Women

The media present mixed messages about the danger of drinking during pregnancy. Scare tactics, such as implying that one drink will irreparably harm the baby, are not only scientifically inaccurate but may also cause unwanted effects; taken literally, they may cause undue anxiety and lead a pregnant woman to make unnecessary decisions (such as abortion). Alternatively, women who ignore these warnings completely may disregard the real risks of drinking.

Contemporary health promotion describes a continuum of risk to the unborn child and a "risk-reduction" or "harm-reduction" approach to treatment. (The interested reader may consult May [1995] for a description of a multiple-level comprehensive approach to the prevention of FAS.) For the woman who has significant problems with her drinking, any reduction—at any time during her pregnancy—will improve the outcome for her baby.

Nevertheless, there is no known safe level of drinking and no benefit to the baby from the mother's drinking. Health Canada's position is that the prudent choice is not to drink during pregnancy or while breast-feeding. The pregnant woman should receive this clear, non-judgmental message from her physician, counsellor, friend or relative.

At a recent conference on FAS, a panel of birth mothers with alcohol-affected children rejected the notion of the "reduce drinking/harm reduction" message. For them, any message that suggested that one or two drinks would not be harmful essentially granted women permission to drink. They stated that if one or two drinks were acceptable, what would stop women from drinking a few more? These panel members contended that women must be informed that it is best to stop drinking altogether.

WOMEN WHO USE OTHER DRUGS DURING PREGNANCY

Although our primary focus has been on the use of alcohol during pregnancy, women who drink during pregnancy are likely also to use other drugs that may affect the fetus. Little is known about combined drug effects.

Streissguth and her colleagues (1991) compared the drug use of women who used cocaine during pregnancy with those who did not. The results, summarized below, are a reminder that alcohol remains the drug about which we should be most concerned. They indicate that women who use cocaine during pregnancy are likely also to use alcohol, and may have a pattern of binge drinking that can be harmful. At present, the effects of cocaine alone on the fetus are not well understood. A smaller-scale study was carried out in Toronto, with similar findings (Graham & Koren, 1991).

TABLE 22-2

Cocaine and Other Drugs in Pregnancy

	NO COCAINE (N = 777)	COCAINE (N = 97)
Any alcohol	56%	82%
Binge alcohol (>5 drinks/occasion)	8%	30%
Cigarettes	31%	89%
Marijuana	14%	68%
Other illicit drugs	4%	33%

Source: Streissguth et al., 1991.

FATHERS WHO DRINK

To date, the data on how prenatal paternal exposure to alcohol affects a fetus is sparse. Animal studies show some effect on organ weights, hormone secretion and immune response. In reviewing the literature, however, the Institute of Medicine clearly states that paternal consumption does not cause FAS. With great caution, they recognized that the combinations of maternal and paternal alcohol abuse are so complex that some anomalies attributed to maternal drinking may be exacerbated by paternal drinking, but this issue requires further research (Stratton et al., 1996).

Even so, fathers play an extremely important role in supporting their partners in not drinking during pregnancy. It can be difficult for the pregnant woman to withstand pressure from her partner, relatives and friends who encourage her to drink with them. On the other hand, pregnancy can be a powerful motivator. With positive support from family, friends and professionals, many women have successfully stopped drinking for the sake of the health of their unborn child.

CONCLUSION

Some communities have established programs to improve pregnancy outcomes through better prenatal care, nutrition and supported living arrangements, but even the most effective community services can be disjointed for lack of integration. For example, often there is no quick access to alcohol and drug counselling due to long waiting lists; pregnant women with children may fear that seeking treatment will result in their children being apprehended, or they may be unable to attend treatment because of inadequate child care. Further, the mother should continue to receive counselling after the baby is born, and she may not make the necessary transition to the appropriate community agency. Alcohol and drug counsellors play an extremely important role in integrating services to minimize the developmental consequences of parental substance abuse.

REFERENCES

Asante, K.O., Conry, J.L., Woodworth, C. & Salahub, A. (2003, February). Multi-discipline assessment of FAS and other alcohol-related diagnoses: A working community model. Symposium conducted at the conference *Fetal Alcohol Spectrum Disorder: Doing What Works,* Vancouver, B.C.

Astley, S.J., Bailey, D., Talbot, T. & Clarren, S.K. (2000). Fetal alcohol syndrome (FAS) primary prevention through FAS diagnosis: II. A comprehensive profile of 80 birth mothers of children with FAS. *Alcohol & Alcoholism, 35*(5), 509–519.

Baer, J.S., Sampson, P.D., Barr, H.M., Connor, P.D. & Streissguth, A.P. (2003). A 21-year longitudinal analysis of the effects of prenatal alcohol exposure on young adult drinking. *Archives of General Psychiatry, 60,* 377–385.

Beletis, S. & Brown, S. (1981). A developmental framework for understanding the adult children of alcoholics. *Focus on Women Journal of Addictions Health, 2,* 187–203.

Bennett, L.A., Wolin, S.J. & Reiss, D. (1988). Cognitive, behavioral, and emotional problems among school-age children of alcoholic parents. *American Journal of Psychiatry, 145,* 185–190.

Callan, V.T. & Jackson, D. (1986). Children of alcoholic fathers and recovered alcoholic fathers: Personal and family functioning. *Journal of Studies on Alcohol, 47,* 180–182.

Christensen, H.B. & Bilenberg, N. (2000). Behavioural and emotional problems in children of alcoholic mothers and fathers. *European Child and Adolescent Psychiatry, 9*(3), 219–226.

Clarke, M.E., Tough, S. & Cook, J.L. (2003). *Attitudes and Practices of Canadian Health Care Professionals toward Alcohol Consumption by Pregnant Women.* Unpublished abstract.

Conry, J.L. (1990). Neuropsychologic deficits in fetal alcohol syndrome and fetal alcohol effects. *Alcoholism: Clinical and Experimental Research, 14,* 650–655.

Conry, J.L. (1996). *Working with Students with Fetal Alcohol Syndrome/Effects: A Resource Guide for Teachers.* Victoria, B.C.: Ministry of Education.

Cooper, E.F. (1991). *Alcohol Use and Abuse by Women.* Congressional Research Report. Washington, DC: Library of Congress.

Dorris, M. (1989). *The Broken Cord.* New York: Harper and Row.

Ebrahim, S.H., Diekman, S.T., Floyd, L.R. & Decoufle, P. (1999). Pregnancy-related alcohol use among women in the United States, 1988–1994. *Prenatal and Neonatal Medicine, 4,* 39–46.

El-Sheikh, M. & Flanagan, E. (2001). Parental problem drinking and children's adjustment: Family conflict and parental depression as mediators and moderators of risk. *Journal of Abnormal Child Psychology, 29*(5), 417–432.

Ernst, C.C., Grant, T.M., Streissguth, A.P. & Sampson, P.D. (1999). Intervention with high-risk alcohol and drug-abusing mothers: II. Three-year findings from the Seattle model of paraprofessional advocacy. *Journal of Community Psychology, 27*(1), 19–38.

Finkelstein, N. (1993). Treatment programming for alcohol and drug-dependent pregnant women. *International Journal of the Addictions, 28*(13), 1275–1309.

Finkelstein, N. (1994). Treatment issues for alcohol and drug-dependent pregnant and parenting women. *Health and Social Work, 19* (1), 7–15.

Gabrielli, W. & Mednick, S. (1983). Intellectual performance in children of alcoholics. *Journal of Nervous and Mental Disease, 171,* 444–447.

Gladstone, J., Levy, M., Nulman, I. & Koren, G. (1997). Characteristics of pregnant women who engage in binge alcohol consumption. *Canadian Medical Association Journal, 156,* 789–794.

Graham, K. & Koren, G. (1991). Characteristics of pregnant women exposed to cocaine in Toronto between 1985 and 1990. *Canadian Medical Association Journal, 144*(5), 563–568.

Grant, T.M., Ernst, C.C. & Streissguth, A.P. (1999). Intervention with high-risk alcohol and drug-abusing mothers: I. Administrative strategies of the Seattle model of paraprofessional advocacy. *Journal of Community Psychology, 27*(1), 1–18.

Grossman, H. (1977). *Manual and Terminology on Classification in Mental Retardation.* Washington, DC: American Association on Mental Deficiency.

Health Canada. (1996). *Joint Statement: Prevention of Fetal Alcohol Syndrome (FAS) Fetal Alcohol Effects (FAE) in Canada.* Ottawa: Government of Canada.

Health Canada. (2000). *Canadian Perinatal Health Report.* Ottawa: Minister of Public Works and Government Services Canada.

Health Canada. (2001). *Best Practices: Treatment and Rehabilitation for Women with Substance Use Problems.* Ottawa: Minister of Public Works and Government Services.

Human Resources Development Canada and Health Canada. (2002). *The Well-Being of Canada's Young Children: Government of Canada Report.* Ottawa: Government of Canada.

Jansen, R.E., Fitzgerald, H.E., Ham, H.P. & Zucker, R.A. (1995). Pathways into risk: Temperament and behavior problems in three- to five-year-old sons of alcoholics. *Alcoholism: Clinical and Experimental Research, 19*(2), 501–509.

Jones, K.L. & Smith, D.W. (1973). Recognition of the Fetal Alcohol Syndrome in early infancy. *Lancet 2*(836), 999–1001.

Jones, K.L., Smith, D.W., Ulleland, C.N. & Streissguth, A.P. (1973). Pattern of malformation in offspring of chronic alcoholic mothers. *Lancet 1*(815), 1267–1271.

Knop, J., Teasdale, T., Schulsinger, F. & Goodwin, D. (1985). A prospective study of young men at high risk for alcoholism: School behavior and achievement. *Journal of Studies on Alcoholism, 46*, 273–278.

Kuperman, S., Schlosser, S.S., Lidral, J. & Reich, W. (1999). Relationship of child psychopathology to parental alcoholism and antisocial personality disorder. *Journal of the American Academy of Child and Adolescent Psychiatry, 38*(6), 686–692.

Lamache, A. (1967). Réflexions sur la descendance des alcooliques. *Bulletin de l'Académie Nationale de Médecine, 151*, 517–524.

Lemoine, P., Harouseau, H., Borteryu, J.T. & Menuet, J.C. (1968). Les enfants des parents alcooliques: Anomalies observées à propos du 127 cas. *Ouest Médical, 21*, 476–482.

Loukas, A., Zucker, R.A., Fitzgerald, H.E. & Krull, J.L. (2003). Developmental trajectories of disruptive behavior problems among sons of alcoholics: Effects of parent psychopathology, family conflict, and child undercontrol. *Journal of Abnormal Psychology, 112*(1), 119–131.

Lund, C. & Landesman-Dwyer, S. (1979). Pre-delinquents and disturbed adolescents: The role of parental alcoholism. *Currents in Alcoholism, 5*, 339–348.

MacDonald, D.R. & Blume, S.B. (1986). Children of alcoholics. *American Journal of Diseases of Children, 140*, 750–754.

May, P. (1995). A multiple-level comprehensive approach to the prevention of Fetal Alcohol Syndrome and other alcohol-related birth defects. *The International Journal of Addictions, 30*(12), 1549–1602.

May, P.A. & Gossage, J.P. (2001). Estimating the prevalence of Fetal Alcohol Syndrome: A summary. *Alcohol Research & Health, 25*(3), 159–167.

Moos, R. & Billings, A. (1982). Children of alcoholics during the recovery process: Alcoholic and matched control families. *Addictive Behaviors, 7*, 155–163.

Morrison, J. (1980). Adult psychiatric disorders in parents of hyperactive children. *American Journal of Psychiatry, 137*, 825–827.

Nylander, I. (1960). Children of alcoholic fathers. *Acta Paediatrica Scandinavica, 49*, Suppl. 121.

Poon, E., Ellis, D.A., Fitzgerald, H.E. & Zucker, R.A. (2000). Intellectual, cognitive, and academic performance among sons of alcoholics, during the early school years: Differences related to subtypes of familial alcoholism. *Alcoholism: Clinical and Experimental Research, 24*(7), 1020–1027.

Robins, L., West, P., Ratcliff, K. & Herjanic, B. (1978). Fathers' alcoholism and children's outcomes. *Currents in Alcoholism, 4*.

Robinson, G.C., Conry, J.L. & Conry, R.F. (1987). Clinical profile and prevalence of fetal alcohol syndrome in an isolated community in British Columbia. *Canadian Medical Association Journal, 137*(3), 203–207.

Rutter, M. (1990). Psychosocial resilience and protective mechanisms. In J. Rolf, A.S. Masten, D. Cicchetti, K.H. Nuechterlein & S. Weintraub (Eds.), *Risk and Protective Factors in the Development of Psychopathology* (pp. 181–214). New York: Cambridge University Press.

Sher, K.J. (1997). Psychological characteristics of children of alcoholics. *Alcohol Health & Research World, 21*(2), 247–254.

Sidhu, J.S. & Floyd, R.L. (2002). Alcohol use among women of childbearing age, United States, 1991–1999. *MMWR Weekly, 51*(13), 273–76.

Sokol, R.J. (1988). Finding the risk drinker in your clinical practice. In G.C. Robinson & R.M. Armstrong (Eds.), *Alcohol and Child/Family Health* (pp. 37–46). Vancouver: FAS Resource Group.

Sokol, R.J. & Clarren, S.K. (1989). Guidelines for use of terminology describing the impact of prenatal alcohol on the offspring. *Alcoholism: Clinical and Experimental Research, 13*, 597–598.

Sokol, R.J., Martier, S.S. & Ager, J.W. (1989). The T-ACE questions: Practical prenatal detection of risk-drinking. *American Journal of Obstetrics and Gynecology, 160*, 863–868.

Steinhausen, H., Nestler, V. & Huth, H. (1982). Psychopathology and mental functions in the offspring of alcoholic and epileptic mothers. *Journal of the American Academy of Child Psychiatry, 21*, 268–273.

Stewart, M., deBlois, S. & Cummings, C. (1980). Psychiatric disorder in the parents of hyperactive boys and those with conduct disorder. *Journal of Child Psychology and Psychiatry, 21*, 283–292.

Stratton, K., Howe, C. & Battaglia, F. (Eds.). (1996). *Fetal Alcohol Syndrome: Diagnosis, Epidemiology, Prevention, and Treatment*. Washington, DC: National Academy Press.

Streissguth, A.P. (1976). Psychologic handicaps in children with fetal alcohol syndrome. *Annals of the New York Academy of Sciences, 273,* 140–145.

Streissguth, A.P., Barr, H.M., Kogan, J. & Bookstein, F.L. (1996). *Understanding the Occurrence of Secondary Disabilities in Clients with Fetal Alcohol Syndrome (FAS) and Fetal Alcohol Effects (FAE): Final Report.* Seattle: University of Washington.

Streissguth, A.P., Grant, T.M., Barr, H.M., Brown, Z.A., Mayock, D.E., Ramey, S.L. et al. (1991). Cocaine and the use of alcohol and other drugs during pregnancy. *American Journal of Obstetrics and Gynecology, 164,* 1239–1243.

Streissguth, A.P., Little, R.E., Herman, C. & Woodell, S. (1979). IQ in children of recovered alcoholic mothers compared to matched controls. *Alcoholism: Clinical and Experimental Research, 3,* 197.

Streissguth, A.P. & Little, R.E. (1994). *Project Cork Institute Medical School Curriculum, Unit 5.* Timonium, MD: Milner Fenwick.

Tarter, R., Hegedus, A., Goldstein, G., Shelly, C. & Alterman, A. (1984). Adolescent sons of alcoholics: Neuropsychological and personality characteristics. *Alcoholism: Clinical and Experimental Research, 8,* 216–222.

Werner, E.E. (1986). Resilient offspring of alcoholics: A longitudinal study from birth to age 18. *Journal of Studies on Alcohol, 47,* 34–40.

Werner, E.E. (1992). The children of Kauai: Resiliency and recovery in adolescence and adulthood. *Journal of Adolescent Health, 12,* 262–268.

West, W.O. & Prinz, R.J. (1987). Parental alcoholism and childhood psychopathology. *Psychological Bulletin, 102,* 204–218.

Whipple, S.C. & Noble, E.P. (1991). Personality characteristics of alcoholic fathers and their sons. *Journal of Studies on Alcohol, 52,* 331–337.

Woodside, M. (1983). Children of alcoholic parents: Inherited and psychosocial influences. *Journal of Psychiatric Treatment and Evaluation, 5,* 51–537.

Chapter 23

Cognitive Deficits Caused by Alcohol and Other Drugs: Treatment Implications

TONY TONEATTO

This chapter will focus primarily on the evidence showing the impact of alcohol on the central nervous system (including fetal alcohol syndrome), and will also give a brief overview of the effects of other psychoactive substances on the brain.

SUBSTANCE-RELATED COGNITIVE DEFICITS

Alcohol

There is no doubt that people who are severely dependent on alcohol suffer significant neuropsychological impairment. In fact, 45 to 70 per cent of people who are alcohol-dependent have resulting deficits in memory, attention, new learning, visuospatial skills, concept formation, cognitive flexibility, set shifting, problem solving and ability to follow complex demands or instructions (Parsons, 1987). CT and MRI scans show that over half of those with chronic alcohol problems have cerebral atrophy (Lishman, 1990). Between 15 per cent and 30 per cent of nursing home patients may have permanent alcohol-induced dementia (Kaufman et al., 1996). Such cognitive deficits as impaired memory or confusion can be observed in the mental status assessment and in neuropsychological tests of people who were alcohol-dependent and have recently detoxified. (However, in most cases the cognitive effects of problem alcohol use do not fully meet the diagnostic criteria for permanent or well-defined diagnostic syndromes such as Korsakoff's syndrome or dementia.) In assessing people with severe drinking problems, it is important to learn whether the person has irreversible cognitive deficits that may affect his or her ability to adjust to an abstinent lifestyle, to cope with life stresses and to benefit from traditional alcohol treatments.

Tarter & Edwards (1986) have categorized people with chronic alcoholism into four groups. The first group consists of young people in the early stages of alcoholism who do not show any disturbances on neuropsychological measures. People in the second group have some neuropsychological abnormalities but are generally not clinically impaired. This group is the primary focus of this chapter. Those in the third group have serious memory disturbances but may otherwise show normal intellectual abilities. People with Korsakoff's syndrome are included in this group. This condition is usually preceded by Wernicke's encephalopathy, which is characterized by confusion, ataxia (involuntary muscle movements) and eye-muscle paralysis. Clients who demonstrate residual alcohol-related amnesia (accompanied by lack of spontaneity and indifference toward their condition) are usually diagnosed with Korsakoff's syndrome only when other cognitive functions (e.g., orientation to time, place and people) are relatively intact. Confabulation, or "making up" experiences, is one way in which such people may cope with severely impaired short-term memory. Nonetheless, these people remain alert and maintain social behaviour, self-care and grooming. The fourth group comprises people whose intellect is impaired and for whom alcohol-induced dementia is a more appropriate diagnosis. These clients may have difficulty in maintaining self-care. Ten per cent of people with alcohol dependence have full-fledged alcohol amnestic syndromes such as Korsakoff's syndrome and dementia.

The Wechsler Adult Intelligence Scale (WAIS) has been one of the most common measures of the effects of severe alcohol use on cognitive abilities. However, evidence is inconsistent on the effects of chronic alcohol use on this measure of intelligence. Some studies have found significant deterioration in people with long-term drinking problems versus the general population (Franceschi et al., 1984), while others have failed to find reliable differences (Grant et al., 1979). Verbal IQ scores tend to fall in the normal range (Tarter & Edwards, 1986) while performance IQ tends to be decreased. These findings reflect the damaging effect of alcohol on perceptual-motor abstraction and co-ordination skills, while less complex sensory or motor functions such as vocabulary, which depend on long-term memory, are less affected. Four WAIS-R subtests—Picture Arrangement, Digit Symbol, Block Design and Object Assembly—seem to consistently yield differences between people with severe alcohol problems and controls, indicating significant deficits in sequential organization and visuospatial skills (Knight & Longmore, 1994).

The Halstead-Reitan Battery (HRB) has also been used widely to investigate cognitive impairment in people with chronic drinking problems. The Category Test, a subtest of the HRB that assesses conceptual learning and problem solving, is the most sensitive test in the battery for measuring the effects of alcohol. The Tactual

Performance Test (which assesses spatial identification and memory) and Trails B (which assesses motor skills) are also sensitive to the effects of alcohol (Parsons & Farr, 1981). However, not all those with alcoholism will show evidence of brain damage on the HRB. Age, education level and the client's WAIS Verbal all correlate significantly with the HRB Impairment Index. The Luria-Nebraska Neuropsychological Battery shows similar results. These tests show that the most reliable effect of chronic alcoholism is a deterioration in the person's abstract cognitive functioning. This deterioration is indicated by a difficulty in forming hypotheses (necessary for effective problem solving), perseveration (persisting with the same pattern of behaviour to the point of inappropriateness) and difficulty in shifting problem-solving strategies (e.g., failing to try new strategies when initial ones are unsuccessful) (Parsons, 1987). Research to date does not indicate that people with long-term drinking problems have deficits in basic perceptual processes, but does reveal disturbances in spatial tasks requiring perceptual analysis, synthesis, orientation and sequencing. These deficits are typical of people in the intermediate stage of alcoholism, which includes those who have developed cognitive and behavioural difficulties but have no diagnosable organic brain syndrome.

Memory function is highly sensitive to central nervous system (CNS) damage and, as a result, is frequently used to assess the presence of brain damage in people with chronic alcohol problems. The Wechsler Memory Scales (WMS) have been widely used in this regard. However, early studies consistently failed to show that memory impairment was a feature of chronic alcohol use (Parsons & Prigatano, 1977; Butters et al., 1977). This finding may demonstrate that many WMS subtests are insensitive to even profound memory damage. However, in a modified version of the WMS, in which a second assessment occurs 30 minutes after the initial testing (Russell, 1988), there is strong evidence of memory deficits (Nixon et al., 1987), especially weak or poor encoding strategies. Similarly, tests that assess memory for geometric designs after a brief delay, such as the Benton Visual Retention Test, have also shown deficits for some people with severe alcohol problems. Short-term memory, in which material is recalled after delays up to 60 seconds, also seems to be impaired. (Brandt et al., 1983).

FETAL ALCOHOL SYNDROME

Prenatal alcohol exposure may result in spontaneous abortion, or in children born with any of the following: facial structure malformations, malformations of the hands and feet, flattened bridge of the nose, cardiac defects, mild to moderate mental retardation, lower birthweight. These effects, which typically include learning and behaviour difficulties, comprise what are known as fetal alcohol syndrome (FAS) and fetal alcohol effects (FAE; for a discussion of the terminology, see Chapter 22). The incidence of FAS is affected by the amount of alcohol a woman consumes while pregnant, when in her pregnancy she was drinking, and the degree of nutritional deficiencies. Nonetheless, milder FAS effects have been reported in children whose mothers had only three alcoholic drinks per day (Day et al., 1999). Learning difficulties commonly observed in children with FAS are also related to clinically significant hearing deficit, another common manifestation of prenatal alcohol exposure (Church & Kaltenbach, 1997). Not surprisingly, children with FAS are also at higher risk for other psychiatric problems, especially antisocial personality disorder and alcohol problems (Famy et al., 1998).

Other Drugs

Long-term use of stimulants such as cocaine has been shown to contribute to memory deficits (van Gorp et al., 1999). Some evidence suggests a link between stimulant use and mild impairments in memory and attention that last for a few months after the person stops use (Strickland & Stein, 1996). However, very few (0.5 per cent) people who seek treatment for stimulant use show permanent brain damage as a result of using stimulants (Kaufman et al., 1998).

Cognitive functioning, especially memory, also appears to be affected by cannabis (Solowij et al., 1995). However, there is little evidence that heavy cannabis use has long-term effects on the brain (Pope & Yurgelun-Todd, 1996), although cannabis may act in the long term on the septal area of the limbic system, an area important for the control of emotion. Effects such as impaired social behaviour, thinking dysfunction and amotivational syndrome (in which the person is apathetic, appears slothful and often gains weight) may reflect pre-existing personal characteristics rather than the direct effects of cannabis.

Prolonged hallucinogen use has been thought to contribute to thinking disorders, amotivational syndrome, deficits in abstract reasoning, and social withdrawal (Morgan, 2000). Yet, as with cannabis, it is not possible to distinguish between the direct effects of hallucinogens and pre-existing personal factors (Krystal & Price, 1992). Phencyclidine (PCP) has also been associated with serious memory deficits, especially within a month or two of use, though the toxic effects appear to be short-term. Glue and other inhalants are well-known for their impact on the brain, possibly as a result of their effects on the cerebellum. There is limited evidence that inhalant use may result in permanent brain atrophy (Yamanouchi et al., 1997). CNS depressants, such as the benzodiazepines, have also been shown to produce significant memory problems months, and sometimes even longer, after the person has stopped using them, even when they are used as intended (Griffiths & Weerts, 1997).

PREDICTING ALCOHOL-RELATED COGNITIVE DEFICITS

Not all people who use alcohol heavily will have cognitive deficits. In fact, the most important determinant of whether alcohol leads to cognitive impairment appears to be the age at which the person begins drinking. Among people with severe alcohol problems, those who began to drink by age 14 show more impairment on measures of abstraction, visuospatial sequencing and verbal memory than those who began to drink at a later age. Frequency, quantity and duration of drinking episodes do not appear to be related to neuropsychological deficits in any simple fashion (Parsons & Leber, 1981), and neither do the length of the person's alcohol use (Hesselbrock et al., 1985) or a family history of alcoholism (Schafer et al., 1991).

While children of people who drink heavily may show dysfunctional personal behaviour and have disturbed family backgrounds, this is not necessarily accompanied by cognitive deficits. When such people do show deficits, the deficits seem to be related to how much and how often the person himself or herself drinks, and to the toxic effects of drinking on brain functioning (Parsons, 1987).

Evidence also shows that people with "primary alcoholism" (those without mental health or serious medical problems before their drinking problems began) were more cognitively impaired than those with "secondary alcoholism," who typically drink to relieve stress.

Note that the cognitive impairment discussed above is not unique to people with severe drinking problems; impairment on the measures discussed above tends to be similar regardless of the source, which may include brain injury, multiple sclerosis or other causes in addition to heavy alcohol use. As Knight and Longmore (1994) note, "it must be acknowledged that there is little of exceptional interest in the neuropsychological performance of chronic alcoholics," especially when it is considered that the direct, neurotoxic effects of alcohol are not the only source of the cognitive deficits observed in people who drink heavily. Secondary factors include malnutrition (Wernicke-Korsakoff syndromes representing the most serious example), seizures, liver disease, concurrent use of other drugs, head injuries and premorbid intellectual functioning (Carlin & O'Malley, 1996).

However, this literature showing evidence of cognitive impairment in people with alcoholism may not adequately account for the role of motivation and attention, which may diminish performance independent of the CNS effects of alcohol. Lack of motivation to perform well or lack of persistence may produce lower performance than that of people in healthier control groups (Cynn, 1992). In addition, educational attainment and IQ have been shown to be related to cognitive deficits among people who drink heavily, with younger and more educated people performing better than those who are older and poorly educated (Tarter & Edwards, 1986).

ALCOHOL-RELATED COGNITIVE DEFICITS AND TREATMENT OUTCOME

Cognitive performance appears to account for only a small part of the variance in the outcome of alcohol use treatment. Donovan et al. (1987) found that people with alcohol-related neuropsychological impairment may be less likely to be employed, but did not find any correlation with relapse rates or drinking patterns. Studies that compare the outcome of alcohol use treatment for people with or without neuro-psychological deficits do not clearly show that deficits play a major role. For example, Teichner et al. (2002) studied people with a cognitive impairment who completed an intensive three-week outpatient program for alcohol use. These people did not do any worse up to 12 months after treatment. Cooney et al. (1991), in contrast, had found earlier that among people with severe alcoholism, those who were cognitively impaired did less well in coping skills therapy, but did as well as people who were cognitively intact in interactional therapy. Of course, cognitive deficits are only one of a range of variables, both external (e.g., psychosocial stability) and internal (e.g., mental health), that influence people's response to treatment. In any case these studies suggest that, for maximum benefit, alcohol use treatment must accommodate a person's cognitive deficits. People with a cognitive impairment *can* be treated successfully.

Although cognitive deficits do not seem to significantly affect treatment outcome, this is true mainly for younger, more mildly impaired people. For older people with more severe impairments, traditional treatments may need to be adapted. These people have conditions such as Korsakoff's syndrome or alcohol-induced dementia that result in severe memory impairments and disorientation. Some clients may appear to be cognitively intact because their conversational skills are normal and they show no obvious deficits such as impaired memory. Some of these people may nonetheless have impaired abstraction, problem solving and perceptual-motor functioning and may experience great difficulty in traditional treatments, which may be attributed to their poor motivation or denial. The cognitive effects of alcohol may interfere with therapy, which requires intact memory and learning and problem-solving skills. In addition, cognitive impairments may affect clients' motivation to use the skills they possess or have been taught. Some studies have found a higher rate of dropout from alcohol use treatment among people with a cognitive impairment (Teichner et al., 2002).

Because deficits may be at their most severe soon after the person stops drinking, it may be necessary to repeat therapeutic interventions made in this period. In fact, repeating elements of treatment is essential for older clients, who typically have more severe cognitive deficits and recover more slowly. As suggested by Goldman (1983), complex therapy should be delayed until cognitive function has recovered. For clients with impairments in memory, concentration and retention, treatment should be structured to ensure that the person is ready for the demands of treatment. Clients who have difficulty coping with residual deficits may also need help to reintegrate into everyday functioning. For the many clients in residential programs who have cognitive deficits, it may be particularly important for therapeutic interventions in the first phase of treatment to be less intense, to allow the client to recover cognitive functioning (McKenna, 1997).

RECOVERY FROM ALCOHOL-RELATED COGNITIVE DEFICITS

Neuropsychological function can improve in the weeks and months after a person stops drinking (Parsons & Nixon, 1998; Schuckit, 2000). This recovery can follow at least two paths: neurobiological recovery from the direct or indirect CNS effects of alcohol, and experience-dependent recovery in which practice, stimulation and activity speed up the client's recovery (Stringer & Goldman, 1988). Deficits in verbal ability (e.g., in verbal paired-associate learning) appear to clear up very quickly, within a month (Goldman, 1983), while some deficits (e.g., abstraction deficits) may persist for years. Similarly, impairments in new learning, visuospatial abstraction, problem solving and short-term memory may persist, especially in older clients. In a series of studies, Goldman (1987) and his colleagues (Ellenberg et al., 1980) showed that verbal functioning (as assessed by the WAIS Verbal scales) and visuospatial learning ability reach normal levels within two weeks of abstinence. Similarly, problem solving and new learning were impaired for one to two weeks after the client stopped drinking. However, on tests requiring complex skills, using novel stimuli or requiring adaptation, clients tended to show persistent deficits. Goldman (1983) summarized the recovery process as follows: Existing verbal abilities (vocabulary) are not impaired after the person stops drinking. Most other abilities, especially when any new learning is involved, are impaired during the first week or two of abstinence. New verbal learning then recovers. Visual-spatial abilities, abstraction and problem solving, short-term memory, and perhaps simple sensory reception show persistent impairment, particularly in older people. With prolonged abstinence, some of these abilities may recover. In general, the more novel, complex and rapid the information processing that a task requires, the longer abilities take to recover.

Age also influences the rate of cognitive recovery. People under age 40 frequently show no functional impairment two to three weeks after they stop drinking, while older clients may require three or more months to recover to a similar extent (Goldman et al., 1983). How much the person drinks and how long he or she has been drinking do not appear to have much influence on rate of recovery. Notably, people who resume drinking after a prolonged abstinence, even at much lower rates, show significantly less cognitive improvement than those who remain abstinent (Yohman, et al., 1985).

Rate of recovery can also be improved by repeating assessments. For example, Ellenberg et al. (1980) showed that repeating the testing materials resulted in improvement, suggesting that experience can improve the client's cognitive functioning. Forsberg and Goldman (1987) showed that clients who were repeatedly tested with a measure of verbal and visuospatial functions made fewer and fewer errors until their scores were normal. These authors also showed that clients learning with one task generalized their learning to different tasks that assessed the same function. This research suggests that experience-dependent learning can reduce the cognitive deficits of alcohol use clients, and that the gains clients make are not task-specific. Parsons (1987) has found that clients who received memory training (sessions on attention, chunking, visual memory, list learning, paired-associates, digit symbol and use of mnemonics) or problem-solving training (sessions on identifying goals and brainstorming) had better memory and problem-solving skills than those who received no training.

Goldman (1983) found the following in rehabilitating clients with alcohol-related cognitive deficits:

1. General activation increases the person's overall cognitive activity and appears to aid recovery by improving his or her efficiency at developing compensatory behaviours, integrating remaining functions, overcoming mental apathy and learning through trial and error.

2. Practice and guided rehearsal teaches the person specific ways to overcome a deficit (e.g., recovery from visuospatial deficits is enhanced through training on visuospatial tasks).

3. Behavioural compensation trains the individual in alternative ways to accomplish cognitive tasks, especially where he or she has had neurological damage (e.g., visuospatial performance may be enhanced through the use of verbal mediators). Goldman (1987) has also stressed the importance of repeating material to ensure that the client has processed it adequately. Since people in the first few weeks of abstinence typically have cognitive "haziness," they may forget much of what they learn during this period. Thus, treatment should be delayed until the person recovers his or her cognitive capacities.

Goldstein (1987) has suggested placing less emphasis on remediating memory impairments, which may often be subtle (except in the case of people with Korsakoff's syndrome). Instead, Goldstein argues that it is more important to focus on teaching problem-solving skills, abstraction skills, how to learn and how to recall what is learned. Goldstein suggests that since clients have a reduced ability to process information (which affects several cognitive domains, including memory), efforts to improve the processing of information will be a useful approach to rehabilitation.

Treatment workers may need to modify their attitudes toward clients with alcohol-induced cognitive impairments, since interpretations of behaviours and attitudes that are appropriate to cognitively intact clients may not apply. For example, what appears to be denial or resistance to treatment may be comprehension or memory difficulties; what seems to be a motivational problem may in fact be a memory problem. Cognitively impaired clients may have initial difficulty in applying abstract principles to their life problems, in reasoning by analogy or in recalling material taught earlier in the program. Thus, the client may give the impression that he or she is not making sufficient effort. These difficulties may be accompanied by emotional reactions such as anger, frustration and depression. Consequently, counsellors must be aware of the client's neuropsychological status and adjust clinical interventions accordingly.

TREATMENT OF MEMORY LOSS

There is a considerable body of research on improving memory in people who have had memory loss or damage due to substance use, disease or injury. The following recommendations are particularly relevant to treating clients with alcohol-related cognitive deficits:

1. Structured therapeutic tasks increase the client's ability to engage in effortful processing (Hertel, 1992). Unstructured, unfocused tasks will confuse and inhibit the client's learning. It is important to maintain a clear focus and structure in both the process and content of therapeutic interventions. Presenting information in modules may also be helpful.

2. "Deeper" encoding of information can be encouraged through elaborative inter-rogation. In this process, the counsellor asks the client "why" questions about the material to be remembered (Pressley & El-Dinary, 1992). This encourages self-referential processing, through which the material becomes personally relevant to the client (Rogers et al., 1977). It also stimulates the activation of episodic memory processes in encoding the material, which enhances retrievability (versus semantic learning; Tulving, 1972).

3. Systematic and planned repetition, especially if it is elaborated with imagery, can help the client to recall information. This can be encouraged, for example, through the client taking notes, which are then regularly reviewed.

4. It is important to enhance cognitive knowledge and skills that instruct the client when to use what he or she has learned, how to apply new learning and in what situations (Pressley & El-Dinary, 1992). This helps the client know the limits of his or her memory and remedial steps to take.

5. The client will better encode and retrieve learning if the practice of important therapeutic information is spaced (i.e., daily and regular sessions) rather than massed (i.e., intensive learning sessions or "cramming"; Payne & Wenger, 1992).

6. Teaching the client how to focus attention, screen out distractions and maintain concentration can help him or her give the necessary attention to the encoding and recall of information.

7. External retrieval cues (e.g., cue cards, making notes) to enhance recall (Zacks & Hasher, 1992) are a practical means of improving the client's daily functioning when his or her deficits do not fully recover.

8. Metamemory (the client's awareness of how his or her own memory works) can be improved through encouraging the client to be mindful of the information to be remembered (i.e., knowing that you know; Plude, 1992).

9. The use of mental imagery and imagination helps the client encode important therapeutic material and learning.

10. Clients may be helped by training in problem-solving strategies, in which they are guided in a step-by-step process that includes defining the problem and selecting and executing reasonable solutions. Training in monitoring the effectiveness of problem-solving efforts helps the person shift strategies (i.e., metacognitive strategies) from ones that will not succeed to ones that may.

SUMMARY

This chapter has surveyed some of the literature on the chronic effects of alcohol on cognition, and the relationship of these effects with the outcomes of treatment. A discussion of some practical techniques to enhance cognitive processing indicates that treatment programs for clients with alcohol-induced cognitive impairments may need to focus on the timing of interventions (to maximize recovery and to minimize forgetting due to residual cognitive deficits); encouragement of creative solutions by counsellors and clients; and education of treatment staff on these clients' cognitive limitations.

REFERENCES

Brandt, J., Butters, N., Ryan, C. & Bayog, R. (1983). Cognitive loss and recovery in long-term alcohol abusers. *Archives of General Psychiatry, 40*, 435–442.

Butters, N., Cermak, L.S., Montgomery, K. & Adinolfi, A. (1977). Some comparisons of the memory and visuoperceptive deficits of chronic alcoholics and patients with Korsakoff's disease. *Alcoholism: Clinical and Experimental Research, 1*, 73–80.

Carlin, A.S. & O'Malley, S. (1996). Neuropsychological consequences of drug abuse. In I. Grant and K.M. Adams (Eds.), *Neuropsychological Assessment of Neuropsychiatric Disorders* (pp. 486–503). London: Oxford University Press.

Church, M.W. & Kaltenbach, J.A. (1997). Hearing, speech, language, and vestibular disorders in the fetal alcohol syndrome: A French study. *Alcoholism: Clinical and Experimental Research, 21*, 495–512.

Cooney, N.L., Kadden, R.M., Litt, M.D. & Getter, H. (1991). Matching alcoholics to coping skills or interactional therapies: Two-year follow-up results. *Journal of Consulting and Clinical Psychology, 59*, 598–601.

Cynn, V.E.H. (1992). Persistence and problem-solving skills in young male alcoholics. *Journal of Studies on Alcohol, 53*, 57–62.

Day, N.L., Zuo, Y., Richardson, G.A., Goldschmidt, L., Larkby, C. & Cornelius, M.D. (1999). Prenatal alcohol use and offspring size at 10 years of age. *Alcoholism: Clinical and Experimental Research, 23*, 863–869.

Donovan, D.M., Walker, R.D. & Kivlahan, D.R. (1987). Recovery and remediation of neuropsychological functions, implications for alcoholism rehabilitation process and outcome. In O.A. Parsons, N. Butters & P.E. Nathan (Eds.), *Neuropsychology of Alcoholism: Implications for Diagnosis and Treatment* (pp. 339–360). New York: Guilford Press.

Ellenberg, L., Rosenbaum, G., Goldman, M.S. & Whitman, R.D. (1980). Recoverability of psychological functions following alcohol abuse: Lateralization effects. *Journal of Consulting and Clinical Psychology, 481*, 503–510.

Famy, C., Streissguth, A.P. & Unis, A.S. (1998). Mental illness in adults with fetal alcohol syndrome. *American Journal of Psychiatry, 155*, 552–554.

Forsberg, L.K. & Goldman, M.S. (1987). Experience-dependent recovery of cognitive deficits in alcoholics: Extended transfer of training. *Journal of Abnormal Psychology, 96*, 345–353.

Franceschi, M., Truci, G., Comi, G., Lozza, L., Marchinettini, P., Galardi, G. & Smirne, S. (1984). Cognitive deficits and their relationship to other neurological complications in chronic alcoholic patients. *Journal of Neurology, Neurosurgery, and Psychiatry, 47*, 1134–1137.

Goldman, M.S. (1983). Cognitive impairment in chronic alcoholics: Endogenous and exogenous processes. *Alcoholism: Clinical and Experimental Research, 38*, 1045–1054.

Goldman, M.S. (1987). The role of time and practice in recovery of function in alcoholics. In O.A. Parsons, N. Butters & P.E. Nathan (Eds.), *Neuropsychology of Alcoholism: Implications for Diagnosis and Treatment* (pp. 291–321). New York: Guilford Press.

Goldman, M.S., Williams, D.L. & Klisz, D.K. (1983). Recoverability of psychological functioning following alcohol abuse: Prolonged visual-spatial dysfunction in older alcoholics. *Journal of Consulting and Clinical Psychology, 51*, 370–378.

Goldstein, G. (1987). Recovery, treatment and rehabilitation in chronic alcoholics. In O.A. Parsons, N. Butters & P.E. Nathan (Eds.), *Neuropsychology of Alcoholism: Implications for Diagnosis and Treatment* (pp. 361–377). New York: Guilford Press.

Grant, I., Adams, K. & Reed, R. (1979). Normal neuropsychological abilities of alcoholic men in their late thirties. *American Journal of Psychiatry, 136*, 1263–1269.

Griffiths, R.R. & Weerts, E.M. (1997). Benzodiazepine self-administered in humans and laboratory animals: Implications for problems of long-term use and abuse. *Psychopharmacology, 134*, 1–37.

Hertel, P.T. (1992). Improving memory and mood through automatic and controlled procedures of mind. In D.J. Herrmann, H. Weingartner, A. Searleman & C. McEvoy (Eds.), *Memory Improvement: Implications for Memory Theory* (pp. 43–60). New York: Springer-Verlag.

Hesselbrock, M.N., Weidenman, M.A. & Reed, H.B. (1985). Effects of age, sex, drinking history and antisocial personality on neuropsychology of alcoholics. *Journal of Studies on Alcohol, 46*, 313–320.

Kaufman, M.J., Levin, J.M., Christensen, J.D. & Renshaw, P.F. (1996). Magnetic resonance studies of substance abuse. *Seminars in Clinical Neuropsychiatry, 1*, 61–75.

Kaufman, M.J., Levin, J.M., Ross, M.H., Lang, N., Rose, S.L., Kukes, T.J., Mendelson, J.H., Lukas, S.E., Cohen, B.M., & Renshaw, P.F. (1998). Cocaine-induced cerebral vasoconstriction detected in humans with magnetic resonance angiography. *Journal of the American Medical Association, 279*, 376–380.

Knight, R.G. & Longmore, B.E. (1994). *Clinical Neuropsychology of Alcoholism.* Hove, U.K.: Lawrence Erlbaum Associates.

Krystal, J.H. & Price, L.H. (1992). Chronic 3,4-MDMA use: Effects on mood and neuropsychological function. *American Journal of Drug and Alcohol Abuse, 18*, 331–341.

Lishman, W.A. (1990). Alcohol and the brain. *British Journal of Psychiatry*, 156, 635–644.

McKenna, C. (1997). Neurocognitive syndromes and neuroimaging in addictions. In N. Miller (Ed.), *The Principles and Practice of Addictions in Psychiatry* (pp. 79–102). Philadelphia: W.B. Saunders.

Morgan, M.J. (2000). Ecstasy (MDMA): A review of its possible persistent psychological effects. *Psychopharmacology, 152*, 230–248.

Nixon, S.J., Kujawski, A., Parsons, O.A. & Yohman, J.R. (1987). Semantic (verbal) and figural memory impairments in alcoholics. *Journal of Clinical and Experimental Neuropsychology, 9*, 311–322.

Parsons, O.A. (1987). Do neuropsychological deficits predict alcoholics treatment course and post-treatment recovery? In O.A. Parsons, N. Butters & P.E. Nathan (Eds.), *Neuropsychology of Alcoholism: Implications for Diagnosis and Treatment* (pp. 273–290). New York: Guilford Press.

Parsons, O.A. & Farr, S.P. (1981). The neuropsychology of drug and alcohol abuse. In S.B. Filskov & T.J. Boll (Eds.), *Handbook of Clinical Neuropsychology* (pp. 320–365). New York: Wiley Interscience.

Parsons, O.A. & Leber, W.R. (1981). The relationship between cognitive dysfunction and brain damage in alcoholics: Causal, interactive or epiphenomenal? *Alcoholism: Clinical and Experimental Research, 14*, 746–755.

Parsons, O.A. & Nixon, S.J. (1998). Cognitive functioning in sober social drinkers: A review of the research since 1986. *Journal of Studies on Alcohol, 59*, 180–190.

Parsons, O.A. & Prigatano, G.P. (1977). Memory functioning in alcoholics. In I.M. Birnbaum & E.S. Parker (Eds.), *Alcohol and Human Memory* (pp. 185–194). Hillsdale, NJ: Lawrence Erlbaum Associates Inc.

Payne, D.G. & Wenger, M.J. (1992). Improving memory through practice. In D.J. Herrmann, H. Weingartner, A. Searleman & C. McEvoy (Eds.), *Memory Improvement: Implications for Memory Theory* (pp. 187–209). New York: Springer-Verlag.

Plude, D.J. (1992). Attention and memory improvement. In D.J. Herrmann, H. Weingartner, A. Searleman & C. McEvoy (Eds.), *Memory Improvement: Implications for Memory Theory* (pp. 150–168). New York: Springer-Verlag.

Pope, H.G. & Yurgelun-Todd, D. (1996). The residual cognitive effects of heavy marijuana use in college students. *Journal of the American Medical Association, 275,* 521–527.

Pressley, M. & El-Dinary, P.B. (1992). Memory strategy instruction that promotes good information processing. In D.J. Herrmann, H. Weingartner, A. Searleman & C. McEvoy (Eds.), *Memory Improvement: Implications for Memory Theory* (pp. 79–100). New York: Springer-Verlag.

Rogers, T.B., Kuiper, N.A. & Kirker, W.S. (1977). Self-reference and the encoding of personal information. *Journal of Personality and Social Psychology, 35,* 677–688.

Russell, E.W. (1988). Renorming Russell's version of the Wechsler Memory Scale. *Journal of Clinical and Experimental Neuropsychology, 10,* 235–239.

Schaeffer, K., Butters, N., Smith, T., Irwin, M., Brown, S., Hanger, P., Grant, I. & Schuckit, M. (1991). Cognitive performance of alcoholics: Longitudinal evaluation of the role of drinking history, depression, liver function nutrition, and family history. *Alcoholism: Clinical and Experimental Research, 15,* 653–660.

Schuckit, M. (2000). *Drug and Alcohol Abuse* (5th ed.). New York: Kluwer Academic.

Solowij, N., Michie, P.T. & Fox, A.M. (1995). Differential impairments of selective attention due to frequency and duration of cannabis use. *Biological Psychiatry, 37,* 731–739.

Strickland, T.L. & Stein, R.A. (1996). Neurobehavioral functioning in chronic cocaine abusers following sustained abstinence. *Archives of Clinical Neurology, 11,* 456–457.

Stringer, A.Y. & Goldman, M.S. (1988). Experience-dependent recovery of block design performance in male alcoholics: Strategy training versus unstructured practice. *Journal of Studies on Alcohol, 49,* 406–411.

Tarter, R.E. & Edwards, K.L. (1986). Multifactorial etiology of neuropsychological impairment in alcoholics. *Alcoholism: Clinical and Experimental Research, 10,* 128–135.

Teichner, G., Horner, M.D., Roitzsch, J.C., Herron, J. & Thevos, A. (2002). Substance abuse treatment outcomes for cognitively impaired and intact outpatients. *Addictive Behaviors, 27,* 751–763.

Tulving, E. (1972). Episodic and semantic memory. In E. Tulving & W. Donaldson (Eds.), *Organization of Memory.* New York: Academic Press.

van Gorp, W.G., Wilkins, J.N., Hinkin, C.H., Moore, L.H., Hull., J., Horner, M.D. & Plotkin, D. (1999). Declarative and procedural memory functioning in abstinent cocaine abusers. *Archives of General Psychiatry, 56,* 85–89.

Yamanouchi, N., Okada, S., Kodama, K., Sakamoto, T., Sekine, H., Hirai, S., Murakami, A., Komatsu, N. & Sato, T. (1997). Effects of MRI abnormalities on WAIS-R performance in solvent abusers. *Acta Neurologica Scandinavica, 96,* 34–39.

Yohman, J.R., Parsons, O.A. & Leber, W.R. (1985). Lack of recovery in male alcoholics' neuropsychological performance one year after treatment. *Alcoholism: Clinical and Experimental Research, 9,* 114–117.

Zacks, R.T. & Hasher, L. (1992). Memory in life, lab, and clinic: Implications for memory theory. In D.J. Herrmann, H. Weingartner, A. Searleman & C. McEvoy (Eds.), *Memory Improvement: Implications for Memory Theory* (pp. 232–248*).* New York: Springer-Verlag.

Chapter 24

Sexuality and Sexual Issues

JEREMY TOMLINSON

INTRODUCTION

We seem to shy away from sex. We tend not to automatically engage in conversations about sexuality with our clients. We tend to consider it too intimate or embarrassing and assume that clients must feel the same way. Yet a holistic approach to counselling includes conversations about all aspects of a person's health: physical, emotional, social, spiritual, intellectual and sexual.

Being aware of the broad range of health issues including sexuality is important when working with clients dealing with substance use issues. Clients may be using alcohol or other drugs to mask sexual feelings or sexualized abuse. A thorough approach to counselling should include discussions that can help clients:

• evaluate their attitudes, values and beliefs about sexuality and sexual health (Guldner & Guldner, 1999; Sanders, 1995)
• look at barriers to healthy sexual experiences (Kleinplatz, 1994)
• increase their comfort with their sexual identity
• enhance their sexual pleasure (Kleinplatz, 1995).

In many training programs for counsellors, sexuality is given scant attention (Guldner & Guldner, 1999). Without additional workshops or other training in sexuality issues after graduation, some counsellors may find it hard to initiate conversations about sexuality during counselling, because they:

• are unaware of their own assumptions about sexuality issues
• feel personal discomfort with sexuality or with communicating about sex

• feel uncomfortable discussing something that feels so personal and intimate, out of concern that clients will feel pushed to discuss issues they are not yet ready to discuss (Carroll et al., 2001)
• fear that the client may be a survivor of sexualized abuse who will feel triggered by the mention of sex (Guldner & Guldner, 1999).

In fact, discussing sexuality with clients may be one of the most important components in a holistic approach to substance use counselling. In other words, start with the assumption that it is okay to discuss sexuality with clients, but ensure that the conversation is sensitive, respectful and well-timed.

Clearly, as counsellors, we have to set appropriate boundaries to ensure clients' safety and well-being as well as our own. However, the result of these boundaries can be that, when we do talk with our clients about sex, we become very clinical and disconnected. It is ironic that we might distance ourselves from clients in conversations at a time that we are encouraging them to connect with their bodies and their partners' bodies. Instead of avoiding the topic, keep in mind that discussions about sexuality can be relaxed, fun and funny.

This chapter will help substance use counsellors feel more comfortable discussing sexuality with clients. It addresses:
• assumptions: attitudes, values and beliefs
• the effect that different substances have on sexuality and sexual response
• different ways to approach the issue of sexuality with clients
• strategies to discuss these issues with clients
• ways to help clients deal with sexual disturbances
• other situations in which a discussion about sexuality and substance use would be appropriate for clients.

The issues raised will be relevant both to clients who are sober and to clients who are still using.

ASSUMPTIONS: ATTITUDES, VALUES AND BELIEFS

With what assumptions about sexuality does a substance use counsellor enter the consulting room? Perhaps more importantly in this context, with what assumptions about *sexuality counselling* does a substance use counsellor enter the consulting room? Our training has taught us to approach clients in a supportive, non-biased, non-judgmental manner, but that does not mean we enter the counselling room in a neutral, value-free way. How could we? We encourage clients to look at their life experiences, explore what they have learned from these experiences and try to integrate that wisdom into their lives. Likewise, we bring our own life experiences and learning into the counselling room, and it is from this position that we facilitate conversations with clients.

How People Define Sex

In order to alleviate some of the discomfort that counsellors or clients might feel regarding sexuality, it will be important for counsellors to examine their own assumptions about sexuality (Ford & Hendrick, 2003; Kleinplatz, 2001a). Let's start with the most basic question: How do you define sex? If a person is "having sex," what does that mean? A number of variables influence people's answers to that question, such as:

• gender (are the participants both female, both male, one of each, more than one of each?)
• age (at different ages, people may find certain sexual activities acceptable or disgusting)
• degree of sexual experience
• knowledge (or fear) of sexually transmitted infections, including HIV (which could lead to avoiding vaginal intercourse, anal intercourse or oral sex)
• desire to become pregnant (so sex will mean vaginal intercourse, particularly at the time of ovulation) or not become pregnant (sex may mean avoiding vaginal intercourse, particularly at the time of ovulation)
• moral or religious values about particular sexual activities or sex outside of marriage.

　　If you ask a client if he or she is sexually active, what exactly do you want to know? Are you asking about sexual intercourse in a monogamous heterosexual relationship? How does the client define the expression "sexually active"? Is kissing a sexual activity? Consider the concept of "foreplay." The word implies that whatever the sexual activity is (kissing, caressing, oral sex), it is not the point, but is leading to something "more," presumably intercourse. However, the experience of kissing, caressing or oral sex may be deeply satisfying for someone as an end in itself. Is self-pleasure (or masturbation) sex? If a person has no partner, but self-pleasures, does that person consider him- or herself sexually active?

　　Learning what sex means for clients can help to build rapport and lead to more in-depth discussions about sexuality. As well, it can help clients expand their own definitions about sexual expression and open them up to new possibilities.

Examining and Avoiding Assumptions

Counsellors do not approach their work in a manner that is "value-free" (Morris, 1993). Consider the assumptions you hold about who has sex. What do you think about sex between unmarried people? Is sex with a partner other than a husband or wife (i.e., extra-marital sex) acceptable? If your initial response was no, what if the couple has an arrangement where they have agreed to have sex with partners outside the primary relationship? Do you assume that they have relationship problems or sexual problems, that they are immoral, oversexed or adventurous? Or do you assume that they are respectful people and good communicators, who have negotiated an open sexual relationship that works for them? How would you feel about someone who, during the counselling session, discussed his or her enjoyment of sex among three or more people at a time? Would you define that as deviant, immoral or adventurous?

In offering comprehensive substance use counselling that includes discussions of sexuality, we, as counsellors, must examine and challenge our own assumptions; we need to ask questions with warmth, genuineness and curiosity. In this way, we can help clients define and explore the meanings that sexual issues have for them in the context of their substance use problems.

THE EFFECTS OF SUBSTANCE USE ON SEXUAL RESPONSE

One of the primary challenges clients face in counselling for substance use is with what they are "giving up." Many clients use alcohol and other substances because they enjoy the emotional, physical and/or spiritual sensations that they have while under the influence. As a result, while counsellors help clients remember the reasons they have decided to quit using, they also need to help them "mourn" the loss—of sensation, of a sense of connection with God or other people, etc.

Aspects of sexuality can be among these losses. Many clients may have enjoyed enhanced desire and sexual pleasure, and decreased inhibitions, while using a substance. Counsellors need to help these clients accept the reality (and mourn the loss) that they may never have quite those same sensations again (Murray, J., personal communication, March 12, 2003), while helping them try to establish other ways to decrease inhibitions and increase desire and sexual pleasure.

Other clients we commonly meet are using substances and have some concerns about their use but are not interested in stopping at the time. A harm-reduction model can help these clients make decisions about safer sex and safer substance use.

Traditionally, although relatively little appears to have been written about this issue of sexuality and substance use, any discussion of substance use in the sex therapy literature has focused on the physical effects of substance use on sexual response in relation to drug and alcohol use (Howard & Hudson, 1997, citing Gold, 1988; Kaplan, 1979; Kolodny et al., 1979; Masters et al., 1969).

More recent research has started to include questions that ask participants about their subjective experiences of sexual contact while under the influence of alcohol or other substances (ACT, 2001; Camden & Islington Community Health Services, 1999; Carroll et al., 2001; Henderson et al., 1995; Palha & Esteves, 2002; Rawson et al., 2002). This trend reinforces the importance of hearing clients' experiences about substance use and sexuality, so counsellors can help to facilitate decision making that is relevant to clients' own lives.

Clearly, substance use can also have a negative effect on people's experience of sex, and on their sexual response. Substance use can:
• reduce desire
• make orgasm more difficult in men and women
• cause problems with erection and ejaculation in men
• reduce lubrication in women.

Whether substance use enhances or lessens the sexual experience depends on different factors, such as:
• how much the person takes
• how the person was feeling when the substance was taken
• the person's environment
• who the person is with
• why the person took the substance (Camden & Islington Community Health Services, 1999).

ALCOHOL

Clients report that alcohol reduces social inhibitions. One of my clients, who reported anxiety about dating and social situations, called alcohol a "social lubricant." He drank before dates and at parties and clubs, because he believed it gave him more courage to interact and connect with potential love interests or sexual partners. Alcohol may also decrease sexual inhibitions, so that people feel more able to be sexually adventurous.

• In smaller amounts, clients report alcohol increases desire (Taylor Seagraves, 1988; Zilbergeld, 1992).
• In larger amounts, or with chronic use, alcohol may cause reduced sexual desire in men (Taylor Seagraves, 1988; Zilbergeld 1992), while it may reduce the intensity and frequency of orgasms in women (Berger et al., 1995).
• Chronic alcohol use can make men produce less testosterone and produce abnormally shaped sperm (Berger et al., 1995).
• In women, the effects of moderate to high alcohol intake on hormone levels have been associated with reduced likelihood of conception. This may be due to reduced ovulation (Gill, 2000).
• Women who drink two standard drinks twice a week may have a higher chance of miscarriage (Friedman & Gradstein, 1992).
• People who have been drinking will probably find it harder to make clear decisions about safer sex (to protect from HIV, sexually transmitted diseases and pregnancy). When drinking, people may find that impaired decision-making places them in unsafe situations where sexual assault is a greater risk.

MARIJUANA

• Many people report decreased inhibitions while using marijuana.
• People who use small amounts of marijuana report increased desire, increased sensuality and intensified body sensations (ACT, 2003; Taylor Seagraves, 1988; Zilbergeld, 1992).

- In larger amounts or with more use over time, people may experience decreased desire, difficulties with erection and difficulty achieving orgasm (Berger et al., 1995; Zilbergeld, 1992).
- Marijuana use may also increase the chance of miscarriage (Friedman & Gradstein, 1992).

COCAINE

- Some clients report that using cocaine (or crack) decreases sexual inhibitions.
- In smaller doses, cocaine has been reported both to increase desire and arousal (Taylor Seagraves, 1988; Zilbergeld, 1992) and to decrease desire (Henderson et al., 1995).
- Acute cocaine use may lead to increased desire and erectile difficulties in men, and difficulties with lubrication in women (Henderson et al. 1995; TRIP, 2003; Zilbergeld, 1992).
- Chronic use can lead to erectile difficulties in men, and decreased desire and difficulties achieving orgasm for both men and women (Henderson et al., 1995; Hernandez & Alfonso, 1997; Rawson et al., 2002; Zilbergeld, 1992).

An interesting challenge exists in work with people who use cocaine. They may so strongly associate good sex with their use of the substance that imagining sex without it is difficult or impossible (Camden & Islington Community Health Services, 1999; Rawson et al., 2002). This appears to be more common for men (Rawson et al., 2002). Camden and Islington Community Health Services (1999) suggest that part of the reason for this is the extent to which cocaine alters reality for people who use it.

HEROIN

- Many people compare a heroin high to an extended orgasm.
- In the initial stages of use, some people report improved sexual functioning (Palha & Esteves 2002).
- Women who have experienced painful intercourse or difficulty with penetration report improvements, likely due to the relaxation and the analgesic effect of the drug (Hernandez & Alfonso, 1997; Palha & Esteves, 2002).
- Men who have had difficulty with rapid ejaculation report that the problem goes away (Palha & Esteves, 2002).
- Many men and women report decreased sexual interest, more difficulty with arousal and more difficulty achieving orgasm as heroin use increases (Palha & Esteves, 2002).

METHAMPHETAMINE

- Methamphetamine ("crystal" or "crystal meth") produces a rush of adrenaline that can influence mood, body movement, sensory perception and sexual function (ACT, 2003).
- It has been described as giving "the ultimate high" (Camden & Islington Community Health Services, 1999).

- It is reported to greatly reduce sexual inhibition, and many people who use it describe an "unrivalled sense of sexual power, liberation and energy" (Camden & Islington Community Health Services, 1999).
- Methamphetamine reportedly allows people to have intense sex for extended periods of time (Murray, 2003a).
- Sexual desire, sensation and arousal become intensified and orgasm is delayed (Rawson et al., 2002; TRIP, 2003).
- A common side-effect for men is difficulty with achieving an erection or with having a softer erection. This is known as "crystal dick."

MDMA
- To discuss MDMA (methylenedioxymethamphetamine, ecstasy or "E") in the context of sexuality raises the earlier topics of how people define sex and how people's experience of a drug depends on their expectations and environment.
- Many people say they do not feel a desire for genital contact while on MDMA; however, the drug is likely to enhance people's communication and sense of connection, intimacy, warmth and openness with one another (Holland, 2001; Klitzman et al., 2002).
- People often want to hold and touch one another when using MDMA, which is why it is referred to as the "hug drug" (Holland, 2001) or the "love drug" (Klitzman et al., 2002).
- Some people find MDMA increases their sexual arousal (Klitzman et al., 2002), and they may want intimate genital contact.
- The desire for closeness that people describe from MDMA may lead to unsafe sexual practices if people want to "connect" without the barrier of a condom between them (Camden & Islington Community Health Services, 1999; Klitzman et al., 2002).
- Some people find MDMA causes difficulty with arousal, achieving erections or achieving an orgasm (Holland, 2001).
- Others find the (genital) sexual experience very intense and enjoyable because of the closeness and intimacy they feel (Camden & Islington Community Health Services, 1999; see also the Safer Sex discussion forum at www.dancesafe.org).

KETAMINE
Ketamine ("special K," "vitamin K" or "K") is not likely to be used to enhance the sexual experience in significant ways; however, it is worthy of mention here because it is a "party drug."

The relevance to sexuality is that a subtle difference in dosage can cause a remarkably different high:
- In small doses, it can cause people to feel drunk and have visual hallucinations.
- People who take even slightly too much may feel dissociated, detached from their bodies, or unaware of where they are (ACT, 2003). For these reasons, conversations about sexual safety and safer sex become paramount.

GHB

GHB ("G") is often taken specifically because of its reputed sex-enhancing abilities. Camden & Islington Community Health Services (1999) warn that there are common misconceptions about how spectacular sex can be when using GHB, so clients may have heard embellished stories.

• Some people who take GHB report a "heightened sense of touch, disinhibition, enhanced erection and increased intensity of orgasm" (ACT, 2003).

• GHB carries a high risk of overdose, because there is a very small difference between an amount that makes people high and an amount that makes them sick or knocks them out (Murray, 2003b).

• Too much GHB, or mixing GHB with other drugs that depress the central nervous system, such as alcohol and tranquilizers, can lead to dangerously low breathing and heart rate, coma or vomiting, which, if the vomit gets into lungs, can lead to death (Camden & Islington Community Health Services, 1999; ACT, 2003).

• The concentration of GHB can vary widely from batch to batch, so the dose that "gave you a good high last time could make you sick or put you in a coma next time" (Murray, 2003b, p. 29).

Counsellors should discuss harm reduction strategies if clients are using this drug. For further information on harm reduction strategies, see Murray (2003b) and ACT (2003).

VIAGRA

Although Viagra (sildenafil citrate) is not normally thought of as a recreational drug, some men use it as an antidote to the erectile difficulties caused by using other drugs. Recently it has become more popular in the gay community for this use.

• Using Viagra poses risks for men who have heart problems.

• Mixing Viagra with club drugs, a strenuous night of dancing and lack of sleep could also put stress on the heart and affect blood pressure (Camden & Islington Community Health Services, 1999).

• If a man mixes Viagra with amyl nitrite ("poppers"), there is a risk that blood vessels could open too far. This could lead to priapism (where blood is unable to leave an erection, causing pain and sometimes permanent damage), unconsciousness, coma, heart attack or stroke (Camden & Islington Community Health Services, 1999).

TALKING ABOUT SEXUALITY IN COUNSELLING

Just as counsellors might hesitate to talk about sexuality, so too are clients likely to be reluctant to approach the issue. Clients will have concerns similar to those of counsellors, such as uncertainty about:

• whether it is appropriate to discuss something so intimate with a counsellor
• how to articulate their thoughts and feelings about sex and sexuality
• whether the counsellor can "handle" the issue.

As a result, clients may not initiate discussion, but may watch for cues and seek reassurance that a conversation about sexuality will be sensitive, supportive and respectful. Counsellors working with substance use issues must consciously create a context and environment in which conversations about sexuality feel as natural, comfortable and non-threatening as possible. Clients will want to know that their counsellors can understand their experience of the issue before they feel safe enough to broach the topic.

A Conducive Environment

Consider the setting where you meet with clients. How do you let clients know that discussing sexuality issues is acceptable or encouraged?

THE WAITING ROOM
Consider your waiting room. Do you have condoms in your waiting room? Consider the posters and other reading material available in your waiting room. Do you hang posters with images that represent a range of sexuality issues, such as:
• information about safer sex
• promotion of tolerance for gay, lesbian, bisexual and transgendered people
• information about birth control
• information about fertility issues?

Brochures are available about these same topics, as well as for safer S/M, safer sex while under the influence of a substance and enhancing sexual pleasure. Brochures may also advertise sex therapists and sex-positive retailers in your community.

Do the magazines in your waiting room have articles, advertising or images related to sexuality, body image or sexualized abuse, which could lead to conversations in your counselling session about these issues? Are there copies of the local (or regional) publication for the gay, lesbian, bisexual, transgendered communities?

THE CONSULTING ROOM
Similarly, the physical environment in the room where you see clients may send messages about your comfort with sexuality issues. As well as the posters, brochures and condoms in the waiting room, the books and journals on your bookshelf are likely to be noticed by many clients.

THE INTAKE FORM
Consider your intake form or your "welcome to the agency/my office" form. Is sexuality mentioned as an issue that some clients discuss?

Sometimes, including a form with a checklist of possible "presenting issues" helps give clients permission to raise difficult issues. You can help clients to raise topics they were unsure about discussing by including sections on the checklist that ask about, for example:

- pregnancy
- fertility
- birth control
- gay, lesbian, bisexual and transgender issues
- sexual disturbances (or sexual difficulties)
- sexual pleasure.

These tools can help normalize the discussion of sexuality in counselling and may help clients to feel they have permission to initiate a conversation.

INTRODUCING THE TOPIC

Whether you are working with individuals, couples or groups, you can invite clients to explore sexuality in conjunction with their treatment for substance use problems. As I introduce myself to clients at our first session, I may mention my previous work at Planned Parenthood, or that I have had specific training about sexuality issues, if I think this information will help clients feel more comfortable speaking about sexuality.

To normalize the idea of talking about sexuality in the context of substance use, I usually say in the first counselling session, "People come to see me about a variety of issues, such as relationship issues, family issues, substance use, childhood trauma, sexuality and bereavement. Those are the common issues, but people come to speak to me about just about anything else you can imagine." When I list these issues to clients, I try to include their presenting issue (if I know what it is ahead of time) so they don't feel their issue is an "uncommon" one. This normalizing statement opens the door to a conversation about sexuality. It also sends the message that "anything you can imagine" has already been discussed with me, so I am unlikely to feel overwhelmed by or uncomfortable with a topic the client considers shocking, difficult or taboo.

Setting Limits

While working in a context of healthy sexuality we try to be as open as possible to the sexual issues clients raise. Nonetheless, we may need to set certain limits.

SAFETY

Safety is one factor. Safety may mean emphasizing condom use and safer sex. It may mean talking with clients about not getting into compromising situations after using alcohol or other substances. Healthy sexuality is consensual. Clients need to understand the importance of not taking advantage of others who have used too much of a substance to be able to properly consent to sexual activity.

LEGAL ISSUES

One legal issue is the age of consent for sexual activity. In Canada, for example, a 14-year-old can consent to sexual activity, unless it is with someone in a position of power over him or her (a supervisor, coach, teacher, etc.). A person between the ages of 12 and 14 can consent, but only if the partner is within two years of the person's own age (e.g., a 13-year-old can consent to sexual activity with a 15-year-old). Age-of-consent laws vary in different jurisdictions.

MOTIVATION FOR SEXUAL CONTACT

Another issue to consider is the client's motivation for sexual contact. Do the client's motivations seem to be healthy, both to you and to the client? For example, if the client is having sex out of boredom, loneliness, compulsion or anxiety, or to avoid other concerns, the sexual behaviour may be unhealthy.

SETTING BOUNDARIES

Counsellors dealing with sexuality and substance use must help clients to set boundaries and define healthy sexuality for themselves. Healthy sexuality may be about an expression of love or caring for another person, or it may be about the physical pleasure. It may be about connection and intimacy. It involves consent from all participants for what activities take place, and when they take place.

Traditional Medical Approaches to Sexual Disturbance

A problem with some traditional approaches to sex therapy is that they have focused on "fixing" the physical manifestations of clients' sexual problems, or as Peggy Kleinplatz suggests, the focus is on the "parts rather than on the people attached" (2001a, p. xxii). Worse, "sexual problems" have been defined in terms of successful heterosexual intercourse (Kleinplatz, 2001b). Kleinplatz (2001a) discusses vaginismus and erectile problems as primary examples of problematic diagnoses.

VAGINISMUS

The *Diagnostic and Statistical Manual of Mental Disorders*, fourth edition (DSM-IV) classifies vaginismus as a "sexual dysfunction" in which "one experiences recurrent or persistent involuntary spasm of the musculature of the outer third of the vagina that interferes with sexual intercourse" (American Psychiatric Association, 1994, p. 505).

What is missing from this definition, of course, is the person attached to the vagina. Does she want to have penetration by a penis at all? If she enjoys oral sex but not vaginal intercourse, the classification is irrelevant and the point is moot. If she does desire vaginal intercourse, are there reasons her body is sending the message that entry to the vagina is uncomfortable? Is she a survivor of sexualized abuse or assault, for example?

In her somewhat ironic explanation, Kleinplatz suggests that the traditional treatment of vaginismus "consists primarily of systematic desensitization to objects in the vagina with the use of graduated, plastic vaginal dilators. The dilators are used to teach patients mastery over their pubococcygeal muscles so that they are able to open and close their vaginas on cue" (2001a, p. xxiii). Clearly it is a problem if counsellors focus more on "training" the woman's vagina than on having a conversation with her about what might be contributing to the issue. We need to:

• talk with her about her perception of what is happening (Keystone, 1994)
• be clear about her history (has she had sexual relationships or sexual experiences in the past that were coercive, violent or abusive?) (Guldner & Guldner, 1999)
• learn whether she really desires vaginal intercourse (Guldner, 1999).

Is intercourse enjoyable for her with her current partner(s), or has it ever been enjoyable for her? Does she worry about becoming pregnant, and, if so, why? Has she had a previously unplanned pregnancy? Are the stresses of work, school or child-rearing interfering in a satisfying sexual relationship? We should encourage clients to visit their family physician for an assessment to rule out organic causes, but we also need to spend enough time talking with them to learn their meaning of their sexual problems.

ERECTILE DIFFICULTIES

Likewise, with erectile difficulties we need to explore the man's own perception of the problem and look for possible causes (Schnarch, 1999). Is he apprehensive about a sexual relationship or sexual activities in which he is involved? Is he concerned that his partner could become pregnant? Does he have fears about HIV or sexually trans-mitted infections? Does he have enough privacy for sexual activity? Are the stresses of work, school or child-rearing interfering?

Although medication like Viagra may be a solution to the *physical* problem, it is important to do a thorough assessment to explore the emotional and social issues involved. It is a good idea to rule out organic causes with his family physician. A few conversations with a counsellor may help him to resolve the issue to his satisfaction.

Other Counselling Approaches to Sexual Problems

POST-MODERN APPROACH

A post-modern, or social constructionist, approach to sexuality counselling looks at cultural influences and the meanings that people draw from them (about their own identities as sexual beings and how they recognize their own sexual experiences) (Atwood & Dershowitz, 1992; Daniluk, 1998; Guldner & Guldner, 1999; Irvine, 1995; Tiefer, 1995; Tisdale, 1994). Sexuality counselling in this approach can help people to understand how they define themselves as male or female or to explore the places masculinity and femininity hold in their lives. People may draw meaning from the sexual activities they choose or choose not to participate in. They may have opinions about others who make choices different from their own. Culture, religion, gender or age can all influence people's sexual value systems, as can the sexual value systems of their families, peers, school or the media. Counselling helps clients to explore alterna-tives and arrive at new possibilities. Rather than focusing on the problem in their sexual lives, clients look to solutions. A solution might be a new way of looking at the situation or a new way to approach the issue.

Couples who discuss sexual issues with their counsellor are likely to have tried many solutions on their own. The couple counsellor can help clients understand how they might be able to solve their problems by:
• helping both partners define the problem in their own words
• helping them talk about how the problem is influencing their sexual life and the relationship in general
• looking at what has worked in the past and how that demonstrated success.

FAMILY SYSTEMS APPROACH

A family systems approach considers the family or couple and issues of power, role, family rules and boundaries to deal with the counselling issue being presented. It looks at patterns and interactions of communication and behaviour, how those interactions affect the family or couple, and how they affect each member. In the context of substance use and sexuality, the counsellor uses these patterns of behaviour and interaction to look at how the person's substance use has affected the family and the couple, and how it has affected sexuality.

For example, substance use can influence a family in different ways. In some families, adults may have violated sexual boundaries while under the influence of alcohol or other substances, by speaking inappropriately with children about sexuality, with inappropriate nudity or with other forms of sexualized abuse. Substance use may have influenced the couple, either by enhancing or diminishing sexual response and frequency. These issues would be discussed during counselling.

The family systems approach also looks at the influence of the family of origin— that is, the family in which a person is raised—on the person's sexual behaviour as an adult. Was the family of origin open to the discussion of sexuality? What language was used? Were genitals described clearly and directly (penis and vagina) or with childish names ("pee-pee") or did the family just speak about "down there"? How was self-pleasure discussed in the family? Was it ever mentioned? How the clients' families approached the discussion of sexuality may affect the couple's problems.

"PRO-CHOICE" APPROACH

Because both the client and the counsellor enter the consulting room with their own histories and understandings of sexual issues, the counsellor should approach the discussion from a "pro-choice" perspective.

Traditionally, the idea of "pro-choice" in sexual health refers to pregnancy-options counselling in which pregnant women and their partners are presented with options of parenting, adoption and abortion in a non-judgmental, supportive environment, and each option is discussed to help the woman or couple make the best choice. For the purposes of this chapter, the idea of pro-choice should be considered in a broader context in which people are given non-biased information and education to help them decide on their best options for the full range of sexual health issues. In addition to offering information, the counsellor also helps clients to explore and critique their values about sexuality, which encourages them to develop and use their own, healthy, personal perspectives (Kleinplatz, 1995; Morris, 1993).

Discrepancies of Desire

Generally, when people have sexual problems related to desire, it is because their level of desire differs from that of their partner. The "desire discrepancy" approach was first discussed by Zilbergeld & Ellison (1980). Reece (1987) further developed the approach in a model for work with gay men but the principles can be applied to couples of any sexual orientation. In essence, these authors suggest that, rather than discussing how one partner has a low sex drive and the other partner has a high sex drive, counselling focuses on the difference in sex drives. Many issues can cause a discrepancy:

• Couples may have problems communicating needs and desire, expressing during sex what feels enjoyable or what is painful or uncomfortable, and understanding patterns of initiating and declining sex.
• Intimacy issues and fear of dependency can lead to someone pulling away from a sexual relationship.
• Sexual guilt or sexualized trauma can lead to shame and influence a couple's sexual activity.
• Alcohol and other drug use can increase or decrease sexual desire.

To deal with these issues, Reece (1987) suggests that counselling can help clients explore the meaning of their discrepancy of desire, by using the following strategies:

• The counsellor can facilitate conversations about how the partners are influenced by, for example, their families of origin, their expectations about gender, their histories of sexualized abuse or trauma and their previous sexual experiences.
• Conversations can look at lifespan and developmental issues. Sexual experiences will change with aging and with time in any relationship. While this may seem obvious, people commonly expect the same sexual relationship they had in the first few weeks of their relationship or when they were younger. Counselling can help clients to combat repetition and boredom by encouraging fantasy or exploration of new activities.
• Sometimes the counsellor can coach clients in communication skills, helping them to better acknowledge pleasure or patterns of initiation.
• Counsellors can help clients explore communication patterns in which, for example, one partner feels rejected because she was turned down for sex, so is reluctant to initiate again, or where one partner becomes visibly tense when the topic of sex comes up, because he is afraid of repercussions if he says he does not feel like sex at the moment.

When Sex Has Occurred Only While under the Influence

Alcohol and other substance use may be inextricably linked with sex and sexuality for some clients. Sometimes, clients who have experienced sexualized abuse or assault can only participate in sexual activity with help from substance use. With these clients, it will be important for counsellors to work on three levels:

- addressing the substance use with harm reduction or abstinence strategies
- working on the client's experience of trauma
- enhancing the sexual experience.

Although we may work simultaneously on the three issues, it will be important for counsellors to negotiate with the client about areas that take priority, and to be mindful of safety at all times.

Other reasons for linking substance use and sexual activity include the following:

- If a person has been using for many years, or is a young person who began using during adolescence, he or she may be unable to identify sex as a comfortable activity while sober.
- A person may rely on substance use to cope with body image issues.
- Substance use can reduce or mask fears of connection and intimacy (and the resulting vulnerability that can occur during sexual contact).
- A person may rely on substance use to reduce inhibitions.

CONNECTING WITH THE BODY: SELF-TOUCH

A client who has been sexual primarily, or solely, while under the influence is probably unfamiliar with his or her body and with which sensations are most enjoyable. To connect with his or her sexual self, the client can be coached with exercises to try at home. A good starting exercise is to suggest the client take a bath or shower with the goal of being aware of the sensuality of touch. For this exercise, encourage the client to avoid touching his or her genitals, but to focus on touching other areas of the body and learning what feels good.

When I discuss self-pleasure, or masturbation, with clients, they are consistently surprised when I suggest that they try self-pleasure specifically with the goal of not having an orgasm. Instead, in this exercise, the goal is to be aware of the touch and to enjoy the fantasy. Experimenting with different lubricants, sex toys or erotica can help clients reconnect with their bodies and themselves as sexual people.

For many people, self-pleasure is associated with shame and embarrassment, so counsellors may need to initiate a conversation about clients' belief systems related to self-touch. You may need to explore the client's religious values, family of origin issues and adolescent experiences. If the client was ever "caught in the act," there may be residual shame, so counselling should work to help resolve these feelings. Clients may see self-pleasure only as a way to "get off" or release tension. They may see it as an activity people do only when no one else is around to be sexual with.

Occasionally, I have seen conflict when members of a couple hold different values about self-pleasure, where one person is comfortable with it and the other is less comfortable, or where one person sees self-pleasure as an activity only for single people, not something that people do once they are in a relationship. More than once, clients have told me that they self-pleasure secretly, because their partners would consider it "cheating," or would feel undesirable.

Counsellors are in an ideal position to help clients see self-pleasure as a legitimate sexual activity. Encourage clients to enjoy their own bodies. Dissuade clients from viewing self-pleasure as something to do "only when no one else is around, " and help them to find time in their lives to add it to the repertoire of sexual activities they enjoy. Clients who have some reticence about learning (or re-learning) to explore their bodies sexually may benefit from reading *Sex for One* by Betty Dodson (1987).

CONNECTING WITH THE BODY: FOR COUPLES

In a similar manner, when you are counselling a couple, you can encourage them to re-explore their bodies together. This is true whether one or both of them are in recovery. The counselling conversation with a couple can be dynamic when speaking with two people who were accustomed to the effect of substance use on their sex life. They may need to explore past hurts, disappointments or betrayals to rebuild trust and intimacy in the relationship. They may need to discuss patterns of initiation and other rituals (such as, "we only have sex on Saturday evenings and it is pretty predictable about who will do what, to whom, in what order.")

If couples have not been sexual for a while, you can suggest exercises for them to do outside the consulting room. Exercises can be used to reconnect around touch, such as taking baths or showers together that focus on non-genital touch, or giving a massage that excludes genital touching.

Schnarch (1997) describes a case where he helped a couple to reconnect to each other by reminding them to notice the person they were touching. Here is how you can help a couple to use the same process. Ask the couple to set aside time when they will be comfortable and undisturbed. For five or 10 minutes, one partner should speak about something, while the other listens attentively without responding verbally. The listening partner should stroke and caress the speaking partner's face and hands. Then they switch, so the other partner speaks while the original speaker actively listens and caresses. Couples may be surprised by the intensity of the intimacy they feel, how different it was to be heard, or how hard it was to listen so intently. Ensure that you debrief this exercise with them in the next session, to help the couple discuss intimacy and connection.

Another exercise to help clients reconnect with their sexual selves is to ask them to set time aside at home and kiss with their tops off but with their clothes on below the waist. This exercise can be particularly helpful with couples who have begun to see one another more as friends than as lovers. As both members of the couple become more comfortable with non-genital touch, hopefully they will eventually feel more ready to re-introduce genital touch to their repertoire of sexual activity.

Other Issues to Discuss in Counselling

DANCE/PARTY SCENE

Most readers will be familiar with raves, dance party events held in a large space (e.g., a warehouse or a tent in a farmer's field). At raves, people dance to techno or trance music with "a beat not coincidentally approximating the rhythm of an exercising heart or a resting fetus" (Holland, 2001, p. 347). The result is an intense feeling of bonding and connection as people join in a feeling of celebration (Holland, 2001). While raves are no longer as popular as they were (Lewis, E., personal communication, March 20, 2003), parties and events continue to happen within the electronic dance music community.

For many people in the electronic dance music scene, party drugs (MDMA, GHB, crystal meth, etc.) are part of the evening's entertainment. Often, people do not attend these events with the intention of sexual connection. However, the environment is certainly sexualized with dancing, the close proximity of other dancers and the heat and sensuality enhanced by the substances consumed. Counsellors can be helpful by discussing harm reduction strategies about substance use and safer sex information with clients who attend these events.

Dance party events, held specifically for gay men and known as "circuit parties," are held in large cities around the world (Toronto, Montreal, Miami, Sydney, etc.), with people sometimes travelling great distances to attend. Party drugs, also known as "party favours," are an important aspect of the experience for many of the participants. Again, although many men report that they do not attend these events seeking sex, the environment is sexualized with the dancers, the heat and sweat, and people dancing bare-chested (ACT, 2001). Harm reduction strategies can be useful with this client population as well (Bad Boy Club Montreal, 2003).

GRIEF, SUBSTANCE USE AND SEXUALITY

Bereavement can lead to increased substance use. When talking with clients about substance use and sexuality, bereavement may be a factor. The grief could be caused by death or other losses. For example, when a couple has experienced a miscarriage, or learned that they will be unable to have children, there is likely to be a loss reaction (Anton, 1992; Kluger-Bell, 1998; Kossman, 2002). After an abortion, a client may experience a grief and loss reaction (Kluger-Bell, 1998; Reardon & Ney, 2000). Particularly in the first year after an abortion, a woman may mourn "what could have been." She may feel sad around what would have been the date of delivery, or on anniversary dates, such as her own birthday. You may also encounter client grief if you work with a community (gay men, for example) in which it is common for clients to have lost several friends or a partner to an AIDS-related death.

Some clients may drink or use other substances to cope with their grief reactions (Beechem et al., 1996; Byrne et al., 1999; Reardon & Ney, 2000). Although research has not shown a causal relationship between grief and substance use, studies do show that some people will increase their substance use after experiencing loss.

Helping a client to work through loss can be an important part of substance use treatment (Beechem et al., 1996). Often, this means simply attending while the client expresses intense sadness or rage about the loss. Redefining the client's feelings as a similar reaction to one of bereavement can help him or her contextualize those feelings.

BDSM

Counsellors who show that they are open to discussing sexuality are likely to encounter clients involved in bondage/discipline, dominance/submission, sadism/masochism (BDSM). The practice of BDSM is hard to define succinctly. However, it involves the use of power and domination for the mutual sexual enjoyment of two or more participants (Payne, 1999). Trevor Jacques writes, "SM is about roles . . . SM is about ritual . . . SM is *not* abuse . . . SM is about fantasy . . . SM is about the Top's needs . . . SM is about the Bottom's needs . . . SM is about the exchange of power . . . SM is about the exchange of trust" (Jacques, 1993, pp. 10–12).

People who participate in BDSM may use fantasy, power and control, humiliation, pain or bondage. Safety is important; a motto of this community is to participate in activities that are "safe, sane and consensual." *Safe* refers to safer sex and emotional safety. For instance, the couple will have a "safe" word, so that if either participant feels things are getting too intense, he or she can stop the activity. *Sane* refers to the importance of being grounded and present during the process. This refers especially to drug and alcohol use, which should be avoided. (Bannon, 1992; Jacques, 1993). *Consensual* refers to all participants consenting to all activities, many of which may have been negotiated in advance.

In BDSM, all participants must be fully aware of their surroundings; to ensure everyone's safety and for this reason alcohol and drug use is highly discouraged.

ETHICAL IMPLICATIONS

Clearly, it is *never* appropriate for counsellors to engage in sexual activity with clients. Occasionally, counsellors may feel aroused during a discussion of sexuality, or they may feel sexually attracted to a client. Always remember the power differential in the client-counsellor relationship. Acknowledge to yourself that you are having those feelings in the moment, and set appropriate boundaries to stop those feelings during the session. It will be important to consult with a supervisor or senior clinician about those feelings.

In the context of "doing no harm" to clients, be sure to approach the issue of sexuality gently and with compassion. You can model comfort with sexuality and normalize the issue for clients, but be aware of their upbringing, religion, possible history of sexualized abuse and possible shame around their sexual history. It is important to introduce the topic of sexuality, but only with sensitivity and at a pace that feels comfortable to the client.

Respect your own limits. If you feel an issue is too personally challenging to discuss, set a limit with the client and help him or her to find a counsellor who will feel more comfortable discussing the issue. If you feel comfortable with the issue, but do not have a lot of information about it, research it by contacting other professionals, or by doing searches in journals and on the Internet. A client can give you information about his or her experience, but do not ask clients to teach you. Remember, they are coming to you for help.

CONCLUSION

Counsellors are in the unique position to be able to share clients' personal stories. We hear about their pain and difficulties, but we can also hear about their successes. We hear about their frustrations, but we can also help to facilitate fulfilment. Discussions about sexuality can allow clients to discuss issues that they may have seen as taboo or too private to disclose to others.

This chapter has invited you to evaluate your own attitudes, values and beliefs about sexuality and sexual health to better help clients evaluate theirs. We have looked at the effects of alcohol and other drugs on sexuality and discussed ways to facilitate conversations about this with clients. We have looked at the impact that substance use can have on a person's definition of his or her own sexual identity and body image and discussed ways to enhance sexual pleasure. Finally, we have looked at certain situations where the discussion of sexuality and substance use becomes especially important.

Discussions about sexuality can be relaxed, fun and funny. They can be insightful, informative and supportive. Clients will benefit from your empathy and confidence in discussing these issues.

BOOKS FOR CLIENTS

Barbach, L.G. (1975). *For Yourself: The Fulfillment of Female Sexuality*. New York: Doubleday.

Bodansky, S. & Bodansky, V. (2002). *The Illustrated Guide to Extended Massive Orgasm*. Alameda, CA: Hunter House Publications.

Chia, M. & Abrams, D. (1996). *The Multi-orgasmic Man*. San Francisco: Harper Collins.

Covington, S. (1991). *Awakening Your Sexuality: A Guide for Recovering Women*. San Francisco: Harper Collins.

Morin, J. (1998). *Anal Pleasure and Health: A Guide for Men and Women*. San Francisco: Down There Press.

Schwartz, P. & Lever, J. (1998). *The Great Sex Weekend: A 48 Hour Guide to Rekindling Sparks for Bold, Busy or Bored Lovers*. New York: G.P. Putnam's Sons.

REFERENCES

AIDS Committee of Toronto (ACT). (2001). *Drug Use & HIV Risk among Gay Men in the Dance/Club Scene in Toronto: How Should AIDS Prevention Programs Respond?* Toronto: author.

AIDS Committee of Toronto (ACT). (2003, March). *Club Drug Info*. Available: www.torontovibe.com.

American Psychiatric Association. (1994). *Diagnostic and Statistical Manual of Mental Disorders* (4th ed.). Washington, DC: author.

Anton, L.H. (1992). *Never to Be a Mother: A Guide for All Women Who Didn't, or Couldn't, Have Children*. San Francisco: Harper Collins.

Atwood, J.D. & Dershowitz, S. (1992, Fall). Constructing a sex and marital therapy frame: Ways to help couples deconstruct sexual problems. *Journal of Sex & Marital Therapy, 18*(3), 196–218.

Bad Boy Club Montreal. (2003, March). *Harm Reduction*. Available: www.bbcm.org.

Bannon, R. (1992). *Learning the Ropes: A Basic Guide to Safe and Fun S/M Lovemaking*. San Francisco: Daedalus Publishing Company.

Beechem, M.H., Prewitt, J. & Scholar, J. (1996). Loss-grief addiction model. *Journal of Drug Education, 26*(2), 183–198.

Berger, G.S., Goldstein, M. & Fuerst, M. (1995). *The Couple's Guide to Fertility*. New York: Doubleday.

Byrne, G.J.A., Raphael, B. & Arnold, E. (1999, October). Alcohol consumption and psychological distress in recently widowed older men. *Australian and New Zealand Journal of Psychiatry, 33*(5), 740–747.

Camden & Islington Community Health Services. (1999). *Sexual Chemistry: Sex, Drugs and Gay Men*. Available: www.candihps.com/pages/reschem.htm.

Carroll, J.F.X., McGinley, J.J. & Mack, S.E. (2001). Exploring the self-reported sexual problems and concerns of drug-dependent males and females in modified, therapeutic community treatment. *Journal of Substance Abuse Treatment, 20*, 245–250.

Covington, S. (1991). *Awakening Your Sexuality: A Guide for Recovering Women*. San Francisco: HarperSanFrancisco.

DanceSafe. (2003, March). *Drug Info*. Available: www.dancesafe.org.

Daniluk, J.C. (1998). *Women's Sexuality across the Lifespan: Challenging Myths, Creating Meanings*. New York: Guilford Press.

Dodson, B. (1987). *Sex for One: The Joy of Selfloving*. New York: Crown Trade Paperbacks.

Ford, M.D. & Hendrick, S.S. (2003). Therapists' sexual values for self and clients: Implications for practice and training. *Professional Psychology: Research and Practice, 34*(1), 80–87.

Friedman, R. & Gradstein, B. (1992). *Surviving Pregnancy Loss: A Complete Sourcebook for Women and Their Families*. Boston: Little, Brown and Company.

Gill, J. (2000). The effects of moderate alcohol consumption on female hormone levels and reproductive function. *Alcohol and Alcoholism, 35*(5), 417–423.

Gold, M. (1988). Alcohol, drugs and sexual dysfunction. *Alcoholism and Addiction, 9*(2), 13.

Guldner, C. & Guldner, D. (1999). *Sex Therapy Manual*. Guelph, ON: University of Guelph.

Guldner, D. (1999, July). Female sexual dysfunction. *American Association of Marriage and Family Therapy Clinical Update, 1*(4), 1–4.

Henderson, D.J., Boyd, C.J. & Whitmarsh, J. (1995). Women and illicit drugs: Sexuality and crack cocaine. *Health Care for Women International, 16*, 113–124.

Hernandez, M. & Alfonso, C.A. (1997). Psychoactive drugs and sexuality. *International Journal of Mental Health, 26*(1), 68–78.

Holland, J. (Ed.). (2001). *Ecstasy: The Complete Guide*. Rochester, VT: Park Street Press.

Howard, B.M. & Hudson, D. (1997). Sexuality, sexual problems, and sexual and physical assault. In S. Harrison & V. Carver (Eds.), *Alcohol and Drug Problems: A Practical Guide for Counsellors* (2nd ed.), 451–472. Toronto: Centre for Addiction and Mental Health.

Irvine, J.M. (1995). *Sexuality Education across Cultures: Working with Differences*. San Francisco: Jossey Bass.

Jacques, T. (1993). *On the Safe Edge: A Manual for SM Play*. Toronto: WholeSM Publishing.

Kaplan, H.S. (1979). *Disorders of Sexual Desire*. New York: Brunner/Mazel.

Keystone, M. (1994, Winter). A feminist approach to couple and sex therapy. *Canadian Journal of Human Sexuality, 3*(4), 321–325.

Kleinplatz, P.J. (1994, June). *The role of eroticism in sexual diversity*. Paper presented at Understanding Sexual Diversity: 16th Annual Guelph Conference and Training Institute on Sexuality.

Kleinplatz, P.J. (1995, June). *Integrating eroticism into sex therapy*. Paper presented at Sexuality Towards Equality: 17th annual Guelph Conference and Training Institute on Sexuality.

Kleinplatz, P.J. (2001a). A critical evaluation of sex therapy: Room for improvement. In P.J. Kleinplatz (Ed.), *New Directions in Sex Therapy: Innovations and Alternatives* (pp. xix–xxiii). Philadelphia: Brunner-Routledge.

Kleinplatz, P.J. (2001b). A critique of the goals of sex therapy, or the hazards of safer sex. In P.J. Kleinplatz (Ed.), *New Directions in Sex Therapy: Innovations and Alternatives* (pp. 109-131). Philadelphia: Brunner-Routledge.

Klitzman, R.L., Greenberg, J.D., Pollack, L.M. & Dolezal, C. (2002). MDMA ("ecstasy") use, and its association with high risk behaviours, mental health, and other factors among gay/bisexual men in New York City. *Drug and Alcohol Dependence, 66*, 115–125.

Kluger-Bell, K. (1998). *Unspeakable Losses: Understanding the Experience of Pregnancy Loss, Miscarriage and Abortion*. New York: W.W. Norton.

Kolodny, R.C., Masters, W.H., & Johnson, V.E. (1979). *Textbook of Sexual Medicine*. Boston: Brown & Co.

Kossman, D.D. (2002, July/August). Barren: Coming to terms with a lost dream. *Psychotherapy Networker, 26*(4), 40–45, 58.

Masters, W.H., Johnson, V.E. & Kolodny, R.C. (1969). *Sex and Human Loving*. Boston: Little, Brown.

Morris, R.W. (1993, Summer). Teaching values in sexuality education: From value-freedom to neutrality and beyond. *Canadian Journal of Human Sexuality, 2*(2), 71–78.

Murray, J. (2003a, January 2). Crystal methamphetamine, crank, speed, tina (Part 2 of a 6 part series, The ABC's of E, G, K and Other Drugs). *Fab, 29.*

Murray, J. (2003b, January 16). G, GHB, liquid E, date rape drug (Part 3 of a 6 part series, The ABC's of E, G, K and Other Drugs). *Fab, 29.*

Palha, A.P. & Esteves, M. (2002). A study of the sexuality of opiate addicts. *Journal of Sex & Marital Therapy, 28*, 427–437.

Payne, P. (1999). *Sex Tips from a Dominatrix*. New York: HarperCollins.

Rawson, R.A., Washton, A., Domier, C. & Reiber, C. (2002). Drugs and sexual effects: Role of drug type and gender. *Journal of Substance Abuse Treatment, 22*, 103–108.

Reardon, D.C. & Ney, P.G. (2000). Abortion and subsequent substance abuse. *American Journal of Drug and Alcohol Abuse, 26*(1), 61–75.

Reece, R. (1987). Causes and treatment of sexual desire discrepancies in male couples. *Journal of Homosexuality, 14*(12), 157–171.

Sanders, G. (1995, Winter). Sexuality, power, and empowerment: One man's reflections on sex therapy. *Canadian Journal of Human Sexuality, 4*(4), 289–298.

Schnarch, D. (1997, September/October). Passionate marriage: Helping couples decode the language of their sexuality. *Family Therapy Networker, 21*(5), 42–49.

Schnarch, D. (1999, January). Male sexual dysfunction. *American Association of Marriage and Family Therapy Clinical Update, 1*(1), 1–4.

Taylor Seagraves, R. (1988). Drugs and desire. In S.R. Leiblum & R.C. Rosen (Eds.), *Sexual Desire Disorders* (pp. 313–374). New York: Guilford Press.

Tiefer, L. (1995). *Sex is Not a Natural Act & Other Essays*. Boulder: Westview Press.

Tisdale, S. (1994). *Talk Dirty to Me: An Intimate Philosophy of Sex*. New York: Doubleday.

Toronto Raver Info Project (TRIP). (2003, March). *Sex/Drugs*. Available: www.torontoraverinfoproject.ca.

Zilbergeld, B. (1992). *The New Male Sexuality*. New York: Bantam Books.

Zilbergeld, B. & Ellison, C.R. (1980). Desire discrepance and arousal problems in sex therapy. In S.R. Leiblum & L.A. Pervin (Eds.), *Principles and Practice of Sex Therapy* (pp. 65–101). New York: Guilford Press.

Chapter 25

Eating Disorders and Substance Use Problems

CHRISTINE M.A. COURBASSON, PATRICK D. SMITH AND FRED J. BOLAND

Eating disorders, especially anorexia nervosa, have one of the highest death rates in psychiatry (Keel et al., 2003). In practice, addiction therapists may unknowingly meet people with concurrent eating disorders; up to 35 per cent of people with substance use problems have eating disorders (National Center on Addiction and Substance Abuse, 2003; Hudson et al., 1992; Jonas et al., 1987; Lacey & Moureli, 1986; Schuckit et al., 1996; Peveler & Fairburn, 1990). For this reason, addiction therapists must be alert to potential food and body image issues in clients.

Concurrent eating and substance use disorders—which affect men and women—can cause many medical, psychological and social problems. Their severity may range from minimal impairment, such as obsessive thoughts about food, body shape and substances, to serious harm, such as the inability to work or assume family responsibility. In fact, some behaviours associated with concurrent eating and substance use disorders can lead to cardiac arrest and death.

TYPES OF EATING DISORDERS

Anorexia Nervosa

The *DSM-IV (TR)* (APA, 2000), lists the following features for anorexia nervosa:

(a) Refusal to maintain body weight at or above 85 per cent of normal for age and height;

(b) Intense fear of gaining weight or becoming fat;

(c) Disturbances in the experience of body shape, weight and/or size;

(d) In females, absence of at least three consecutive menstrual cycles.*

The *DSM-IV* distinguishes between a restricting subtype and a binge-eating/purging subtype of anorexia nervosa. People with the restricting subtype restrict their food intake and do not regularly binge-eat or purge. However, people with the eating/purging type regularly binge-eat or purge. Fasting, excessive exercise, self-induced vomiting, or misusing laxatives, diuretics or enemas are ways they may purge.

People with anorexia are usually easy to identify, as they are emaciated. However, emaciation can also be attributed to the lifestyle associated with substance use, so clinicians in addiction treatment settings rarely explore the possibility of eating disorders in clients.

Anorexia nervosa can affect most major organ systems. Starvation can seriously compromise the cognitive abilities of people who have this disorder; re-feeding may be necessary before beginning any psychotherapy. Some people recover fully after the first treatment (see "Treatment Considerations," p. 402), while others may struggle with the disorder for many years (APA, 2000). As many as 18 per cent of people who have anorexia die from starvation, dehydration, suicide, electrolyte imbalance or from problems related to a concurrent alcohol disorder (Theander, 1992; Herzog et al., 2000).

People with the restricting subtype of anorexia nervosa are probably the hardest to treat, as they are highly controlled, disciplined and rigid in their behaviour. They are often unwillingly brought into treatment by concerned, often panicking, family members. They consider weight loss as an outstanding achievement, and weight gain as evidence of no self-control. They tend to have obsessions and compulsions related to food, body shape and weight; these obsessions and compulsions may worsen with increased malnutrition.

---

*Reprinted with permission from the *Diagnostic and Statistical Manual of Mental Disorders* (4th ed., text revision). Copyright 2000 American Psychiatric Association.

Bulimia Nervosa

The *DSM-IV* criteria for bulimia nervosa (APA, 2000) are:

(a) Recurrent episodes of binge-eating, defined as eating more than an average person would in a discrete period of time (e.g., within two hours) and feeling of lack of control over eating behaviour during a binge;

(b) Regular engagement in some form of purging (vomiting, laxatives, diuretics, strict dieting, fasting or compulsive exercise) to prevent weight gain;

(c) Minimum average of two binge-eating and purging episodes a week for at least three months;

(d) Persistent over-concern with body shape and weight; the disturbance is not associated with anorexia nervosa.*

The *DSM-IV* distinguishes between purging-type and nonpurging-type bulimia nervosa. People with the purging type typically self-induce vomiting or misuse laxatives, diuretics or enemas. In comparison, people with the nonpurging type use other inappropriate compensatory behaviours (fasting or excessive exercise) and tend not to self-induce vomiting or misuse laxatives, diuretics or enemas on a regular basis.

People with bulimia are perhaps the hardest to identify, because their weight is typically within the normal range (Fairburn, 1984). A skilled clinician may recognize salivary gland enlargement, scars/bruises/calluses on the client's hands, or loss of dental enamel from repeated vomiting. Approximately one-third of people with bulimia have substance use problems. Although rare, esophageal tears, gastric rupture and cardiac arrhythmias are some of the fatalities of the disorder (APA, 2000). The mortality rate for bulimia nervosa can be as high as three per cent (Herzog et al., 2000).

Binge-Eating Disorder

Binge-eating, a new category of eating disorder proposed by APA (2000), has been listed as a research criteria, and its prevalence is increasingly recognized. It is characterized by a period of at least six months, for at least two days per week, in which the person has:

(a) Recurrent episodes of binge-eating with a lack of control and in a discrete period of time (an amount of food much larger than most people would eat in a similar period of time under similar circumstances).

---

*Reprinted with permission from the *Diagnostic and Statistical Manual of Mental Disorders* (4th ed., text revision). Copyright 2000 American Psychiatric Association.

(b) At least three of the following: (1) eating more rapidly than normal, (2) eating until feeling uncomfortably full; (3) eating large amounts of food when not physically hungry, (4) eating alone because of embarrassment over the amount of food eaten, (5) feeling disgusted with oneself, depressed or very guilty after overeating.

(c) Marked distress regarding binge-eating.*

People who binge-eat do not use compensatory behaviours (purging, fasting, excessive exercise). As a result, they may gain a large amount of weight and be identifiable by their size. Some identify depression, anxiety and tension as prompting events for their binge-eating; some say that bingeing renders them numb. Its increasingly recognized prevalence makes it likely that binge-eating disorder will one day be among the classified eating disorders.

Eating Disorder Not Otherwise Specified

Eating disorders that are severe but may miss one criterion of the criteria considered above are called eating disorder not otherwise specified. Behaviours associated with these disorders can seriously endanger people's lives and need to be given due consideration. Clinicians need to identify and treat such eating disorders without waiting for clients to meet diagnostic criteria.

CAUSES OF EATING DISORDERS

There is no single defined cause of eating disorders. Various theories, ranging from genetic to socio-cultural, attempt to explain the causes of eating disorders. While they are often debated, most theories about eating disorders share the common feature that causes are multifactorial.

Many factors, such as those related to personality (Vitousek & Monke, 1994), genetics (Strober, 1991) and family (Vandereycken et al., 1989) are associated with eating disorders; however, such factors may be causes or consequences. The presence of different factors varies from person to person; counsellors must be aware of the range of contributing factors and be able to address these factors as they emerge in clients.

---

*Reprinted with permission from the *Diagnostic and Statistical Manual of Mental Disorders* (4th ed., text revision). Copyright 2000 American Psychiatric Association.

Biological Factors

It has been suggested that eating disorders may be due to a deficit in pituitary function (Sheldon, 1939). Various neurotransmitters have been shown to be involved both in eating behaviours and in mood (Fichter, 1992). However, we do not know whether neuroendocrine malfunctioning is the cause or result of eating disorders.

People who have juvenile diabetes have an increased incidence of eating disorders (Rodin et al., 1986). In part, this may be due to their having to chronically restrict the rich high-calorie food that their peers enjoy and possibly to the rigidity of their diets.

Cultural and Gender Factors

Some theories suggest that Western culture produces eating disorders. Thinness, especially for women, is associated with success, femininity, attractiveness, self-control and many other desirable characteristics; fatness is linked with laziness, lack of discipline, ugliness and other negative characteristics.

Women have been socialized more than men have to value appearance concerns. As a result, women tend to internalize an ideal of thinness and to fear fatness. Perceived deviations from the unrealistic ideal are associated with body dissatisfaction and low self-esteem. Indeed, the perceived rewards for thinness are so great for women that, no matter what the source of their low self-esteem or body dissatisfaction, losing weight is often seen as a solution.

Paradoxically, while women experience excessive cultural pressure to be thin, they are also more socialized than are men to interact with food and to use food as a coping mechanism or for pleasure. Often the same women's magazine will contain articles that suggest the comforting nature of food and articles that recommend ways to diet and avoid these very foods. A woman may deprive herself of the foods from which she derives most pleasure—high-calorie, rich foods. The restriction may create obsessive thinking about these foods.

This socially induced thinness also sets up a serious conflict with the physiological forces that protect the woman's body. Many theories suggest that healthy weight is determined by a physiological "set point" mechanism that is influenced a great deal by genetics (Bennett & Gurin, 1982; Keesey & Powley, 1986). The body's response to weight loss is to seek to maintain its fat stores by slowing down metabolic rate (Bennet & Gurin, 1982). (The fact that 95 per cent of people treated for obesity gain back the weight they lose supports this theory.) The chronic, strict dieting seen in people who have bulimia and anorexia places them so far below their healthy weight that their bodies react as if they were starving.

A study by Keys et al. (1950) suggests that semi-starvation in and of itself can generate and maintain symptoms of eating disorders.

Some professions are associated with eating disorders (ballet dancers, fashion models, jockeys and wrestlers) because of the lean body they demand (Garner & Garfinkel, 1980).

Obesity is another risk factor for eating disorders. A high proportion of people with bulimia have a history of obesity. Obesity often results in social punishment for fatness (ridicule, embarrassment, etc.); people who are or have been obese have more reasons to believe that dieting will answer their problems (Loro & Orleans, 1981).

Psychological Factors

Psychoanalytic explanations for eating disorders have ranged from a wish for and fear of oral impregnation (Waller et al., 1940), to the adolescent's hopeless efforts to gain control in a world encroached upon by the mother. Weight and shape may be one of the few areas of the person's life amenable to control. Refusing to eat can be a way of expressing autonomy. This refusal can then become an obsession and lose its original power to alleviate feelings of ineffectiveness and low self-esteem (Bruch, 1977).

A promising new theory that may help to explain eating disorders is the emotion regulation theory. According to this theory, people with eating disorders binge-eat or starve themselves to cope with stress. People with eating disorders are uncomfortable with emotions, and they use food in excess or restriction to modulate their emotions (Safer et al., 2001).

Cognitive Factors

Cognitive theories suggest that eating disorders stem from dysfunctional beliefs and maladaptive information processing. Dichotomous ("black/white") thinking, overgeneralization and superstitious thinking, especially around weight, shape and food issues, are extremely common among people with eating disorders (Fairburn, 2001). These cognitive problems tend to worsen as the weight loss becomes more dramatic.

The construct of *expectancy* (what people expect from something, whether it is based on real facts or incorrect assumptions) has been used to study cognitive mediators of behaviour (Kirsch, 1985; Rotter, 1954). Expectancy models of alcohol use can help predict differential drinking patterns and motivation to maintain drinking behaviours. For example, people who expect that alcohol will reduce their tension are more likely to drink than are those who believe that alcohol will not reduce their tension (Stacy et al., 1990). Similarly, the expectancy theory has recently been applied to understanding eating disorders—differential dieting and eating expectancies may play a significant role in predicting various behaviours associated with eating disorders (Hohltein et al., 1998).

Interrelated Mental Health and Substance Use Factors

Because they are associated with poor impulse control, personality disorders may place people at higher risk for bulimia (Piran et al., 1988) and substance use problems.

Although depression is strongly associated with bulimia nervosa (and alcohol problems), most depression is probably secondary to the bulimia and is alleviated as the bulimic behaviour decreases (Cooper & Fairburn, 1983). Although neurochemical abnormalities, especially those involving serotonin, can be associated both with depression and with eating disorders (Fava et al., 1989), it is currently impossible to tell whether these abnormalities are a consequence or a cause of eating disorders.

Because of the high rate of co-existence of eating disorders and problem substance use, Brisman & Siegel (1984) have proposed that some people may become addicted to specific substances (food or drugs), while others may become addicted to the euphoria brought about by starvation. This theory remains greatly disputed on the basis that people with eating disorders do not meet the tolerance and physical dependence criteria of substance use problems (Wilson, 1993).

THE RELATIONSHIP BETWEEN EATING DISORDERS AND SUBSTANCE USE

An association between problem substance use and bulimia is easy to document. Estimated rates of prevalence for concurrent eating disorders in people with a substance use problem can be as high as 35 per cent, and 50 per cent of people with eating disorders admit to using substances (Goldbloom et al., 1992; National Center on Addiction and Substance Abuse, 2003; Schuckit et al., 1996). People with concurrent eating and substance use disorders have similar misconceptions about food, substances and their bodies. Food and substances become maladaptive tools they use to try to either gain some control over or take refuge from stresses in their lives. Whether the person uses food or substances, or a combination of these, to control stress or take refuge from stress, and the extent of such disordered behaviour, is influenced by a combination of emotions or fear of emotions, deficits in adaptive coping strategies and physical needs.

For example, a person may have eaten almost nothing during the day. In the afternoon following an argument with a co-worker she feels angry, is uncomfortable with the feeling of anger and unsuccessfully tries to push the anger away. When she gets home, she prepares a healthy dinner but is interrupted by a telephone call from her mother, who disagrees with her about something. Being very hungry, the woman feels irritable and ends the conversation abruptly. Now she feels angry and guilty, and she reaches for a drink to calm her. The drink temporarily soothes her, and she drinks more to feel even better. Then she becomes tormented by thinking about the calories in the alcohol and feels she has ruined her diet. This makes her more anxious, and, since she has already broken her diet, she feels she may as well eat something. However, the starvation and alcohol lead her to eat uncontrollably. She feels guilty about her lack of control and purges to get rid of the calories. Then she drinks more to cope with her feeling of guilt about the binge-eating.

In this way, cycles are established, revolving around emotions, interpersonal interactions and an inability to cope with stressors without resorting to disordered eating and substance use. The psychological and physiological conditions also become intertwined. The emotional problems brought about by problematic eating can lead a person to use substances and vice versa. The maladaptive behaviours are usually only effective in the short term, and eventually lead to more severe long-term consequences.

COMMON FACTORS ASSOCIATED WITH PROBLEMATIC EATING BEHAVIOUR AND SUBSTANCE USE

To recover from concurrent eating and substance use disorders, a person must learn to identify and adaptively address his or her own precipitants and reinforcers to the problem behaviours. Understanding the different factors that may help maintain problems with both substance use and eating behaviour can help clinicians more effectively address the problem behaviour.

Psychosocial

People who have concurrent eating and substance use disorders tend to:
• have obsessive thoughts about food, body shape and substances (Katz, 1990)
• restrict their food intake or use food or substances to numb or avoid emotions
• lack control over the amount of substances they use and food they eat (except for people who have the restrictive sub-type of anorexia) (Krahn, 1991; Wilson, 1993)
• be preoccupied with, and continue to use, food or substances despite experiencing harm from such use
• have strong feelings of shame associated with the eating and substance use behaviours and often deny the behaviours or keep the behaviours secret, decreasing the likelihood they will seek or comply with treatment.

These features make it hard to treat concurrent eating and substance use disorders. People with these concurrent disorders often withdraw prematurely from treatment programs, experience a chronic course of the illnesses and need longer courses of treatment. They also tend to have many other medical and psychosocial problems. Among people seeking substance use treatment, those who screened positive for concurrent eating and substance use disorders had greater comorbidity for depression, mania, panic disorders, social phobia, schizophrenia, as well as schizophreniform disorders, conduct disorders and gambling disorders, than did all other treatment-seekers (Courbasson et al., 1999).

Other research suggests that people with these concurrent disorders are at risk for depression, impulsiveness, anxiety, obsessiveness and social withdrawal (Boland & Butt, 1989; Hatsukami et al., 1984; Hatsukami et al., 1982). Increased incidence of disturbed childhoods and sexual abuse is also associated with people who either have an eating disorder or have a substance use disorder. People who have concurrent eating and substance use disorders show more likelihood of having experienced childhood abuse than does the population in general (Walker et al., 1988).

Clients with concurrent substance use and eating disorders are more likely to:
- have problems with more than one substance
- have experienced more adolescent antisocial behaviour problems, more self-reported suicidal thoughts and attempts, and more previous treatment for mental health problems (Perlman & McKenna, 1988)
- have been hospitalized for psychiatric problems
- have a history of stealing, abuse of diuretics and social impairment (Hatsukami et al., 1986).

Precipitants

The following precipitants, either alone or in combination, are commonly observed in people with concurrent substance use and eating disorders.

EMOTIONAL AND PSYCHOLOGICAL TRIGGERS
Various emotions (positive and negative) typically precede problematic eating/restricting/purging and substance use. These include elation, anxiety, anger, boredom, sadness, frustration, loneliness and rejection (Arnow et al., 1995; Marlatt & Gordon, 1985). Increases in stress level, or relatively sudden increases in concern over appearance, are also associated with bingeing and purging. Other patterns of triggers may be uniquely associated with a person's bingeing (e.g., need to punish one's self or impulsivity).

DIETING
Dieting also encourages bingeing, as the starved body reaches for as much food as it can, when it can. The stricter the diet, the more severe the binge (Vanderheyden & Boland, 1987). Chronic dieters and people with bulimia nervosa have many foods they label as forbidden when dieting. Paradoxically, these "taboo" foods easily trigger binges, because consumption of even small amounts symbolizes the breaking of the diet (Knight & Boland, 1989).

ALCOHOL USE
Alcohol consumption has been shown to disinhibit eating in dieters in much the same way as consumption of "taboo" foods (Polivy & Herman, 1976).

Reinforcers

Although concurrent eating and substance use disorders can cause severe problems, the short-term benefits people achieve through these behaviours temporarily outweigh the consequences. These benefits are known as "reinforcers."

ANOREXIA

People with anorexia derive satisfaction from being hungry and feeling in control; some even describe a type of high they achieve from the starvation.

BINGE-EATING

People who binge-eat usually feel an initial pleasure in anticipating tasting and eating the rich "taboo" foods that they crave and normally exclude from their diet. Bingeing often brings temporary relief from the tension and negative mood that helped trigger the binge. For many, eating fills a void, creating a way not to feel. In these ways, people can use a food binge much like someone else might use alcohol or drugs: to achieve a desirable effect.

As a binge progresses (the typical binge lasts 30 to 60 minutes), the negative consequences begin to appear. There is a return of negative mood states and feeling out of control. People will often end their binge by going to bed, often with feelings of disgust and self-hatred. The fear of weight gain and the pain, nausea and bloating that accompany overeating may eventually help stop the binge.

PURGING

Terrified of gaining weight, and as a way to release abdominal discomfort caused by the large amount of food, a person may then purge by self-inducing vomiting, using laxatives or exercising immediately after the binge. These behaviours tend to "lock in" the binge-purge cycle, as the purging is powerfully rewarded physically, by relief of nausea and bloating, and psychologically, by reduced anxiety over weight gain. Eventually, the purging becomes a way to control the negative effects of the binge. A person with bulimia will often avoid bingeing unless there is an opportunity to purge shortly after. For some people with bulimia, it is the purging, rather than the bingeing, that releases the tension.

PHYSIOLOGICAL REINFORCERS

In some cases, a physiological response to a binge on refined carbohydrates may help maintain the binge-purge cycle. Refined sugars are absorbed directly into the blood, causing an acute rise in blood glucose levels. The body then releases large amounts of insulin to bring down the blood sugar level. In people who binge-purge and chronically diet, this process can serve as a stimulus to eat (Spitzer & Rodin, 1987). Also, because most of the calories consumed during the binge are soon purged, there is a possibility of insulin overshoot, resulting in an acute hypoglycemic state that may contribute to mood instability and craving for more sugar.

SUBSTANCE USE

Some people feel out of control when they binge-eat. Because they have already broken their restriction rule, they feel that they may as well break their rules about substance use, in an effort to feel better. For others, the purge does not reduce tension enough, or they might be feeling shame for bingeing or starving, so they use substances to cope with these feelings.

ASSESSMENT OF EATING DISORDERS

For several reasons, clinicians often overlook the need to assess for eating disorders in clients who seek treatment for substance use problems:
• Clinicians may be unaware of the significant prevalence of these concurrent disorders. In clients who are severely underweight, clinicians often attribute emaciation to the substance use.
• People with bulimia are often of average weight, so the eating disorder is less noticeable.
• Clinicians may not ask men about eating disorders because of the myth that eating disorders are exclusively female problems.
• People with eating disorders are unlikely to disclose the problems because they deny the illness, feel shame about the behaviours and lack motivation to seek or comply with treatment.

Signs of Eating Disorders

The following signs indicate the need for assessment for eating disorders.
• anorexia nervosa: emaciation, thinning of head hair and the appearance of lanugos (fine hair) on face and body
• bulimia nervosa: signs of repeated self-induced vomiting, such as scarring on the hands from teeth abrasion, loss of tooth enamel, recurrent dental cavities, bursting of veins around the eyes, and salivary gland enlargement (swelling on the right and left sides of the lower jaw)
• binge-eating disorder: obesity with reports of mindless eating.
When asking questions about these signs, a non-judgmental stance, validation, honesty and perseverance can help establish a therapeutic alliance that may promote clients' openness.

Assessment Tools and Procedures

The Eating Disorder Examination (Cooper & Fairburn, 1997) is a semi-structured interview to assess specific psychopathology of eating disorders (patterns and restraint over eating; dietary rules; control; guilt about eating; preoccupation with food, eating, calories, weight and shape; bingeing; purging; fear of weight). This comprehensive interview provides ample information about the client's problems.

The *Structured Clinical Inventory for the Diagnostic and Statistical Manual IV Axis I (SCID)* (First, et al., 1995) is somewhat less comprehensive but checks for *DSM-IV* criteria. It can be followed by a self-report questionnaire to expand the assessment when the person screens positive for an eating disorder (Crowther & Sherwood, 1997; Fairburn, 2001).

Quick screening can also be done on the Internet (e.g., Healthy Place, 2003). User-friendly Internet measures can have good psychometric properties, although anyone using them must be cautioned that these do not replace a formal psychiatric evaluation.

Clinicians must collect a thorough history of the client's functioning, family dynamics, peer relationships, present or past abuse, body weight, eating patterns and weight control measures, attitudes toward food, shape and weight, and previous attempts at treatment. Also, psychiatric history must be covered, as mood, anxiety and personality disorders are common additional comorbid problems (Crowther & Sherwood, 1997). A thorough medical check-up must always complement a psychological assessment of eating disorders (for a list of medical complications, see Kaplan & Woodside, 1987).

TREATMENT CONSIDERATIONS

Inpatient and Outpatient Treatments

ANOREXIA

For anorexia, inpatient treatment is recommended for severely underweight and undernourished clients (less than 75 per cent of healthy weight) (APA, 2000). Inpatient treatment has been effective and invaluable in reversing the effects of malnutrition and stabilizing clients biochemically and physically. This stabilization can be necessary before treatment can begin to address the substance use problem.

Psychotherapy is limited until a good therapeutic relationship is established to help clients learn to self-regulate and self-care (Gootsitt, 1997). The closer to healthy weight at time of discharge, the lower the risk of relapse to the disordered eating behaviour (APA, 2000).

BULIMIA AND BINGE-EATING DISORDER

Treatment for bulimia and binge-eating disorder is mostly outpatient (Beumont et al., 1997). Hospitalization is usually only recommended when it is medically necessary to stabilize the patient. The goal of inpatient treatment for bulimia is not recovery but treating medical aspects of the disorder in hospital.

Outpatient treatments may be medical or psychotherapeutic. Clients are usually treated medically as outpatients when it is clear that they are uninterested in psychological treatment (Garner & Needleman, 1997). Medical maintenance focuses on keeping the person alive, for example, by administering intravenous fluids to hydrate the person.

Pharmacological Treatments

Pharmacological treatments have been explored for bulimia and anorexia. Tricyclic antidepressants (e.g., imipramine, desipramine) can be beneficial, at least in the short term (fewer than eight weeks). Long-term antidepressant use is less successful, often resulting in frequent changes of drugs required, a high dropout rate from treatment and a high relapse rate when medication is withdrawn (Mitchell, 1988).

Psychological Treatments and Education

Psychological treatments for eating disorders may be offered on an individual or group basis, in outpatient, inpatient or day hospital programs. Many therapists use a variety of techniques from different theoretical orientations.

Any psychological treatment must be undertaken only with medical supervision; if clients are so nutritionally compromised that they cannot think clearly, psychological treatment will not be effective. Medical supervision ensures that the client is medically able to participate in psychological treatment and can safely be treated as an outpatient. The physician may perform blood and urine tests, and an ECG to check for hydration status, nutritional deficiencies, and any cardiac abnormalities.

Concurrent eating and substance use disorders tend to be chronic and to be associated with serious psychological and medical outcome. For this reason, professionals trained in concurrent treatment can most effectively help clients with such disorders.

COGNITIVE BEHAVIOUR THERAPY

Cognitive behaviour therapy is generally more effective than pharmacotherapy for eating disorders. In some cases, the best treatment is a combination of the two (Agras et al., 1992). Cognitive behaviour therapy:

- addresses chronic and maladaptive thought patterns, especially underlying assumptions about weight, body image and self-worth; for example, that personal worth can be inferred solely or predominantly from weight and/or body shape (Garner, Needleman & Lawrence, 1997)
- corrects client's errors in reasoning and the underlying assumptions that helped develop and help maintain the eating disorder (Wilson et al., 1997)
- challenges dichotomous thinking by using behavioural exercises to evaluate a particular belief from a different perspective (Garner, Vitousek & Pike, 1997).

Regular weigh-ins are common in this treatment (Wilson et al., 1997). Clients are educated about issues such as weight regulation, negative effects of laxatives and symptoms of starvation (Garner, Vitousek & Pike, 1997; Wilson et al., 1997). The therapist makes recommendations to help clients normalize their eating behaviours and curb restrictive dieting. Self-control strategies and problem-solving skills help the client avoid eating-disordered behaviours (Wilson et al., 1997; Garner, Vitousek &

Pike, 1997). Relapse-prevention techniques (Wilson et al., 1997) help clients antici-pate problems and prepare various ways of coping with them (Wilson et al., 1997).

The length of cognitive behaviour therapy treatment for bulimia or binge-eating disorder is typically three months; for anorexia, the treatment period is often longer (Garner, Needleman & Lawrence, 1997). See Fairburn et al. (1993) for a manual and Fairburn (1995) for a self-help version of this therapy.

NUTRITION EDUCATION
Nutrition education, preferably from a dietitian trained in eating disorders treatment, can help the client:
• reach and maintain normal nutritional status
• attain normal eating behaviours and a normal attitude to food (APA, 2000; Beumont et al., 1997)
• recognize hunger and satiety cues and develop appropriate responses to those cues (Beumont et al., 1997).

FAMILY THERAPY
Family therapy is also often useful, especially with young patients living at home (Brownell & Foreyt, 1985; Garner & Garfinkel, 1985).

FEMINIST APPROACH TO THERAPY
The feminist approach to therapy differs from other therapies in the following ways:
• It addresses sexual abuse, confrontation of perpetrators, exploration of legal options and victim support services (Wooley, 1995).
• The therapeutic relationship is more egalitarian than that of other psychotherapies.
• It emphasizes empowerment of the client, socio-political aspects of eating disorders (Perlick & Silverstein, 1994) and interpersonal relationships (Garner, Needleman & Lawrence, 1997) to heighten the client's understanding of the role of victimization of clients (including sexual abuse), identity confusion and role conflicts (Garner, Needleman & Lawrence, 1997).
• Its goals are "self-differentiation, self-determination, and informed refusal" (Wooley, 1995).

PSYCHOANALYTIC AND PSYCHODYNAMIC THERAPIES
Psychoanalytic and psychodynamic therapies address:
• developmental issues
• identity formation and gender role expectations
• body image concerns
• sexual and aggressive problems
• affect regulation
• interpersonal conflicts
• family dysfunction
• coping styles and problem solving (APA, 2000).

Some therapists believe that eating disorders do not have unique underlying processes, and so they use a traditional interpretive framework. Others believe that these disorders are distinctive, and so traditional psychodynamic therapy must be modified to meet the special psychological and physical needs of clients with eating disorders (Garner, Needleman & Lawrence, 1997). Recently, therapists have been integrating traditional psychodynamic therapy with principles of symptom management (Crisp, 1997).

MEDITATION

Meditation, or the process of focusing on one "thing" at a time, has recently been considered as a very useful tool in recovery for eating disorders. It may modify the deregulated processes associated with binge-eating (Kristeller & Hallett, 1999). Research suggests that meditation can:

- promote relaxation and reduce both emotional and physiological upheaval (Beauchamp-Turner & Levinson, 1992; Sothers & Anchor, 1989)
- increase awareness of physiological signals and thereby help the person recognize and respond to normal satiety cues (Kristeller & Hallett, 1999)
- improve self-acceptance and decrease the appeal of binge-eating as an escape (Heatherton & Baumeister, 1991).

DIALECTICAL BEHAVIOURAL THERAPY

Dialectical behavioural therapy (DBT) has been adapted for the treatment of bulimia nervosa and binge-eating disorder, and has been shown to reduce the number of binges and purges (Safer et al., 2001; Telch et al., 2001). DBT has also been demonstrated to be an effective treatment for substance use disorders (Linehan et al., 1999; Linehan & Dimeff, 2000). Standard DBT treatments include:

- individual therapy
- group skills training
- telephone coaching
- consult team meetings for clinicians.

The treatment is premised, in part, on the view that clients have deficits in emotion regulation and interpersonal skills for which they compensate with maladaptive, problematic behaviours. DBT treatments therefore involve increasing clients' problem-solving skills while also teaching them:

- mindfulness skills to heighten their awareness of behaviours, thoughts, emotions and body and to become non-judgmental
- interpersonal effectiveness skills to help them attend to relationships while balancing priorities and demands
- emotion experiencing and regulation skills to observe and describe emotions and reduce their emotional vulnerability
- distress tolerance and crisis survival skills.

In addition to teaching these skills and coaching clients as they incorporate the skills into their lives, the DBT model also incorporates treatment strategies that are effective with client populations who tend to become polarized and resistant to treatment.

DBT Adaptations for Bulimia and Binge-Eating

Dialectical behavioural therapy (DBT) has been recently adapted for the treatment of bulimia nervosa and binge-eating disorder, and has been shown to reduce the number of binges and purges (Safer et al., 2001; Telch et al., 2001). However, people with active substance use problems or severe depression were excluded from the trials.

People who have concurrent substance use disorders are often ineligible to participate in treatments for eating disorders. They must start with treatment for one disorder and then move to another treatment to address the other.

This approach overlooks the crucial interrelationships among eating and substance use disorders. Consequently, as one disorder improves, the other deteriorates, and clients may go through several cycles of treatment (Sutherland et al., 1993).

Recently, Courbasson & Dixon (2003) of the Centre for Addiction and Mental Health have adapted DBT for concurrent eating and substance use disorders. This enhanced DBT blends elements from previous separate adaptations for eating and substance use disorders and incorporates new elements tailored specifically for clients with both disorders.

Clients learn about eating and substance use disorders, and how to break the cycle of problematic eating, maladaptive decision-making and physical and mental health problems. They are also encouraged to build balanced structure in their lives to help break out of their isolation, develop new skills and areas of interest, develop mastery, structure positive activities and improve self-care. The emphasis is on flexibility and adaptation to change. Helping clients explore their expectancies and challenge their rules about substance use, eating and dieting allows clients and clinicians to co-construct an individually tailored understanding of the problem and a plan to resolve the problem. Relapse prevention strategies (Marlatt & Gordon, 1985) are also an integral part of the treatment.

This recent concurrent treatment is promising; early findings suggest improvements in healthy eating, stopping and reducing substance use, treatment retention, development of healthy identity and decreased distress (Courbasson, 2001; McMain et al., 2001). We hope that further research will show this treatment to be effective across a variety of settings.

SELF-HELP GROUPS

Self-help groups for eating disorders are available in the community and may be appropriate for some clients. The National Eating Disorder Information Centre in Toronto, Canada, can supply excellent handouts relevant to consciousness-raising of how society shapes women's attitudes and behaviour in destructive ways. A feminist-oriented literature, such as *Fat Is a Feminist Issue* (Orbach, 1982), or *Making Peace with Food* (Kano, 1989) can be useful. For exercises and homework assignments for improving body image, see Butters & Cash (1987) and Wooley & Kearney-Cooke (1986).

Treatment of Concurrent Substance Use and Eating Disorders

We suggest that it is best for people who are struggling with eating disorders and substance use problems to be treated concurrently for both sets of issues. A client with a concurrent eating and substance use disorder should be referred to a therapist familiar with treating both disorders. If that is not possible, the therapist responsible for assessing and treating the eating disorder should work together with the addiction therapist, if possible.

The therapist must use judgment when deciding whether a client who needs residential treatment can be managed in a substance use treatment unit; the therapist should include a medical professional in this decision process.

If the behaviours associated with the eating disorder cause a client to miss groups and be unavailable for substance use treatment, the client must be referred to more suitable treatment for the eating disorder. Further, it is important not to underestimate the potential medical complications that may not be apparent without close medical screening and monitoring.

If the addiction counsellor is the only source of help for the client with a concurrent eating disorder, this counsellor is obligated to become more familiar with factors related to eating disorders and with appropriate treatment strategies, and to arrange for medical support from a physician. For more information on how to make these arrangements, see the list of recommended readings on p. 416.

ISSUES TO CONSIDER

Gender and Eating Disorders

GENDER DIFFERENCES IN CHILDHOOD AND ADOLESCENCE

In childhood and adolescence, girls engage in bingeing and purging weight-loss behaviours more than boys do. Compared with their non-dieting same-sex peers, girls who try to lose weight are more upset about their shape than are boys who try to lose weight (Ackard et al., 2001). When trying to lose weight, girls with body dissatisfaction and low self-esteem are less likely to engage in physical activity than are boys who have the same concerns. Adolescent girls report more use of laxatives and vomiting as weight control methods than do adolescent boys (Field et al., 1999).

Compared with boys who do not have eating disorders, boys with eating disorders have more mental and physical health problems, and have experienced more sexual and physical abuse. Girls who have eating disorders, compared with girls who do not, are more likely to engage in sexual risk-taking and substance use (Lock et al., 2001).

GENDER DIFFERENCES IN AGE OF ONSET

The age of onset of eating disorders is generally later in men than in women. Men are also more likely to have an occupation or a sport where weight control is seen to influence performance (Braun et al., 1999).

GENDER DIFFERENCES IN ADULTHOOD

Although eating disorders and body image disturbance are common in men, more women than men report such problems (Barry & Grilo, 2002).

Women with concurrent eating disorders, especially bulimia nervosa, and drinking problems usually develop the eating disorder before the alcohol problem (Higuchi et al., 1993).

Women are more likely than men are to label their eating as a binge and to experience negative emotions as a result of the label (LaPorte, 1997). They are more likely to eat to try to cope with negative emotions, especially anxiety, anger, frustration and depression (Tanofsky et al., 1997).

Women who binge-eat are more likely to engage in compensatory behaviours (fasting, extreme exercise) than men are. Apart from this, few gender differences have been seen in the relationship between binge-eating and substance use (Ross & Ivis, 1999). Women with bulimia have a stronger desire to be thin, whereas men report more issues with perfectionism and trust (Joiner et al., 2000).

Among people who are obese and binge-eat, men eat more than women do when bingeing (Geliebter et al., 2001) and are more likely to binge because of negative emotions, such as depression or anger. Women in this group tend to binge after dieting or restricting their eating. These gender differences may be related to gender-role expectations (Costanzo et al., 1999).

Men with anorexia have a better prognosis than do women and tend to be in better physical condition after treatment (Deter et al., 1998). Having been sexually harassed is associated with eating disorder behaviours in women, but not in men (Harned & Fitzgerald, 2002).

Sexual Orientation

Heterosexual women have the highest incidence of eating disorder symptoms and concerns with body size and shape; heterosexual men have the lowest incidence. The incidence of eating disorders in gay men and lesbians rests between the two heterosexual groups (Strong et al., 2000). Heterosexual females and gay men are more likely to engage in binge behaviours than heterosexual males or lesbians are. Gay men also engage in more exercise than do either of the heterosexual groups. Heterosexual women are more likely to want to lose weight than lesbians are. Of these four groups, heterosexual men are the most likely to be obese and the least concerned about weight (Schneider et al., 1995).

Culture and Ethnicity

Rates of eating disorders vary among different racial and ethnic groups, and they also change over time as cultures evolve. Cultural change—as time passes and also when a person moves into a new culture—is associated with increased vulnerability to eating disorders (particularly if such change involves physical aesthetics) (Miller & Pumariega, 2001). While the prevalence of eating disorders has been mainly in Western societies, these disorders may be increasing in other countries, as they adopt Western ideas and ideals (Lovejoy, 2001).

CULTURE AND ETHNICITY IN CHILDREN AND ADOLESCENTS

African-American adolescent girls are more satisfied with their bodies and have lower rates of dieting or disordered eating than do Caucasian girls in the United States (Franko & Striegel-Moore, 2002). African-American boys engage in binge-eating more than African-American girls do, followed by Caucasian boys, and Caucasian girls. The rates of binge-eating increase with age for Caucasians but decrease with age for African-Americans (Johnson et al., 2002).

Because of the influence of Western culture, the proportion of young women at risk for disordered eating in Hong Kong may become similar to that of North America and Europe (Lee, 2001).

CULTURE AND ETHNICITY IN ADULTS

Caucasians and Asians have greater body discrepancy (difference between current and ideal) than do African-Americans (Gluck & Geliebter, 2002). Compared with Caucasian women, African-American women appear to be more satisfied with their weight and appearance, are less likely to control their weight unhealthily, and engage less in problematic eating and restricting. However, they have higher rates of obesity than Caucasian women do (Atlas et al., 2002; Lovejoy, 2001).

CONCLUSION

The results of concurrent substance use and eating disorders can be very harmful, and even fatal. Clinicians need to understand the different factors associated with both substance use and disordered eating, and the way in which the psychological and physiological conditions become intertwined.

The best outcomes for people who are struggling with eating disorders and substance use problems may be found when both sets of issues are treated concurrently. To effectively help such clients, addiction counsellors should become familiar with eating disorders, their causes and treatment, and their interrelationship with substance use disorders. Addiction counsellors should also be prepared to arrange for medical support from a physician.

REFERENCES

Ackard, D., Neumark-Sztainer, D., Hannan, P.J., French, S. & Story, M. (2001). Binge and purge behavior among adolescents: Associations with sexual and physical abuse in a nationally representative sample: The Commonwealth Fund survey. *Child Abuse and Neglect, 25*(6), 771–785.

Agras, W.S., Rossiter, E.M., Arnow, B., Schneider, J.A., Telch, C.F., Raeburn, S.D. et al. (1992). Pharmacologic and cognitive-behavioral treatment for bulimia nervosa: A controlled comparison. *American Journal of Psychiatry 49*, 82–87.

American Psychiatric Association. (2000). *Diagnostic and Statistical Manual of Mental Disorders* (4th ed., text revision). American Psychiatric Association. Washington, DC: author.

Arnow, B., Kenardy, J. & Agras, W.S. (1995). The Emotional Eating Scale: The development of a measure to assess coping with negative affect by eating. *International Journal of Eating Disorders, 18*(1), 79–90.

Atlas, J.G., Smith, G.T., Hohlstein, L.A., McCarthy, D.M. & Kroll, L.S. (2002). Similarities and differences between Caucasian and African American college women on eating and dieting expectancies, bulimic symptoms, dietary restraint, and disinhibition. *International Journal of Eating Disorders, 32*(3), 326–334.

Barry, D.T. & Grilo, C.M. (2002). Eating and body image disturbances in adolescent psychiatric inpatients: Gender and ethnicity patterns. *International Journal of Eating Disorders, 32*(3), 335–343.

Beauchamp-Turner, D.L. & Levinson, D.M. (1992). Effects of meditation on stress, health, and affect. *Medical Psychotherapy: An International Journal, 5*, 123–131.

Bennett, W. & Gurin, J. (1982). *The Dieter's Dilemma*. New York: Basic Books.

Beumont, P.J.V., Beumont, C.C., Touyz, S.W., Stephen, W. & Williams, H. (1997). Nutritional counselling and supervised exercise. In D.M. Garner & P. Garfinkel (Eds.), *Handbook of Treatment for Eating Disorders: 2nd Ed.* (pp. 178–187). New York: Guilford Press.

Boland, F.J. & Butt, J. (1989). *Increased signs of eating disorders in women with alcohol problems.* Paper presented to Canadian Psychological Association, Halifax.

Braun, D.L., Sunday, S.R., Huang, A. & Halmi, K.A. (1999). More males seek treatment for eating disorders. *International Journal of Eating Disorders, 25*(4), 415–424.

Brisman, J. & Siegel, M. (1984). Bulimia and alcoholism: Two sides of the same coin? *Journal of Substance Abuse Treatment, 1*, 113–118.

Brownell, K.D. & Foreyt, J.P. (1985). Obesity. In D.H. Barlow (Ed.), *Clinical Handbook of Psychological Disorders: A Step-by-Step Treatment Manual* (pp. 299–343). Philadelphia: University of Pennsylvania, School of Medicine, Dept. of Psychiatry.

Bruch, H. (1977). Psychological antecedents of anorexia nervosa. In R.A. Vigersky (Ed.), *Anorexia Nervosa* (pp. 1–10). New York: Raven Press.

Butters, J.W. & Cash, T.F. (1987). Cognitive behavioral treatment of women's body image dissatisfaction. *Journal of Consulting and Clinical Psychology, 55*(6), 889–897.

Cooper, P.J. & Fairburn, C.G. (1983). Binge-eating and self-induced vomiting in the community: A preliminary study. *British Journal of Psychiatry, 142,* 139–144.

Costanzo, P.R., Musante, G.J., Friedman, K.E., Kern, L.S. & Tomlinson, K. (1999). The gender specificity of emotional, situational, and behavioral indicators of binge eating in a diet-seeking obese population. *International Journal of Eating Disorders, 26*(2), 205–210.

Courbasson, C.M.A. (2001). DBT for concurrent eating and substance use disorders. *The DBT Bulletin, 1*(1), 3.

Courbasson, C.M.A. & Dixon, L. (2003). *Building Balance: A Facilitators' Guide to Skills Training in Dialectical Behaviour Therapy for Concurrent Eating Disorders and Substance Use Problems.* Submitted for publication.

Courbasson, C.M.A., Smith, P.D. & Cleland, P.A. (1999). *Substance use disorders, anorexia, bulimia, and concurrent disorders.* Paper presented at the 10th Annual Meeting of the American Academy of Addiction Psychiatry, Nassau, Bahamas (December).

Crisp, A.H. (1997). Anorexia nervosa as flight from growth: Assessment and treatment based on the model. In D.M. Garner & P. Garfinkel (Eds.), *Handbook of Treatment for Eating Disorders: 2nd Ed.* (pp. 248–277). New York: Guilford Press.

Crowther, J.H. & Sherwood, N.E. (1997). Assessment. In D.M. Garner & P. Garfinkel (Eds.), *Handbook of Treatment for Eating Disorders: 2nd Ed.* (pp. 34–49). New York: Guilford Press.

Deter, H.-C., Koepp, W., Zipfel, S. & Herzog, W. (1998). Male anorexia nervosa patients in the long-term course of the disease, *Nervenarzt, 69*(5), 419–426.

Fairburn, C.G. (1984). Bulimia: Its epidemiology and management. *Psychiatric Annals, 13*(12), 953–961.

Fairburn, C.G. (1995). *Overcoming Binge Eating.* New York: Guilford Press.

Fairburn C.G. (2001). *Eating Disorders and Obesity: A Comprehensive Handbook.* New York: Guilford Press.

Fairburn, C.G. & Cooper, Z. (1993). The Eating Disorder Examination (12th edition). In C.G. Fairburn & G.T. Wilson (Eds.), *Binge Eating: Nature, Assessment, and Treatment* (pp. 317–360). New York: Guilford Press.

Fairburn, C.G., Marcus, M.D. & Wilson, G.T. (1993). Cognitive-behavioral therapy for binge eating and bulimia nervosa: A comprehensive treatment manual. In C.G. Fairburn & G.T. Wilson (Eds.), *Binge Eating: Nature, Assessment, and Treatment* (pp. 361–404). New York: Guilford Press.

Fava, M., Copland, P.M., Schiveiger, U. & Herzog, D.B. (1989). Neurochemical abnormalities of anorexia nervosa and bulimia nervosa. *American Journal of Psychiatry, 146,* 963–971.

Fichter, M.M. (1992). Starvation-related endocrine changes. In Halmi, K.A. (Ed.), *Psychobiology and Treatment of Anorexia Nervosa and Bulimia Nervosa* (pp. 193–220). Washington, DC: APA.

Field, A.E., Camargo, C.A. Jr., Taylor, C.B., Berkey, C.S., Frazier, L., Gillman, M.W. et al. (1999). Overweight, weight concerns, and bulimic behaviors among girls and boys. *Journal of the American Academy of Child & Adolescent Psychiatry, 38*(6), 754–760.

First, M.B., Spitzer, R.L., Gibbon, M. & Williams, J.B.W. (1995). *Structured Clinical Interview for DSM-IV Axis I Disorders.* Biometrics Research Department, New York State Psychiatric Institute, Department of Psychiatry. New York: Columbia University.

Franko, D.L & Striegel-Moore, R.H. (2002). The role of body dissatisfaction as a risk factor for depression in adolescent girls: Are the differences Black and White? *Journal of Psychosomatic Research, 53*(5), 975–983.

Garfinkel, P.E. & Garner, D.M. (1982). *Anorexia Nervosa: A Multidimensional Perspective.* New York: Brunner/Mazel.

Garner, D.M. & Garfinkel, P.E. (1980). Socio-cultural factors in the development of anorexia nervosa. *Psychological Medicine, 10,* 647–656.

Garner, D.M. & Garfinkel, P. (Eds.). (1997). *Handbook of Treatment for Eating Disorders (2nd ed.).* New York: Guilford Press.

Garner, D.M., Needleman, L.D. & Lawrence, D. (1997). Sequencing and integration of treatments. In D.M. Garner & P. Garfinkel (Eds.), *Handbook of Treatment for Eating Disorders: 2nd Ed.* (pp. 50–63). New York: Guilford Press.

Garner, D.M., Vitousek, K.M. & Pike, K.M. (1997). Cognitive-behavioural therapy for anorexia nervosa. In D.M. Garner & P. Garfinkel (Eds.), *Handbook of Treatment for Eating Disorders: 2nd Ed.* (pp. 94–144). New York: Guilford Press.

Geliebter, A., Hassid, G. & Hashim, S.A. (2001). Test meal intake in obese binge eaters in relation to mood and gender. *International Journal of Eating Disorders, 29*(4), 488–494.

Gluck, M.E. & Geliebter, A. (2002). Racial/ethnic differences in body image and eating behaviors. *Eating Behaviors, 3*(2), 143–151.

Goldbloom, D.S., Naranjo, C.A., Bremner, K.E. & Hicks, L.K. (1992). Eating disorders and alcohol abuse in women. *British Journal of Addiction, 87*(6), 913–919.

Goodsitt, A. (1997). Eating disorders: A self-psychological perspective. In D.M. Garner & P.E. Garfinkel (Eds.), *Handbook of Treatment for Eating Disorders: 2nd Ed.* (pp. 205–228). New York: Guilford Press.

Harned, M.S. & Fitzgerald, L.F. (2002). Understanding a link between sexual harassment and eating disorder symptoms: A mediational analysis. *Journal of Consulting & Clinical Psychology, 70*(5), 1170–1181.

Hatsukami, D., Eckert, E.D., Mitchell, J.E. & Pyle, R.L. (1984). Affective disorder and substance abuse in women with bulimia. *Psychological Medicine, 14,* 701–704.

Hatsukami, D., Mitchell, J.E., Eckert, E.D. & Pyle, R.L. (1986). Characteristics of patients with bulimia only, bulimia with affective disorder, and bulimia with substance abuse problems. *Addictive Behaviors, 11,* 399–406.

Hatsukami, D., Owen, P., Pyle, R.L. & Mitchell, J.E. (1982). Similarities and differences on the MMPI between women with bulimia and women with alcohol abuse problems. *Addictive Disorders, 7,* 435–439.

Healthy Place. (2003). Psychological tests. Available: www.healthyplace.com/site/tests/psychological.asp.

Heatherton, T.F. & Baumeister, R.F. (1991). Binge eating as escape from self-awareness. *Psychological Bulletin, 110*(1), 86–108.

Herzog, D.B., Greenwood, D.N., Dorer, D.J., Flores, A.T., Ekeblad, E.R., Richards, A. et al. (2000). Mortality in eating disorders: A descriptive study. *International Journal of Eating Disorders, 28*(1), 20–26.

Higuchi, S., Suzuki, K., Yamada, K., Parrish, K. et al. (1993). Alcoholics with eating disorders: Prevalence and clinical course: A study from Japan. *British Journal of Psychiatry, 162*, 403–406.

Hohltein, L.A., Smith, G.T. & Atlas, J.G. (1998). An application of expectancy theory to eating disorders: Development and validation of measures of eating and dieting expectancies. *Psychological Assessment, 10*(1), 49–58.

Hudson, J.I., Weiss, R.D., Pope, H.G. Jr., McElroy, S.K. & Mirin, S.M. (1992). Eating disorders in hospitalized substance abusers. *American Journal of Drug & Alcohol Abuse, 18*(1), 75–85.

Johnson, W.G., Rohan, K.J. & Kirk, A.A. (2002). Prevalence and correlates of binge eating in White and African American adolescents. *Eating Behaviors, 3*(2), 179–189.

Joiner, T.E. Jr., Katz, J. & Heatherton, T.F. (2000). Personality features differentiate late adolescent females and males with chronic bulimic symptoms. *International Journal of Eating Disorders, 27*(2), 191–197.

Jonas, J.M., Gold, M.S., Sweeney, D. & Pottash, A.L.C. (1987). Eating Disorders and cocaine abuse: A Survey of 259 cocaine abusers. *Journal of Clinical Psychiatry, 48*, 47–50.

Kano, S. (1989). *Making Peace with Food.* New York: Harper and Row.

Kaplan, A.S. & Woodside, D.B. (1987). Biological aspects of anorexia nervosa and bulimia nervosa. *Journal of Consulting and Clinical Psychology, 55*, 645–653.

Katz, J.L. (1990). Eating disorders: A primer for the substance abuse specialist: I. Clinical features. *Journal of Substance Abuse Treatment, 7*(3), 143–149.

Keel, P.K., Dorer, D.J., Eddy, K.T. & Franko, D. (2003). Predictors of Mortality in Eating Disorders. *Archives of General Psychiatry, 60*(2), 179–183.

Keesey, R.E. & Powley, T.L. (1986). The regulation of body weight. *Annual Review of Psychology, 37*, 109–133.

Keys, A., Biozek, J., Henschel, A., Mickelsen, O. & Taylor, H.L. (1950). *The Biology of Human Starvation.* Minneapolis: University of Minnesota Press.

Kirsch, I. (1985). Response expectancy as a determinant of experience and behavior. *American Psychologist, 40*, 1189–1202.

Knight, L.J. & Boland, F.J. (1989). Restrained eating: An experimental disentanglement of the disinhibiting variables of perceived calories and food type. *Journal of Abnormal Psychology, 98*, 412–420.

Krahn, D.D. (1991). The relationship of eating disorders and substance abuse. *Journal of Substance Abuse, 3*, 230–254.

Kristeller, J.L. & Hallett, C.B. (1999). An exploratory study of a meditation-based intervention for binge eating disorder. *Journal of Health Psychology, 4*(3), 357–363.

Lacey, J.H. & Moureli, E. (1986). Bulimic alcoholics: Some features of a clinical sub-group. *British Journal of Addiction, 81*(3), 389–393.

LaPorte, D.J. (1997). Gender differences in perceptions and consequences of an eating binge. *Sex Roles, 36*(7–8), 479–489.

Lee, S. (2001). From diversity to unity: The classification of mental disorders in 21st-century China. *Psychiatric Clinics of North America, 24*(3), 421–431.

Linehan, M.M. & Dimeff, L.A. (2000). *Extension of Standard Dialectical Behavior Therapy (DBT) to Treatment of Substance Abusers with Borderline Personality Disorder (DBT-S). Treatment Procedures Manual.* Manuscript submitted for publication.

Linehan, M.M., Schmidt, H., Dimeff, L.A., Craft, J.C., Kanter, J. & Comtois, K.A. (1999). Dialectical behavior therapy for patients with borderline personality disorder and drug-dependence. *American Journal on Addictions, 8*(4), 279–292.

Lock, J., Reisel, B. & Steiner, H. (2001). Associated health risks of adolescents with disordered eating: How different are they from their peers? Results from a high school survey. *Child Psychiatry & Human Development, 31*(3), 249–265.

Loro, A.D. & Orlens, C.S. (1981). Binge-eating in obesity: Preliminary findings and guidelines for behavioral analysis and treatment. *Addictive Behaviors, 6,* 155–166.

Lovejoy, M. (2001). Disturbances in the social body: Differences in body image and eating problems among African American and white women. *Gender & Society, 15*(2), 239–261.

Marlatt, G.A. & Gordon, J.R. (1985). *Relapse Prevention.* New York: Guilford Press.

McMain, S., Korman, L., Courbasson, C.M.A. & Smith, P.D. (2001). Traitements spécialisés des personnes ayant des problèmes concomitants de santé mentale et toxicomanie: un modèle intégrant la thérapie dialectique comportementale. *Santé Mentale au Québec, 26*(2), 132–156.

Miller, M.N & Pumariega, A.J. (2001). Culture and eating disorders: A historical and cross-cultural review. *Psychiatry, 64*(2), 93–110.

Mitchell, P.B. (1988). The pharmacological management of bulimia nervosa: A critical review. *International Journal of Eating Disorders, 7,* 29–41.

Orbach, S. (1982). *Fat Is a Feminist Issue II.* New York: Berkeley Books.

Perlick, D. & Silverstein, B. (1994). Faces of female discontent: Depression, disordered eating, and changing gender roles. In P. Fallon, A. Melanie et al. (Eds.), *Feminist Perspectives on Eating Disorders* (pp. 77–93). New York: Guilford Press.

Perlman, A. & McKenna, T. (1988). A comparison of bulimic and non-bulimic chemical dependency patients. *Hazelden Professional Update, 7,* 1–6.

Peveler, R. & Fairburn, C. (1990). Eating disorders in women who abuse alcohol. *British Journal of Addiction, 85*(12), 1633–1638.

Piran, N., Lerner, P., Garfinkel, P.E., Kennedy, S. & Brouilette, C. (1988). Personality disorders in restricting and bulimic forms of anorexia nervosa. *International Journal of Obesity, 1,* 589–600.

Polivy, J. & Herman, C.P. (1976). The effect of alcohol on eating behavior: Disinhibition or sedation? *Addictive Behaviors, 1,* 121–125.

Rodin, G., Daneman, D., Johnson, L., Kenshole, A. & Garfinkel, P.E. (1986). Anorexia nervosa and bulimia in insulin-dependent diabetes mellitus. *International Journal of Psychiatric Medicine, 16*, 49–57.

Ross, H.E. & Ivis, F. (1999). Binge eating and substance use among male and female adolescents. *International Journal of Eating Disorders, 26*(3), 245–260.

Rotter, J.B. (1954). *Social Learning and Clinical Psychology.* New York: Prentice Hall.

Safer, D.L., Telch, C.F. & Agras, W.S. (2001). Dialectical behavior therapy for bulimia nervosa. *American Journal of Psychiatry, 158*, 632–634.

Schneider, J.A., O'Leary, A. & Jenkins, S.R. (1995). Gender, sexual orientation, and disordered eating. *Psychology & Health, 10*(2), 113–128.

Schucklit, M.A., Tippe, J.E., Anthenelli, R.M., Bucholz, K.K., Hesselbrock, V.M. & Nurnberger, J.I. (1996). Anorexia nervosa and bulimia nervosa in alcohol-dependent men and women and their relatives. *American Journal of Psychiatry, 153*, 74–82.

Sheldon, J.H. (1939). Anorexia nervosa. *Proceedings of the Royal Society of Medicine, 32*, 738–740.

Sothers, K. & Anchor, K.N. (1989). Prevention and treatment of essential hypertension with meditation-relaxation methods. *Medical Psychotherapy: An International Journal, 2*, 137–156.

Spitzer, L. & Rodin, J. (1987). Effects of fructose and glucose preloads on subsequent food intake. *Appetite, 8*, 135–145.

Stacy, A.W., Widaman, K.F. & Marlatt, G.A. (1990). Expectancy models of alcohol use. *Journal of Personality and Social Psychology, 58*(5), 918–928.

Strober, M. (1991). Family-genetic studies of eating disorders. *Journal of Clinical Psychiatry, 52*, 9–12.

Strong, S.M., Williamson, D.A., Netemeyer, R.G. & Geer, J.H. (2000). Eating disorder symptoms and concerns about body differ as a function of gender and sexual orientation. *Journal of Social & Clinical Psychology, 19*(2), 240–255.

Sutherland, L.A., Weaver, S.N., McPeake, J.D. & Quimby, C.D. (1993). The Beech Hill Hospital eating disorders treatment program for drug dependent females: Program description and case analysis. *Journal of Substance Abuse Treatment, 10*(5), 473–481.

Tanofsky, M.B., Wilfley, D.E., Spurrell, E.B., Welch, R. et al. (1997). Comparison of men and women with binge eating disorder. *International Journal of Eating Disorders, 21*(1), 49–54.

Telch, C.F., Agras, W.S. & Linehan, M.M. (2001). Dialectical Behavior Therapy for binge eating disorder. *Journal of Consulting and Clinical Psychology, 69*, 1061–1065.

Theander, S. (1992). Chronicity in anorexia nervosa: Results from the Swedish long-term study. In W. Herzog, H. Deter & W. Vandereyken (Eds.), *The Course of Eating Disorders* (pp. 214–227). New York: Springer-Verlag.

Vandereycken, W., Kog, E. & Vanderlinden, J. (1989). *The Family Approach to Eating Disorders: Assessment and Treatment of Anorexia Nervosa and Bulimia.* New York and London: PMA Publishing.

Vanderheyden, D.A. & Boland, F.J. (1987). A comparison of normals, mild, moderate and severe binge-eaters, and binge-vomiters using discriminant function analysis. *International Journal of Eating Disorders, 6,* 331–337.

Vitousek, K. & Monke, F. (1994). Personality variables and diagnoses in anorexia nervosa and bulimia nervosa. *Journal of Abnormal Psychology, 103,* 137–148.

Walker, C.E., Bonner, B.L. & Kaufman, K.L (1988). *The Physically and Sexually Abused Child: Evaluation and Treatment.* Toronto: Pergamon Press.

Waller, J.V., Kaufman, M.R. & Deutsch, F. (1940). Anorexia nervosa: Psychosomatic entity. *Psychosomatic Medicine, 2,* 3–16.

Wilson, G.T. (1993). Binge eating and addictive disorders. In C.G. Fairburn & G.T. Wilson (Eds.), *Binge Eating: Nature, Assessment and Treatment* (pp. 97–120). New York: Guilford Press.

Wilson, G.T., Fairburn, C.G. & Agras, W.S. (1997). Cognitive-behavioral therapy for bulimia nervosa. In D.M. Garner & P.E. Garfinkel (Eds.), *Handbook of Treatment for Eating Disorders: 2nd Ed.* (pp. 67–93). New York: Guilford Press.

Wolley, S.C.M. (1995). Maelstrom revisited. *American Psychologist, 50,* 943–944.

Wooley, S.C. & Kearney-Cooke, A. (1986). Intensive treatment of bulimia and body-image disturbance. In K.D. Brownell & J.B. Foreyt (Eds.), *Handbook of Eating Disorders* (pp. 476–502). New York: Basic Books.

RECOMMENDED READINGS

General Reference Books
Any of the following four books would serve as an excellent general reference to all aspects of eating disorders and their treatment:

Brownell, K.D. & Foreyt, J.P. (1986). *Handbook of Eating Disorders.* New York: Basic Books.

Garner, D.M. & Garfinkel, P.E. (Eds.). (1985). *Handbook of Psychotherapy for Anorexia Nervosa and Bulimia.* New York: Guilford Press.

Garner, D.M. & Garfinkel, P.E. (Eds.). (1997). *Handbook of Treatment for Eating Disorders: 2nd Ed.* New York: Guilford Press.

Schlundt, D.G. & Johnson, W.G. (1990). *Eating Disorders: Assessment and Treatment.* Boston: Allyn and Bacon.

Articles
For a very readable and comprehensive summary of information related to eating disorders, see:

Garner, D.M., Rocket, W., Olmsted, M.P., Johnson, C. & Coscina, D.V. (1985). Psychoeducational principles in the treatment of bulimia and anorexia nervosa. In D.M. Garner & P.E. Garfinkel (Eds.), *Handbook of Psychotherapy for Anorexia Nervosa and Bulimia* (pp. 513–512). New York: Guilford Press.

Non-technical Books

Popular non-technical books that are useful in therapy for both client and therapist:

Fairburn, C. (1985). *Overcoming Binge Eating*. New York: Guilford Press.

Hutchinson, M. (1985). *Transforming Body Image*. New York: Crossing Press.

Kano, S. (1989). *Making Peace with Food*. New York: Harper and Row.

Orbach, S. (1982). *Fat Is a Feminist Issue II*. New York: Berkeley Books.

Polivy, J. & Herman, C.P. (1983). *Breaking the Diet Habit: The Natural Weight Alternative*. New York: Basic Books.

Tribole, E. & Resch, E. (1996). *Intuitive Eating*. New York: St. Martin's Press.

Information from Organizations

The following organizations offer newsletters and information about therapists, self-help groups, workshops and conferences on eating disorders.

THE NATIONAL EATING DISORDER INFORMATION CENTRE
Toronto General Hospital
200 Elizabeth Street 2-332
Toronto, ON M5G 2C4

ANOREXIA NERVOSA AND BULIMIA FOUNDATION OF CANADA
P.O. Box 3074
Winnipeg, MN R3C 4E5

BULIMIA ANOREXIA NERVOSA ASSOCIATION
c/o Psychological Services, University of Windsor
Windsor, ON N9B 3P4

HERSIZE
223 Concord Avenue
Toronto, ON M6H 2P4

BASH (BULIMIA, ANOREXIA, SELF-HELP) MAGAZINE
6125 Clayton Avenue, Suite 215
St. Louis, MS 63139
U.S.A.

RADIANCE MAGAZINE
P.O. Box 31703
Oakland, CA 94604-9937
U.S.A.

Chapter 26

Concurrent Disorders

GERRY COOPER AND KIM CALDERWOOD

INTRODUCTION

Concurrent disorders have become the focus of a growing body of scientific literature over the past 10 to 20 years. However, accounts of concurrent disorders are not a new phenomenon. Reports of co-existing psychiatric and substance use disorders date back many decades. For example, Freed (1975) lists almost 200 references, including some works that were published in the 1930s. Indeed, the academic association between psychiatric syndromes and substance use problems dates back about 200 years to Benjamin Rush, one of the pioneers of North American psychiatry (Glass, 1989).

Several factors account for the relatively recent increase in attention to concurrent disorders. First, tremendous strides have been made in knowledge about the biological basis of various mental health and substance use disorders (e.g., Andrews et al., 2000; Chaudron & Wilkinson, 1988; Petrakis et al., 2002).

Second, improvements to diagnostic taxonomies and procedures, in both the psychiatric and substance use fields, have helped clinicians to accurately identify concurrent disorders in clients (e.g., the American Psychiatric Association's DSM classification system [APA, 1994]). Not surprisingly, as clinicians have become more precise in examining clients' treatment needs, the prevalence of such problems has been found to be much greater than previously thought.

The third factor concerns the societal trend of psychiatric deinstitutionalization, through which large numbers of severely mentally ill people have been discharged from mental health facilities to live in the broader community, often without sufficient supports (Brown et al., 1989). This development has essentially created a new group of clients who encounter community-based problems previously unknown to many of them—including homelessness, unemployment and easy access to psychoactive substances. (A helpful overview of the post-deinstitutionalization era in Canada—including reforms to the mental health service delivery system and developments within the substance use treatment system—can be found in Health Canada [2001], Appendix D.)

Health care systems in North America have generally been overwhelmed by the number of deinstitutionalized clients and their associated needs. To further exacerbate the situation, mental health treatment systems and substance use treatment systems have historically operated as two mutually exclusive entities (Galanter et al., 1988; Howland, 1990). Each system was designed to provide care for either substance use or psychiatric disorders, typically not both. According to Gottheil and colleagues (1980):

> [O]ften [clients with concurrent disorders] are shuttled back and forth, or they fall through the cracks of the system and are lost to treatment, or they are treated in both [psychiatric and substance use] clinics with conflicting methods and confusing effects (p. xii).

More recently, these challenges have led several national organizations to focus on concurrent disorders and co-ordinate their efforts to address them. For example, advances have been made to bridge knowledge gaps through the funding of crossover demonstration treatment programs and associated research projects (Brown et al., 1989; SAMHSA, 2002). Others have directed their attention toward system-level improvements at a regional level (Carmichael et al., 1997; Calderwood & Christie, 2003). Developments like these have contributed to the thinking about concurrent disorders, and have helped to influence the creation and content of best practice consensus documents in both Canada and the United States (Health Canada, 2001; SAMHSA, 2002).

From the foregoing, three observations are warranted:

1. Concurrent disorders are very prevalent, particularly among people who use the psychiatric and substance use treatment systems.
2. The level and types of care provided to people with concurrent disorders have frequently failed to respond adequately to their unique treatment needs.
3. Innovative approaches (at both the micro and macro levels) hold considerable promise for successfully responding to individuals with concurrent disorders.

This chapter addresses issues including definitions and diagnoses, prevalence, etiology, and obstacles to effective treatment (from both micro and macro perspectives). As a prelude to discussing some recommendations for treatment and service delivery, we will comment on a recent conceptual model that informs best practice guidelines. The recommendations we will provide are based on a summary of the literature and the emerging positions articulated in the principal consensus documents.

TERMINOLOGY, DEFINITIONS AND DIAGNOSES

There is growing agreement to use one of the two similar terms "concurrent disorders" or "co-occurring disorders" to describe the presence of substance use disorders alongside psychiatric disorders (and vice versa). Historically, however, achieving consensus on phraseology has been difficult. For example, pejorative terms such as "comorbidity," "MICA" (mentally ill chemical abuser) and "SAMI" (substance abusing mentally ill) have appeared in professional literature; it is not uncommon to find them in use even today.

Over the years, some authors have used very similar (and at times overlapping) terms to describe conditions quite distinct from what we now call concurrent disorders. Fisher et al. (1989) used "dual diagnoses" to refer to concurrent mental retardation and psychiatric disorders. A similar term, "dual disorders" (Daley et al., 1987), has been used for concurrent disorders, but the use of the word "dual" was thought to be a misnomer, since people often have more than two disorders. The absence of a broadly accepted single term hints at a range of opinions concerning etiology and treatment; some may conclude that the field is generally devoid of agreement about these issues.

To the contrary, as new knowledge helps inform the discourse, tremendous strides have been made over the past decade toward consensus on what comprises concurrent disorders. For example, two similar terms are favoured in North America—in Canada the term is "concurrent disorders," while in the United States the preferred term is "co-occurring substance abuse disorders and mental disorders" (or simply "co-occurring disorders"). Despite the preference for different terminology, the respective definitions used by the Canadian and American consensus panels closely parallel one another, as can be seen from the following excerpts. Health Canada's (2001) definition states:

> In general terms, the concurrent disorders population refers to those people who are experiencing a combination of mental/emotional/psychiatric problems with the abuse of alcohol and/or psychoactive drugs. More technically speaking, and in diagnostic terms, it refers to any combination of mental health and substance use disorders, as defined for example on either Axis I or Axis II of DSM-IV (p. v).

The definition given by the United States Substance Abuse and Mental Health Services Administration (SAMHSA; 2002) reads:

> [P]eople with co-occurring substance abuse disorders and mental disorders are individuals who have at least one mental disorder as well as an alcohol or drug use disorder. While these disorders may interact differently in any one person (e.g., an episode of depression may trigger a relapse into alcohol abuse, or cocaine use may exacerbate schizophrenic symptoms), at

least one disorder of each type can be diagnosed independently of the other. . . . Co-occurring disorders may include any combination of two or more substance abuse disorders and mental disorders identified in the DSM-IV.

In both definitions, the *DSM-IV (Diagnostic and Statistical Manual of Mental Disorders,* 4th ed.; APA, 1994) is cited as a basis of diagnosis, and any combination of mental health and substance use disorders may be identified as concurrent disorders. This adoption of a common set of definitions is useful to both the mental health and substance use treatment systems. (Interestingly, the term "co-occurring" frequently appears in Health Canada's best practices document [2001], alongside "concurrent".)

Despite the field's emerging agreement regarding lexicon, terms such as "concurrent" and "co-occurring" remain somewhat generic and, therefore, are limited in their ability to precisely describe specific types of concurrent disorders. While they help us to understand in a basic way what is being discussed (the combination of substance use problems and mental illness rather than, say, mental illness in people who are developmentally delayed), they do not address the complicated interplay between people's substance use problem(s) and their mental health.

There are many kinds of complex psychiatric disorders, including the general classifications of schizophrenia, mood disorders, anxiety disorders and personality disorders (each of these categories can be further subdivided). In addition, a wide variety of psychoactive substances exist which, of course, can be used alone or in combination. They include stimulants (e.g., amphetamines, caffeine, cocaine, nicotine), sedatives (e.g., alcohol, barbiturates, benzodiazepines, inhalants), narcotics (e.g., heroin, morphine) and hallucinogens (e.g., cannabis, LSD, PCP).

Clearly, then, the possible combinations of psychiatric disorders with substance use problems are numerous. In addition, symptoms may vary depending on the whether the person is intoxicated or in a state of withdrawal. Finally, some people's substance use problems predate their mental disorders, while for others the reverse is true. For example, a clinician might ask the following of a person who is depressed and has an alcohol problem:

• Is this client's drinking motivated by relatively recent feelings of sadness?
• Is the person's drinking an attempt to help him or her cope with a long-standing serious depression?
• Is his or her depression a direct result of heavy and chronic alcohol use?

The answers to this puzzle are critical to determining what therapeutic approaches will have the greatest likelihood of success.

It is essential, then, that health care providers base assessment and treatment on each client's unique characteristics. People with concurrent disorders have a wide range of different clinical presentations; this truly is a heterogeneous population. For example, while the people described below are all said to have concurrent disorders, their symptoms and complaints are quite diverse. (These illustrations are consistent with Ryglewicz & Pepper's (1996) classification scheme, as cited in Health Canada [2001].)

Jim, 45, has antisocial personality disorder and has cocaine use problems.

Mary, 30, has bouts of severe anxiety (e.g., panic attacks) and increasingly has taken to using alcohol to cope with her nerves.

Tom, 22, has been diagnosed with schizophrenia, and his social use of cannabis intensifies his symptoms.

Susan, 67, has a long history of depression, and has been increasing her use of alcohol and benzodiazepines for many months without her physician's awareness or approval.

To complicate matters further, while the above scenarios appear to be quite distinct, in some cases psychiatric symptoms can be masked and/or mimicked by psychoactive substance use (Ross et al., 1988b)—so these clients may at times present with very similar symptom profiles. This reinforces the importance of conducting proper screening and assessment on a regular and ongoing basis. A provisional diagnosis, usually made once a person has been safely detoxified and at the outset of treatment, should be adjusted accordingly as new and clinically significant information becomes apparent (Ananth et al., 1989). Widely accepted diagnostic classification systems, such as the *DSM-IV* (APA, 1994), should be used consistently, since they outline standard criteria for rendering diagnoses based on observable symptoms.

That being said, in some communities there may be limited access to a psychiatrist or licensed professional who is permitted to provide a formal diagnosis. Moreover, there may be stark contrasts in the scope of the responsibilities of different clinicians, depending on how well-resourced their treatment systems are. For example, clinical scope is generally greater in less well-resourced areas such as rural and remote communities.

For these reasons, we approach the issue of diagnosis from a much broader perspective. While not all clinicians are capable (legally or otherwise) of rendering a formal diagnosis of, for instance, schizophrenia, a clinician may know enough about the symptoms of schizophrenia to know when a psychiatric assessment and/or intervention is required. Even in the absence of a formal diagnosis in cases such as this, clinicians should take careful note of the client's symptoms and adjust their practice behaviour accordingly.

The diagnostic picture is further complicated by the existence of smaller subgroups within the concurrent disorders population. For example, young people with chronic mental illnesses have been described as "hypervulnerable—chemically, psychologically and socially—to the effects of even mild or recreational use of drugs and alcohol" (Brown et al., 1989, p. 567). Psychiatric treatments for such people often include pharmacotherapy, but even modest amounts of alcohol can interact with medication to produce a compounded effect (Schmidt, 1989). To make accurate diagnoses, clinicians may therefore need to examine their values and their beliefs about what it means to have a substance use problem.

The importance of moving beyond the general concurrent disorders terminology to specifically consider the unique needs of individuals is reinforced by the consensus documents identified earlier. For example, the SAMHSA report to the United States Congress specifically discusses prevention approaches for children/adolescents, adults and older adults. In addition, the report identifies several high-risk groups, discusses the barriers that members of these groups face in accessing help, and examines effective interventions. The groups include:

• people with concurrent medical conditions
• homeless people
• women
• people with trauma
• people who have been involved with the criminal justice system
• youth
• people from rural areas
• members of racial and ethnic minorities.

Health Canada's report, for comparison, identifies five subgroups as follows:

• Group 1: people with co-occurring substance use and mood or anxiety disorders
• Group 2: people with co-occurring substance use and severe and persistent mental disorders
• Group 3: people with co-occurring substance use and personality disorders
• Group 4: people with co-occurring substance use and eating disorders
• Group 5: people with other co-occurring substance use and mental health disorders. (Health Canada, 2001).

PREVALENCE

Problem substance use is quite common among people with psychiatric disorders, as are mental health problems among people with substance use disorders. However, many prevalence studies have limitations, so it is difficult to establish precisely just how common these phenomena really are. For example, the SAMHSA group concluded after an exhaustive review of the literature that there is "a significant lack of prevalence data on co-occurring disorders" (2002, p. 3).

Although the extent of concurrent disorders in the general population is not clear, several studies, particularly in the United States, have tried to estimate the prevalence (e.g., Weissman & Meyers, 1980; Helzer & Pryzbeck, 1988; Schmidt, 1989). The two U.S. studies that are cited most often are the Epidemiologic Catchment Area (ECA) study (Regier et al., 1990) and the National Comorbidity Survey (NCS; Kessler et al., 1994). Both were quite extensive. The ECA interviewed more than 20,000 people from five geographical areas, including people living both in the community and in institutional settings. A few years later the NCS, a nationally representative study, interviewed 8,098 non-institutionalized people between the ages of 15 and 54 years.

Essentially, both of these studies found that people with substance use problems and those with mental health problems have a higher risk of developing concurrent disorders than the general population. According to the United States Surgeon General's 1999 report on mental health (which drew heavily upon these studies):

> Forty-one to 65 per cent of individuals with a lifetime substance abuse disorder also have a lifetime history of at least one mental disorder, and about 51 per cent of those with one or more lifetime mental disorders also have a lifetime history of at least one substance abuse disorder (U.S. Department of Health and Human Services, 1999).

Similar findings have also been reported in Canadian studies (Health Canada, 2001).

Estimates of the prevalence of concurrent disorders within clinical populations vary according to the person's diagnosis, the location and type of treatment program being studied, and the procedures used in the research study. Regier et al. (1990) found that among people in mental health or substance use treatment centres, the odds of having a substance use disorder are about double those in the general population. It is generally thought that about half of all people receiving psychiatric treatment also have a substance use problem (or problems), while as many as three-quarters of all people in treatment for substance use have some form of co-existing psychiatric problem(s) (Health Canada, 2001). For the most part, a person's risk of having a concurrent psychiatric problem increases with the number of substances used.

Due to the seriousness of their symptoms, people with concurrent disorders are more likely to eventually find their way into treatment than those with less complicated problems (Woody et al., 1990). This suggests that people with concurrent disorders comprise a greater proportion of the client population than do people with substance use problems uncomplicated by a psychiatric disorder or psychiatric problems uncomplicated by substance use problems. People with only one type of disorder would be more likely than those with concurrent disorders to recover on their own.

Despite being overrepresented in clinical populations, most people with concurrent disorders do not seek help for their problems (U.S. Department of Health and Human Services, 1999; SAMHSA, 2002; Health Canada, 2001). In addition, the studies cited above contribute little to our understanding of those who do not seek help and those who do seek treatment but are unsuccessful in obtaining it. In other words, the needs of people with concurrent disorders are not necessarily reflected in study samples (Cooper et al., 1990). Many people with concurrent disorders have reportedly been served poorly or not at all, due to the inflexible nature of, on one hand, agencies' admission criteria and mandates and, on the other hand, the structures of treatment systems (Carey, 1989). Such clients are often denied treatment in substance use programs because of their psychiatric condition, and denied treatment at psychiatric facilities because of their substance use problems. Not surprisingly, resistance to seeking treatment is often reinforced, since information about denied treatment is informally circulated amongst clients and family members.

Among people with concurrent disorders who have sought treatment, there have been many accounts of less than optimal care being rendered. This likely has resulted in many clients leaving the formal helping system altogether, or "falling through the cracks." This rather bleak scenario has spawned such unflattering expressions as "the patient shuffle" and "system misfits," and references to clients being "ping-ponged" or "pigeonholed." Comprehensive published accounts of people who have been poorly served in this way are rare, but anecdotal data suggest that such people are plentiful (Willauer et al., 1990). The effect of traditionally poor clinical service upon prevalence rates within treatment systems is not known. It is hoped though that over time, and as clinical practice improves, greater numbers of those needing help will receive it.

ETIOLOGY

With respect to the cause of concurrent disorders, it appears that the jury is still out. Some claim that two-thirds of all cases are a direct result of prior alcohol use problems (McEvoy, 1989). Others contend that substance use problems often result from a variety of psychiatric illnesses, as people attempt to self-medicate. For example, Carpenter & Hasin (1998) found that drinking to cope with negative emotional states was a risk factor for eventual alcohol dependence, and Hall and colleagues (1979) found that as many as 50 per cent of study participants reported self-medication-type behaviours.

The self-medication hypothesis has considerable support from other researchers. Reich and colleagues (1974) found that, contrary to the assumption that alcohol is used to counteract depressive symptoms, subjects drank excessively primarily during the manic phase of bipolar disorder, and did so to reduce their manic symptoms. Ross and colleagues (1988a) reported a predictive relationship between the severity of substance use problems and the likelihood of psychiatric problems.

Some interesting gender differences have been observed, which may contribute to the etiologic picture. Generally, women have a later age of onset of alcoholism than men (Winokur et al., 1970) and, correspondingly, psychiatric problems frequently predate substance use problems in women (Fine, 1980). The reverse is true for men (Hesselbrock et al., 1985).

Clearly, the age of onset of substance use problems and/or psychiatric problems is an important factor. It has been demonstrated that early commencement of alcoholism and of additional psychiatric syndromes is significantly related to a family history of alcoholism (Powell et al., 1982). Other factors that should be considered include the absence of social support mechanisms (Lin et al., 1979) and the presence of stressors, such as homelessness (Koegel et al., 1988). Each of these variables can influence illness symptoms and their prevalence.

Despite beliefs about etiology, it is critical to recognize the heterogeneity of this client population and to address each person's situation as unique. Some clients will want to explore what caused each disorder and/or which came first; others will prefer a solution-focused approach. Clinical approaches should be client-centred and tailored to individual needs. In some situations it will not be difficult to determine what caused the disorders and/or which came first. In other instances, the client's situation will be so complex that a cause-effect relationship cannot be easily identified.

OBSTACLES TO EFFECTIVE TREATMENT

Treatment services have frequently failed to help people with concurrent disorders. It is not uncommon, for example, for divergent philosophies to interfere with a co-ordinated approach to care. Providers may disagree on issues such as the role of medications, the use of confrontation and the need for abstinence as a prior condition for treatment. Many researchers have also found, unfortunately, that substance use problems and/or mental health problems often go undetected, and are misdiagnosed or otherwise improperly treated due to inappropriate staff attitudes and/or lack of skills (Howland, 1990; Melinyshyn et al., 1996; Minkoff, 1994, 1996, 1997). This latter point has been directly related to the limited availability of appropriate training in medical and other professional schools. Few treatment programs attempt to identify and fully assess a client's psychiatric and substance use status, and even fewer complement their findings with corroborative data from family members and/or biochemical laboratory tests.

For the few clients who are correctly identified as having concurrent disorders, there are few specialized programs to which they can be referred (by "specialized," we mean that the program can treat clients with concurrent disorders through an integrated approach, such that both substance use and mental health problems are addressed by the clinical team; see "Recommendations for Treatment Efficacy"). Programs that do provide these services are often not well known to potential referral agents. In many cases, clinicians hesitate to refer clients to other agencies because they have concerns about confidentiality and related issues (Bean-Bayog, 1987). The absence of any large-scale advocacy group for people with concurrent disorders—a group that could influence policy-makers, practitioners and administrators—may also have contributed to this state of affairs (Kopolow, 1981).

As mentioned earlier, people with concurrent disorders are more likely to seek and/or obtain treatment than those who have uncomplicated substance use problems or psychiatric problems. At the same time, clients with multiple problems have been turned away from some programs because service providers prefer not to handle difficult cases, because programs lack the resources required to address complex cases, or because mandates for programs are categorical (i.e., they mandate the treatment of either mental health problems or substance use problems, but not both; Aiken et al., 1975). Other barriers include lack of training, insufficient knowledge regarding effective service delivery, and philosophical differences across programs (Howland, 1990; Minkoff, 1994, 1996, 1997; SAMHSA, 2002). Even when people with concurrent disorders do receive professional help, often only one of their problems is addressed

(Hood et al., 1996; Ontario Ministry of Health and Long-Term Care, 1999). Problems that have impeded the integration of the treatment systems for psychiatric problems and substance use problems include lack of leadership (Sciacca, 1998a, 1998b) and separate funding mechanisms (Minkoff, 1994, 1996, 1997).

As problems intensify for people with the most severe forms of concurrent disorders, they often utilize a broad range of services, including intrusive services. For example, people with concurrent disorders are more frequent users of emergency medical services (Howland, 1990) and they have a greater likelihood of being hospitalized (Drake & Wallach, 1989; Ford et al., 1991; Stoffelmayr et al., 1989) than the general population or those with only one type of disorder. These people are more likely than others to be arrested (Ford et al., 1991) and are at a greater risk for suicide and violence (Howland, 1990). They also have a lower level of community adjustment than the general population or people with only one type of disorder (Ford et al., 1991), including higher rates of homelessness, disconnection from social support systems, unemployment and vocational disability (Sloan & Rowe, 1995).

Though this is a relatively recent area of analysis, social stigma has kept many people from seeking help for their concurrent substance use and mental health problems. For example, in their review of 38 natural recovery studies, Sobell and colleagues (2000) found that of the nine that provided information on barriers to entering alcohol or other drug treatment programs, eight described participants who had concerns about being stigmatized or labelled. The authors note that these factors parallel research on why people had *delayed* seeking treatment for substance use problems.

Similar findings have been found with regard to the treatment of mental disorders. Stigma reduces a person's access to resources, opportunities and participation in society, according to the U.S. Surgeon General's report (U.S. Department of Health and Human Services, 1999). Social stigma has in fact been found to be the primary factor that interferes with help-seeking behaviour by people with mental illness and, moreover, the main reason why many—perhaps most—people with a diagnosable mental illness do not seek help (Herman, 1993; Regier et al., 1993).

Stigma has been found to be a rather complex phenomenon; it is not a dichotomous entity (that is, one that is either present or is not; Goffman, 1963). In some instances, stigmatizing behaviours are found in the most supportive of clinicians. Clients with some types of disorder may experience more stigma than those with other disorders, and stigma can emanate from clients themselves toward other clients (Kittel Canale, 2001).

Fortunately, this scenario is undergoing rapid change:
• Concurrent disorder mutual aid groups are being formed in many communities.
• More clinicians are receiving specialized training.
• Some targeted public education programs are having an impact (Campbell et al., 2002).
• Governmental position documents herald a commitment to change (Health Canada, 2001).

RECOMMENDATIONS FOR TREATMENT EFFICACY

Much work still needs to be done to more fully understand concurrent disorders and to empirically demonstrate the effectiveness of various therapeutic approaches— particularly as they pertain to client subgroups with special needs or those at high risk. However, considerable consensus has emerged on treatment principles for general adult populations. What follows is a synthesis of this consensus, which is based on published program descriptions, case studies, best advice reports and best practice models. Recommendations are divided into two sections, those focusing on clinical issues (micro level) and those concerning system integration (macro level).

These recommendations may be used to guide planning for successful concurrent disorders interventions. Naturally, the degree to which these principles are implemented will affect the probability of consistently positive outcomes. It may not be within the mandate of individual clinicians, services or organizations to enact each of these principles; however, the importance of being attentive to both micro- and macro-level perspectives cannot be overstated. Important contributions can come from committed individuals at each level; system change begins with individual initiative.

A Conceptual Framework

Both the Canadian and American consensus papers subscribe to a perspective that considers the provision and co-ordination of services as being driven by the severity of clients' problems. This notion is perhaps best expressed in the conceptual model outlined by SAMHSA (2002); it appears below as Figure 26-1. The model outlines four quadrants of integrated care that basically respond to "symptom multiplicity and severity rather than specific diagnoses" (SAMHSA, 2002, p. 18). In this model, there exists a continuum of problem severity with regard to both mental disorders and substance use disorders. In turn, levels of service and system co-ordination are also found on a corresponding continuum. In this way, the model can accommodate clients whose problems are severe and persistent, as well as those whose problems may be in the early stages of development. Additionally, the model is fluid in that clients can move back and forth depending on the stage of their illness and the status of their recovery.

Importantly, both the mental health and substance use treatment systems appear to be accepting this model. In doing so, both systems are moving toward a common language and demonstrating that concurrent disorders are an important priority. Each system acknowledges and supports the important role played by the other and, in so doing, the two systems demonstrate their mutual responsibility for resolving the conundrum of concurrent disorders treatment.

FIGURE 26-1

Service Co-ordination by Severity of Concurrent Disorders

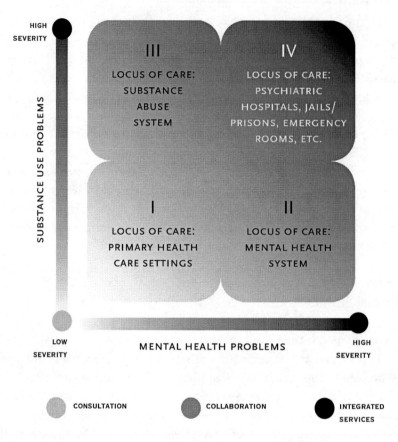

Source: Adapted from SAMHSA (2002).

Clinically Oriented Recommendations

All clients presenting to all services within the mental health and substance use treatment systems should be screened for the presence of concurrent disorders. Further, it should be the expectation, rather than the exception, that staff at these services will identify some form of concurrent disorders with these clients. Health Canada's best practices document (2001) states that such screening is a precursor to a more comprehensive assessment process and should be conducted in two stages. In "Level I," clinicians proceed with an index of suspicion and ask non-threatening, straightforward questions. "Level II" makes use of validated instruments that are quick and easy to administer.

Complete detoxification, ideally from all psychoactive substances (at least those that are not absolutely medically necessary; exceptions may be made for, for example, antipsychotic medications), should occur prior to assessment and treatment planning. (In this regard, withdrawal management services have recently begun to offer services in a client's home or other safe environments, away from an agency or institutional setting.) At this stage, clients should also be made aware that any social and/or non-medical substance use would likely exacerbate and complicate their mental health status.

A comprehensive assessment of the client's presenting problems (both mental health and substance use) and strengths (e.g., support systems) should occur as soon as the client is free of intoxication and/or withdrawal. To the extent possible, it would also be helpful at this stage to establish formal diagnoses, obtain an understanding of the client's psychosocial functioning and explore how the client's substance use interacts with his or her mental disorder(s). The assessment should incorporate laboratory measures, such as urinalysis, and solicit corroborative input from family members whenever possible.

Alternatively, if a formal diagnosis is not possible at this stage, a provisional diagnosis of the client's problems, along with an individualized treatment plan, would suffice. Both the client and family members should be involved as much as possible. The provisional diagnosis should be reviewed periodically throughout the course of treatment, and interventions should be adjusted accordingly.

When attempting to match interventions to the client's needs, it is crucial to adhere to several principles, including the following:
• Approaches must be flexible.
• Abstinence is usually the most desirable treatment goal; however, clinicians must be patient, and should recognize that abstinence may be harder to achieve for clients with concurrent disorders.
• Prior abstinence is not necessarily a requirement for treatment to begin.
• Mental health and substance use interventions are employed as indicated.
• A holistic orientation is required.
• For many clients, confrontational interventions may actually hinder the recovery process.
• A range of residential and community-based/outpatient options may be necessary for some clients.
• Special attention should be given to the provision of safe and supportive housing for the client.
• Treatment outcome will likely be a function of the type and severity of a client's disorders but appropriately matching the treatment to each client's needs will improve the chance of a good outcome.

Treatment should simultaneously address psychiatric and substance use problems under "one program roof," and ideally from a single clinician or team; this has been termed "program integration" in the Canadian best practices document (Health Canada, 2001). Failing an integrated system with co-ordinated programs, extensive communication between the various treatment components by one case manager (who has major responsibility for the case) is recommended as a bare minimum.

The intensity of treatment and support should be determined by the client's needs, by the specific type of concurrent disorders experienced, and by the presence or absence of additional considerations (e.g., clients with special needs or those at high risk).

The unified clinical team should ideally comprise professionally trained mental health and substance use treatment staff (including physicians to administer and monitor pharmacotherapy) supplemented, as required, by people stabilized in their own recovery (i.e., members of mutual aid groups).

For more severe forms of concurrent disorders, treatment should be open-ended. Emphasis should be placed on ongoing care (after-care), with extensive use of case management workers and rigorous outreach efforts.

Clients should be encouraged to use mutual aid programs. A member of the clinical team should help them locate a group in which they feel comfortable. In some cases, new groups may need to be established, with a special orientation to concurrent disorders. Increasingly, mutual aid groups (and other forms of assistance) can be found on the Web. They have been an effective source of information and support for many people (Cooper, 2004; Ferguson 1996, 1997; Finn, 1996; Griffiths & Cooper, 2003). Health Canada (2001) calls attention to one Web-accessible mutual aid group, Dual Recovery Anonymous (which is targeted to people with concurrent disorders), as being an especially attractive option for those who live in rural communities and have little access to specialized services.

System-Oriented Recommendations

Building links and working together across agencies is often referred to as "co-ordination" or "system level integration." This is an important aspect of clinical work, because clients' experiences in other health care and social service systems greatly impact the effectiveness of the addiction and mental health interventions they receive.

Baker (1991) highlights the fact that achieving co-ordination is a slow, evolutionary process that must be based on a shared ideology about the need for integration. Zweben (1993) emphasizes the importance of communication, the clarification of different assumptions in each system, and the development of a common language. She also suggests that inadequate capacity and long waiting lists can hinder attempts to network effectively. Sciacca & Thompson (1996) discuss the need for a formulated and integrated philosophical perspective, redefined roles and non-judgmental acceptance of symptoms. Health Canada (2001) stresses the importance of the meaningful involvement of consumers and family members in system planning and development.

Systems can become more integrated through:
• shared information systems
• a resource directory for both formal services and mutual aid groups
• substance use treatment programs and mental health programs sharing the same

location
- centralized intake and referral at a single lead agency (which would provide a current directory of addiction and mental health services, advocacy and adequate follow-up)
- case management and multidisciplinary continuous-treatment teams
- the sharing of staff, with workers spending time working at a different program or agency
- cross-training (workers in the two systems train each other)
- joint training (workers in both systems are trained together)
- the combination of funding sources
- case conferences in which workers from various agencies come together to discuss clinical challenges or specific client cases
- inter-agency agreements that formalize shared communication and clinical procedures
- a common assessment tool (Unfortunately, at present there is no standard assessment tool, in part because it is very challenging to devise one that meets the needs of all agencies across the two systems.)
- a common evaluation for cost-effectiveness and outcomes, including joint program review, joint ongoing monitoring and a consumer feedback process
- use of the Internet and "telepsychiatry," which can be an effective way of providing training and professional development to clinicians, particularly those in rural and remote communities (Health Canada, 2001).

CONCLUSION

People with concurrent disorders form a complex and heterogeneous population. They are often demanding of the clinician's time, effort and creativity. It is hoped that a greater awareness of these clients and their needs will lead in the future to consistent identification, accurate diagnoses and improved treatment. According to Minkoff, "the most significant predictor of treatment success is . . . an empathic, hopeful, continuous treatment relationship . . . in which integrated treatment and coordination of care can take place through multiple treatment episodes" (Mental Illness Education Project, 2000).

As mentioned earlier, it is crucial that clients have a single case manager who coordinates all aspects of their treatment over time. People with concurrent disorders often have problems that are chronic and subject to setbacks. Change is likely to occur slowly and incrementally. Consequently, being the case manager for this type of client may represent a large commitment. Clinicians who are not working in a specialized treatment setting for clients with concurrent disorders might be advised to seek administrative backing for this time- and energy-consuming task.

Clearly, clients with concurrent disorders demand and deserve more than the predominant short-term approach to treatment. Ultimately, only a long-term commitment to this client population will save money, effort and staff time. Most importantly, long-term care will alleviate considerable suffering by clients and their families.

ON-LINE SOURCES OF INFORMATION AND ASSISTANCE

Increasingly, people use the Internet to locate credible information, therapist-delivered treatment and peer-based support for personal problems (Ferguson, 1996). This is also true of those seeking to learn about and/or recover from concurrent disorders. For this reason, we have listed a number of Web sites that offer a variety of perspectives on this topic. This is not an exhaustive list, but it provides a fair indication of the type of material that can be found with the help of a search engine. It is always advisable to carefully authenticate sources of information as being credible and reputable.

Arizona Integrated Treatment Consensus Panel. (1999). *Providing Integrated Services for Persons with Co-occurring Mental Health and Substance Abuse Disorders.* Phoenix: Arizona Department of Health Services. Available: www.hs.state.az.us/bhs/finalreport.pdf.

Health Canada. (2001). *Best Practices: Concurrent Mental Health and Substance Use Disorders.* (Cat. No.: H39-599/2001-2E). Ottawa: Minister of Public Works and Government Services Canada. Available: www.hc-sc.gc.ca/hecs-sesc/cds/pdf/concurrentbestpractice.pdf.

Health Canada. (2002). *Summary Report of the Workshop on Best Practices for Concurrent Mental Health and Substance Use Disorders.* Ottawa: author. Available: www.hc-sc.gc.ca/hecs-sesc/cds/publications/mental_health/toc.htm.

New South Wales Office of Drug Policy. (no date). *Discussion Paper* and *Service Delivery Guidelines.* Available: www.druginfo.nsw.gov.au/information_&_resources/dual_disorders

SAMHSA. (2002). *Substance Abuse and Mental Health Services Administration Report to Congress on the Prevention and Treatment of Co-occurring Substance Abuse Disorders and Mental Disorders.* Rockville, MD: author. Available: www.samhsa.gov/news/cl_congress2002.html.

SAMHSA. (2003). *Strategies for Developing Treatment Programs for People with Co-occurring Substance Abuse and Mental Disorders.* Rockville, MD: author. Available: www.nccbh.org/cooccurringreport.pdf.

Sciacca, K. *Dual Diagnosis Website.* (1996). Available: http://users.erols.com/ksciacca/.

South West Sydney Area Health Service. (no date). *MIDAS Dual Diagnosis Home Page.* Available: www.swsahs.nsw.gov.au/areaser/Midas/default.asp.

Treatment Improvement Exchange. (no date). *Dual Disorders Special Topic.* Rockville, MD: Center for Substance Abuse Treatment/SAMHSA. Available: www.treatment.org/Topics/dual.html.

Trupin, E. & Boesky, L.M. (2001). *Working Together for Change: Co-occurring Mental Health and Substance Abuse Disorders among Youth Involved in the Juvenile Justice System. An Online Tutorial for Juvenile Justice, Mental Health, and Substance Abuse Treatment Professionals.* Delmar, NY: National GAINS Centre for People with Co-occurring Disorders in the Justice System/University of Washington. Available: www.gainsctr.com/curriculum/juvenile/index.htm.

U.S. Department of Health and Human Services. (1999). *Mental Health: A Report of the Surgeon General.* Rockville, MD: author. Available: www.surgeongeneral.gov/library/mentalhealth/home.html.

U.S. National Alliance for the Mentally Ill. (no date). *Dual Diagnosis: Mental Illness and Substance Abuse.* Available: www.nami.org/helpline/dualdiagnosis.htm.

REFERENCES

Aiken, M., Deward, R., DiTomaso, N., Hage, J. & Zeitz, G. (1975). *Coordinating Human Services: New Strategies for Building Service Delivery Systems.* San Francisco: Jossey-Bass.

American Psychiatric Association. (1994). *Diagnostic and Statistical Manual of Mental Disorders* (4th ed.). Washington, DC: author.

Ananth, J., Vandewater, S., Kamal, M., Brodsky, A., Gamal, R. & Miller, M. (1989). Missed diagnosis of substance abuse in psychiatric patients. *Hospital and Community Psychiatry, 40*(3), 297–299.

Andrews, G., Goldner, E.M., Parikh, S.V. & Bilsker, D. (Eds.). (2000). *Management of Mental Disorders.* Vancouver: World Health Organization Collaborating Centre for Mental Health and Substance Abuse.

Baker, F. (1991). *Coordination of Alcohol, Drug Abuse, and Mental Health Services* (Technical Assistance Publication Series, Number 4). Rockville, MD: U.S. Department of Health and Human Services.

Bean-Bayog, M. (1987). Inpatient treatment of the psychiatric patient with alcoholism. *General Hospital of Psychiatry, 9*, 203–209.

Brown, V.B., Ridgely, M.S., Pepper, B., Levine, I.S. & Ryglewicz, H. (1989). The dual crisis: Mental illness and substance abuse. *American Psychologist, 44*(3), 565–569.

Calderwood, K. & Christie, R. (2003). *Increasing Linkages between Addiction and Mental Health Services in Ontario: Final Report on the Concurrent Disorders System Models Project.* Toronto: Centre for Addiction and Mental Health.

Campbell, H., Gagnon, C.A., Long, W. & Cooper, G. (2002). *Reducing stigma through a public educational campaign which targets key influencers.* Paper presented at the 27th International Congress on Law and Mental Health, Amsterdam.

Carey, K.B. (1989). Emerging treatment guidelines for mentally ill chemical abusers. *Hospital and Community Psychiatry, 40*(4), 341–349.

Carmichael, D., Tackett-Gibson, M., O'Dell, Jayasuriya, B., Jordan, J. & Menon, R. (1997). *Texas Dual Diagnosis Project Evaluation Report.* Submitted to the Texas Commission on Alcohol and Drug Abuse, Texas Department of Mental Health and Mental Retardation. College Station, TX: Public Policy Research Institute, Texas A&M University.

Carpenter, K.M. & Hasin, D. (1998). A prospective evaluation of the relationship between reasons for drinking and DSM-IV alcohol-use disorders. *Addictive Behaviors, 23*(1), 41–46.

Chaudron, C.D. & Wilkinson, D.A. (1988). *Theories on Alcoholism.* Toronto: Addiction Research Foundation.

Cooper, G. (2004). Exploring and understanding online assistance for problem gamblers: The pathways disclosure model. *eCOMMUNITY: International Journal of Mental Health and Addiction, 1*(2). Available: www.pasinfo.net/journal/v1i2/v1i2a04article.html.

Cooper, G., Graham, D., Hill, J.M. & Huneault, N. (1990). Chronic mental illness and substance abuse: A needs assessment. *Rural Community Mental Health Newsletter 17*(1), 5.

Daley, D.C., Moss, H. & Campbell, F. (1987). *Dual Disorders: Counselling Clients with Chemical Dependency and Mental Illness.* Centre City, MN: Hazelden.

Drake, R.E. & Wallach, M.A. (1989). Substance abuse among the chronic mentally ill. *Hospital and Community Psychiatry, 40*, 1041–1045.

Ferguson, T. (1996). *Health Online.* Reading, MA: Addison-Wesley.

Ferguson, T. (1997). Health care in cyberspace: Patients lead a revolution. *The Futurist, 31*(6), 29–33.

Fine, E.W. (1980). The syndrome of alcohol dependency and depression. In E. Gottheil, A.T. McLellan & K.A. Druley (Eds.), *Substance Abuse and Psychiatric Illness.* New York: Pergamon Press.

Finn, J. (1996). Computer-based self-help groups: On-line recovery for addictions. *Computers in Human Services, 13*(1), 21–41.

Fisher, W., Piazza, C. & Page, T.J. (1989). Assessing independent and interactive effects of behavioral and pharmacologic interventions for a client with dual diagnoses. *Journal of Behavioral Therapy and Experimental Psychiatry 20*(3), 241–250.

Ford, L., Snowden, L.R. & Walser, E.J. (1991). Outpatient mental health and the dual-diagnosis patient: Utilization of services and community adjustment. *Evaluation and Program Planning, 14*, 291–298.

Freed, E.X. (1975). Alcoholism and schizophrenia: The search for perspectives. A review. *Journal of Studies on Alcohol 36*(7), 853–881.

Galanter, M., Castaneda, R. & Ferman, J. (1988). Substance abuse among general psychiatric patients: Place of presentation, diagnosis and treatment. *American Journal of Drug and Alcohol Abuse, 14*(2), 211–235.

Glass, I.B. (1989). Psychiatric education and substance problems: A slow response to neglect. *International Review of Psychiatry, 1*, 17–19.

Goffman, Erving. (1963). *Stigma: Notes on the Management of a Spoiled Identity.* Englewood Cliffs: Prentice-Hall.

Gottheil, E., McLellan, A.T. & Druley, K.A. (1980). *Substance Abuse and Psychiatric Illness.* New York: Pergamon Press.

Griffiths, M. & Cooper, G. (2003). Online Therapy: Implications for Problem Gamblers and Clinicians. *British Journal of Guidance and Counselling, 31*(1), 113–135.

Hall, R.C.W., Stickney, S.K., Gardner, E.R., Perl, M. & LeCann, A.F. (1979). Relationship of psychiatric illness to drug abuse. *Journal of Psychedelic Drugs, 11*(4), 337–342.

Health Canada. (2001). *Best practices: Concurrent Mental Health and Substance Use Disorders.* (Cat. No.: H39-599/2001-2E). Ottawa: Minister of Public Works and Government Services Canada. Available: www.hc-sc.gc.ca/hecs-sesc/cds/pdf/concurrentbestpractice.pdf.

Helzer, J.E. & Pryzbeck, T.R. (1988). The co-occurrence of alcoholism with other psychiatric disorders in the general population and its impact on treatment. *Journal of Studies on Alcohol, 49*(3), 219–224.

Herman, N.J. (1993). Return to sender: Reintegrative stigma-management strategies of ex-psychiatric patients. *Journal of Contemporary Ethnography, 22*(3), 295–330.

Hesselbrock, M.N., Meyer, R.E. & Keener, J.J. (November 1985). Psychopathology in hospital-ized alcoholics. *Archives of General Psychiatry, 42*, 1050–1055.

Hood, C., Mangham, C., McGuire, D. & Leigh, G. (1996). *Exploring the Links between Substance Use and Mental Health: A Discussion Paper and a Round Table.* Ottawa: Health Canada.

Howland, R.H. (1990). Barriers to community treatment of patients with dual diagnoses. *Hospital and Community Psychiatry, 41*, 1134–1135.

Kessler, R.C., McGonagle, K.A., Zhao, S., Nelson C.B., Hughes, M., Eshleman, S. et al. (1994). Lifetime and 12-month prevalence of DSM-III-R psychiatric disorders in the United States. Results from the national comorbidity survey. *Archives of General Psychiatry, 51*, 8–19.

Kittel Canale, M. (2001). *Stigma of Addiction: Final Report.* Toronto: Centre for Addiction and Mental Health.

Koegel, P., Burman, M.A. & Farr, R.K. (1988). The prevalence of specific psychiatric disorders among homeless individuals in the inner city of Los Angeles. *Archives of General Psychiatry, 45*, 1085–1092.

Kopolow, L.E. (1981). Client participation in mental health service delivery. *Community Mental Health Journal, 17*(1), 46–53.

Lin, N., Ensel, W.M., Simeone, R.S. & Kuo, W. (1979). Social support, stressful life events, and illness: A model and an empirical test. *Journal of Health and Social Behaviour, 20*, 108–119.

McEvoy, L. (1989). Alcoholism often goes undetected in psychiatric patients. *The Medical Post*, June 20, 40.

Melinyshyn, M., Christie, R. & Shirley, M. (1996). *Travelling the Same Road: A Report on Concurrent Disorders in Ontario*. Toronto: Addiction Research Foundation.

Mental Illness Education Project. (2000). *Dual Diagnosis: A Lecture by Ken Minkoff M.D.* [video]. Brookline, MA: author.

Minkoff, K. (1994). Models for addiction treatment in psychiatric populations: Methodologies for providing addiction treatment to psychiatric populations have been emerging relatively slowly. *Psychiatric Annals, 24*, 412–417.

Minkoff, K. (1996). Integration of addiction and psychiatric treatment. In N.S. Miller (Ed.), *The Principles and Practice of Addictions in Psychiatry* (pp. 191–199). Philadelphia, PA: W.B. Saunders.

Minkoff, K. (1997). Integration of addiction and psychiatric services. In K. Minkoff & D. Pollack (Eds.), *Managed Mental Health Care in the Public Sector: A Survival Manual* (pp. 233–245). Australia: Harwood Academic Publishers.

Ontario Ministry of Health and Long-term Care. (1999). *Making It Happen: Implementation Plan for the Reformed Mental Health System.* Toronto: author.

Petrakis, I.L., Gonzalez, G., Rosenheck, R. & Krystal, J.H. (2002). Comorbidity of alcoholism and psychiatric disorders: An overview. *Alcohol Health and Research World, 26*(2), 81–89.

Powell, B.J., Penick, E.C., Othmer, E., Bingham, S.F. & Rice, A.S. (1982). Prevalence of additional psychiatric syndromes among male alcoholics. *Journal of Clinical Psychiatry, 43*(10), 404–407.

Regier, D.A., Farmer, M.E. & Rae, D.S. (1990). Comorbidity of mental disorders with alcohol and other drug abuse: Results from the epidemiologic catchment area study. *Journal of the American Medical Association, 264*, 2511–2518.

Regier, D.A., Narrow, W.E., Rae, D.S., Manderscheid, R.W., Locke, B.Z. & Goodwin, F.K. (1993). The defacto US mental and addictive disorders service system. Epidemiologic Catchment Area prospective 1 year prevalence rates of disorders and services. *Archives in General Psychiatry, 50*, 85–94.

Reich, L.H., Davies, R.K. & Himmelhoch, J.M. (1974). Excessive alcohol use in manic-depressive illness. *American Journal of Psychiatry, 131*(1), 83–86.

Ross, H.E., Glaser, F.B. & Germanson, T. (1988a). The prevalence of psychiatric disorders in patients with alcohol and other drug problems. *Archives of General Psychiatry, 45*, 1023–1031.

Ross, H.E., Glaser, F.B. & Strasny, S. (1988b). Sex differences in the prevalence of psychiatric disorders in patients with alcohol and drug problems. *British Journal of Addiction, 83,* 1179–1192.

Ryglewicz, H. & Pepper, B. (1996). *Lives at Risk: Understanding and Treating Young People with Dual Disorders.* New York: The Free Press.

SAMHSA. (2002). *Substance Abuse and Mental Health Services Administration Report to Congress on the Prevention and Treatment of Co-occurring Substance Abuse Disorders and Mental Disorders.* Rockville, MD: author. Available: www.samhsa.gov/news/cl_congress2002.html.

Schmidt, L.A. (1989). *Prevalence and correlates of problem drinking in a psychiatrically treated population.* Paper presented at the Annual Meeting of the American Public Health Association, Chicago.

Sciacca, K. (1998a). From the field: Tennessee initiates statewide dual diagnosis program development. *Alcoholism and Drug Abuse Weekly, 10*(7), 5.

Sciacca, K. (1998b). On co-occurring addictive and mental disorders: A brief history of the origins of dual diagnosis treatment and program development. Available: www.erols.com/ksciacca/brifhst.htm.

Sciacca, K. & Thompson, C.M. (1996). Program development and integrated treatment across systems for dual diagnosis: Mental illness, drug addiction, and alcoholism (MIDAA). *Journal of Mental Health Administration, 23,* 288–297.

Sloan, K.L. & Rowe, G. (1995). Substance abuse and psychiatric illness. *The American Journal on Addictions, 4,* 60–69.

Sobell, L.C., Ellingstad, T.P. & Sobell, M.B. (2000). Natural recovery from alcohol and drug problems: Methodological review of the research with suggestions for future directions. *Addiction, 95*(5), 749–764.

Stoffelmayr, B.E., Benishek, L.A., Humphreys, K., Lee, J.A. & Mavis, B.E. (1989). Substance abuse prognosis with an additional psychiatric diagnosis: Understanding the relationship. *Journal of Psychoactive Drugs, 21,* 145–152.

U.S. Department of Health and Human Services. (1999). *Mental Health: A Report of the Surgeon General.* Rockville, MD: author. Available: www.surgeongeneral.gov/library/mentalhealth/home.html.

Weissman, M.M. & Meyers, J.K. (1980). Clinical depression in alcoholics. *American Journal of Psychiatry, 137,* 372–373.

Willauer, S., Cooper, G., Graham, D., Todd, L. & Mainer, B. (1990). *Dual Disorders Needs Assessment: Phase I Interim Report.* Sudbury, ON: Addiction Research Foundation.

Winokur, G., Reich, T., Rimmer, J. & Pitts, F.N. (1970). Alcoholism: III. Diagnosis and familial psychiatric illness in 259 alcoholic probands. *Archives of General Psychiatry, 23,* 104–111.

Woody, G.E., McLellan, A.T. & O'Brien, C.P. (1990). Research on psychopathology and addiction: Treatment implications. *Drug and Alcohol Dependence, 25*, 121–123.

Zweben, J.E. (1993). Dual diagnosis: Key issues for the 1990s. *Psychology of Addictive Behaviors, 7*, 168–172.

Chapter 27

Counselling People Who Use Substances about Blood-Borne Pathogens

WENDY WOBESER, CATHERINE OLIVER, PETER M. FORD AND HANNAH KAUFMAN

INTRODUCTION

Human immunodeficiency virus (HIV), hepatitis C virus (HCV) and hepatitis B virus (HBV) raise many issues for people who use substances and for substance use counsellors. Counsellors need to know how these diseases are contracted and how they impact people over time. They must be prepared to counsel clients in a manner that prevents the transmission of disease and equips people who have been diagnosed to manage the challenges of substance use and disease.

This chapter begins with an overview of the diseases and then addresses counselling issues within the context of disease. As professional team members of the Clinical Immunology Outpatient Clinic at Kingston General Hospital, we are particularly focused on HIV disease; however, the prevalence of HCV and/or HBV at our clinic is ever-increasing. All of our clients are infected with HIV, and over one-third are co-infected with HCV and/or HBV; most of these clients have a history of substance use problems.

Overview of Blood-Borne Pathogens

HIV can lead to AIDS. HBV and HCV can result in cirrhosis and liver cancer. When combined, HIV and HCV infection can be particularly deadly. Among people who inject drugs, infection with HCV is most common (because it is more easily transmitted than HIV and more people have HCV and can thus transmit the infection), followed by HIV and finally HBV. The majority of people infected with HCV and HIV develop a chronic infection; the virus continues to circulate in the blood and they can infect others. The majority of people who are infected with HBV, on the other hand, eventually recover and become immune. However, in the acute phase, HBV is the most deadly of the three viruses. It is also the only one for which there is a preventive vaccine. People who use substances, particularly those using needles, should be vaccinated for HBV.

Modes of Transmission

HIV, HBV and HCV are transmitted primarily by exchange of body fluids from infected to uninfected people. The body fluids most likely to transmit are blood (HIV, HBV and HCV) and semen/vaginal secretions (HIV, HBV). Maternal milk can transmit HIV from mother to child. Sexual and mother-to-child transmission of HCV does occur, but is uncommon. Other body fluids such as sweat, saliva and urine are incapable of transmitting these viruses. The major modes of transmission are:

Injection with blood-contaminated syringes (and possibly other drug injection paraphernalia such as water, cookers, swabs in the case of infection with HCV). Infected blood transfusions or infected blood products, such as Factor VIII preparations for hemophiliacs, are modes of transmission for all three blood-borne pathogens. Although a significant proportion of HCV infection in the last two decades was a result of infected blood transfusions, most new infections in North America are a result of injection drug use.

Sexual/anal intercourse. Because of the trauma to mucous membranes lining the anus and rectum, anal intercourse is the most frequent mode of sexual transmission, but oral sex with ingestion of semen and vaginal intercourse are also capable of transmission. In developing countries, vaginal intercourse is the predominant mode of HIV transmission, with genital ulceration due to other sexually transmitted diseases facilitating the spread by this route. Sexual transmission is less common for HCV than HIV or HBV.

Mother-to-baby transmission of HIV and HBV may occur in the womb, but probably most commonly occurs at birth. Infants may also be infected by HIV through breast-feeding, since breast milk of infected mothers may contain HIV-infected lymphocytes. HBV is also likely transmitted by breast milk.

Household transmission of HBV is possible from a person who is HBsAg positive (i.e., has circulating virus and is highly infectious, see HBV section, below). All household contacts of an HBsAg person who are not immune should be vaccinated. Household transmission is very uncommon for HIV or HCV; however, sharing a razor or toothbrush with an infected person may increase risk in the case of HCV.

EFFECTS OF BLOOD-BORNE PATHOGENS

HIV

The effects of HIV infection vary considerably from one person to the next, although at some point, usually several years from the time of infection, the immune system starts to fail. The phase where the patient appears well may last from two years to more than 10 years after infection; only about 50 per cent of infected people show signs of the disease after 10 years. The remainder appear well, but are capable of spreading the disease to others. Once infected, a person remains capable of transmitting the infection for the rest of his or her life.

HCV

HCV primarily infects liver cells. Most people with HCV remain relatively asymptomatic until end-stage complications, such as cirrhosis, become manifest. A number of symptoms, such as fatigue, may manifest throughout the course of infection. It is estimated that 10 to 30 per cent of people infected with HCV will develop cirrhosis over 20 to 30 years, and 1 to 5 per cent will develop hepatocellular carcinoma (a type of liver cancer). Alcohol ingestion increases the risk of developing cirrhosis. Unlike HIV, some people infected with HCV can rid themselves of the virus (approximately 20 per cent) although most become chronic carriers who can infect others. It is not completely understood why some people can and others cannot clear the virus; however, the deciding factor appears to be differences in one's immune response to the infection.

HBV

Like HCV, HBV primarily infects liver cells. Most infections resolve on their own within six months. However a few people infected with HBV will develop a severe, life-threatening acute infection with liver failure. Another small group will develop a chronic infection with circulating virus (termed HBsAg positive) and chronic liver inflammation, which can result in cirrhosis and hepatocellular carcinoma. Occasionally HBV infection is associated with other clinical syndromes such as arthritis and kidney inflammation. As previously explained, HBV is preventable by vaccine.

TESTING

HIV

A number of laboratory tests can detect whether a person has been infected with HIV. The screening tests detect antibodies to the virus. These antibodies may take up to six weeks and in a few cases as long as three to four months after infection to appear. During this time, HIV screening tests are negative, but the patient is capable of transmitting the infection—the so-called "window period."

The main screening test is the ELISA test, which occasionally produces false positive results. When the ELISA is positive, a confirmatory test called the "Western blot" (the name refers to the laboratory procedure) is usually carried out. The Western blot is regarded as the gold standard in HIV testing. All positive Western blot tests should be repeated for confirmation. When test results are indeterminate (e.g., an ELISA positive and a Western blot negative), the laboratory will repeat both tests. When counselling either before or after testing for HIV, it is important to remember that a person exposed to risk within the previous three to four months may be in the window period (infected, but without developed antibodies that show up on testing), and should be tested again after a period of at least three months from last exposure. For many people who inject drugs who continue to expose themselves to potential infection, a single negative test is meaningless; repeated testing is required until risk behaviour has ceased. Further, the viral levels in the blood of an infected person during the window period are extremely high and the person, highly infectious. People who are thought to be in the window period must be counselled to practise safe sex and to avoid behaviour that might put others at risk.

Progression of HIV to AIDS

There is often confusion about the difference between being infected with HIV and having AIDS. Someone with a positive confirmatory or Western blot test is infected with HIV, but that person does not have AIDS until he or she becomes physically ill with some of the disease manifestations described below.

As the HIV infection progresses, the virus destroys the macrophages and the immune system's "helper" lymphocytes. These cells help protect the body against infection, and damage to them results in the loss of immunity to a whole range of micro-organisms, many of which never trouble people with intact immune systems. The decline in immune function occurs over several years and may be slowed by a number of drugs that inhibit viral growth but, unfortunately, do not kill the virus. It has recently become possible to measure the amount of virus in the bloodstream— the "viral load"—and this is used to guide treatment. A high viral load indicates that the current therapy is not working, and a reduction in viral load after starting a new treatment indicates that the drug is effective.

HCV and HBV

Like the tests for HIV, commonly used tests for HCV detect antibodies to the virus. As with HIV, there is a window period during which a person may have circulating virus (usually at high levels) before antibodies become detectable. Antibodies are usually not detectable for three months after infection and may require up to six months to appear. Most people who have antibodies to HCV also have circulating virus and are potentially infectious. For HBV, a test called HBsAg is a marker that a person has circulating virus and is highly infectious. People with antibody to HBsAg do not have circulating virus, and are not infectious.

TREATMENT OF BLOOD-BORNE DISEASES

HIV

Treatment advances in HIV in the last 10 years have been significant. Treatments are becoming less complex, but for success a patient must still adhere to a strict medication regimen. Patients who frequently miss doses are likely to develop resistant virus, which remains in the body and may re-emerge if future drug regimes fail. Failure to adhere to the drug therapy remains the most common cause of disease progression in the treated person. While the new drugs have changed HIV from a death sentence into a chronic, manageable illness, they also have a significant incidence of side-effects. Many of these side-effects not only make patients feel chronically unwell, they may also change their appearance due, for example, to changes in fat distribution. There are no dramatic new developments in HIV therapy expected in the next few years. Although people who use substances can be adequately treated for HIV, they represent a significant challenge and management of the addiction is needed for HIV treatment success. These challenges result from chaotic and unstable living situations which may interfere with the rigid treatment regimen necessary for effective management of HIV. Enrolment in a treatment program should precede treatment of HIV where possible.

As the immune system declines in people with HIV and the risk of infection increases, it is possible to provide prophylactic therapy to prevent a number of common infections such as candida (thrush), herpes and pneumocystis (which causes a severe pneumonia). Ongoing care and monitoring are usually provided either by regional HIV/AIDS clinics—which, in Canada, have been established with provincial funding in most major cities—or by interested family physicians. With close super-vision, both the duration and quality of life can be improved. There is thus an incentive for HIV-positive individuals to seek appropriate medical care.

In addition to attacking the immune system, HIV also attacks the central nervous system, and may cause dementia. This is usually only pronounced in the late stages of the disease and its incidence has been much diminished with the use of antiviral drugs. Dementia in the terminal stages of the disease may not only complicate management, but can also cause considerable strain and distress to caregivers and patients alike.

An additional problem in HIV/AIDS patients is the occurrence of certain tumours. These include Kaposi's Sarcoma, a tumour rarely seen other than in AIDS patients, intracranial lymphoma and, in females, cervical cancer. Treating cancers in persons with HIV is complicated by the presence of underlying problems with the immune system making it difficult to tolerate tumour treatment.

HCV

Treatment advances have also been seen with HCV. The current standard treatment consists of once-weekly pegylated Interferon injections and oral Ribavirin. This treat-ment usually causes mild flu-like symptoms, and may also cause depression or exacerbate existing depression, with some suicides being reported. Long-term response rates are still less than 60 per cent and considerably lower with HIV and HCV co-infection, which is often present in people with substance use problems.

The toxicities of the treatments for HIV and HCV overlap, further complicating the treatment of these two diseases when they occur together. The cost per year for both HIV and HCV treatment is significant (i.e., three-drug therapy for HIV is about $8,000 to $14,000). The availability of these drugs varies from province to province; some are provided free (e.g., AZT) and many others are funded through a variety of public and private drug plans. When patients are expected to pay for these expensive drugs, HIV/AIDS health care providers face major problems ensuring that patients receive available treatment.

HBV

Treatments for HBV are available but are limited in their effectiveness. New treat-ments are being developed. It is important that household members of persons with chronic active HBV be vaccinated against this virus.

EPIDEMIOLOGY

Who Is Infected?

When HIV/AIDS first appeared in North America in 1981, it was recognized in homosexuals. Although it was also noted to occur in other groups, such as people who inject drugs and Haitian immigrants, for several years HIV/AIDS was regarded in North America as a "gay" disease. By the late 1980s, however, it became clear that there was a second major epidemic of HIV infection in the injection drug–using population of some, but not all, cities in the United States.

In the early 1990s, epidemics of HIV infection were recognized in three groups:
• homosexuals
• people who inject drugs
• heterosexuals.

All three groups overlap to some extent, particularly the latter two. What is less generally appreciated is that the rate of spread differs in all three groups.

The chance of a person becoming infected with HIV depends on:
• how risky his or her behaviour is
• the likelihood of infection of the person's partner(s)
• the number of partners the person has.

The slow rise of numbers among heterosexuals has given a false sense of security regarding this group. Vaginal intercourse with an infected male, even without condom use, carries a relatively low risk of transmission in the intact vagina and, despite the impression given by the media, the average heterosexual does not have multiple partners. Female-to-male spread is even less likely. But because initially, most infected females used drugs or worked in the sex trade or both, their non–drug-using male partners slowly began to appear in the statistics, and now heterosexual spread in the non–drug-using population is increasing and reflected in the rising number of newly infected women—many of whom were unaware that they were at risk.

Prison Populations

The prevalence of HIV and HCV in prison populations is generally about 10 times that of the non-prison population. A number of studies showed that the rate of HIV and HCV in the general prison population five years ago was two per cent and 33 per cent respectively and has likely risen since then. The prevalence of HCV in people known to use drugs in prisons was much higher, around 80 per cent, for those regularly sharing injection equipment (Ford et al., 2000).

Urban Populations

Once HIV and HCV enter a city's injection drug use population—in both developed and developing nations—they spread very quickly. For example, in 1988 the incidence of HIV-positivity in people who inject drugs in Bangkok jumped from 16 per cent in the spring to 46 per cent in the fall, and more than 75 per cent were infected before the first AIDS case appeared. The current prevalence of HIV in people who inject drugs varies considerably in the Western hemisphere, being very high in cities such as Vancouver, Baltimore, Sydney and Seattle. (See section on "Harm Reduction" later in this chapter for information about how some cities have addressed these issues.)

PRACTICAL APPROACHES TO COUNSELLING

Unfortunately, for some people a visit to a doctor's office or clinic for an HIV test is the first time they learn about the transmission of blood-borne diseases. While elementary and high school curricula can provide current knowledge to students, for people past their high school years the facts about risk have to be learned elsewhere. Quick items on the news, uncensored information about a distant relative's death from AIDS or vague impressions of life-saving medications do little more than confuse the public and misrepresent the truth.

As the front line to people with potential high risk of infection, counsellors of clients in treatment programs should design their programming to include prevention and management of blood-borne diseases. The intake assessment should itself be a screening of risk factors. The client's motivation for treatment, mental health history, formal and informal support systems, sexual partners, substance use and barriers to behavioural change should all be considered for level of risk of infection. Although many clients are aware of their HIV/HCV/HBV status and of effective disease-management practices, the counsellor cannot assume this. The client should be advised that he or she is being assessed for disease-related risk factors; the personal inquiry and weight the counsellor gives to these issues may raise the level of the client's awareness and bring disease transmission into a relevant context for the person. Once risk factors are established a client may require counselling for anxiety and an expedient referral to be tested for disease. The client and his or her associates who are at risk have then gained access to health-status monitoring and other supportive services.

In our clinical setting, we routinely meet patients who were aware of their risk factor(s) for an extended period of time, in some cases for years, but have delayed testing. Some clients adopt avoidance as their coping strategy, but if disease is present and risk behaviours continue, they are not only placing others at risk of infection, but also effectively compromising their own long-term health outcome. Similar self-harm and harm to others is sometimes seen in those who continue to deny their positive test results.

A counsellor can enhance a client's level of well-being through the provision of referrals to HIV-related services and a commitment to co-ordinated, co-operative care with other health care providers and agencies. A client who has supported access to HIV-related services is more apt to follow through with integrating new information and learning positive coping strategies, and is likely to experience improved long- and short-term outcomes. Referrals and linkages with community agencies, family doctors and hospital-based clinics can decrease uncertainty and increase the client's and family's ability to cope (Hilton, 1992). Care must be taken, however, when referring clients to community HIV/AIDS support agencies. These service providers continue to be widely perceived as politically radical and "gay." Clients may choose not to associate with these agencies. Client education about the service provider and an introduction to a contact person may reduce these objections.

Care must also be taken to refer clients to service providers that are receptive to people who use substances. Establishing health care linkages and improving support networks can be a major breakthrough toward health and self-care for these clients— replacing a culture of marginalization and disenfranchisement with acceptance and self-esteem.

HIV Testing: Pre- and Post-Test Counselling

Pre-test and post-test counselling are important when caring for a person who is concerned about HIV. Clients considering testing must be aware of the following three provisions as outlined by the Canadian Medical Association (1995):

1. HIV testing should be done only after the individual has provided informed consent.
2. Clients have available to them the choice of different testing sites, which may offer up to three different identification modes: nominal, non-nominal and anonymous testing. For nominal testing, the patient's full name and contact information are used throughout the process. Non-nominal testing involves providing the principal staff person (usually a registered nurse) with full name and contact information, but using a code for all test requisitions and test tubes, and later decoding results to match them to the patient. For anonymous testing the patient provides an alias and no contact information to the principal staff person. The patient will later present him- or herself to the test site and use the same alias to receive test results. A substance use counsellor should advise clients of identification options and help them make an informed choice. Public Health Units offer nominal, non-nominal and anonymous testing. Hospital clinics tend to offer only non-nominal testing.
3. A substance use counsellor should ensure that the client fully understands that medical records are strictly confidential; no one can have access to them without the patient's consent (unless the medical record is subpoenaed by a court of law).

Even with a full understanding of these three provisions a client may choose not to be tested. At this point and onward, appropriate counselling about risk reduction is imperative.

A client's decision to proceed with testing brings complex risks and concerns. The process of being tested can produce anxiety and depression, discrimination in the workplace and/or in relationships and, most strikingly, suicide risk. The counsellor must understand these concerns and help the person through the testing process, and while he or she is awaiting results (Marks & Goldblum, 1989). The substance use counsellor must also understand the issues that arise during HIV testing. The purpose of this is two-fold. First, the substance use counsellor can, with clients, assess further learning needs to reinforce complete and appropriate counselling. Second, because HIV counselling is rarely accomplished in one or two sessions, the client has an improved chance of information retention and behaviour change if both HIV health care personnel and substance use counsellors provide consistent and complementary counselling.

The HIV pre-test session involves:
- assessment of the patient's knowledge of HIV, including reasons for testing/retesting
- discussion of disease transmission (sexual intercourse, blood transmission, sharing needles, mother to baby)
- discussion of relevant risk behaviours (sexual practices, drug and alcohol use)
- exploration of the psychological effects of testing, including an assessment of individual coping mechanisms, support systems and suicide risk
- discussion of the testing process (e.g., that there is typically a two-week wait for results), test limitations, retesting requirements if in window period, and meaning of test results
- discussion of risk-reduction strategies and need for future testing if risk behaviour(s) continue
- obtaining informed consent.

Regardless of whether test results are negative or positive, they should always be given *in person*.

If the test results are negative, the HIV post-test session should include:
- interpretation of the result
- reinforcement of risk-reduction strategies
- addressing the need for retesting if the client is in the window period and /or continues to engage in risk behaviours
- discussion of false sense of security and potential to minimize the significance of risk factors.

If the test results are positive, the HIV post-test session should include:
- interpretation of the result (infected with the virus, not diagnosed with AIDS and reassurance that a confirmatory test was performed to rule out a false positive)
- discussion of issues important to the patient
- discussion of coping and support systems, including decisions about disclosure
- assessment of mental status
- referral for additional support (mental health agencies, HIV/AIDS support agencies, benefit packages and/or disability plans).

The diagnosis of HIV infection is often the only thing the client remembers from this post-test counselling session. It is important to hold follow-up sessions over the next few days and weeks.

Other issues to explore during the initial and/or follow-up post-test sessions, if the test is positive, should include:
• the client's responsibility to disclose his or her status to current and future sexual partners
• the client's responsibility to never share needles
• the client's disclosure to Public Health (for confidential contact and disease surveillance purposes) of past and present sexual partners and of others with whom the client engages in shared risk behaviours
• prevention of transmission (practising safe sex and safe drug use, avoiding donations of blood, organs, tissue and sperm, avoiding breast-feeding, protecting others from blood, semen or vaginal fluids)
• stages of HIV disease and the importance of regular medical follow-up
• ongoing discussion of issues important to the patient
• ongoing assessment of mental status, coping skills and comprehension
• discussion of health enhancement through proper nutrition, rest, fitness, stress reduction and elimination of substance use.

All clients, with or without substance use problems, may be overwhelmed by a diagnosis of HIV infection. Newly diagnosed individuals are prone to increased risk behaviours, such as needle sharing and unsafe sex, due to mental health complications, increased substance use and anxiety. Because denial, as a coping strategy, allows for continued substance use, challenging a client's use can result in decreased acceptance of the diagnosis, depression or suicide. Uncertainty about health, life expectancy and the impact of HIV on everyday functioning can lead clients to try to assert maximum control over their lives. This can take the form of either seeking or avoiding knowledge about their illness, and either increased or decreased substance use (Weitz, 1989). Clients may be overwhelmed by illness, grief and a sense of loss. This powerful focus can result in a client's overlooking or avoiding either the substance use or the HIV infection, again leading to high-risk activities, anxiety, depression and suicide. The counsellor must be alert to these possibilities.

Counsellors are also prone to use avoidance and control behaviours to manage anxiety: a "parallel process" they sometimes fall into with clients. The counsellor's behaviour may, for example, unwittingly enable the client's high-risk activities, especially increased substance use. For example, when counsellors insist that clients newly diagnosed with HIV totally abstain from substance use, this may remove clients' only coping strategy, leading them to increased feelings of anxiety and loss of self control, which may in turn increase their substance use. Prior to entering a formal substance use program, a goal of moderating a client's substance use may increase that client's motivation, and help the counsellor with this complicated engagement process. Counselling strategies that provide information, including the strategies for behaviour change, while enhancing self-esteem, have also been shown to increase the likelihood of behaviour change. Any person who tests positive for HIV should also be tested for HCV and HBV, and the counsellor should be aware of those results. The modes of transmission of all three are similar, but HCV and HBV are much more easily transmitted by injection drug use than HIV, although both forms of hepatitis are transmissible sexually. Patients with active HCV or HBV disease of the liver should be strenuously counselled to avoid any alcohol, which accelerates disease progression. There is no evidence that even low levels of consumption are safe.

Long-Term Vulnerabilities

Like HIV, HBV and HCV disease, substance use problems present complex and emotionally charged issues. The combination of disease and substance use problems exacerbates the stressors for both, and long before the person presents for counselling, he or she has likely been stigmatized and marginalized from the larger community.

Because counsellors are often members of the "mainstream" community from which clients are excluded, counsellors and clients may have difficulty establishing a common ground for building rapport and establishing trust. The onus is on the counsellor to create a therapeutic environment that is free of biased attitudes; only then will the client begin to risk exploring matters of concern. How effectively the counsellor hears, and communicates his or her resolve to "start where the client is at," will determine the extent to which the relationship develops so that therapeutic intervention can be accomplished.

To break through the barriers of the disenfranchised toward improved health and self-care, the counsellor must be prepared to help the client with problems he or she may have with managing daily living activities (Grube & Chernesky, 2001). Concrete concerns of housing, budgeting, medication costs, transportation and a balanced nutritional diet are recurring themes in counselling sessions. For many clients, functional barriers impede efforts to fulfil these needs. These barriers include:
• illiteracy
• missing documents (e.g., birth certificate, social insurance card, up-to-date tax returns)
• inability to maintain routines or keep scheduled appointments
• difficulty navigating service systems (e.g., encountering an automated phone message results in many slammed receivers).

Numerous emotional barriers challenge even the initiation of help-seeking behaviours. These may include:
• depression
• feelings of worthlessness
• a pervasive sense that the social services system is punitive by design
• previous encounters with health care services that have reinforced these notions of inadequacy.

Counselling a person with HIV disease and substance use problems requires a multi-issue approach. The client who attends counselling may believe that issues other than his or her substance use problems or HIV status are more immediate and significant. The counsellor needs to be open to assist with issues relevant to the client, as well as specific issues of substance use and disease. The counsellor must have a wide range of expertise, linkages to a wide range of services and be an effective networker to establish contacts within agencies. The counsellor acts as an advocate for policy change that can result in improved inclusion and adequate service provision.

The counsellor must also be sensitive to additional difficulties often faced by people infected with HIV. Multiple losses have already been experienced, and more are anticipated: abandonment by family and friends, death of close friends, loss of health, loss of energy, loss of financial independence, loss of social respectability, loss of ability to contribute at work, and thus loss of job satisfaction/fulfilment, deteriorating physical appearance and forfeiting of dreams. The effects of HIV disease are not only physically disfiguring, but also physically, mentally and emotionally debilitating. Many of these issues affect people with substance use problems as well. The similarities between the burden of disease for the person with HIV and for the person with substance use problems are staggering.

The goals of counselling should include ongoing disease education, life-skills training, awareness of and changes in attitudes toward one's circumstances and ultimately changes in behaviour. Motivation, incentives and barriers to change should be explored and used in the counselling process to enhance support systems and to minimize the avoidance of other major issues, such as substance use.

As previously mentioned, improved therapies are transforming HIV from a lifethreatening disease (AIDS) to a chronic illness with many of the same emotional, social and financial issues as other chronic conditions. Although this is good news, people infected with HIV must be able to manage long-term use of expensive medications, an emotional shift from thinking about and planning for imminent death to retrieving a lost social and work life as their health stabilizes, and changing their relationship and family roles. Many people, having adjusted to a shortened lifespan, do not cope well with these changes. Counsellors must not assume that the transition will be a completely easy one for their clients.

HIV AND SPECIAL POPULATIONS

Women and HIV

RISK OF INFECTION

Traditionally, society has considered women at low risk for HIV infection. Many women themselves have naively bought into this misconception and continued risk behaviours. Others have had risk imposed on them through physical and/or sexual abuse during childhood or as adults. Still others are unaware of personal risk, as they are not informed of their partner's sexual and/or needle-sharing practices. Over the last decade, the incidence of HIV infection has taken a sharp upturn in women, particularly young women. In the Northeastern United States, women are now the fastest-growing group testing HIV-positive. In Canada this trend is clearly present and growing, but women have not yet surpassed the other two major groups of HIV-infected people (men who have sex with men and people who inject drugs). In recent years, our clinic has supported an increasing number of women who learn of their risk only after being infected by a bisexual male partner. Interestingly, women who appear to have been infected by a partner who injects drugs are more likely to be aware of their partner's habit. The primary risk factors associated with a diagnosis of HIV among women are heterosexual contact and injection drug use (Health Canada, 2003).

PRESENTATION OF DISEASE

Women and men with HIV show some differences in presentation and complications, although the survival times are probably much the same in similar socio-economic groups. Women may present with recurrent and persistent vaginal candidiasis and may also have recurrent problems with pelvic inflammatory disease. In addition, there appears to be an increased risk of cervical cancer. Because HIV in women is less familiar to physicians in Canada, it is often missed in the early phase, particularly when it presents as recurrent pelvic inflammatory disease. Although there has been some suggestion that AIDS is a more rapidly fatal disease in women than in men, this appears to be so only because more of the female cases come from lower socio-economic groups. Women do no worse than males from the same groups. Statistics on males are skewed by the fact that many homosexuals with AIDS come from the middle class with better access to health care and money to pay for treatment (Ford & Ford, 1995).

ISSUES FOR COUNSELLORS

Fully understanding the nature of risk offers little comfort to many heterosexual women. The psychological trauma of learning that their partner is sexually involved with someone else (and that the "someone else" is a man), or that their partner has a history of injection drug use, along with financial dependencies, concern for the well-being of the children and fear of an inability to achieve intimacy because of stigmatization of disease, is a difficult challenge for women. As well, women infected with HIV with a history of injection drug use have a significantly higher risk for domestic violence. Their risk increases with disclosure of HIV-positive status to their sex and needle-sharing partners (North, 1994). Frequently women place their own well-being at the bottom of their priorities and do not have the financial and emotional resources to look after themselves.

Women who are HIV positive should be assessed for the risk of domestic violence and offered appropriate intervention. Targeted HIV intervention strategies should be developed for women who use drugs, for survivors of domestic assault and rape, and for assailants. In addition, if domestic violence is in the picture, extreme caution should be used when considering partner notification.

An HIV-positive pregnant woman who does not receive any antiretroviral treatment has up to a 25 per cent chance of giving birth to an infected infant. By treating the HIV (treatment is often started after the third month of pregnancy), transmission rates can be as low as one to two per cent. There is thus good reason to counsel and test pregnant women regardless of their perception of risk, because there is a real benefit to timely treatment.

PRISON POPULATIONS

Substance use is common among inmates of correctional institutions. Inmates are dependent on sharing the limited supply of illicit injecting equipment. Inmates with infectious disease who inject their drugs are often so dependent on sharing needles that they exercise great caution to ensure their health status is not revealed, even to the point of not availing themselves of any health care for the duration of their incarceration. For this reason, the spread of infection may be far greater than in the non-incarcerated community. Once inmates are released from prison, this concentration of disease is dispersed into the wider community.

Men and women who have recently finished lengthy incarcerations have limited skill sets for assessing and managing community supports and health care programs, finding adequate accommodation and budgeting on social assistance funds. These people are vulnerable to reintegration failure and may consciously or subconsciously seek re-entry into the familiar world of incarceration. Back inside, the chances for controlling substance use or receiving adequate heath care are again challenged.

HARM REDUCTION

Harm reduction programs such as needle exchange and methadone clinics have proven to be effective strategies for stemming the spread of disease. Besides the use of sterile injecting equipment, the positive effects on a client from regular daily contact with a skilled health advisor are enormous. The staff member is alert to assess both gradual and sudden changes in the person's presentation, as well as to provide progressive education about many health matters. Because people with substance use problems often have their first and only interaction with a skilled counsellor at such a setting, the counsellor must provide concrete information about HIV, HCV and HBV, help the client to access testing, and follow through with referrals to treatment programs and heath care agencies. The health care agencies and the street-care programs must work as colleagues to ensure client care is maximized without compromising patient confidentiality. Arrangements in which the street-care program dispenses daily HIV medications, along with methadone or needles, or directly refers a client for priority medical assessment, are helping clients better manage their disease.

Glasgow and Edinburgh make a fascinating and instructive comparison in terms of the benefits of harm reduction strategies. At the beginning of the HIV epidemic, Glasgow already had a needle exchange program in place because of concern about the spread of hepatitis. Edinburgh did not have such a program; in fact the police closed the only pharmacy in the city prepared to sell clean needles and syringes to people who inject drugs. At the end of the 1980s, the prevalence of HIV in the injection drug use population in Edinburgh was over 70 per cent; in Glasgow it was around five per cent. There is now mounting evidence that needle exchange and methadone treatment programs, coupled with education, can reduce risk behaviour and probably the spread of HIV. Such programs often provide the only point of contact for health care workers with this population.

In Canada, needle exchange programs slow the escalation of infection rates rather than stop infection. This has recently been demonstrated in Vancouver, where the prevalence of HIV and HCV in people who inject drugs and are street involved is above 20 per cent and 80 per cent respectively. Other major Canadian cities such as Montreal, Toronto and Ottawa show a similar trend. Those who are at particular risk appear to be females and people who use cocaine. Though many people who inject drugs have been immunized for HBV, the levels of HBV infection in that population are at least 10 times higher than in the general population (Alary & Hankins, 2002; Burchell et al., 2002; Tyndall et al., 2001).

For a comprehensive and reasonably compact review of the subject of injection drug use and HIV/AIDS, the reader is referred to Des Jarlais et al. (1992). The reader may also wish to look at *Reducing the Harm Associated with Injection Drug Use in Canada* (FPT Committee on Population Health et al., 2001). A disturbing trend we have noticed locally, and with increasing prevalence, concerns prescription narcotics. Patients receiving prescriptions or daily dispensing of narcotics are routinely threatened and physically assaulted for any narcotics that are part of their medication regime. One patient revealed that he was severely beaten by assailants who hoped that medical intervention would be required, so that they would be able to access greater dosages of painkillers through him as he recovered. Most disturbing is that the assaults are perpetrated by other clients of the same services; it is widely believed that intimidation and bullying behaviours also find their targets among fellow patients in the HIV clinic.

COUNSELLOR CONCERNS

Professional counsellors should expect during their career to encounter clients either infected with or affected by blood-borne diseases. The counsellor should have a solid knowledge of HIV, HCV and HBV. This information is of benefit to the client only if the counsellor has first become aware of his or her own personal attitudes regarding disease (HIV in particular), a broad range of sexual practices, addiction, drug-seeking behaviours, progressive disability and death.

Many feelings are generated when staff face HIV issues. These feelings can either help or hinder the provision of improved services and treatment. An agency that institutionally faces issues such as homophobia, AIDS phobia, and fears of transmission and death sets an example to staff, clients and the community. This can be a painful and difficult process, but the payoff is enormous. Crisis can be prevented or minimized, staff and clients can more freely voice their own fears and concerns, and adequate information and referral sources are more likely to be in place before they are needed. As counsellor tensions, biases and anxiety are openly addressed through non-threatening peer consultation, each counsellor is able to work more efficiently and with professional objectivity.

An aspect of professional objectivity that cannot be overlooked is the need to be ever-vigilant in assessing potential for violence. The client may be at great risk of inflicting harm on himself or herself or others. Suicidal ideation is common in these clients; attempts occur and are sometimes successfully completed. Yet extreme behaviours are also often targeted outward in the form of calculated attacks or uncontrolled outbursts of verbal and/or physical rage. Targets vary from people believed by clients to be the source of their disease, to professionals who are perceived by clients as withholding desired medications (especially if the client feels he or she should be prescribed a much greater dose of narcotics). Extreme occasions may occur, such as when a client threatens staff or other service users and needs to be barred from future service.

CONCLUSION

People who use substances are at an increased risk for infection of blood-borne diseases. As a group, they share key risk factors:
• needle sharing
• compromised immune status
• decreased inhibitions leading to unsafe sex
• unsafe drug use practices
• low self-esteem.

Any one of these factors can lead to HIV/HCV/HBV infection and related health problems. In combination, the risk dramatically increases. The person may not be aware of the risk of transmission, or may not bring up the issue during substance use counselling. Because of these circumstances, all clients with a history of substance use require counselling about blood-borne diseases, their transmission, prevention and impact on both the client and his or her associates.

Providing a variety of other prevention programs can prevent an epidemic of disease in a specific community, as well as stabilize prevalence of infection. These might include:
• needle exchange programs
• methadone
• supervised injection sites
• distribution of condoms and latex squares
• education
• testing for disease.

REFERENCES

Alary, M., Hankins, C. & Le Réseau SurvUDI. (2002). Surveillance épidémiologique de l'infection par le virus de l'immunodéficience humain chez les utilisateurs de drogures par injection. Rapport interimaire, Novembre, 2002. Le Réseau SurvUDI.

Burchell, A., Clazavara, L.M., Major, C., Remis, R.S., Corey, P., Myers, T., Millson, P.E., Wallace, E. & the Polaris Study Team. HIV incidence among persons undergoing repeat diagnostic testing in Ontario, 1992–2000. *Canadian Journal of Infectious Diseases, 13*(Suppl. A, 48A). Abstract 315.

Canadian Medical Association. (1995). *Counselling Guidelines for HIV Testing.* Ottawa: Canadian Medical Association.

Des Jarlais, D.C., Friedman, S.R., Choopanya, K., Vanichseni, S. & Ward, T.P. (1992). International epidemiology of HIV and AIDS among injecting drug users. *AIDS, 6*(10), 1053–1068.

Ford, P.M. & Ford, S.E. (1995). AIDS and women. *Journal of the Society of Obstetrics and Gynecology, 17*, 1229–1235.

Ford P., Pearson, M., Sankar-Mistry, P., Stevenson, T., Bell, D. & Austin, J. (2000). HIV, hepatitis C and risk behaviour in a Canadian medium security federal penitentiary. *Quarterly Journal of Medicine, 93*, 113–119.

FPT Committee on Population Health, FPT Committee on Alcohol and Other Drug Issues, FPT Committee on AIDS, FPT Heads of Corrections Working Group on HIV/AIDS. (2001). *Reducing the Harm Associated with Injection Drug Use in Canada.* Ottawa: Minister of Public Works and Government Services. Available: www.hc-sc.gc.ca/hecs-sesc/cds/publications/injection_drug/toc.htm.

Grube, B. & Chernesky, R.H. HIV/AIDS case management tasks and activities: The results of a functional analysis study. *Social Work in Health Care 32*(3), 41–63.

Health Canada. (2003, April). *HIV/AIDS Epi Update.* Available: www.hc-sc.gc.ca/pphb-dgspsp/publicat/epiu-aepi/hiv-vih/women_e.html.

Hilton, A. (1992). Perceptions of uncertainty: Its relevance to life-threatening and chronic illness. *Critical Care Nurse, 12*, 7–73.

Marks, R. & Goldblum, P. (1989). The decision to test: A personal choice. In J. Dilley, C. Pies & M. Helquist (Eds.), *Face to Face: A Guide to AIDS Counseling* (pp. 49–58). San Francisco: University of California AIDS Health Project.

Murrill, C.S., Weeks, H., Castrucci, B.C., Weinstock, H.S., Bell, B.P., Spruill, C. & Gwinn, M. (2002). Age-specific seroprevalence of HIV, hepatitis B virus, and hepatitis C virus infection among injection drug users admitted to drug treatment in 6 US cities. *American Journal of Public Health, 92*(3), 385–387.

North, R.L. & Rothenberg, K.H. (1994). Partner notification and the threat of domestic violence against women with HIV infection. *New England Journal of Medicine, 329,* 1194–1196.

Tyndall, M., Johnston, C., Craib, K., Li, K., Spittal, P., O'Shaughnessy, M. & Schecter, M. (2001). HIV incidence and mortality among injection drug users in Vancouver—1996–2000. *Canadian Journal of Infectious Diseases, 11*(Suppl. B) 69B, p. 354.

Weitz, R. (1989). Uncertainty in the face of AIDS. *Journal of Health and Social Behaviour, 30,* 270–281.

GENERAL REFERENCES

Adler, M. (Ed.). (1987). *The ABCs of AIDS.* London: British Medical Journal.

Dilley, J., Pies, C. & Helquest, M. (Eds.). (1990). *Face to Face: A Guide to AIDS Counselling.* Berkeley AIDS Health Project. San Francisco: University of California.

King, A., Beazle, R.P., Warren, W.K., Hankins, C.A., Robertson, A.S. & Radford, J.L. (1987). *Canada Youth and AIDS Study.* Kingston, ON: Queen's University.

McKenzie, N.F. (Ed.). (1991). *The AIDS Reader: Social, Political and Ethical Issues.* New York: Meridian.

Meridith, L. (1996). *Establishing Links: Violence against Women and Substance Abuse.* London, ON: Centre for Research on Violence against Women and Children.

Miller, C.L., Johnston, C., Spittal, P.M., Li, K., Laliberte, N., Montaner, J.S. & Schechter, M.T. (2002). Opportunities for prevention: Hepatitis C prevalence and incidence in a cohort of young injection drug users. *Hepatology, Sept. 36*(3), 737–742.

Ostrow, D. (Ed.). (1990). *Behavioral Aspects of AIDS.* New York: Plenum Medical Company.

Chapter 28

Working with Mandated Clients

CATE SUTHERLAND, MICHAEL NAYMARK AND RANIA SHUGGI

INTRODUCTION

This chapter addresses the assessment and treatment issues that mandated clients present to addiction treatment agencies. Similarities and differences in clinical approaches are described. Practical suggestions are provided for how to establish an effective liaison with the referral agents in allied sectors and how to develop a constructive counselling relationship with the client.

The purpose of this chapter is to provide information that will:
• increase your understanding of mandatory clients and related processes
• dispel the myth that it is difficult to deal with mandated clients
• show that the management of these clients is only slightly different from that of non-mandatory clients
• outline techniques to help you work with mandated clients and their referring agents.

While agencies deal with mandatory clients from a variety of sources, this chapter will address four sources in particular:
• probation and parole offices
• the Ontario Works Addiction Services Initiative (as an example of a program which mandates people receiving social support payments into addiction treatment)
• driving while impaired (DWI) clients
• Drug Treatment Courts (DTCs).

Each source presents somewhat different issues in terms of programming and more particularly in terms of the relationship between the agency providing treatment and the "referral agent."

OVERVIEW OF ISSUES IN TREATMENT

Motivation

During the last 10 years or so, governments in Canada have increasingly recognized the wisdom of providing access to treatment to people whose legal or other problems are caused by their substance use. As a result, addiction services are seeing increasing numbers of mandatory clients. This trend causes concern for some workers in the addiction field.

There is a commonly held belief that mandated clients are, in general, unmotivated, and that management of such clients is more difficult than that of non-mandated clients. This is not necessarily true. Addiction agencies have traditionally worked primarily with clients who voluntarily seek assistance, and an influx of involuntary clients may be disconcerting. Some agencies may have long waiting lists and may feel compelled to save counselling energy for someone who is really interested in help. This touches on another problem—the belief, inherent in the addiction field, that you cannot help a person who does not want to be helped. The unmotivated client is often perceived as unco-operative and unlikely to benefit from compulsory intervention. This can be true in some cases—a few clients may choose to be unco-operative and gain little or nothing from their involvement with your agency. Still, it is the experience of counsellors who have worked with high numbers of mandated clients that most are compliant and easily engaged. If some initial resistance is noticed, remember that motivation is not a static attribute; it is a process, and so is behaviour change. It is possible for a person to begin these processes at your agency.

Even clients who present with no apparent motivation or desire for help can be provided with appropriate services, which might be a catalyst for starting the process of change. Work by Prochaska & DiClemente (1984) outlines stages of behaviour change based on their transtheoretical model. See Chapter 2 for more information on motivational interviewing.

When working with mandated clients, consideration should be given to the definitions of "voluntary" and "involuntary." Webster's Dictionary states that "voluntary" implies "freedom and spontaneity of choice or action without external compulsion." By this definition, how many clients are truly voluntary? Most clients who present at an addiction agency are propelled by external pressure (perhaps they have lost their jobs or families, suffered serious health problems or are in legal or financial trouble), it is just that the external compulsion of mandated clients is more visible. Available research indicates that involuntary clients do as well as voluntary clients (Anglin et al., 1998).

In addition to these considerations, there are two critical factors that can influence an agency's effectiveness with mandatory clients: the counsellor's attitude and expectations, and the agency's relationship with the referral agent.

Counsellor's Attitude

The counsellor's attitude and expectations will, in most cases, set the tone and determine the outcome of the interview. A client will react to the immediate presentation of the counsellor, who is in a position to create a type of self-fulfilling prophecy. If the counsellor expects a lack of co-operation or motivation, resistance or annoyance, those expectations will be transmitted to the client and will affect the treatment outcome: low expectations plus low effort equals poor outcome—to change the outcome, change the expectations and effort. Though positive expectations and high effort will not be successful in every case, at least the worker can be satisfied that appropriate and proactive attempts were made to engage the client in the process.

Ideally, the goal is to create an environment in which the client can openly examine his or her attitudes and behaviours, start the process of motivation and make personal, informed decisions about his or her alcohol and/or other drug use. Fortunately, immediate emotional insight is not always necessary for ultimate therapeutic success. Sometimes simply exposing the client to a non-judgmental, positive treatment situation can precipitate constructive changes. A long-standing AA member once used this analogy when asked to give his views on the benefits of mandatory attendance in treatment. He said, "If you throw mud at the wall, some of it is bound to stick." Following this analogy, it would seem that the initial job of the counsellor is to prepare the wall in such a fashion that it is more receptive to the mud.

Agency Relationship to Referral Agent

The second critical factor in an agency's effectiveness is its relationship with the referral agent. Not all mandatory clients will have a referral agent in the traditional sense. While many will be referred by a third party such as a probation/parole officer, employer, social support worker or child protection worker, the attendance of others will be dictated by a legal authority. For instance, in many jurisdictions, the vehicle licensing authority requires that convicted impaired drivers complete a remedial measures program before consideration is given to lifting the suspension of their driver's licence. Also, in two jurisdictions in Canada, people can apply to have their drug-related criminal charges heard in the Drug Treatment Court, and the rules and regulations of that program guide the referral relationship. Details of these programs and client issues are contained later in this chapter. To effectively manage the more common type of mandatory client, however, a co-operative relationship must be established between your agency and the referral agent and/or the referring agency.

SERVICE AGREEMENTS
It is crucial that you meet with the referring agency to clarify respective roles and expectations. This will make the job much easier in the long run and help prevent misunderstandings. Service agreements between organizations that outline details of

working relationships are now common, and should be developed by the agency's management staff. A meeting may then be arranged between the staff of the respective agencies or, at least, between selected staff who know the job well and are versed in the particular situations that may arise. At this meeting, be very specific in your discussions and put your agreements and the results of your discussions in writing. Suggested topics include the following:

Who will make the actual referral, the referral agent or the client?

When it is practical, it is recommended that the referral agent make the referral and schedule the initial appointment. This arrangement helps reinforce for the client that it is the referral agent/agency who requires the client's attendance and helps the counsellor maintain a neutral position.

What type of information does your agency need upon referral?

Consider providing the referral agency with copies of your intake/referral form.

What types of services will your agency provide or not provide?

For example, a residential treatment agency may require that travel arrangements be made by the client and referring agency; or, an agency may see couples to discuss addiction-related issues, but not provide more general types of relationship counselling.

What type and how much information will be relayed back to the referral agent?

Keep in mind that appropriate consent forms must be signed and that the client may allow only certain information to be released. Also remember that, regardless of the arrangement between your agency and the referral agency, the counsellor's first obligation is to the client. Informed consent is obtained only after it is explained to the client what his or her rights are, what type of information will be released and to whom it will be released. If the client is at all reluctant to consent to release of information, remember that it is not the job of the counsellor, but of the referral agent, to resolve this issue (though the counsellor may provide information about the possible repercussions of not providing consent).

Further, there may be a grey area regarding the exchange of information when your agency is under contract to provincial correctional services. Depending on the jurisdiction in which you work, agency staff in these circumstances may technically be considered employees of the provincial correctional ministry and, as such, permitted to exchange information with other employees of that ministry without the written consent of the client. Still, this is open to interpretation and you are best advised to discuss the matter with your agency's legal counsel and the legal branch of the Ministry of Correctional Services in your jurisdiction.

Will the information be conveyed to the referral agent verbally or in written form?

Consider that if you insist that most information be given verbally, you save yourself and the agency a lot of work (although accurate note-taking of each conversation by both the counsellor and the referral agent is, of course, crucial). Written reports may then only be necessary some of the time. If the referral agent insists that all communication be written, then compromise with form letters. For example, a form letter from a community treatment agency that provides assessments might read:

Mr. _____ was seen on this date for a standardized addiction assessment.

The assessment indicates . . .

The following treatment plan was negotiated: . . .

Who reschedules missed appointments?

Again, you can save some work by maintaining that it is the referral agent's responsibility to ensure that clients are aware of and attend appointments. If an appointment is missed, simply let the referral agent know; it is the referral agent's job, not yours, to enforce any existing mandatory conditions to attend. This will also help preserve your counselling relationship with the client.

Insist that the referral agent take full responsibility for explaining to the client the purpose of the referral to the addiction agency.

Ask that the referral agent briefly tell the client what to expect when he or she arrives at your office. Hopefully, this will prevent people from showing up at your office for appointments without knowing fully why they are there or what is going to happen.

Request detailed information from the referral agent regarding the other terms and conditions of the mandatory attendance.

Such terms may include, for example, abstinence from alcohol and/or other drugs. Develop a clear understanding of your responsibility vis-à-vis reporting breaches of these conditions to the referral agent. If a client discloses substance use to you, are you prepared to report this information, which may cause irreparable damage to the counselling relationship but may be in the best interests of the client or public safety?

Once the details of the working relationship have been ironed out, ask to attend a staff meeting at the referring agency to help ensure that everyone understands the guidelines for the working relationship; you can also provide a detailed explanation of the philosophy, policies, procedures and services of your agency. Ideally, one person from the referral agency can act as a liaison between the respective agencies. The purpose of a liaison is to provide clear communication routes and to reduce the likelihood of inappropriate referrals. This meeting also provides a good opportunity to invite other staff members to visit your facility site(s). Their familiarity with your physical plant as well as your services will be useful when preparing their clients for a referral to your agency.

In summary, with the right attitude and a little preparatory work, a counsellor can create an environment in which a mandated client is more likely to benefit from involvement with the agency. As a bonus, the counsellor may find that working with mandatory clients can be challenging and satisfying.

SOURCES OF MANDATED CLIENTS

Probation or Parole Clients

Addiction treatment providers are seeing increasing numbers of mandatory referrals from probation and parole offices. People convicted of an offence and incarcerated in a provincial or federal correctional facility are usually required to participate in both institutional programs during incarceration and community substance use treatment programs following their release. Also, there has been increased emphasis in the courts in recent years on sentencing options that include rehabilitative conditions. As part of the sentence following a criminal conviction, a judge may order that the person accept help for a particular problem, mandated by a condition in a probation or parole supervision order by which the person has agreed to abide. The problem areas might include, for example, emotional health concerns or financial difficulties. Substance use is often a key factor in crime, and probation or parole conditions and/or correctional treatment plans will frequently mandate that the client participate in substance use treatment programs.

THE CLIENT INTERVIEW

Though most agencies follow a standardized format in client interviews, there are several matters it is recommended you address when beginning an interview with a correctional client. First, ensure that the client understands why he or she is at your agency. Ask directly, "Can you tell me why your probation/parole officer (PO) arranged this interview?" Hopefully, you will get a relatively accurate response and can proceed to the second matter. If not, explain your understanding of the purpose of the interview. This will present two options, depending on the client's attitude: if the client is resistant, refer him or her back to the PO, whose job is to provide a proper explanation and enforce the treatment condition; if the client is compliant or seems reasonably so, proceed.

Second, determine how the client feels about having to attend for treatment. Again, be blunt: "How do you feel about being required to attend here?" Do not settle for vague answers, such as "It's OK." Take some time to find out how the client really feels, whether the response is positive or negative. If you receive a negative reaction regarding the required attendance, simply acknowledge it and, perhaps, empathize. For example, politely say, "Thank you for being honest with me. I can understand how someone might feel that way," and move on. This is a subtle but very important point. It establishes, from the beginning, that honesty during the interview is expected and will not be judged or have any negative repercussions.

Third, declare your neutrality. Ensure that the client understands that it is not your agency that requires his or her attendance and that you are not an extension of the legal system. Explain that your agency has a co-operative relationship with the probation or parole office, but that the focus of your responsibility is to provide appropriate substance use treatment services. Occasionally a client will equate his or her required attendance with your agency's desire or need for money. Most counsellors have probably heard a variation of the following by a mandatory referral at some point in their career: "If it wasn't for people like me having to come here, you wouldn't have a job." If this is true, don't insult the client's intelligence by denying it. Some substance use treatment services have contract or service agreements with referral agencies that fund a counsellor position or part of one to provide services to selected clientele. If this is the case with your agency, don't debate the money issue, lightly acknowledge it: "Yes, the agency does receive some funding from them," and proceed to the next part of the interview. If your agency doesn't receive separate funds for the mandatory services it provides, you can briefly comment on that fact.

You may encounter substantial negativity or resistance from the client regarding his or her mandatory attendance. To make the interview (and future sessions) productive, it is important to try to nullify the initial resistance. Try and appeal to the client's adult and logical sensibilities. Acknowledge that his or her attendance is probably not completely voluntary, but point out the advantages of complying and the disadvantages of not doing so. You might say something like the following (in a professional and respectful tone):

> I know it probably doesn't seem that you had a choice about whether to come here. Still, you could have chosen to not comply with the treatment condition and deal instead with the resulting legal charges. I realize that doesn't seem like much of a choice, but it's still a choice. The fact that you are here tells me that you are concerned about making decisions that are in your best interest. Now you have another choice to make—you can just go through the motions here or you might consider trying to make the best of it. Alcohol and/or other drug use was an issue in your criminal charge and resulted in your referral here. This might be an opportunity to examine your drinking and/or drug using patterns and behaviours and the advantage to you would be figuring out ways to prevent future problems.

It is also recommended that you address the issue of consent to release/exchange information before you begin the assessment process. Carefully review with the client a written consent form that addresses the limits of confidentiality. Answer all questions honestly and, if the client is not prepared to sign the form, it is recommended that you not proceed. Instead (as mentioned earlier), refer the client back to the PO to discuss the options. This is an important step to help avoid a future misunderstanding that could undermine the therapeutic relationship with the client.

Now, proceed with the interview. It will be surprising to some counsellors that, from this point on, the interview should be conducted in exactly the same way as with a referral from any other source. There are no tricks or special techniques needed to interview correctional clients. Typically, they are no more or less truthful, forthright or co-operative than any other client. In fact, some counsellors consider it easier to work with correctional clients because, in a sense, a treatment plan has already been set by the probation or parole supervision order. For example, a typical probation condition might read, "Attend for, and be amenable to, alcohol counselling or treatment as directed by a Provincial Probation Officer." After a standardized assessment to determine which treatment services would be most appropriate for the client, ask the client if he or she is willing to attend, and make arrangements for the provision of those services. (See Chapter 3 for more information on assessment and treatment planning.) Even clients who are "precontemplators" can be offered services appropriate to that stage of change. Still, remember it is not your job to enforce the probation or parole condition for addiction treatment. That is the probation or parole officer's job. It will not be necessary anyway in most cases. Correctional clients, like anyone else, respond positively to being treated with dignity and respect, and appreciate consideration of their opinions and feelings about situations and circumstances.

Some correctional clients, especially those with extensive criminal histories or who have spent time in federal institutions for more serious offences, may have features of antisocial personality disorder. These people often make an extremely positive first impression and may be charming and convincing in their claims that their referral is a misunderstanding. This may be true, but is unlikely. Though the counsellor's first obligation is to the client, neither naiveté nor cynicism will benefit the therapeutic relationship. It is important to maintain clear and open communications with the PO and ensure the client fully understands that such communication is ongoing.

ADDITIONAL ASSESSMENT CONSIDERATIONS

Although service delivery to correctional clients requires only minor adjustment in practice for counsellors, there are a number of considerations to keep in mind. As noted earlier, correctional clients are more likely to have features of an antisocial personality and a small percentage may be psychopathic; research has shown that the latter can be dangerous. While most referrals will not be at high risk for violent behaviour, counsellors should be aware of these possibilities and educate themselves accordingly.

Some correctional clients may have been victims of neglect and abuse in childhood and spent many years in institutional settings. As a result, they may have deficits and needs in many areas. The assessment should encompass a variety of life areas thought to be affected by substance use problems. This is particularly true for correctional clients, where problems in social relationships, employment, mental health and the legal system are prevalent.

Ontario Works Addiction Services Initiative

Ontario Works (OW) is an example of an initiative to provide assistance to clients receiving social support payments in cases where substance use may pose a barrier to employment. Other jurisdictions may have similar initiatives. It is expected that by 2005, OW will have implemented its Addiction Services Initiative (ASI) in every municipality in Ontario in partnership with local addiction treatment systems. The primary benefits for the OW client include immediate access to community addiction treatment services and the removal of most obstacles (e.g., waiting lists) that prevent or complicate the person's participation in treatment and ancillary supports. OW can also assist in overcoming other barriers to treatment such as lack of finances, transportation, social or family stability and child care.

An agency involved in the ASI will have a service agreement with OW, outlining:
• the types of services offered,
• the manner in which they are provided
• details about respective roles and expectations.

Staff should be familiar with this agreement. It is also helpful to know how the OW process works, in terms of how the client, starting at OW, eventually ends up in your office. While procedures will vary slightly by municipality, OW has outlined a very simple, generic process.

Each OW office will have staff who co-ordinate the ASI. In addition to screening clients to be referred for addiction assessment and treatment, that OW employee acts as a liaison between the addiction treatment provider and the general OW workers, and ensures that the client understands his or her rights. The criteria for referral for screening are clients whose substance use may be a barrier to employment. Such clients can self-identify or may be identified by their assigned OW worker.

THE CLIENT INTERVIEW

The counsellor can expect that by the time the OW client attends at the agency, he or she understands his or her rights in the situation and the implications related to the Participant's Agreement. If the client is not a self-referral, the OW staff will also have discussed with him or her the reasons for the referral for screening and, subsequently, for substance use treatment. It is the counsellor's obligation to confirm at the beginning of the OW client's first appointment that these matters have been discussed with the client. An OW client, like any other, has the right to expect that he or she will be fully informed. If these matters have not been discussed with the client before the referral for treatment, you may wish to discuss this with a supervisor in your agency so adjustments can be made to the referral process.

If the client is a self-referral to the ASI, proceed as you would with any other voluntary client: complete the assessment, develop an individualized treatment plan and help the client carry it out. Pay particular attention to, and document, any obstacles to accessing treatment and to supports that may help the client achieve and maintain his or her treatment goals. Discuss these obstacles and supports with the client and develop suggested solutions. This information should be reported to the OW contact, who will collaborate with the counsellor and client to remove the obstacles and provide reasonable supports.

If the OW client is not a self-referral, but has agreed to attend your agency, it is most productive to assume intended compliance. Remember that mandatory referral does not equate to an unco-operative client. Asking what the client knows about the services your agency provides is a comfortable and safe place to start the interview. Based on the nature and tone of the response, you'll probably get an indication of the client's feelings about attending. If the response is negative, don't respond immediately.

Clarify any misinformation about your services and fill in any gaps, then ask the client this simple question: "What would you like to accomplish during your involvement with this agency?" This starts the work in a positive frame, acknowledges the importance of the client's preferences and opinions and indicates that he or she will have some control in the situation. These are important factors, which demonstrate respect for the client. The client's response will act as the springboard from which the work will begin.

Based on the collective experience of the workers in the program to date, the client's answer will probably demonstrate a willingness to engage or, at least, to explore issues. But suppose the client's answer indicates a high degree of negativity and resistance, something like, "I don't want to accomplish anything! I don't have a problem. I'm only here because they said I had to come." A counsellor can still very easily work with this OW client, but the direction of the interview will need to become solution-focused.

Because OW recognizes the harm-reduction perspective and, for clients referred under the ASI, substance use has been identified as a barrier to employment, the counsellor's logical response to such a declaration may be, "Oh, OK. I guess I'm curious then about how you're going to resolve the situation with Ontario Works." This should generate a conversation about the "situation," which is that OW thinks the client's substance use is interfering with his or her employability, and the client disagrees. The counsellor can then offer to help the client explore the problems presented by the situation, and to find possible solutions. It is possible that substance use is not the problem, but experience so far indicates that OW's identification and referral process is reliable. A highly resistant client may be a true precontemplator, and might benefit from information and techniques suggested in the "stages of change" theory. The client might also agree to become engaged in the process simply to rule out substance use, or may suggest that he or she will "prove" it's not a factor by participating in employment programs in the expected manner. Regardless, the counsellor can still use the client's involvement as an opportunity to explore issues related to his or her substance use, and possibly reduce harm caused by it.

Just as referral source is not a defining factor in motivation, neither is income source. Clients in receipt of social assistance have always been on the case loads of addiction workers, as have clients with other income sources. OW clients will be no more or less difficult to work with than other clients. In fact, the implementation of OWASI might make the treatment process easier for both client and counsellor. OW has a vested interest in positive outcomes. This can benefit the client, who receives increased social support, and also the financial support needed for treatment and recovery. For counsellors, the encouragement and removal of financial obstacles provided by OW can help to make their job easier, and provide impetus in the process of motivating the client.

Drug Treatment Courts

Drug Treatment Courts (DTCs) are a relatively new innovation in the criminal justice system's approach to people with substance use problems. They also represent a new type of partnership between the courts and treatment. Their operation highlights a number of issues faced by treatment providers working with mandated clients.

The first DTC opened in Miami-Dade County, U.S.A., in 1989, as a response to the backlog of drug-related cases awaiting trial. It attempted to go beyond merely expediting the processing of these cases by addressing the substance use problems that kept offenders recycling through the justice system (Harrison & Scarpitti, 2002). There are currently two DTCs in Canada: the Toronto DTC, established in December 1998, and the Vancouver DTC, established in December 2001. DTCs have been established internationally in a wide range of jurisdictions, including Jamaica, Ireland, Scotland, Australia, New Zealand and Brazil. By far the largest number of drug courts is in the United States, where, as of 2003, about 800 DTCs had been established, with 500 more in the planning stage (National Association of Drug Court Professionals [NADCP], 2003).

DTCs programs provide court-supervised treatment for drug-dependent people charged with drug offences (e.g., possession of a drug, trafficking in small amounts of that drug to support their drug use), with the goal of reducing drug use and criminal recidivism. While participating in a DTC program, clients attend treatment and also attend special court sessions where they report their progress to a court team that has ongoing involvement with the clients in that DTC. The court responds to the clients' progress, and compliance or non-compliance with the program, with a range of graduated sanctions and incentives (penalties and rewards). Sanctions can include:
• admonishments from the DTC judge
• community service hours
• more frequent attendance at court
• brief periods of incarceration.
    Incentives include:
• praise in open court
• presentation of certificates for reaching program benchmarks
• reduced court attendance
• opportunity to leave individual court sessions early.

In order to complete the program, clients are required not only to discontinue their drug use, but must also achieve a degree of social stability, in the form of stable housing and employment, that will help ensure ongoing recovery and avoidance of criminal behaviour. Drug use by clients is monitored by regular drug testing. Participants who complete a DTC program receive more lenient sentences; rather than the period of incarceration they would normally expect for their particular charges, they receive non-custodial sentences (e.g., probation).

DTCs differ from standard court diversion programs in which the court directs an offender to work on a substance use problem and then return at the end of a specified period; the court has limited or no contact with these offenders. DTCs instead feature intensive, ongoing monitoring by the court, both to ensure that public safety is not jeopardized, and to utilize the court's power to increase overall compliance with the program. The team approach taken by the judge, prosecutor, defence counsel and probation representative, with representation from treatment, is a hallmark of the DTC approach, and stands in distinct contrast to the adversarial process that characterizes the standard legal approach. Direct, frequent contact between the client and the DTC judge is another defining characteristic. Many people charged with drug offences and drug-related crime have serious substance use problems that are the primary cause of their criminal behaviour. They become trapped in a cycle of drug use, criminal behaviour and incarceration. From the judicial perspective, DTCs are a way to stop perpetuating this cycle, and to use the power of the court for therapeutic ends (with emphasis on rehabilitation rather than punishment), with the aim of increasing public safety. DTCs represent a new judicial paradigm known as "therapeutic jurisprudence," currently receiving a great deal of attention in Canada and the United States, which involves the use of courts as therapeutic tools (Hora et al., 1999).

At the same time, the court-treatment partnership reflects concerns that treatment alone is often ineffective in engaging or retaining drug-dependent people who are involved in criminal behaviour (Belenko, 1999). The DTC concept is based on the notion that the treatment and criminal justice systems need to work together to be effective since neither system has been effective in isolation. DTCs have shown promise in terms of their effectiveness in reducing drug use and recidivism, although there is a need for further evaluation (Turner et al., 2002; Belenko, 2001).

DTCS AND MANDATORY TREATMENT

While DTCs are voluntary programs, they have some of the characteristics of mandated programs. They are voluntary in that offenders choose to apply, through a lawyer, for admission to a DTC but are not required to; they can always elect to go through the standard legal process. In the Toronto DTC, clients can also withdraw from the program at any time, and return to the standard legal process. Still, the choice between a DTC or the standard legal process has been described by critics as a false choice because, for many people, the alternative to entering a DTC program is a jail sentence (though there are people who choose the regular judicial route, preferring jail when the sentence is likely to be shorter than the year-plus DTC program). However, because someone who chooses to enter the DTC is subject to intensive, ongoing monitoring by the court, and can be exposed to court-imposed legal penalties, including brief periods of incarceration, these clients, ironically, subject themselves to some of the conditions of mandatory programs.

CANADIAN VS. AMERICAN DTC MODELS

When the Toronto DTC was created, it differed from the American DTC model in a number of crucial respects, as detailed below. These distinctions reflect differences in the health, judicial and political systems in the two countries, and in the political culture related to illicit drug use in which they operate (Bentley, 1999). In subsequent years, many American programs have evolved in the direction of the Canadian model.

• With few exceptions, there are no sanctions for drug use in the Canadian DTCs, while many American courts have sanctions from the first use onward, culminating in discharge from the program after several uses.

• The Canadian DTCs focus on the most severe substance use problems (cocaine and heroin dependence as opposed to marijuana, which is targeted by many American DTCs).

• The Canadian programs admit people with more serious charges (e.g., trafficking) and more lengthy criminal records than many American programs (e.g., some U.S. DTCs deal only with first-time offenders charged with possession).

• The two existing DTCs in Canada have dedicated treatment programs. In the United States, it is more common for a DTC program to refer clients to one of several different treatment providers, none of them dedicated DTC treatment programs.

• American DTCs emphasize the disease model of addiction and 12-step models of treatment, while the Canadian programs follow a broader bio-psychosocial approach.

• To enhance communication between the treatment and court teams, the Toronto DTC employs a "court liaison," who facilitates communication between the teams, providing information to each team about the other's concerns and recommendations and about client progress in treatment and appearances in court. While the Vancouver DTC has a similar position, such a role is rare in American DTCs.

• A high degree of involvement with community stakeholders is a defining feature of Canadian DTCs. In the Toronto program, for example, community service providers receive referrals from the dedicated treatment program, and community partners provide consultation and oversight to the DTC program and participate in its promotion and ongoing development. American DTCs have less community involvement.

ISSUES FOR TREATMENT PROVIDERS IN THE OPERATION OF DTC PROGRAMS

The treatment-related issues addressed in the following sections have emerged from the experience of the dedicated treatment program of the Toronto DTC, which provides drug-specific treatment for cocaine- and heroin-dependent clients (methadone maintenance treatment is available to the latter group), utilizing individual and group formats. There are stabilization, intensive treatment and after-care phases in the program. Treatment staff provides assessment, intensive case management and individual counselling services.

Assessment Issues

In the Toronto DTC, assessment proceeds in several stages. As with any assessment process, it provides information for determining whether the program is a good match for the applicant and explains the program to clients. The nature of the DTC program creates some unique issues that are best addressed in the assessment phase.

While the DTC initially appears to be an attractive option to many clients (who may apply to avoid jail, or to obtain release from custody by the DTC if they are already in jail at the time of their application to the program) these clients must be able to make an informed choice about the program. Treatment staff must explain the requirements and expectations of the program throughout the screening and assessment process. It can be helpful to point out that the client may be able to serve his or her jail sentence with little difficulty, while the program is very demanding, and possibly longer than the actual sentence would be.

Some applicants do not actually have a substance use problem, but want to avoid legal consequences. Their involvement in the program would reduce the DTCs' credibility in the eyes of the public, community stakeholders and other clients. The assessment process screens out such applicants by asking detailed questions about their substance use.

Given the rigour and complexity of the program, it is necessary to identify applicants with severe cognitive impairment or mental health issues which might interfere with their meeting program requirements.

The issue of motivation for treatment as a criterion for acceptance into the program is a complex one. Both the treatment and court teams would prefer a motivated client. In practice, motivation is difficult to determine, even though clients are asked about their motivation at several points in the assessment process. Some applicants are able to give a smooth, polished presentation, and can sound motivated when they are not, while others are less articulate or sophisticated, though no less motivated. In the Toronto DTC, it is generally felt that penalizing the latter group by denying them admission is unfair. It is also generally recognized that enhancement of motivation is part of the work of the program, rather than a given before the client is accepted.

Issues for Clients

There is a wide range of clinical and social issues that heroin- or cocaine-dependent clients face, especially those who have spent a lot of time on the streets. These include:
• trauma
• violence and/or abuse
• homelessness
• stigmatization
• unemployment
• child welfare issues
• HIV/AIDS exposure
• lack of social supports.

Some additional issues for DTC clients (described below) are amplified by the very nature of the program.
• **Motivational issues**: clients are generally externally motivated by the pressure of their legal problems, and the desire to avoid being in custody. The shift to a more internal motivation for recovery is important for sustaining changes. It can be

difficult for a client to focus on his or her personal reasons for recovery when there are repeated reminders of external pressures (e.g., court sessions; drug testing).

- **Authority issues**: because of their history, many clients resent and mistrust authority, especially the justice system. In a DTC, authority is a constant presence that some clients react to with defiance or false compliance.
- **Issues with program structure**: a DTC program works in part by providing clients with structure (e.g., treatment and court sessions, drug tests, rules around compliance). This can be challenging for clients who have difficulty adhering to any kind of routine, particularly those who are accustomed to a street lifestyle.

Treatment staff help clients with authority and structure issues by:

- listening to clients who have difficulty tolerating program demands or encounters in court
- continually providing explanations for program rules and decisions, and their relevance to a client's recovery
- highlighting any gains that clients make that are attributable to the structure of the program.

At the same time, counsellors highlight the role of the client's own efforts to make changes, and the positive effects these changes have on his or her life, not just on his or her legal status. This helps clients shift from external to internal motivation, as does a constant focus on the clients' personal goals and on the adverse consequences of drug use (over and above the legal consequences) that clients identify.

Based on clinical experience, clients respond best to treatment when the following elements are in place:

- a dedicated treatment program, including immediate access to treatment for new clients, staff who are familiar with the unique issues of a DTC (who can provide clients with support and consistency) and the sense of comfort and community that results from being with others who have similar issues and program experience
- recognition of the need for constant processing of a client's experience of the program
- clear boundaries and rules, with room for flexibility in exceptional circumstances
- clear explanations of confidentiality and reporting considerations
- intensive case management by the therapists who make use of a network of partnerships with other service providers
- a holistic, bio-psychosocial approach to recovery
- progress benchmarks (e.g., graduation from one treatment phase to the next) with recognition by the treatment and court teams
- opportunities to interact with non-DTC clients, to help normalize the issues that DTC clients deal with, and to reduce stigmatization.

CLIENT TREATMENT ISSUES

- **Flexibility**: In any program, there is a tension between the therapeutic value of reinforcing program expectations and the desire to individualize an approach to meet a given client's needs. In a DTC, this challenge is magnified because consistency in the application of rules is a central value in any court. Further, in a program in which clients generally have difficulty with structure, flexibility with some clients may be perceived by others as permission to avoid program requirements. The question, "What message will this decision send to other clients?" is a frequent refrain when deciding whether to be flexible with the application of a program requirement. There is also a strong desire that the program be seen as fair and equitable, and this requires consistency. In the Toronto DTC, these concerns are a frequent topic of discussion, and in practice there are factors that allow for flexibility. Because there is a consistent court team, they become familiar enough with the clients to know their individual circumstances, which means that making some decisions on a case-by-case basis is logical. In addition, if some clients complain, for example, that other clients are "getting a break" when they are not, counsellors can take this opportunity to point out what positive things another client might have done to merit the court's flexibility.

- **Program expectations of client progress**: In any program, there can be incongruence between the program's expectations of client progress and a person's own process of recovery. In a DTC, such incongruence may seem to have more implications than usual for clients, because their progress is being scrutinized by the court. At the same time, clients can benefit from the focus that program expectations provide. In such circumstances, counsellors explain to the court team the clinical reasons, if applicable, for a client's slow progress while remaining open to the possibility that the client might benefit from some pressure, with the addition of appropriate treatment supports.

- **Counselling and the court**: Counsellors may find that there is a blurring of the line between the therapeutic and the judicial. Court-related processes and sanctions may be seen as therapeutic, and counsellors can be increasingly inclined to frame them as such, and to recommend them. For example, the sanction of increased court attendance might be seen as providing additional support, in the form of increased structure and focus, for a client who is having difficulty with his recovery. This can be confusing for counsellors who are generally unaccustomed to allying themselves with the power of the court, yet see the value in doing so. The desire to have some power vis-à-vis the court is also relevant. For example, counsellors may want to participate when the court team considers sanctions for a client. Once the treatment team is involved in recommending whether a given sanction will be effective, the distance between the treatment domain and the court domain diminishes.

RESOLVING THE ISSUES

The issues described above arise in a unique partnership. They force both counsellors and court team members to articulate and challenge their own assumptions, and to constantly re-think the issues in a variety of ways, including:

- being aware that neither the judicial nor the clinical approach has been effective on its own with this client group, and that there is a need to work together
- mutual understanding of each team's main concerns in terms of its professional roles, values, ethics, standards, procedures and who its client is (e.g., the Crown Prosecutor's primary "client" is the public, not the person in the treatment program), and the extent to which a DTC approach challenges all of these dimensions of each team's work

• the benefits of cross-educating the court team to promote understanding of drug use issues, the change process, the recovery process, motivational issues and the issues— emotional, practical and social—that must be addressed to ensure a successful client
• increasing familiarity over time with the members of the court team, which enhances trust, respect and consideration of each other's views
• encouraging regular, ongoing communication between the treatment and court teams (e.g., case conferencing, joint retreats, designated liaison staff to facilitate communication, ongoing collaboration through membership on joint committees).

In summary, DTCs highlight the issues faced by counsellors who work with mandated clients—even though clients are not "mandated" in the usual sense of the word. By providing treatment staff with opportunities to co-operate with and influence the justice system's responses to drug-dependent people, DTCs constantly challenge addiction workers to examine their own assumptions, beliefs and values about how change occurs, about the courts and about the client population that uses these programs. By actively embracing these challenges, counsellors can learn to provide more comprehensive, sophisticated and effective support to a complex client group.

Driving While Impaired (DWI) Clients

Drinking and driving remains the single largest criminal cause of death and injury in Canada. About one thousand people die each year in Canada in motor vehicle crashes involving a drinking driver, and many more are seriously injured or disabled (Mayhew et al., 2002). In 2000, alcohol was involved in:
• 35.6 per cent of motor vehicle fatalities (Mayhew et al., 2002)
• 40 per cent of marine vehicle fatalities (Lifesaving Society, 2000)
• 71.5 per cent of snowmobile and 56.7 per cent of all-terrain vehicle fatalities (Beirness & Desmond, 2000).

Beirness et al. (2002) estimated that in 2001, 1.7 million Canadians drove when they thought they were impaired. Studies of the contribution of drinking and driving to alcohol-related mortality indicate that it is the largest single source of alcohol-related deaths in Canada (Single et al., 1999).

It is currently illegal to drive with a blood alcohol content (BAC) over 80 mg per cent. Penalties for impaired driving include a maximum possible penalty of life in prison for impaired driving causing death. All provinces and territories also have their own highway traffic laws that allow the authorities to impose additional sanctions on drivers convicted of Criminal Code drinking and driving offences. Most provinces also impose minor sanctions on drivers with a BAC lower than the Criminal Code legal limit of 80 mg per cent. These include fines and brief (12–24 hours) suspensions of driving privileges. Most provinces also require the convicted driver to attend counselling sessions, mandatory remedial programs and/or evaluations by medical specialists. Consequently, counsellors in the addiction field are seeing an increasing number of clients who have been referred for remedial measures or treatment as a prerequisite to licence reinstatement.

DEMOGRAPHICS AND PERSONALITY CHARACTERISTICS OF DWI OFFENDERS

The impaired driving population is predominantly male, although one recent research study suggests that the number of women who report driving while believing they were over the legal limit is increasing (Beirness et al., 2002). This study also reported that drivers aged 30 to 39 were the largest group of impaired drivers, at 27 per cent, followed by those aged 40 to 49 (26 per cent) and 50 to 64 (20 per cent). Drivers aged 18 to 25 represented 14 per cent of impaired drivers and those aged 26 to 29 represented eight per cent (Beirness et al., 2002). Drivers aged 65 years and over made up the remaining five per cent. However, other data indicate that younger drivers are most likely to drive after drinking (Centre for Addiction and Mental Health, 2003).

Research has shown that certain personality types and psychiatric disorders are more commonly found among DWI offenders (Macdonald & Mann, 1996). For example, many offenders exhibit some degree of hostility, sensation-seeking behaviour and an external locus of control (Cavaiola & Wuth, 2002). It is useful for the counsellor to think of these characteristics as providing a causal explanation for the DWI behaviour (e.g., sensation seekers prefer novel or varied stimulation, and therefore drink in one location and travel elsewhere for another drink; Wieczorek et al., 1991). Research also shows that depression, antisocial tendencies and attention-deficit/hyperactivity disorder are more common in DWI offenders (Macdonald & Mann, 1996).

Levels of drinking problems observed in DWI offenders are, on average, higher than those observed in the general population but lower than those observed among clients in treatment for alcohol problems (Vingilis, 1983). For example, data from the Back on Track Remedial Measures Program indicate relatively low levels of specific alcohol-related problems in clients of this program: fewer than 10 per cent of participants report having experienced a blackout, fewer than seven per cent report having passed out due to alcohol use in the past 12 months and fewer than five per cent report regularly experiencing hangovers on Sunday or Monday mornings. Although no clients reported that they had tried to cut down their drinking but failed, this may be a reflection of the resistance that most clients exhibit in the early stages of the program, as it is also clear that there are substantial levels of alcohol problems in this population. A follow-up study of convicted second offenders in Ontario found a significantly elevated mortality rate in this group, with specific causes of this elevation the same as those responsible for elevated mortality rates in people with severe alcohol problems (i.e., cirrhosis of the liver, alcohol dependence syndrome, accidents and violence, including motor vehicle collisions; Mann et al., 1993).

Indicators of other drug use appear to be relatively low among Back on Track clients. A total of 11 per cent report using drugs other than those prescribed by a physician, 0.5 per cent report having abused prescription drugs, and 0.8 per cent report having sought help for their drug use.

TREATMENT PROGRAMS

Research has shown that a combination of a remedial program or alcohol treatment with either driver's licence restriction or suspension is the most effective method for reducing recidivism and collisions for all levels of offenders (Wells-Parker et al., 1995; Mann et al., 1988; DeYoung, 1997). Multiple intervention types (i.e., education or treatment plus follow-up) were most effective for multiple and first offenders (Wells-Parker et al., 1995). In addition, based on the widely accepted value of early intervention for problematic substance use and other problems (Bien et al., 1993), and of swift linking of consequences to behaviours (Vingilis, 1990), most counsellors recommend that interventions occur as soon as possible after conviction (Beirness et al., 1997).

Remedial programs consist of a mandatory screening or assessment followed by an education intervention for those identified as lower risk and a treatment intervention for those identified as being in the early stages of a substance use problem or at higher risk of re-offending. These programs draw on techniques used in alcohol treatment, but have a drinking and driving focus. For those offenders assessed as having a serious substance use problem, a third level of intervention exists which usually involves a referral to a substance use treatment program. Your agency may see clients who fall into this third category.

ASSESSMENT

The assessment process is used to identify which type of intervention listed above is best suited to the client's needs. Because research has shown that DWI offenders have a tendency to deny or under-report their drinking and other drug use behaviours (Lapham et al., 2001), assessment instruments that incorporate indirect indicators of substance use and related problems have been developed for this population. The most reliable of these instruments are the Mortimer-Filkins (M-F) test and the Research Institute on Addictions Self Inventory (RIASI) (Nochajski et al., 1994). Another widely used instrument in Canadian remedial programs is the Substance Abuse Subtle Screening Inventory (SASSI) (Miller, 1994). In addition to the screening instruments, the BAC level at the time of the arrest and the impaired driving offence history can also be considered when deciding what type of program is most appropriate for the client.

Even most first offenders report having driven under the influence many times prior to their arrest. As screening instruments tap into indirect indicators of substance use and risk of involvement with the legal system, counsellors may be surprised when some DWI clients, who in most other clinical settings would be assessed as low risk, are referred to the high-risk program based on these instruments. Where the recommendation is based on a well-validated assessment instrument (e.g., RIASI, M-F), the research evidence supports the recommendation of a more intensive program for these clients. Examples of two levels of remedial programming in Manitoba and Ontario are given below.

EDUCATION (LOW RISK)

In Manitoba and Ontario, people assessed as low risk (e.g., some first offenders or others who are at low risk of re-offending) are assigned to an educational program, which is a one-day workshop designed to help clients learn how to separate drinking

from driving. Topics covered include:
• how alcohol and other drugs affect driving performance and safety
• the legal and personal consequences of an impaired driving conviction
• how to avoid drinking and driving in the future.

The workshops are interactive and group work is encouraged.

TREATMENT (HIGH-RISK)

In Manitoba and Ontario, people assessed as being at higher risk of re-offending are assigned to a high-risk or treatment program. The high-risk program in Manitoba is nine hours long, and 16 hours long in Ontario. The topics covered are the same as those covered in the educational program. However, there is a greater emphasis on therapeutic interventions such as coping skills, reducing or preventing problem use of alcohol and other drugs and avoiding relapse. Group sizes are smaller than in the education program.

Remedial measures programs for convicted drinking drivers can address a variety of topics and employ many strategies to assist behaviour change. Wells-Parker et al. (1995) found that programs that combined educational and therapeutic activities, along with continued monitoring, were most successful in reducing recidivism and collisions. Based on available evidence, Mann et al. (1997) identified the following as components to be considered for remedial programs:
• alcohol and traffic safety education
• motivational enhancement to cut down problem drinking
• raising client's awareness regarding his or her drinking patterns
• identification of high-risk situations and planning
• rehearsal of alternative coping skills
• social support for reduced drinking or abstinence
• promotion of lifestyle changes
• information on further treatment options
• the opportunity to choose abstinence or moderate drinking as a program goal.

FOLLOW-UP

Although not all provinces have a follow-up requirement, follow-up has been recommended in the context of impaired driving programs (Mann et al., 1997), based on evidence that it improves the effectiveness of addiction treatment (Moos, 2003). Follow-up takes place anywhere between one month and one year following the intervention and can be conducted in person or by telephone. This provides the client with the opportunity to review the program goals or discuss any substance use problems he or she may have experienced since the last contact. In turn, the counsellor has the opportunity to address any concerns he or she may have had during the intervention and assess whether or not they put the client at risk to recidivate if his or her licence is reinstated.

Although research has not determined that a specific follow-up duration is associated with improved outcomes, evidence shows that monitoring over the span of six months to one year or longer is associated with the largest impact on recidivism rates

(Mann et al., 1988).

RELATIONSHIPS WITH STAKEHOLDERS

In most provinces and territories, remedial program completion is a requirement for licensing and falls under the jurisdiction of the vehicle licensing authority. The program itself is operated by an agency other than the licensing authority. This allows a separation between the administrative aspect of licence suspension and the therapeutic aspect of the remedial program.

Regardless of the programming model, communication between licensing authorities, program administrators and program providers is essential for the success of these programs. Clients seek information about their remedial requirements from various sources, and it is important that the message they receive is consistent. If there is any doubt as to what type of program the client should complete (e.g., if the client was convicted out-of-province), it is important that the client clarify the program requirement with the province or state that issued the conviction, and obtain this information in writing.

REPORTING REQUIREMENTS

Counsellors should also clarify with the client the reporting requirements of the administration and licensing authorities. In Ontario, there are three main levels of reporting requirements.

Reporting to Program Administrators

All remedial programs have participation requirements that are usually determined by the licensing authority. For example, some remedial programs require clients to abstain from alcohol and other drug use on days of contact with the program. Counsellors who observe clients who have not met a requirement should report such cases to the program administration, who will decide what action should be taken.

Reporting to the Licensing Authority

Some clients may successfully meet the program requirements and pass the course, but counsellors may still have some clinical concerns about their driving ability. Clients who exhibit any of the following symptoms during the program are referred for medical review:

• seizure
• disorientation
• balance or co-ordination problems
• tremors
• agitation or sedation
• gross memory impairment.

The licensing authority may require people with any of these symptoms to complete a medical assessment with an addiction specialist before reinstating their driver's licence.

Reporting to Law Enforcement

If a counsellor learns that his or her client is driving while intoxicated (i.e., he or she has driven to the appointment intoxicated and intends to drive when the session is over), the counsellor should take steps to prevent the client from driving. Depending on the level of co-operation from the client, the counsellor may need to involve local law enforcement officials.

In light of all the potential instances in which counsellors and administrators may share information about the client, it is important that this exchange of information be clearly explained to the client, and consent to release this information be obtained. If this has not been done at the administrative level when the client registers for the program, the counsellor must obtain the consent before admitting him or her. If consent is not obtained, the client should not be admitted to the program.

WORKING WITH DWI CLIENTS

As with all clients mandated to treatment, the DWI client is often initially resistant to the process and may manifest this resistance through anger at the remedial process or the counsellor (see stages of resistance, below). Research shows that a logical, supportive and empathic approach works best in helping clients deal with these issues (Lazarus & Fay, 1982). DWI clients tend to exhibit an external locus of control (Cavaiola & DeSordi, 1999), attributing the events that led them to their impaired conviction to chance or bad luck.

Cavaiola et al. (2002, p. 136) provide a useful description of the stages of resistance that clients referred to remedial programs or addiction treatment may experience. These are summarized as follows:

- **Stage 1—Anger:** The client is angry over referral to the remedial program. "I'm not an alcoholic! I don't need to be here."
- **Stage 2—Testing the Limits:** The client tests the agency or legal system and may even attempt to bargain with counsellors. "These stupid rules don't apply to me—no one will notice if I miss a few sessions."
- **Stage 3—Compliance:** The client is merely going through the motions. "I'll do anything you tell me—I just want to get this over with."
- **Stage 4—Anger (part 2):** The client is angry at being forced to examine drinking behaviour and being forced to take responsibility for the DWI offence as a drinking-related event.
- **Stage 5—Self-Depreciation:** The client feels angry at himself or herself and may experience some non-clinical depression related to the DWI offence. "I was stupid to drive after drinking so much."
- **Stage 6—Acceptance:** The client willingly accepts responsibility for the offence and in some cases, the need for counselling or attendance at a mutual aid group.

When trying to understand the client's anger, it is important to consider what has already happened to the client before this point in the system. He or she has already gone through the court process, paid fines and had his or her licence suspended; in some cases the client may not have been aware of the remedial requirement until several months into the suspension period. Based on client satisfaction ratings for the Back on Track Remedial Measures program, one of the most helpful things counsellors can do is clearly lay out the program plan and expectations during the first contact with the client. Counsellors should also address any hostility the client exhibits and set the tone for subsequent interactions. By maintaining neutrality and dealing with clients in a non-judgmental manner, counsellors can help clients overcome their resistance.

CONCLUSION

This chapter has examined general issues in the addiction treatment system concerning work with mandated clients. It has also considered issues specific to particular groups of "mandatory" clients who may participate in specially created programs and/or receive treatment in a generic substance use treatment service.

Many problems that addiction agencies have when dealing with mandatory clients are the result of unclear policy or lack of communication between the agency and the referral agent. Preparatory work must be done, and roles and expectations defined. Other problems may be more the result of the counsellor's attitude than the client's. There is a tendency to categorize and make assumptions about clients based on the referral source. The assumption that the manner in which a client comes to us dictates the level of motivation and success is fundamentally wrong. Each client presents at an addiction agency with his or her own agenda, expectations and needs. Counsellors also have expectations and needs when a client enters treatment, but must recognize that when these expectations are unrealistic or inaccurate, they may bias the management of the client and affect the outcome. Although one must be realistic, it is more productive to start from a positive stance.

In summary, effective management of mandatory clients entails three factors: shedding preconceptions about such clients; the development of a satisfactory relationship with the referral agent/agency; and a positive orientation of the client. It is productive for workers in the addiction field to look at this situation as an opportunity and a challenge to provide services to groups of people who, in many cases, would not have taken the initiative to seek help.

REFERENCES

Anglin, M.D., Prendergast, M. & Farabee, D. (1998, March). *The effectiveness of coerced treatment for drug abusing offenders.* Paper presented at the 1998 meeting of the Office of National Drug Control Policy's Conference of Scholars and Policy Makers, Washington, DC. Available: www.ncjrs.org/ondcppubs/treat/consensus/anglin.pdf.

Beirness, D.J. & Desmond, K. (2000). *Alcohol Involvement in Recreational Vehicle Fatalities in*

Canada. Ottawa: Traffic Injury Research Foundation.

Beirness, D., Mayhew, D. & Simpson, H. (1997). *DWI Repeat Offenders. A Review and Synthesis of the Literature.* Ottawa: Health Canada.

Beirness, D.J., Simpson, H. & Desmond, K. (2002). *The Road Safety Monitor 2002: Drinking and Driving.* Ottawa: Traffic Injury Research Foundation.

Belenko, S. (1999). Research on drug courts: A critical review. *National Drug Court Institute Review, 1*(1), 1–42.

Belenko, S. (2001). *Research on Drug Courts: A Critical Review 2001 Update.* New York: The National Center on Addiction and Substance Abuse at Columbia University.

Bentley, Justice Paul. (1999). Canada's First Drug Treatment Court. 31C.R. [Criminal Reports], 5th, p. 257.

Bien, T.H., Miller, W.R. & Tonigan, J.S. (1993). Brief interventions for alcohol problems. A review. *Addictions, 88,* 315–336.

Cavaiola, A.A. & DeSordi, E. (1999). *Locus of control in a group of DWI offenders versus non-offenders.* Paper presented at the 74th annual meeting of the Eastern Psychological Association, Providence, RI.

Cavaiola, A.A. & Wuth, C. (2002). *Assessment and Treatment of the DWI Offender.* New York: Haworth Press.

Centre for Addiction and Mental Health. (2003). Monthly variation in self-reports of drinking and driving in Ontario. *CAMH Population Studies eBulletin, July/Aug 2003, No. 21.* Toronto: author. Available: www.camh.net/pdf/eb021_ddmonthly.pdf.

DeYoung, D.J. (1997). Evaluation of the effectiveness of alcohol treatment, driver licence actions and jail terms in reducing drunk driving recidivism in California. *Addiction, 92,* 989–997.

Harrison, L.D. & Scarpitti, F.R. (2002). Progress and issues in drug treatment courts. *Substance Use and Misuse, 37*(12,13), 1441–1467.

Hora, P.F., Schma, W.G. & Rosenthal, J.T. (1999). Therapeutic jurisprudence and the drug treatment court movement: Revolutionizing the criminal justice system's response to drug abuse and crime in America. *Notre Dame Law Review, 74*(2), 439–537.

Lapham, S., C'de Baca, J., Chang, I., Hunt, W. & Berger, L. (2001). Are drunk-driving offenders referred for screening accurately reporting their drug use? *Drug and Alcohol Dependence, 66,* 243–253.

Lazarus, A.A. & Fay, A. (1982). Resistance or rationalization? A cognitive-behavioural perspective. In P.L. Wachtel (Ed.), *Resistance: Psychodynamic and Behavioural Approaches* (pp. 115–132). New York: Plenum.

Lifesaving Society. (2000). *Boating Fatalities in Canada.* Available: www.lifesaving.ca/ls2/

Publications/Boating_Fatalities_Rpt_EN.PDF.

Macdonald, S. & Mann, R.E. (1996). Distinguishing causes and correlates of drinking and driving. *Contemporary Drug Problems, 23*, 259–290.

Mann, R.E., Anglin, L., Wilkins, K., Vingilis, E.R. & Macdonald, S. (1993). Mortality in a sample of convicted drinking drivers. *Addiction, 88*, 643–647.

Mann, R.E., Koski-Jannes, A., Room, R., Mitchell, B., Harrison, S., Stoduto, G. et al. (1997). *Remedial Programs for Convicted Drinking-Drivers. Part 2: Implementing a Systematic Program in Ontario*. Toronto: Addiction Research Foundation.

Mann, R.E., Vingilis, E.R. & Stewart, K. (1988). Programmes to change individual behaviour: Education and rehabilitation in the prevention of drinking and driving. In M.D. Laurence, J.R. Snortum & F.E. Zimring (Eds.), *The Social Control of Drinking and Driving* (pp. 248–269). Chicago: University of Chicago Press.

Mayhew, R., Brown, S.W. & Simpson, H.M. (2002). *The Alcohol Crash Problem in Canada, 1999*. Ottawa: Transport Canada.

Miller, G.A. (1994). *The Substance Abuse Subtle Screening Inventory Manual (SASSI)*. Bloomington, IN: The SASSI Institute.

Moos, R.H. (2003). Addictive disorders in context: Principles and puzzles of effective treatment and recovery. *Psychology of Addictive Behaviours, 17*, 3–12.

National Association of Drug Court Professionals. (2003). *Drug Courts Today*. Available: www.nadcp.org.

Nochajski, T.H., Miller, B.A. & Parks, K.A. (1994). *Effectiveness of the RIASI for Screening Convicted DWI Offenders*. Buffalo, NY: Research Institute on Addictions.

Prochaska, J. & DiClemente, C. (1984). *The Transtheoretical Approach: Crossing the Traditional Boundaries of Therapy*. Homewood, IL: Down Jones/Irwin.

Single, E., Robson, L., Rehm, J. & Xie, X. (1999). Morbidity and mortality attributable to alcohol, tobacco, and illicit drug use in Canada. *American Journal of Public Health, 89*, 385–390.

Turner, S., Longshore, D., Wenzel, S., Deschenes, E., Greenwood, P., Fain, T. et al. (2002). A decade of drug treatment court research. *Substance Use and Misuse, 37*(12, 13), 1489–1527.

Vingilis, E.R. (1983). Drinking drivers and alcoholics: Are they from the same population? In R.G. Smart, F.B. Glaser, Y. Israel, H. Kalant, R.E. Popham & W. Schmidt (Eds.), *Research Advances in Alcohol and Drug Problems*, Vol. VII (pp. 299–342). New York: Plenum Press.

Vingilis, E.R. (1990). A new look at deterrence. In R.J. Wilson & R.E. Mann (Eds.), *Drinking and Driving Advances in Research and Prevention* (pp. 99–115). New York: Guilford Press.

Wells-Parker, E., Bangert-Drowns, R., McMillen, R. & Williams, M. (1995). Final results form a meta-analysis of remedial interventions with drink/drive offenders. *Addiction, 9,* 907–926.

Wieczorek, W.F., Miller, B.A. & Nochajski, T.H. (1991). *The relationship of sensation seeking, hostility and childhood hyperactivity to multiple location drinking among DWI offenders.* Paper presented at the Research Society on Alcoholism Annual Meeting, Marco Island, FL.

Chapter 29

Helping People Who Use Heroin and Cocaine

DAVID MARSH, MICHAEL NAYMARK, WAYNE SKINNER AND JULIA DRAKE

INTRODUCTION

Although heroin and cocaine use is often portrayed as glamorous in modern music and cinema, people with problems related to these drugs are arguably the most stigmatized of all people with substance use problems. While heroin and cocaine have very different pharmacological effects (heroin depresses nervous activity via opioid receptors, while cocaine stimulates the central nervous system through enhanced dopamine effects), the societal response to the two drugs is similar. It is illegal to produce, sell or possess heroin and cocaine, except in very limited medical situations, throughout most of the world. Heroin and cocaine are perceived as being more dangerous and addictive than most other drugs, and elicit strong responses from politicians, law enforcement officers and the judicial system, to the point that constitutionally protected rights, such as freedom from being searched without just cause, are considered differently in the context of possession of these substances. When helping people who have heroin and cocaine use problems, counsellors need to consider the environmental and societal impact of these drugs, as well as the impact of the drugs themselves.

Heroin and cocaine use and dependence affect only a small minority of the population. The most recent Canada-wide study, done in 1994, found that 3.8 per cent of adults aged 15 or older reported ever using cocaine, and a smaller percentage reported ever using heroin (Single et al., 1999). In 2000, an Ontario survey found 8.3 per cent of men and 4.8 per cent of women reported use of cocaine in their lifetime, but of all adults surveyed, only 1.2 per cent reported use in the last 12 months, showing a

651

decline in use from two per cent in 1984 (Adlaf & Ialomiteanu, 2001). Participants in this survey also reported their income. Those with an annual income of over $80,000 reported the highest levels of lifetime use, or 9.4 per cent of that group. Surveys of Ontario high-school students show that past-year cocaine use declined during the 1980s but increased from 1.5 per cent in 1993 to 4.8 per cent in 2003, with the largest increases occurring in Northern and Western Ontario (Adlaf & Paglia, 2003). Adult surveys in Canada have never occurred with sufficient regularity or sample size to track changes in heroin use. The *Ontario Student Drug Use Survey* found a steady level of past-year heroin use, with never more than 2.5 per cent of those surveyed from 1977 to 2003 reporting use (Adlaf & Paglia, 2003). The studies show that only a minority of those who report use of heroin or cocaine in their lifetime report use in the past year; most people who try these drugs do not develop repeated daily use with dependence.

To help any client with a drug problem, counsellors need to understand how a drug works and what motivates a person to use it. The assessment and treatment process should examine the quantity and frequency of drug use and the method of administering the drug. Counsellors must also investigate and understand clients' patterns of drug use and how drugs have affected life-functioning areas, including relationships with peers and family and employment. In addition, counsellors need to appreciate the physical and psychological processes that clients are likely to encounter as they withdraw from a substance on which they are dependent.

Although the number of people who use heroin or cocaine is fairly low, the problems related to use are significant. A notable similarity between heroin and cocaine is that their impact—on people who use them and on society—is enormous. These drugs can lead to serious problems including non-fatal and fatal overdose, severe disruption of social function, elevated criminal involvement, unstable housing and poor physical and psychological health (Fischer et al., 1999). Because the production and distribution of these drugs is illegal, the content or purity is never known to the people who use them, and therefore overdose death is a significant risk. In a 33-year follow-up study of people who use heroin, 284 of 581 participants died, with overdose being the leading cause of death, followed by deaths caused by violence (i.e., homicide, suicide or accident; Hser et al., 2001).

Because heroin and cocaine can both be injected, people who use these drugs also face the risks associated with injection drug use. These can include local injuries and infections in the skin, and more serious and life-threatening conditions, such as infections of the heart valves (Kahan & Marsh, 1998). In addition, people who use these drugs risk becoming infected with blood-borne diseases such as viral hepatitis and human immunodeficiency virus (HIV), which can be spread by sharing injection equipment. In Canada, the proportion of HIV infections attributed to injection drug use increased substantially until about 1997, but is now in decline (Health Canada, 2003). Heroin and cocaine use can also lead to unprotected high-risk sexual activity, which can also spread HIV (Marsh, 2000). Also at increased risk of being infected with HIV and of developing AIDS are the sexual partners of and the infants born to people who inject drugs. In this age of HIV and other blood-borne diseases, it is clear that some consequences of drug use can be more hazardous than drug use itself. While it is important to work to prevent and treat substance use problems, we must recognize that despite our efforts, drug use will continue, and that it is also important to reduce the harmful consequences of drug use.

This chapter examines problems related to the use of cocaine and opioids, particularly heroin. It also describes some of the factors that counsellors should consider when working with clients who are dependent on these powerful drugs.

HEROIN

What Is Heroin?

The term "opiates" refers to drugs that are made from the opium poppy; the term "opioids" includes the opiates, and also synthetic drugs with similar effects. Opioids include prescribed or over-the-counter painkillers, such as morphine and codeine, and illegal drugs, of which heroin is the most infamous. Opioids can be administered by snorting, swallowing, injecting or by inserting the drug in the rectum.

Heroin is usually a white or brownish powder, which is dissolved in water and then injected. Injection is popular with people who use opioids for their psychoactive effects because this method results in the fastest and most intense "high."

History

Opiates have been used both medically and non-medically for centuries. In the mid- to late-19th century, when morphine was freely available and unregulated, approximately four per cent of the adult population of the United States used it regularly. As societal attitudes toward alcohol and other drug use changed around the turn of the century, national and international restrictions were introduced in an effort to control or decrease opiate use.

Heroin was introduced in 1898 as a powerful cough suppressant for tuberculosis sufferers and as a more potent analgesic than morphine, but it was soon apparent that heroin use could lead to dependence. Opioids such as Dilaudid® (hydromorphone) and Demerol® (meperidine) were first developed as analgesics to replace natural opiates and, it was hoped, to prevent drug dependence. But both the natural opiates and opioid synthetics are now known to produce dependence.

Effects of Opioids

Many opioids are used clinically in North America. For example, morphine is used to relieve pain in post-operative care and in the terminally ill, and codeine is found in many cough suppressants. Canada is unusual among western nations in permitting the availability of codeine preparations without a prescription.

Heroin's short-term effects include a "rush" of euphoria and tranquility often accompanied, in the first-time user, by nausea and vomiting. Heroin's pleasurable high can make people who use it oblivious to their surroundings.

People who use heroin regularly develop tolerance to its effects, so that the more they use, the more of the drug they require to achieve the same effect. People who use the drug also develop physical dependence (expressed as withdrawal), psychological dependence and (despite the harm the drug does to them) compulsive use. For those who use opioids regularly, withdrawal may occur as early as a few hours after the last administration. Withdrawal often includes diarrhea, abdominal cramps, restlessness, uneasiness, sweating, muscle aches, runny nose and eyes, chills, nausea and strong cravings for the drug. Physical withdrawal peaks at two to three days after the last drug use, and resolves within five to seven days. For clients entering abstinence-oriented treatments for opioid dependence, the first step is identification and treatment of withdrawal. See Chapter 10 for more information on the physical effects of opioid use.

Treatment of Opioid Dependence

In the early 1990s in Ontario (particularly in Toronto), evidence from increasing heroin overdose deaths, waiting lists for treatment and other sources suggested a dramatically increased need for treatment of opioid dependence (Brands et al., 2000). Through collaboration of several stakeholders, there has been a rapid expansion in methadone maintenance treatment across Ontario since 1996, leading to many benefits for those previously unable to access treatment easily (Brands et al., 2000; Brands et al., 2002). As treatment availability has expanded in the community, the proportion of outpatients seen at the Centre for Addiction and Mental Health (CAMH) identifying opioids (including heroin) as their primary problem substance has fallen from 14 per cent in 1999 to five per cent in 2002 (CAMH, 2000; 2002).

CLIENT ASSESSMENT

While methadone maintenance is the treatment for opioid dependence with the broadest evidence base, it is important to start the treatment of those with opioid use problems with a comprehensive assessment and evaluation of all the available treatment options (Health Canada, 2002a). A comprehensive assessment of a client using opioids should include:

• a review of the frequency and route of drug use
• the choice and combinations of opioids and other drugs that are used
• the readiness and motivation for behaviour change
• the nature of co-occurring mental health problems
• the social and physical complications of drug use.

Treatment options to be considered in collaboration with the client include any appropriate combination of mutual aid groups, abstinence-based residential and outpatient counselling, methadone maintenance treatment and harm reduction approaches.

ISSUES IN TREATMENT
Mental Health

People with opioid dependence have very high rates of co-occurring mental health problems (Mirin et al., 1988; Rounsaville et al., 1983). Depression is a common complaint, along with other mood disorders. These clients often report eating disorders, anxiety, panic and anger management concerns. Females who use opioids are likely to have experienced physically abusive relationships in childhood or adulthood, so counsellors must be sensitive to this issue in treatment. An effective care plan identifies and includes these other dimensions while beginning the process of building a strong therapeutic alliance.

Counsellor's Attitude and Expectations

Because of the lifestyle that often accompanies illicit drug use, clients using heroin may be caught up in an environment where dishonesty and manipulation are the norm. But, as with counselling any substance use problem, therapists working with clients who use heroin should avoid negative expectancies (i.e., the attitude that "junkies can't change"). These client groups have likely already encountered negative attitudes from family, friends, the police and other health care professionals. It's important that substance use counsellors encourage and support these clients, for whom self-esteem issues may be crucial.

In treatment, counsellors should strive to establish a therapeutic relationship of trust, honesty, openness and respect, but one with clear, consistent boundaries. Jerome Frank (1976) states that, in all forms of psychotherapy, counsellors should:
• strive to inspire the client's hope
• provide opportunities for both cognitive and experiential learning
• enhance the client's sense of mastery by providing or stimulating success experiences
• encourage the client to work through and apply what he or she has learned in therapy to day-to-day living.

When treating clients for heroin use, counsellors must have realistic expectations. Change is a process which usually occurs gradually over an extended period of time. (For a more extensive discussion of the stages of treatment in methadone maintenance and counselling approaches for this client group, please see *Methadone Maintenance: A Counsellor's Guide to Treatment* [CAMH, 2003]).

Harm Reduction

Abstinence from opioids may be the most appropriate long-term goal for people who use these drugs. But because many people reject treatment that requires abstinence, harm reduction (reducing drug-related harm for clients, their families, their employers and for society) is a helpful alternative. "Harm reduction" is defined as the attempt to reduce serious risks to clients' health through strategies such as health education, immunization and screening, which may support, but do not require, abstinence. Because of the threat of HIV infection, harm reduction strategies are an essential component of any alcohol and other drug treatment program. These strategies complement prevention and treatment efforts, and emerge from the expectation that we can't prevent or treat all problems. See Chapter 11 for more information about harm reduction.

WORKING WITH CLIENTS

When a counsellor first meets with a person with an opioid use problem, an intensive response is required to address acute care needs. For example, the client might need help with withdrawal management, and may also lack social support, even for basic things such as housing and funds for subsistence. The counsellor must be attuned to and identify the needs of the client in care. These needs change as the client moves from the phases of initial withdrawal, to preliminary drug-free status, to active change, and to a stage of building new patterns of living that include alternatives to drug use. Beyond that, the client has the persistent challenge of maintaining change over the long run. This is often the hardest part, even after the client has gone through the difficult process of relinquishing drug use.

Client Needs

In planning care, it is important to support the client in treatment options that are appropriate for his or her level of need. There is evidence that people who use opioids can do well in the full range of addiction services—from outpatient through day treatment, to short- and long-term residential care. Intensive interventions, such as residential programs, may be a counsellor's first choice for clients who are severely dependent, who are unhealthy, who have few "healthy" social supports and whose lifestyle leaves them no opportunity for a break from drug use. But the client's readiness to engage in a particular type or level of care is a crucial variable to know and work with.

TREATMENT APPROACHES

While the intensity of care that the client receives during the active treatment phase is important, counsellors need to ensure that ongoing, external care and support are available to the client. The extent of the care plan—ensuring the client has access to support over an extended span of time—is at least as important to the client's long-term success as whatever front-end plans are made. Several treatment approaches that can be offered alone or in combination are described below.

Mutual Aid Groups

The key to success in arranging social support is finding someone whom the client sees as a positive force in his or her life. Mutual aid groups such as Narcotics Anonymous (NA) or Methadone Anonymous (MA) can have a positive impact on some clients. Some people with opioid use problems have found help in Alcoholics Anonymous (AA) groups, particularly if no specialized NA or MA group exists in their community. Clients gain long-term benefits by attending open groups, and by obtaining a sponsor and working through the personal change process outlined by the 12 steps. However, because mutual aid groups tend to be abstinence-oriented, clients unwilling to accept abstinence as an immediate requirement might be reluctant to try this treatment approach. See Chapter 9 for more information on mutual aid groups.

Motivational Interviewing

The needs of people with severe heroin dependence change from client to client and within the same client over time. Counsellors can assess each client's readiness for change by helping him or her evaluate the advantages and disadvantages of continuing drug use and of stopping. By matching interventions to the client's readiness to address a particular problem, counsellors help the client make important changes. See Chapter 2 for more information about the stages of change and motivational interviewing.

Cognitive and Behavioural Therapy

Cognitive therapy has much in common with motivational interviewing techniques. Both rely on an empathic, collaborative therapeutic relationship, in which the therapist and client work together to find solutions, but with cognitive therapy, the theoretical framework is elaborated. Cognitive therapy relies on structured sessions, homework assignments, self-monitoring, guided discovery, analysis of the advantages and disadvantages of drug use and other techniques to explore the client's cognitive system. The client and therapist examine and clarify the client's basic beliefs, automatic thoughts and facilitating beliefs that lead to drug use. This therapy helps the client to replace existing thoughts and beliefs with patterns that do not lead to drug use and, over time, to acquire the cognitive tools necessary to maintain a change in behaviour.

Behavioural therapy techniques can be extremely helpful in treating drug use problems. Therapy can include techniques such as contracting and goal setting. A widely used approach for clients in methadone programs for heroin addiction is contingency management, which relies on variations in methadone doses as positive and negative reinforcement for providing drug-free urine samples. In some programs, the methadone dose is decreased after a urine sample is found to contain drugs; in others, methadone therapy ceases if a certain number of positive urine samples are detected. However, there is a lack of evidence to support that decreasing dosage is effective in promoting decreased drug use. The Ontario Methadone Maintenance Guidelines (CPSO, 2001) state that dose reduction is not used as a negative reinforcement for drug use. Instead, "carry privileges" (allowing clients to take home some doses of methadone) are designed to motivate clients.

Psychodynamic Therapy

While psychodynamic therapy has been used to help clients who use heroin, some clients, particularly in the early stages of treatment for opioid dependence, may lack the ego strength to benefit from this form of therapy, in which a relatively silent therapist encourages the client to engage in free association. On the other hand, time-limited, structured psychodynamic psychotherapies have been well studied and found to be effective for drug clients with more severe mental health problems (Woody et al., 1995). In this form of psychodynamic therapy, the time limit, the focus on a single theme in relationships, the direction of the content toward present-day experiences rather than past traumas, and the more active role of the therapist all serve to limit the degree of client regression. This may explain why structured, time-limited psycho-dynamic approaches have been shown to be beneficial rather than to destabilize patients, as can happen when too much therapeutic focus is placed on past traumas before the client has the ability to tolerate these difficult emotions without relapsing to drug use.

Group and Individual Therapy

The above-noted therapeutic approaches can be applied in either group or individual treatment settings. Group therapy has its benefits, including a cost saving for treatment programs, but there are some cautions to consider. It may be difficult for some clients to be open and honest in groups when their former experiences with others who use drugs, with dealers or with the legal system, have taught them to be secretive. There is a high rate of more serious mental health problems among those who inject drugs. Although certain people, because of their psychiatric condition, may be unable to participate in group therapy, group sessions can be of great value to many clients. In each case, clinicians must be sensitive to the client's needs.

Family Therapy

Heroin and other opioid use is especially known to isolate the people who use these drugs. Counsellors should work with these clients to identify and promote social support among family members and friends who are concerned and willing to play a supportive role. Some research looking at the treatment of people with opioid use problems shows that the involvement of even one family member or peer can improve treatment outcome (Wermuth & Scheidt, 1986; Weidman, 1985), and that family therapy is valuable. For people with a history of illicit drug use who are raising children, family therapy may help prevent the development of drug problems in another generation. In the case of clients in methadone programs, family members are often misinformed or ignorant about opioid dependence and methadone maintenance. Family therapy can help them be more supportive and understanding of the needs of their drug-involved partner or relative. See Chapter 21 for more information on addiction and the family.

Methadone Maintenance Treatment

Methadone is a synthetic drug that was developed in the 1940s as a substitute for morphine. Since the 1960s, methadone has been used to treat withdrawal symptoms, and as a maintenance medication for people who are dependent on heroin or other opioids. Methadone has become the lead treatment response for opioid dependence.

Clients in methadone maintenance treatment (MMT) usually drink a methadone solution daily in the presence of a nurse or pharmacist. A single dose for a stabilized client lasts at least 24 hours. When taken daily at an appropriate dose, methadone relieves cravings and withdrawal symptoms but does not cause sedation or euphoria. As a result, methadone enables clients to perform mental and physical tasks without impairment—in other words, to lead "normal" lives. In addition, sufficient doses of methadone can block the euphoric effects of self-administered opioids, which reduces the likelihood that people will continue to use substances that can cause problems for them.

Counselling is an important part of methadone programs. McLellan et al. (1993), for example, found that counselling helps increase the effectiveness of methadone maintenance. Methadone patients can benefit from any of the counselling approaches described in this chapter when matched with client readiness and need.

Researchers have found that adequate doses of methadone, combined with supportive therapy, reduce illicit opioid use (Brands et al., 2002). Methadone treatment has also been found to reduce criminal activity and HIV transmission, and to improve social health, productivity and physical health (Health Canada, 2002a). It also lowers the risks in pregnancy for pregnant women who are addicted to opioids (Brands, 1998).

In addition to its benefits for the people who use drugs and the people close to them, methadone maintenance has economic benefits for society. For example, America's National Institute on Drug Abuse (NIDA, 1995) estimated the following annual costs, in U.S. dollars, to maintain an opioid addict in New York in 1991:

• $43,000 for someone untreated and living on the street
• $34,000 for someone in prison
• $11,000 for someone in a residential drug-free program
• $2,400 for someone in methadone maintenance treatment.

Several American studies have estimated the benefit-to-cost ratio for methadone programs as high as about four to one (NIDA, 1995).

In Canada, the authority to prescribe methadone is issued by the Bureau of Drug Surveillance of Health Canada in consultation with the provincial bodies that license and regulate physicians. Recently, the federal government devolved responsibilities for regulating methadone treatment to provincial ministries of health and to colleges of physicians and surgeons. These groups are now responsible for issuing guidelines regarding limits on dosage and take-home medicine, counselling requirements and special rules for pregnant women (Health Canada, 2002b).

COCAINE

As noted earlier, only a small percentage of the population currently uses cocaine, and not all of those people are drug-dependent; estimates of dependence among current cocaine users (i.e., reporting use within the last 12 months) range from 16 to 24 per cent (Platt, 1997; Substance Abuse and Mental Health Services Administration, 2001). However, those who do become dependent on cocaine can expect a wide range of criminal justice, medical, social and psychological problems, some associated with substance use issues that are unique to cocaine. It is believed, for example, that people who inject cocaine are at a higher risk for the transmission of blood-borne diseases such as HIV and hepatitis C because of their need to inject frequently, increasing the risk of using contaminated needles (Health Canada, 2000). In 2000, over one-third of clients in treatment in Toronto indicated a problem with cocaine, making it the illicit drug most likely to prompt those who use it to seek treatment (Research Group on Drug Use, 2001).

Dependence and Recovery Issues

PHYSICAL AND PSYCHOLOGICAL EFFECTS

Cocaine is a naturally occurring stimulant that can be extracted from the leaves of the coca plant, native to South America. It has potent euphoric and stimulant effects, and it is these effects that appeal to those who use it recreationally. Neurologically, it is the drug's action on the mesolimbic area, in the so-called "reward pathways" of the brain, which is believed to account for the reinforcing effects of cocaine and the persistence and intensity of cocaine use (Platt, 1997). One famous study found that laboratory monkeys given the option of self-administering cocaine did so to the exclusion of eating and drinking, until the cocaine use was stopped by exhaustion, convulsions or death (Bergman & Katz, 1998). Cocaine appears to block the reuptake of dopamine by presynaptic neurons, which results in an increased concentration of dopamine at the post-synaptic receptors, effectively resulting in increased activity in the brain's pleasure centre.

The positive short-term psychological and behavioural effects of this neuropharmacological activity can include the following:
• euphoria
• alertness
• heightened sense of power and confidence
• increased energy
• increased sociability
• enhanced self-esteem
• increased libido.

As with other substances, the short-term effects can differ among those who use cocaine. For example, some people may become quiet and reclusive or have reduced interest in sex. Less pleasurable effects associated with short-term use include insomnia and agitation. Physiologically, the high is accompanied by decreased appetite and increased heart rate, blood pressure and respiration, which can create medical problems in people with latent or overt problems in areas affected by cocaine use.

Over the long term, the pleasurable psychological effects of cocaine are counterbalanced by agitation, restlessness, insomnia, anxiety and, not infrequently, paranoia and auditory hallucinations during use (which subside quickly after a brief drug-free period). Short-term memory problems are typical. People who use cocaine chronically are at risk for a range of medical complications, including headaches, chronic insomnia, severe weight loss, cardiovascular problems (arrhythmias and heart attacks) and neurological problems (convulsions and strokes). In addition, there are medical risks associated with the specific route of drug administration employed (e.g., respiratory problems in those who smoke crack cocaine). With heavy use, people develop tolerance to the pleasurable psychological effects of the drug; at the same time, sensitization to the convulsion-inducing potential of the drug develops, so that the risk of seizures increases with chronic use.

Along with the direct effects of the drug on those who use chronically, there is a wide range of indirect effects of chronic use that are extremely negative. They include the following:
• homelessness and poverty
• stigmatization and social ostracism
• involvement in the drug trade and related physical violence, as either a victim or a perpetrator
• physical or medical problems (often compounded by homelessness and a street lifestyle)
• mental health issues (e.g., depression and paranoia) that are drug-related or compounded by drug use
• social isolation
• polydrug use.

ROUTE OF ADMINISTRATION
The intensity of cocaine's effects is influenced by the route of drug administration that is used; the more quickly the drug reaches the brain, the more intense the euphoria and the shorter-lived the effects (NIDA, 2003). Cocaine is generally administered in one of three ways: by intranasal inhalation ("snorting") of the powdered form of the drug (cocaine hydrochloride), by smoking "crack" (cocaine in smokable form, produced by processing cocaine powder with baking soda and heating it), or by injection of either powder cocaine or pulverized crack cocaine. Cocaine reaches the brain quickly: in several minutes by the intranasal route; in about 10 to 30 seconds by injection; and in three to eight seconds by smoking. Both smoking and injection of the drug produce an initial brief "rush"—an intense feeling of euphoria and well-being—followed by a relatively milder, but still intense, euphoria. There is little or no rush from snorting the drug, but there are heightened feelings of energy and well-being.

The high from a small amount of cocaine (about 40 to 100 mg) lasts about 20 minutes when snorted, and about 10 minutes when the drug is smoked or injected, and is followed by an intense "crash," characterized by depressed mood, irritability, restlessness and drug cravings. The need to relieve these negative feelings results in further drug use, and it is this swing from euphoria to crash that gives cocaine such a strong potential for dependence. The cycle can be repeated for a period of hours or days. Smoking or injection of cocaine seems to intensify both the rush and the crash.

While some people who are cocaine-dependent use the drug daily, a binge pattern of use is also common, in which the drug is used repeatedly for a period ranging from hours to several days, until the binge is stopped by exhaustion or lack of funds. A marked psychological dependence can arise, with people who use it experiencing strong cravings for cocaine, even when not actively using it.

DIFFERENCES BETWEEN COCAINE DEPENDENCE AND OTHER DRUG DEPENDENCE

People who use cocaine generally see themselves as a distinct group within the population of those who use alcohol and other drugs, with a good deal of justification. There are several aspects of cocaine use and dependence that differentiate it from other drugs. For those who use cocaine, there are differences in the drug use experience, lifestyle, the consequences of drug use and self-image. The reasons for these differences include the following:
• The effects of cocaine are very short-lived, requiring repeated administration, money to buy the drug and frequent excursions to obtain it.
• The cravings are more intense, frequent and persistent than with most other substances.
• Relapses can be frequent, especially early in recovery.
• Cocaine is expensive and criminal behaviour is often necessary to support chronic use.
• Cocaine is illegal.
• Cocaine's effect on the libido can result in more sexual acting out.
• The withdrawal process is relatively uncomplicated with few medical risks.
Treatment providers need to take these differences into consideration by providing cocaine-specific interventions and programming, either individually or in groups.

Crack

As noted earlier, crack is the smokable form of cocaine. Its effects are similar to those of powder cocaine, only the euphoria is more intense, as are the crash and the drug cravings. Part of the appeal of powder cocaine is the intensified social experience it engenders, while for many people who use crack, it is the intense high itself that is the goal of the drug use experience. In many treatment programs, the majority of clients using cocaine use crack, as opposed to powder or injected cocaine, although the use of these latter forms of cocaine is on the increase in some areas (RGDU, 2001). According to a recent survey of drug use in Toronto, crack has become "the most popular drug on the streets" in Toronto, and accounted for 26 per cent of all drug seizures in 2001, compared with six per cent for cocaine powder (RGDU, 2001).

Crack can be bought in smaller amounts than cocaine powder, making it cheaper to buy, which has been a major factor in its widespread use. It is also a factor in the lack of social "cachet" attached to crack use, as compared with powder cocaine use. Ironically, the lower expense is illusory for those who use it chronically, who may intend to limit themselves to small purchases on any given occasion, but ultimately find themselves spending much more than anticipated.

The general public has a negative image of people who use crack. They're seen as failures and criminals with a penchant for violence. Treatment providers who have not had experience dealing with cocaine clients may also have a negative image of people who use crack. Clients in treatment for crack problems may be seen as excitable, disruptive and manipulative; overall, they are seen as "difficult." Unfortunately, these perceptions mirror the very harsh views that people who use crack have of themselves. By the time they present for treatment, most clients dependent on crack see themselves as shameful losers. The stigma associated with crack use often contributes to delays in seeking help. Many people are reluctant to admit the precise nature of the drug problem they have, saying that they're alcoholics, for example, rather than revealing to family members that they're addicted to crack.

These disparaging images of people with crack use problems are simplistic and distorted. For example, while some people may be prone to violent behaviour due to the drug's effects, most crack-related violence occurs in relation to the buying and selling of the drug (Roth, 1994). In fact, there is a stronger relationship between violent crime and alcohol than there is between violent crime and illicit drugs (Pernanen et al., 2002; Roth, 1994). Furthermore, as is the case with other clients with substance use problems, violence is rarely, if ever, seen in a treatment setting among those with crack use problems. There is also the myth that people who use crack are inveterate criminals. While there is no doubt that some finance their drug use by resorting to property crimes, there are many who do not, perhaps because they are employed or because their level of use does not require huge amounts of money. For many people with crack use problems who engage in criminal behaviour, crime follows the onset of the addiction.

Treatment of Clients Who Use Cocaine

CLINICAL PRESENTATION AND MANAGEMENT

Notwithstanding the dangers of stereotyping, clinicians have observed some characteristic behavioural features when working with people who have cocaine use problems (whether they use powder cocaine or crack), especially in a group format. Working with cocaine groups can be an energy-intensive, demanding experience— not surprising with a client population that is attracted to the effects of a stimulant drug. Clients can be boisterous, intense, talkative, active, restless and impulsive. A typical group in the early stage of treatment can feel chaotic: some clients may be cross-talking or joking, others may be sharing food and yet other clients may be standing up and moving around out of sheer inability to stay seated. This group disorder can suddenly shift into focused, intense discussion. As the time since clients' last episode of cocaine use increases, the restlessness gradually subsides and is replaced by more modulated behaviour, more manageable cravings and increased comfort with treatment and treatment norms. Initially some clients present with an "attitude"—arrogance or bravado—and may be disdainful or critical of the treatment program or the staff. This is usually a defence against the shame they are experiencing around their cocaine use and around the need for outside assistance (Wallace, 1991).

In general, clients with cocaine use problems often question treatment advice, information or recommendations; while this may give the impression of resistance to treatment or defiance of authority, this generally is not how clients feel. Once they decide that what they're hearing really makes sense, they will likely accept treatment advice, rather than reject it in an oppositional fashion. Clients with cocaine use problems often seem hungry for information and education about the psychological and physiological aspects of dependence and recovery. They respond especially well to counsellors who demonstrate an understanding of the mechanisms of drug cravings, and have an ability to point out, in a non-judgmental way, when clients are "conning" (deceiving) others or themselves.

To manage disruptive conduct during treatment, a review of the program's communication and behavioural norms is generally all that is required. It helps if treatment staff:
• can tolerate some disorder
• can respond to clients with patience and humour
• are willing to avoid power struggles and to "pick their battles"
• can maintain behavioural boundaries in a clear but non-confrontational manner.

Medically speaking, management of acute withdrawal following cocaine use is relatively uncomplicated. The main symptoms of withdrawal are lengthy periods of sleep (if there has been prolonged use of cocaine), increased appetite, irritability, agitation, drug craving and depressed mood. Guilt, remorse and discouragement about cocaine use and the associated consequences may be particularly strong at this time. Some clients may express suicidal ideation; if this is the case, a suicide assessment needs to be conducted, however, most clients can make it through these feelings with support and encouragement. An improvement in mood and general health is usually experienced within three to four days of appropriate care and support. Several days in a detox unit may be useful if there has been a protracted binge, especially if the client has no social support or lives in an unstable environment.

People with cocaine use problems are often enthusiastic and motivated participants in treatment. There are a number of reasons for this. By the time they seek treatment, most are past the point of denying that they have a problem. They are well aware that they are dependent on cocaine, and have experienced extremely negative consequences. Further, many have reached the point of hating the drug, because they experience agitation and paranoia when they use it. For these reasons, they are often well past the point of believing that cocaine is not a problem in their lives, and are willing to put a great deal of effort into treatment.

DIMENSIONS OF TREATMENT

A wide variety of treatment approaches has been used to treat cocaine problems. The settings vary from outpatient clinics to day programs, 28-day inpatient programs and therapeutic communities. There is wide variation in the intensity and length of treatment programs as well, from several hours per week of brief treatment to full-time programming lasting six months or longer. The modalities used include cognitive-behavioural, psychodynamic, 12-step, therapeutic community and multidimensional approaches (as seen in many short-term residential substance dependence programs).

Most empirical studies focus on the relative effectiveness of various forms of treatment, the duration of positive effects and the interaction between specific treatment approaches and client characteristics. Interestingly, the literature is consistent in showing that treatment often has a significant positive impact on levels of cocaine use regardless of the modality used (e.g., Simpson et al., 1999; Crits-Christoph et al., 1999). However, there are a number of important findings related to specific dimensions of cocaine treatment.

- **Setting**: Outpatient treatment seems to be as effective as inpatient for most, but not all, people who use cocaine. There is some evidence that people with more severe psychosocial problems accompanying their substance use have better outcomes with residential treatment (Health Canada 2000; Simpson et al., 1999).
- **Intensity**: Cocaine treatment needs to be intensive to be successful. Studies have demonstrated that four or five days a week of treatment contact is more effective than one or two days a week, and that providing multiple treatment components (e.g., individual counselling, family therapy, biofeedback or acupuncture to deal with cravings) improves outcomes and retention in treatment (Health Canada, 2000).
- **Retention**: With few exceptions, studies indicate that the longer that people with cocaine use problems stay in treatment, the more likely they are to maintain reductions in their cocaine use (Simpson et al., 1999).
- **Modality**: As indicated above, many forms of treatment are effective. Since the early 1990s the effectiveness of cognitive behaviour therapy (CBT) and relapse prevention (RP) approaches, relative to other treatment approaches, has been shown in a number of studies (Health Canada, 2000). These approaches are very systematic and well documented (Carroll, 1998). However, there is strong evidence for the relative effectiveness of other modalities as well, such as 12-step-oriented individual and group counselling. One very large-scale study (Crits-Christoph et al., 1999) suggests that providing clear and simple treatment goals (e.g., abstinence as conveyed in a 12-step approach) may be of crucial importance. In addition, many treatment programs in Canada and the United States employ several modalities simultaneously (e.g., CBT/RP, group counselling, psychoeducational sessions and alternative treatments). More study is needed to explore the effectiveness of the various combinations of treatment components being used, and the ways in which combined modalities can enhance outcomes.

• **Severity**: Clients with higher levels of psychosocial problems (including unemployment, anxiety or depression, and criminal justice system involvement) and more severe cocaine dependence have better outcomes the longer they stay in treatment (Crits-Christoph et al., 1999).

UNIQUE TREATMENT ISSUES

While the general principles of substance use treatment are applicable to the treatment of cocaine issues (e.g., a counsellor taking an active role in sessions; a counsellor addressing substance use as an issue in its own right, not just as a symptom of other issues), there are a number of cocaine-specific treatment concepts and approaches that are useful. These include:
• a cocaine-specific assessment
• an ongoing focus on drug cravings
• a focus on relapse and relapse prevention
• teaching coping strategies
• a case management approach
• phased treatment
• intensive treatment and support (discussed above)
• addressing the use of other substances.

Assessment

During the assessment of cocaine problems, several issues have particular relevance for clients and their treatment. These include:
• the route of administration
• use of other drugs (sometimes minimized by clients)
• social needs
• child welfare issues
• legal/criminal justice concerns.

The last two issues may be particularly difficult for clients to disclose, due to both shame and concerns about confidentiality.

Cravings

A cocaine craving is an urge to use cocaine. People experience cravings at a cognitive level (i.e., a desire to use while thinking about cocaine's positive effects) or a physical level (e.g., an empty feeling in the stomach or stomach cramps). Persistent cravings are a defining feature of cocaine use and cocaine recovery, but they are often misunderstood. A person with a cocaine use problem who indicates that he or she is still experiencing cravings several months into his or her treatment is often accused of not doing enough work toward his or her recovery. The reverse is true—cravings can be expected to persist for months, albeit at decreasing levels of intensity, even in clients who are well-motivated and committed, and even among clients who are abstinent.

There are a number of reasons for this. One reason is that the psychological effects of cocaine are tremendously reinforcing and enhance a person's mood and self-esteem in a wide range of situations. In addition, powerful classical conditioning occurs with cocaine use, whereby internal and external stimuli that are frequently present when a person is using cocaine will be strongly associated with cocaine use. Even when cocaine is no longer present, these stimuli may evoke an urge to use. Some of these stimuli may be very complex and intense (e.g., sexual behaviour), making the conditioning effect hard to extinguish, or they may be very common and hard to avoid. The various stimuli that are present when an individual uses and the situations in which cocaine use is reinforcing are collectively called "triggers." Cravings later on in recovery may also be a response to the feelings raised by current or early life issues (e.g., issues of self-esteem, relationships, childhood or social needs) that emerge as people have more time away from cocaine.

Cravings, triggers and the skills needed to cope with them are a major focus of cocaine treatment. Clients readily cite cravings as the immediate precipitant of an episode of cocaine use. Initially cravings may arise suddenly and spontaneously, and clients may feel powerless and discouraged in relation to them. It is reassuring for clients to learn that cravings can be analysed, understood and managed.

Some of the guidelines for working with cravings include:
- Normalize the cravings—clients should be aware that cravings can continue well into recovery and are not a sign of failure.
- Teach skills for handling cravings and the situations that elicit them.
- Educate about the causes of cravings (e.g., the impact of conditioning effects).
- Identify the symptoms of cravings—the physical sensations, thoughts and feelings associated with the craving state.
- Reassure clients that they have the power to control whether and how intensely cravings occur (e.g., by avoiding trigger situations, increasing their repertoire of skills for coping with those situations or managing the actual cravings once they occur).
- Emphasize the need for a range of coping techniques, not just one or two.
- Identify triggers.
- Identify high-risk situations (i.e., situations in which the client is at high risk for using cocaine, such as social events, or when the client is experiencing negative emotions).

Identifying triggers and high-risk situations is an early task of cocaine treatment. Once clients are aware of these, counsellors can discuss with them the means of coping with these situations. Coping techniques may include anything from total avoidance to applying new responses when in the situation. While clients with cocaine use problems will have their own individual triggers, three common triggers that many clients experience are sex, money and the presence of cocaine.

While clients with cocaine use problems can do a lot to reduce the risk of being triggered, clients often end up experiencing cravings. In these instances, clients can use cognitive and behavioural techniques to help them to avoid acting on the cravings. In general, these techniques include:
- seeking support (e.g., calling a support person when experiencing the craving; talking about the craving)
- escaping (i.e., leaving a high-risk or triggering situation)

• opting for distraction (e.g., watching television; exercising)
• using positive self-talk (e.g., "This will pass")
• reviewing the benefits of not using cocaine
• anticipating likely negative consequences of drug use
• practising relaxation and other stress management techniques.

Relapse

The term "relapse" is ambiguous. It has been used to refer to anything from one episode of post-recovery use to a return to pre-treatment use patterns. In this section, "relapse" refers to any use of cocaine following treatment, although it is perhaps clearer to talk about a "use" or "uses." Discussed in this way, relapse does not mean a return to old use patterns or an indication that the person is back at square one.

While many people with cocaine use problems stop using cocaine during and after treatment, relapse is a common phenomenon, even the norm for those in cocaine recovery, because of the complex issues surrounding cocaine dependence. A relapse does not necessarily indicate a lack of commitment or treatment failure (although it is important to address each use that occurs in order to reduce the risk of returning to high levels of use). In fact, it can be useful to conceptualize episodes of use as part of recovery. While a relapse is not necessary for a client's successful recovery, a properly handled relapse is an opportunity for the client to learn more about his or her triggers and coping skills. It can also help bring to the surface a client's fear and ambivalence about stopping his or her use.

Analysis of relapses is a fundamental treatment activity. It involves:
• the investigation of the antecedents of the use
• the circumstances of the use itself
• the consequences of the use.

This kind of exploration makes it clear to clients that cocaine use is not a single event, but a process which culminates in the consumption of cocaine. The process can include circumstances, decisions and actions that may begin long before the actual use of the drug, or may involve motivational issues that create a vulnerability to drug triggers. Either way, the analysis needs to consider the personal factors (e.g., craving level, motivation, emotional state, personality) and environmental factors (e.g., availability of cocaine, sexual cues, environmental stressors, such as homelessness) that are involved in a relapse and how they interact, rather than focus on one type of factor only (Festinger et al., 2001).

To summarize, the principles for responding to a cocaine use in treatment are:
• normalize the use
• analyse the use
• understand each use as a process, not an event.

Coping Skills

Cocaine treatment programs have adopted many of the principles and techniques of relapse prevention and CBT, even when these are not the main treatment modalities. The notion of the client as a "learner," the analysis of cravings and of relapses and the combination of cognitive and behavioural coping techniques have become standard features of treatment. Initially, clients often feel totally out of control in their cocaine use and are desperate for some immediately usable techniques for dealing with it. Providing clients with simple and effective tools for reducing their use or dealing with cravings is very motivating and empowering.

Case Management

Resources permitting, a case management model is recommended in working with clients who have cocaine use problems. Many clients enter treatment with a variety of pressing problems that may affect their ability to focus on and benefit from cocaine treatment. These include criminal charges, the need for income assistance, homelessness or inappropriate housing (e.g., living with others who use or living with an abusive partner), child welfare issues and employment issues. It is difficult for clients to concentrate on their treatment and maintain their recovery unless these issues are under some degree of control. At the same time, with appropriate support, a client's work on these issues can be directly related to his or her work in treatment, and may provide additional motivation for recovery. A case management model provides the support, liaising, advocacy and structure that clients need in order to focus on moving forward with these issues.

Phased Treatment

Most substance dependence programs, whether brief or long-term, use a phases-of-treatment model. There is often an intensive treatment phase, followed by a lengthy after-care phase. The intensive treatment phase may be skill-focused or more holistic (i.e., it may include various combinations of group therapy, stress management training, nutrition education and recreational therapy). After-care programming may consist of support groups and/or individual counselling; where treatment resources are scarce, 12-step groups are often recommended. Platt (1997) cites a number of articles discussing the stages of recovery from cocaine dependence. Common to all of them is the notion that clients need a period of stabilization in which to adjust to the experience of working on their cocaine problem. This is why treatment programs have a stabilization or preparation phase prior to engaging clients in more intensive treatment. Clients with cocaine use problems can certainly benefit from such a structure; because of their substance use, it can be difficult for them to start with intensive treatment; they may also have issues around social needs and stability, and be reluctant to accept help. Tasks undertaken during this phase include:

• development of basic recovery skills (e.g., identifying and managing cravings)
• assessment of client's treatment needs, including mental health issues, with referrals to specific clinical and adjunctive services where appropriate
• development of a degree of stability in relation to social needs (housing, income assistance, medical support and legal involvement)
• learning, and adjusting to, the norms, expectations and procedures of the treatment program (e.g., attendance and working in a group format)

• identification of client goals
• motivational assessment and enhancement.

Use of Other Substances

People who are cocaine-dependent often use other substances, most commonly alcohol and/or cannabis. The use of these substances may have preceded the onset of cocaine use, or the substances may have been used primarily to either enhance the cocaine high or take the "edge" off the high or the crash. Some clients may have had a long-standing dependence on these other substances, but view their use as non-problematic because the associated problems pale in comparison to those created by cocaine use. Higgins & Wong (1998) cite studies indicating that up to 60 per cent of people dependent on cocaine are alcohol-dependent, and 30 per cent meet the criteria for marijuana dependence. The use of other substances by people in cocaine recovery is a concern from two perspectives: there is a possibility of developing a dependence on these substances, and a likelihood that even infrequent use could ultimately lead some people back to cocaine use. The experience of many clinicians is that episodes of cocaine use in recovery often start with use of alcohol or marijuana, and that most people with substantial abstinence from cocaine are abstinent from other substances.

Most people in treatment for cocaine dependence choose abstinence from cocaine as a treatment goal; however, they may be uncomfortable with the notion of abstinence from all psychoactive substances. Some clients may not be willing to work toward abstinence from other substances initially, but may decide over time to adopt abstinence, while others may continue to use other substances. Finally, some clients may not be able or willing to meet abstinence requirements, but with support may make important positive changes in their cocaine use and in other parts of their lives. From a harm reduction perspective, a requirement to commit to abstinence from all substances constitutes a barrier to treatment entry, thereby deterring people from obtaining the substantial benefits they could derive from a treatment experience. Ideally, clients should be offered a choice of either abstinence or harm reduction options, depending on their goals and individual circumstances.

Additional Treatment Issues

Other aspects of treatment that deserve attention include working with family members, gender issues and group versus individual approaches. Although they will be touched upon only briefly in this section, each of these topics could be the focus of a lengthier examination.
• **Family issues**: Some families only learn about a family member's problem cocaine use when he or she experiences a sudden crisis related to, for example, legal or financial problems, or a relationship problem. In these circumstances, families are essentially "in shock," and can benefit from realistic information and expectations about cocaine dependence and recovery, and from ongoing support.
• **Gender issues**: Women who are cocaine-dependent may have to deal with issues of prostitution, a history of trading sex for cocaine, domestic violence, child welfare

issues and sexual assault. They may experience shame and anxiety around these issues and therefore find it hard to participate in mixed-gender groups. Even all-female groups may be intimidating if the other women in the group have no understanding of or familiarity with the experiences of women with cocaine use problems. It is important for treatment providers to create opportunities for women to deal with the above issues, in a safe and supportive setting.

· **Group versus individual approaches**: Group counselling is the reality in most substance use programs, and there are distinct benefits to this approach that go beyond issues of cost savings. Groups can reduce the shame clients feel about their cocaine use and the behaviours and issues that accompany it by demonstrating that they're not alone. Clients learn from the recovery successes and failures of other group members, and can gain inspiration from those who are doing well. They can also learn to deal with the interpersonal issues that may be triggers to cocaine use. Individual approaches are also beneficial, as they allow for a more concentrated focus and for greater individualization of treatment.

CONCLUSION

Among illegal drugs, heroin and cocaine are the most powerful and addictive substances available, and clients who inject these drugs face some of the greatest risks of drug use. Because clients may expose others to the risk of HIV, hepatitis and other diseases, their drug use also has a major impact on society.

In the addiction field, we often refer to the "treatment continuum." When people are on the low end of the continuum, the goal is to prevent problems from developing. On the other end, the goal is to treat problems that have emerged. Since it might be hard to find a place for harm reduction in this model, it is useful to think about a new model—a circular model that has three key points on it: prevention, treatment and harm reduction. Working at any point of this circle helps the person in treatment, and also helps to keep others safer from drug-related harm.

In dealing with the high-risk behaviours associated with heroin or cocaine use, harm reduction complements treatment initiatives. Where people are willing to move to less risky behaviours or to stop the risky behaviour altogether, access to treatment is essential. But there will always be those who are not ready or able to stop, and because of this, it is necessary to minimize the harmful consequences for these people, their significant others and the community. As long as people have access to drugs as appealing and addictive as cocaine and heroin, a full range of responses is required to ensure optimal effect.

REFERENCES

Adlaf, E.M. & Ialomiteanu, A. (2001). CAMH Monitor eReport: Addiction and mental health indicators among Ontario adults, 1977–2000. *CAMH Research Doc. Series, 10.* Available: www.camh.net/research/population_life_course.html.

Adlaf, E.M. & Paglia A. (2003). *Drug Use among Ontario Students, 1977–2003: Findings from the OSDUS.* Toronto: Centre for Addiction and Mental Health.

Bergman, J. & Katz, J.L. (1998). Behavioral pharmacology of cocaine and the determinants of abuse liability. In S. Higgins & J. Katz (Eds.), *Cocaine Abuse: Behavior, Pharmacology, and Clinical Applications* (51–74). Chicago: Academic Press.

Brands, B. (Ed.). (1998). *Methadone Maintenance: A Physician's Guide to Treatment.* Toronto: Addiction Research Foundation.

Brands, B., Blake, J. & Marsh, D.C. (2002). Changing patient characteristics with increased methadone maintenance availability. *Drug and Alcohol Dependence, 66*(1), 11–20.

Brands, J., Brands, B. & Marsh, D.C. (2000). The expansion of methadone prescribing in Ontario, 1996–1998. *Addiction Research, 8*(5), 485–496.

Carroll, K.M. (1998). *A Cognitive-Behavioral Approach: Treating Cocaine Addiction.* Rockville, MD: National Institute on Drug Abuse.

Centre for Addiction and Mental Health. (2000). *Balanced Scorecard, 1999–2000.* Toronto: author.

Centre for Addiction and Mental Health. (2002). *Balanced Scorecard, 2001–2002.* Toronto: author.

Crits-Christoph, P., Siqueland, L., Blaine, J., Frank, A., Luborsky, L., Onken, L.S. et al. (1999). Psychosocial treatments for cocaine dependence. *Archives of General Psychiatry, 56*(June), 493–502.

Festinger, D.S., Rubenstein, D.F., Marlowe, D.B. & Platt, J.J. (2001). Relapse: Contributing factors, causative models, and empirical considerations. In F.M. Tims, C.G. Leukefeld & J.J. Platt (Eds.), *Relapse and Recovery in Addictions.* New Haven and London: Yale University Press.

Fischer, B., Medved, W., Gliksman, L. & Rehm, J. (1999). Illicit opiates in Toronto: A profile of current users. *Addiction Research, 7*(5), 377–415.

Health Canada. (2000). *Cocaine Use Recommendations in Treatment and Rehabilitation.* Ottawa: Minister of Public Works and Government Services, Cat. No. H49-155/2001E. Ottawa: author.

Health Canada. (2002a). *Methadone Maintenance Treatment: Literature Review.* Ottawa: author.

Health Canada. (2002b). *Methadone Maintenance Treatment: Best Practices.* Ottawa: author.

Health Canada. (2003). HIV/AIDS among injection drug users in Canada. *HIV/AIDS Epi Update* (April 2003). Available: www.hc-sc.gc.ca/pphb-dgspsp/publicat/epiu-aepi/hiv-vih/idus_e.html.

Higgins, S. & Wong, C. (1998). Treating cocaine abuse: What does research tell us? In S. Higgins & J. Katz (Eds.), *Cocaine Abuse: Behavior, Pharmacology, and Clinical Applications* (pp. 343–357). Chicago: Academic Press.

Hser, Y.I., Hoffman, V., Grella, C.E. & Anglin, M.D. (2001). A 33-year follow-up of narcotics addicts. *Archives of General Psychiatry, 58*, 503–508.

Kahan, M. & Marsh, D.C. (1998). Medical assessment of opioid-dependent patients. In B. Brands (Ed.), *Methadone Maintenance: A Physician's Guide to Treatment.* Toronto: Addiction Research Foundation.

Marsh, D.C. (2000). HIV and substance abuse. In B. Brands, P. Selby, M. Kahan & L. Wilson (Eds.), *Physician's Handbook for Medical Management of Alcohol- and Drug-Related Problems* (2nd ed.). Toronto: Centre for Addiction and Mental Health.

McLellan, A.T., Arndt, I.O., Metzger, D.S., Woody, G.E. & O'Brien, C.P. (1993). The effects of psychosocial services in substance abuse treatment. *Journal of the American Medical Association, 269*(15), 1953–1959.

Mirin, S.M., Weiss, R.D., Michael, J. & Griffin, M.L. (1988). Psychopathology in substance abusers: Diagnosis and treatment. *American Journal of Drug and Alcohol Abuse, 14*(2), 139–157.

National Institute on Drug Abuse. (1995). *Methadone Maintenance Treatment: Translating Research into Policy.* Manual prepared for the American Methadone Treatment Association Conferences, NIDA International Forum, 1995. Bethesda, MD: author.

National Institute on Drug Abuse. (2003). *Research Report Series—Cocaine Abuse and Addiction.* Available: www.drugabuse.gov/ResearchReports/Cocaine/cocaine3.html#effects.

Pernanen, K., Cousineau, M-M., Brochu, S. & Sun, F. (2002). *Proportions of Crimes Associated with Alcohol and Other Drugs in Canada.* Ottawa: Canadian Centre on Substance Abuse. Available: www.ccsa.ca/pdf/ccsa-009105-2002.pdf.

Platt, J.J. (1997) *Cocaine Addiction: Theory, Research, and Treatment.* Cambridge, MA and London, U.K.: Harvard University Press.

Research Group on Drug Use. (2001). *Drug Use in Toronto 2001.* Available: www.city.toronto.on.ca/drugcentre/rgdu01/pdf/rgdu_2001.pdf.

Roth, J.A. (February 1994). Psychoactive substances and violence. *Research in Brief, U.S. Dept. of Justice.* Available: www.druglibrary.org/schaffer/GOVPUBS/psycviol.htm.

Rounsaville, B.J., Glazer, W., Wilber, C.H., Weissman, M.M. & Kleber, H.D. (1983). Short-term interpersonal psychotherapy in methadone maintained opiate addicts. *Archives of General Psychiatry, 40*, 629–636.

Substance Abuse and Mental Health Services Administration (SAMHSA). (2001). *National Household Survey on Drug Abuse 2001*. Department of Health and Human Services. Available: www.oas.samhsa.gov/nhsda/2k1nhsda/vol1/toc.htm.

Simpson, D.D., Joe, G.W., Fletcher, B.W., Hubbard, R.L. & Anglin, M.D. (1999). A National evaluation of treatment outcomes for cocaine dependence. *Arch. Gen. Psychiatry, 56*(June), 507–514.

Single, E., Truong, M.V., Adlaf, E.M. & Ialomiteanu, A. (1999). *Canadian Profile: Alcohol, Tobacco and Other Drugs 1999*. Ottawa: Canadian Centre on Substance Abuse and the Centre for Addiction and Mental Health.

Wallace, B. (1991). *Crack Cocaine: A Practical Treatment Approach for the Chemically Dependent*. New York: Brunner/Mazel.

Weidman, A. (1985). Engaging the families of substance abusing adolescents in family therapy. *Journal of Substance Abuse Treatment, 43*, 927–938.

Wermuth, L. & Scheidt, S. (1986). Enlisting family support in drug treatment. *Family Process, 25*, 25–33.

Woody, G.E., McLellan, A.T., Luborsky, L. & O'Brien, C.P. (1995). Psychotherapy in community methadone programs: A validation study. *American Journal of Psychiatry, 152*, 1302–1308.

Chapter 30

Introduction to the Treatment of Problem Gambling

NINA LITTMAN–SHARP

Information, training and research on problem gambling has been increasingly available in the last few years, in response to the rapid expansion of legalized gambling and consequent concerns about problematic gambling behaviour. There is now a large and growing body of information and experience for new practitioners to access. This chapter introduces the assessment and treatment of people with gambling problems. Although substance use counsellors will find a great deal that is familiar, and will have a head start in this area, there are significant differences in working with this population.

GAMBLING IN A SOCIETAL CONTEXT

There has been a remarkable proliferation of legal gambling opportunities around the world in recent years, representing an increasing source of revenue for governments and charities. The first commercial casino in Canada opened in Winnipeg in 1984. Since then, over 50 permanent casinos have been added. By 2000, there were 44 permanent horse racetracks and about 60,000 video lottery terminals (VLTs) and slot machines in Canada (Korn, 2000). From 1992 to 2000, net gambling revenues from casinos increased by 573 per cent, and revenue from VLTs and slots increased by 1,369 per cent (Azmier, 2001). There have also been expanding opportunities for bingo, off-track betting, Internet gambling and many other games of chance.

Governments' reasons for expansion in this area become very clear when revenues are examined. The Province of Ontario anticipates net earnings from gambling of $2.3 billion in 2002–03, representing about 3.5 per cent of total revenues (Ontario Ministry of Finance Quarterly Update, September 2002). Across Canada, the proportion of provincial revenues coming from gambling have on average increased considerably (see Figure 30-1). Provincially run gambling across Canada, consisting of commercial casinos, VLTs and lotteries, produced gross revenues in 2000 of $9.04 billion. The average net loss per Canadian adult was $394.26 (Azmier 2001).

FIGURE 30-1

Gambling Revenue As a Percentage of Provincial Source Revenue

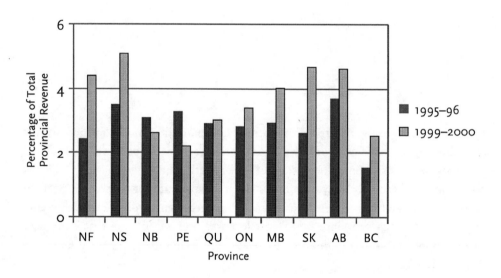

Source: Canadian Centre on Substance Abuse (1997); Azmier (2001). Used by permission.

In addition to government revenues, advantages cited for increased gambling include job creation, economic expansion, increased tourism, support for Aboriginal communities, prevention of illegal gambling, and enhanced revenues for charities. Ontario, for instance, guarantees $100 million of gambling revenue to charities annually through the Ontario Trillium Foundation.

Gambling as a pastime is now far more accepted than it was a decade or two ago, and attracts a broader portion of the population. For instance, a trip to the casino is now a commonplace and respectable outing for women or seniors. Lottery tickets, illegal prior to the Olympic lottery held in 1970, are now a normal part of everyday life. Eighty-three per cent of Ontario adults engaged in some form of gambling in the past year, according to a 2001 study (Wiebe et al., 2001). Gambling is now highly accessible, not just in casinos or racetracks, but also in convenience stores, by phone and on the Internet. In many parts of Canada, VLTs are or have been available in bars and corner stores. Gambling advertising is also ubiquitous, and its messages further normalize gambling behaviour.

Messages from the gambling industry do not typically include the real odds of winning. It is probably a rare gambler who thoroughly understands the odds and makes his or her bets consistent with that knowledge. Cognitive distortions associated with problem gambling will be discussed later in this chapter. However, mistaken beliefs about gambling are part of the current social fabric. For instance, in a survey by the Consumer Federation of America (1999), 27 per cent of respondents believed their best plan for financing their retirement was through lottery winnings rather than through saving and investing.

There is some movement to balance the weight of explicit and implicit pro-gambling messages. All provinces provide funding to promote responsible gambling and to support prevention, research and treatment. For instance, in Ontario 2 per cent of slot machine revenues are earmarked for this purpose. Such initiatives include training for casino staff, self-exclusion programs, 24-hour helplines, prevention packages for youth, and treatment services.

Along with the upswing in gambling opportunities has come an increase in the number of people seeking treatment for problem gambling. Callers to the Ontario Problem Gambling Helpline seeking treatment resources increased by 49 per cent between 1998 and 2002 (Ontario Problem Gambling Helpline statistics, 2003). A 2001 survey on gambling and problem gambling in Ontario found that 3.8 per cent of individuals 18 years or older reported moderate or severe gambling problems (Wiebe et al., 2001). This translates into about 340,000 Ontarians with such problems. Another 9.6 per cent report minor problems with gambling that indicate some risk. Studies consistently find that levels of problem gambling in youth are about double those of adults (AADAC, 2000; Shaffer et al., 1999).

The downside to gambling expansion can be found in damage to individuals, families and communities affected by problem gambling. Excessive gambling affects people's finances, employment, relationships, and physical and mental health, and these effects can range from mild to extreme. The results may include chronic poor levels of functioning, bankruptcy, job loss, legal trouble, family breakups or child neglect. A gambling problem generally affects a number of people in a widening circle of stress and loss.

DEFINITIONS AND GUIDELINES

Game Characteristics and Their Impact

Gambling involves wagering something of value on the result of an event whose outcome is uncertain. In essence it is a game played with probabilities; the person who correctly predicts the outcome wins something valuable from the one who does not. Games differ along a number of dimensions. In order to understand problem gambling, it is necessary to know some characteristics of the games, and how these characteristics affect the player.

One parameter of games is whether their outcomes can be predicted at all through skilled or knowledgeable play. For instance, bingo, slot machines and lottery tickets all have random outcomes; you cannot predict what will happen based on what has happened in the past. On the other hand, horse racing and sports betting involve some knowledge or skill; it is possible to increase the odds of winning through a greater understanding of the game. However, there is still so much randomness in these activities that it is almost impossible to predict outcomes well enough to win consistently. Also, betting venues make money by ensuring that the odds are with the house.

Whatever the type of gambling, people tend to search for patterns in the outcomes in order to predict what will happen the next time. These attempts can range from intensive research on game factors to superstitious beliefs about lucky days of the week. Such beliefs are given credibility by the fact that wins occur relatively frequently, even though overall losses are greater than wins. The longer a person gambles, the more money he or she is likely to lose. However, wins provide intermittent reinforcement which, as any behaviourist knows, is one of the best ways to ensure that a behaviour continues.

Another set of game characteristics has to do with how quickly a bet and outcome are completed, and how soon the next bet can be made. The old weekly lotteries gave a long break between the bet and the result. Now corner stores are filled with instant-win tickets. Horse racing used to offer only as many chances to bet as there were races in that location on that day. Off-track betting venues now allow continuous wagering on races all over the world. Slot machines and VLTs can complete a betting cycle in seconds. The quicker the betting cycle, the more potentially addictive the behaviour becomes (see Schwarz, 1984, for a discussion of schedules of reinforcement as they affect learning behaviour).

The literature has tended in the past to divide games into "action" and "escape" types, and the people playing them at problematic levels as "action" and "escape" gamblers. These two types tended to be associated with males and females respectively. There is some truth to this division. Interactive, higher-stakes games with a skill component tend to attract people who are looking for challenge and an adrenaline rush.

Solitary, smaller-stakes random games such as slot machines are often preferred by people who want to get away from the stresses in their lives. However, there are many overlaps in both the game characteristics and in the motivations of the people who play them. For example, an escape game may be approached with excitement or with pseudo-scientific research, while an action game may be engaged in out of a desire to escape unpleasant feelings. When gambling becomes a problem, motivations will likely change; the initial enjoyment of play may become a desire to win, and then to win back losses. In the end some people play chiefly to avoid thinking about the destructive effects of their gambling.

A couple of further points should be made about the games. First, private games or bets are somewhat different in that there is no "house edge"; odds are potentially equal. While this does not prevent problems from developing, playing against friends tends to limit the financial damage. Second, some activities, such as stock market trading, can be defined as gambling under certain conditions These include rapid trading rather than investment over the longer term, an excessive focus on the behaviour and a preference for high-risk, high-yield trades.

Problem versus Non-problem Gambling

Clearly not all gambling leads to problems. Most people gamble safely, either for entertainment, to socialize or to try their skill or luck. They limit their time and spending to what they can afford, see their losses as the cost of the entertainment, see their wins as due to chance rather than ability and have many activities besides gambling to meet their needs.

The level of gambling involvement may be seen on a continuum:

No gambling → casual social gambling → serious social gambling → risky gambling → problem gambling → pathological gambling

These are not discrete categories but possible points along a range of involvement. People who engage in serious social gambling may enjoy their game more than other activities, and may dedicate considerable time to it, but not to the point where it damages their relationships or other pursuits. Problem gambling varies in intensity, from mild to severe. The term "pathological gambling" arises from medical models, and is generally used to identify the most severe gambling problems.

Professional gamblers are missing from the list above. Such individuals do exist, but are unlikely to come to the attention of counsellors. Gambling for the sake of income must be done as a business, in an orderly fashion, without emotional involvement. Margins tend to be low, so considerable self-discipline is needed. Many people seeking treatment say that, after a series of wins, they began to think of themselves as professional gamblers; so this persona, although rare in fact, is important to consider when dealing with the belief systems that underlie problem gambling.

DSM-IV Criteria

The following are the criteria for pathological gambling from the *Diagnostic and Statistical Manual of Mental Disorders* (American Psychiatric Association, 2000):

A. Persistent and maladaptive gambling behaviour as indicated by five (or more) of the following:

1. is preoccupied with gambling (e.g., preoccupied with reliving past gambling experiences, handicapping, or planning the next venture, or thinking of ways to get money with which to gamble)
2. needs to gamble with increasing amounts of money in order to achieve the desired excitement
3. has repeated unsuccessful efforts to control, cut back, or stop gambling
4. is restless or irritable when attempting to cut down or stop gambling
5. gambles as of a way of escaping from problems or of relieving a dysphoric mood (e.g., feelings of helplessness, guilt, anxiety, depression)
6. after losing money gambling, often returns another day to get even ("chasing" one's losses)
7. lies to family members, therapist, or others to conceal the extent of involvement with gambling
8. has committed illegal acts such as forgery, fraud, theft, or embezzlement to finance gambling
9. has jeopardized or lost a significant relationship, job, or educational or career opportunity because of gambling
10. relies on others to provide money to relieve a desperate financial situation caused by gambling

B. The gambling behaviour is not better accounted for by a manic episode.

Some additional common indicators of problem gambling are:
• spending more time and money on gambling than the person can afford
• experiencing health problems, including stress and anxiety, due to gambling
• attempting to use gambling as a source of income
• borrowing money to gamble or cover losses
• believing a system of gambling will produce wins.

Several instruments aside from the *DSM-IV* can be used to help identify a gambling problem. They include the South Oaks Gambling Screen (SOGS; Lesieur & Blume, 1987), the Canadian Problem Gambling Index (CPGI; Ferris & Wynne, 2001) and short screens developed by the Alberta Alcohol and Drug Abuse Commission (AADAC, n.d.) and Turner & Horbay (1998). There are also screens specifically for adolescents. References to these instruments can be found at the end of the chapter (Shaffer et al., 1994; Winters et al., 1993).

Gambling problems may emerge in the course of other kinds of treatment, but they often remain hidden unless specific questions are asked. Unless all clients are screened, clinicians will likely ask only if they suspect that such a problem exists. The following is a list of indicators that might suggest a gambling problem. Some may be reported by family members. If several of these issues emerge in the course of treatment, screening is advisable.

FIGURE 30-2

Warning Signs That May Indicate a Gambling Problem

IN ADULTS

MONEY
- Financial problems exist despite an adequate income.
- Debts are building up.
- Money has gone missing from a bank account or wallet, or valuables have disappeared.
- There is a lot of borrowing, cash advances, living off credit cards, etc.
- A person takes a second job, but there is no change in his or her finances.
- RRSPs, insurance plans, etc., have been cashed in or allowed to lapse.
- A person obtains money illegally.

BEHAVIOUR
The person:
- avoids family functions or other social events
- neglects responsibilities or makes excuses
- drops other leisure activities to focus on gambling
- arrives late for work or other commitments
- disappears for large blocks of time
- spends a lot of time on sports statistics, racing forms or phone calls.

RELATIONSHIPS
The person:
- withdraws from family and friends
- appears preoccupied
- appears deceptive or secretive about his or her behaviour, particularly around money
- seems edgy, reactive or defensive
- changes sleep, eating or sexual relationship patterns.

IN ADOLESCENTS
The young person:
- can't account for missing money
- skips school
- borrows or steals money from friends or family
- sometimes has large amounts of unexplained cash
- has a fake ID, casino entry card, or racetrack or ProLine receipts among belongings
- is preoccupied with video arcades, Internet gambling sites or day trading
- has left a trail of Internet visits or credit card charges to gambling sites.

UNDERSTANDING PROBLEM GAMBLING

Similarities to and Differences from Substance Use

Problem gambling is similar in many ways to problem substance use. The two behaviours serve many of the same purposes, including escape (sometimes to the point of dissociation), excitement, pleasure and socialization. Those affected have similar subjective experiences of preoccupation, craving, tolerance and loss of control. There are overlaps in the neurobiology associated with each disorder (Comings et al., 1996), and evidence exists of common genetic factors (Slutske et al., 2000). In addition, substance use and problem gambling both affect a person's functioning: individuals are subject to depression, low self-esteem, anxiety and chronic stress, as well as family, legal, employment and financial problems. In both cases, the negative consequences tend to lead to more of the behaviour, creating similar cycles of addiction. Both groups tend to become the focus of attention in their families, and to take on childlike, irresponsible roles there. In both cases, models among families and peers influence the person's behaviour, and the impact on relationships of substance use and problem gambling is alike in many ways. Both sets of families suffer high rates of dysfunction, as well as serious consequences for children (for some effects on children, see Darbyshire, 2001). Most importantly, similar strategies work well with both groups.

Despite these many similarities, problem gambling has some unique features. It is a disorder that relates in large measure to belief systems and cognitive distortions, which are associated with the random schedule of reinforcement mentioned above. An estimated 50 per cent of people with gambling problems have had a big win early in their gambling history (Turner & Liu, 1999). Although gambling includes an effect of adrenaline, perhaps endorphins and other neurotransmitters, and sometimes a subjective experience of withdrawal, the physiological impact is minimal compared with that of substance use.

People with gambling problems are generally healthier and more clear-headed than those with substance use problems. They are more likely to be employed, and on average they are higher functioning. However, their financial problems are usually more severe. No matter how much a person spends on alcohol or other drugs, he or she cannot spend as much as a person can gamble in a single night, or even a single bet. Because the problem is much easier to hide than is substance use, people with gambling problems are often able to build up huge levels of debt. Money trouble is the issue that brings the problem to light in most cases. Although illegal behaviour is common in both disorders, problem gambling is more likely to lead to financial crimes (Meyer & Stadler, 1999). Consequences for families are particularly severe, including the chronic fear and uncertainty that go with devastating financial loss and the hidden nature of the problem.

Although relapse is common in both disorders, only in gambling is it possible to encounter relapse as a winning experience. People with gambling problems can be difficult to keep in treatment when they win. And although individuals are vulnerable to both disorders for many of the same reasons, there are additional precursors for problem gambling. For instance, many people with gambling problems come from families that place a high value on money and material wealth. They may be particularly business-oriented, and perceive gambling as an investment. Interestingly, the persistence and determination that is so effective elsewhere in the lives of such entrepreneurial people tends also to be applied to their gambling, with disastrous results.

The Pathways Model

Many stereotypes exist about problem gambling, but there is no "typical problem gambler." People with gambling problems do have many common experiences. But their backgrounds, needs and personalities vary enormously, and so a single treatment modality will not work for everyone. One useful approach to understanding etiology is Blaszczynski's pathways model (2000), which identifies three major routes to gambling problems. It divides people with gambling problems into three general types: "normal," emotionally vulnerable, and those with biologically based impulsivity.

People in the first group, essentially healthy before their problems begin, are described as falling victim to circumstances such as easy access to gambling, poor judgment and misunderstanding of the odds. Such symptoms as preoccupation, anxiety or depression are results, rather than causes, of their gambling. These people are high-functioning and have many resources. They tend to respond quickly to fairly minimal treatment, and are more likely to successfully reduce (rather than stop) their gambling, if this is their choice.

Those in the second group are predisposed to a gambling problem through a history of precursors such as addiction or mental health problems, including trauma, anxiety and depression. They gamble to escape from negative moods. These people are also affected by the same triggers—such as easy access and misunderstanding the odds—as those in the "normal" group. Given their vulnerability, abstinence is generally the most realistic goal for people in this group.

The third group comprises people with a biologically based tendency to impulsive behaviour. For instance, attention-deficit/hyperactivity disorder is one very common precursor to problem gambling; research suggests that as many as 20 per cent of those with gambling problems have ADHD (Specker et al., 1995). Such people are likely to have a number of concurrent problems, such as substance use, poor school or work performance, emotional lability, chronic boredom and inadequate social skills. Gambling provides exciting stimulation and an apparent chance to excel. The same precursors that affect people in the first two groups also apply here. These people are generally poor candidates for the goal of reduced gambling.

The pathways typology is a good reflection of clinical experience, and suggests that individuals require differential treatment based on their particular etiology.

Problem Development

Eric gambled occasionally with his wife and friends. When he was laid off at work, having time on his hands, he decided to visit a casino. He won the equivalent of a week's salary playing blackjack, and went home exultant. In the next two weeks he visited the casino four times, on two occasions winning several hundred dollars. He began gambling several times a week. When his wife, Anna, expressed concern, he began to conceal his trips. Eric continued to have some wins, but his net losses were depleting their savings. When Anna tried to withdraw money from their joint account and found it empty, she confronted Eric. He confessed to gambling "a bit too much," and promised to cut back and start looking more seriously for work. However, within a week he was back at the casino, betting his entire unemployment cheque. Although eventually he found a new job, the family continued to have to struggle almost entirely on Anna's salary. Eric's occasional wins paid some bills, but more and more frequently any wins were simply gambled away, and he would leave the casino with barely enough to get home. Eric visited the casino so frequently that he was often unavailable to his family. Within a year the couple was on the verge of separation.

To an outside observer, Eric's apparently irrational behaviour might seem baffling. A person with a gambling problem may lose money over and over again, and yet go back repeatedly to lose more. Typically the frequency, the bet size and the duration of gambling episodes increase over time. Negative consequences multiply, and still the person appears to seek a different outcome from the same behaviour.

Blaszczynski would describe Eric as a "pathway two gambler": he is depressed and escapes from unpleasant realities by gambling, and is also triggered by easy access (lots of free time) and a misunderstanding of the odds. Let's look at the experience from Eric's point of view.

Worried about unemployment and his family's finances, and feeling depressed and inadequate, Eric is delighted by his unexpected success at the casino. The experience is far more pleasant and rewarding than his job hunt, and apparently far more lucrative. When twice more he leaves with more money than he arrived with, Eric feels even more powerful and successful, and his view that gambling is easy money is confirmed.

Blackjack players who use care and a knowledge of the game can minimize their losses, leaving the house with an edge of about 3 per cent. Eric's initial wins are not unusual; given the small house edge, outcomes often fluctuate fairly broadly. However, over time even the best players will lose to the house. At the point where Eric might acquire an understanding of these odds, he is already deeply engaged in the belief that he can make money by gambling. The initial wins have been so salient, particularly in combination with his unhappiness and feelings of failure elsewhere, that later losses seem only a temporary aberration on the road to more wins.

Once Eric's losses reach a certain point, the need to win his money back becomes imperative, and it becomes harder and harder to give up on the large amounts already invested. His belief that he will eventually come out a winner justifies his spending, all the concealment and the expenditure of time. Nonetheless, his self-esteem outside the casino inevitably takes a beating, increasing the contrast between his depressing life and the thrill of winning.

Not all people with gambling problems progress in similar ways. Men tend to begin gambling earlier, in their teens, and generally progress more gradually into serious problems. Women tend to start gambling later, in their thirties or forties, progressing much more quickly to problem levels (probably because on average they have less money to spend). Some gambling problems fluctuate in severity, depending on such factors as the person's circumstances, income and employment, and the availability of gambling venues.

A wish to win money is not always the focus of gambling, at least initially. While many people with gambling problems seek a "big win," others are motivated chiefly by the potential for escape in playing for hours on end, or simply by enjoyment of the game. For such people, interest in money centres on having enough to keep playing. But even when money is not the initial motivator, as losses mount people may become increasingly preoccupied with the need to win in order to resolve financial problems.

Turner et al. (2003) examined the characteristics and early gambling experiences of people with and without gambling problems, to determine differences that might act as precursors to the development of problems. They found five basic risk factors:
• a big early win
• susceptibility to boredom
• a poor understanding of randomness
• a tendency to use escape as a way of coping
• a stressful life with a lack of support and direction around the time that gambling began.

Impulsivity and interpersonal anxiety also correlated with problem gambling, and those with gambling problems were more likely to have started when a new opportunity to gamble presented itself. The more of these factors that were present, the more likely a person was to have a gambling problem.

Turner also identified some factors that reduced the risk of problem gambling, including:
• financial security
• supportive friends
• having hopes and dreams for the future
• doing well at work

• using support rather than escape to cope
• knowledge of randomness
• the setting of limits on betting.

These findings fit well with Blaszczynski's model: they identify situational and cognitive factors, factors relating to pre-existing poor coping, and links to biologically based precursors such as impulsivity.

Cognitive Distortions

Turner's finding of a relationship between problem gambling and a poor understanding of random events is particularly relevant to treatment approaches. Some practitioners emphasize cognitive approaches almost exclusively, seeing problem gambling as a disorder of thinking (Ladouceur & Walker, 1998). In fact, incorrect assumptions about the odds are very common among gamblers in general, whether or not their gambling is problematic. Such misperceptions are encouraged by misleading game characteristics. For instance, slot machines can give the appearance that the player has some control, whereas the outcome is actually determined by a random number program.

However, people with gambling problems are significantly more likely to have skewed beliefs about their chances of winning. Toneatto (2001) describes a variety of cognitive distortions to which such people are prone, including superstitions, attributional biases (e.g., attributing wins to skill rather than to chance) and beliefs in control over luck. He notes that those with gambling problems tend to overrate their own gambling skills, and to selectively remember wins rather than losses. The classic "gambler's fallacy" is the belief that results will even out—that a series of losses means that one is "due" for a win.

"Random" does not mean "evenly distributed"; in fact, randomness includes streaks that look decidedly non-random. Thus it is perfectly possible for someone to win consistently by chance for some time, and then to lose for some time, again by chance. People with gambling problems tend to ascribe the winning streak to some special attribute of their own, and the losing streak to unlikely chance or circumstances. The core of cognitive distortions is the belief that one can predict or control the outcome of events that are completely or largely unpredictable.

Concurrent Disorders

GAMBLING AND SUBSTANCE USE

Research suggests that problem gambling and problem substance use co-occur at rates much higher than chance. Grant et al. (2002) cite studies reporting alcohol use disorders in 19 to 48 per cent of clinical samples of those with gambling problems. A literature review by Griffiths et al. (2002) notes that between 7 per cent and 19 per cent of adults with substance use problems also had gambling problems. Griffiths also finds high levels of co-occurrence in studies of adolescents.

Given these figures, clients who misuse substances need to be screened for gambling problems. If the two problems are concurrent, they clearly exacerbate each other. Impaired judgment and impulsivity due to substance use may dramatically increase gambling losses, while financial, work and family difficulties stemming from gambling problems will likely worsen the circumstances triggering substance use. Treatment priorities will depend on the client and on the severity of each issue. However, identifying and assessing gambling problems will not always lead to an interest in treatment. Clients who use substances often have a number of serious problems, and may see any gambling concern as well down their list of priorities. Aftercare is often a good time to focus on the gambling issue; at that point the client may be under less stress, and may also be at particular risk of increasing other problem behaviours to substitute for the missing substance.

This risk is substantiated by the large number of people entering treatment for gambling problems who report a past history of substance use. Many mention that they turned to gambling because they thought it would be a safer alternative. Therefore education and prevention for clients with substance use problems is highly recommended.

GAMBLING AND OTHER PROCESS ADDICTIONS

Gambling can be described as a process addiction. Peele (1980) theorizes that any experience can be addictive if is powerful and absorbing enough to detract from other involvements. If an activity reduces negative feelings and/or increases positive ones, while impairing self-esteem and the ability to cope, the activity will tend to increase in a worsening spiral. Excessive shopping, work, video game play and Internet use are other common process addictions. Some sexual behaviours also come under this heading, and clinical observations and research on problem gambling suggest it co-occurs quite frequently with sexual addictions (Taber, 1985; Boughton & Brewster, 2002). In fact, past or current experience with other process addictions is quite common among those with gambling problems.

Problem gambling almost by definition includes trouble managing money. Some of those affected live on as little as possible so they have more to gamble with, but many are impulsive spenders. In Boughton & Brewster's (2002) study of women with gambling problems, 24 per cent identify a current problem with compulsive shopping, while 43 per cent say they had such a problem in the past.

The Internet is, of course, connected with gambling because of burgeoning on-line betting opportunities. Numerous other Internet activities, such as chat groups, pornography searches and fantasy games, tend to eat up many hours, stretching far into the night—similar in some ways to gambling all night. Note that casinos are among the very few recreation centres that are open 24 hours a day; people with gambling problems often take advantage of this opportunity. Behaviours that go on for many hours and interfere with sleep may have some common results. For example, long-term sleep loss has been related to poor judgment and depression, as well as many health problems (Dement & Vaughan, 1999); and isolation is inevitable for someone who spends most of his or her day gambling and/or on-line.

GAMBLING AND MENTAL HEALTH PROBLEMS

The neurobiology of problem gambling has been the focus of increasing study (e.g., Comings et al., 1996; Carrasco et al., 1994). This research has linked levels of neurotransmitters, including dopamine and serotonin, to increased rates of problem gambling, and notes that these neurotransmitters are often implicated in impulse control disorders. Grant et al. (2003) summarize some promising pharmacological treatments that have been tried for people with gambling problems, including mood stabilizers, SSRIs and naltrexone. Some researchers theorize that problem gambling is one of an impulsive-compulsive spectrum of disorders (e.g., Hollander& Wong, 1995). "Compulsive gambling" is a common term, particularly in popular literature. It suggests a person with an irresistible compulsion to gamble. This usage tends to associate the behaviour with obsessive-compulsive disorder. However, the *DSM-IV* (APA, 2000) identifies problem gambling as an impulse control disorder. Obsessive-compulsive behaviours provide no pleasure, but are carried out to avoid anxiety. Gambling by contrast is a pleasurable activity; it is not until the point of complete desperation and disgust that people report gaining no pleasure from it.

In fact, attention-deficit/hyperactivity disorder, which affects impulse control and concentration, is far more common in those treated for problem gambling than is obsessive-compulsive disorder. As mentioned earlier, studies suggest that about 20 per cent of people with gambling problems have ADHD (Specker et al., 1995). Gambling provides the high level of stimulation they need in order to avoid boredom and depression, and also lends a sense of belonging and accomplishment that is often missing due to their poor functioning. The intense excitement of gambling, and the person's lack of impulse control, make self-restraint particularly difficult. Littman-Sharp and Jain (2000) describe the relationship of ADHD and problem gambling with depression and personality issues, and make suggestions for treatment.

Researchers have found higher rates of depression among those with gambling problems (e.g., McCormick et al., 1984; Cunningham-Williams et al., 1998). Becona et al. (1996) found a positive correlation between the severity of depression and that of pathological gambling. Both situationally caused and endogenous depressions are common in people with gambling problems. It is not surprising that someone who has put himself or herself into serious debt, along with other troubles, would feel depressed as a result; and a depressed mood in a gambling client does not necessarily indicate a major mood disorder. However, as represented by Blaszczynski's type two or emotionally vulnerable gambler, some people with endogenous depression use gambling to lift their mood. In some cases, gambling may be stressful enough to put a vulnerable individual into a depression that does not lift even when circumstances improve. Such cases should be referred for psychiatric assessment, and if possible work should continue in collaboration with a psychiatrist.

In Boughton & Brewster's (2002) study on women with gambling problems, 63 per cent had visited a professional for help with depression, and 53 per cent had done so for an anxiety disorder. Again, some anxiety may be a result rather than a cause of gambling, and may relate to fears over money, threats to housing, pressure from creditors, etc. Physical symptoms of stress, such as stomach pain and insomnia, are very common. However, if the anxiety is persistent and predates the gambling, if there is a family history of anxiety disorders or if there are puzzling physical symptoms (Law, 2001), a referral should be made for a mental health assessment.

Personality disorders or related traits are also frequently found in those with gambling problems. Narcissistic personality traits are relatively common in clinical settings, often in conjunction with ADHD or other impulsivity problems. Some researchers have found high levels of antisocial personality disorder in this population (e.g., Blaszczynski & McConaghy, 1989). Once again, we must distinguish between causes and effects. People with gambling problems often behave selfishly or irresponsibly as they become caught up in a cycle of betting, chasing their losses and seeking more money to gamble. The behaviour is not always characteristic of the person, and it is sometimes the realization of how far they have strayed from their true personality and values that motivates people to seek treatment.

It is essential to carefully screen for suicidality. Between 4 per cent and 31 per cent of people with gambling problems report suicide attempts (Sullivan, 1994; Schwartz & Lindner, 1992). Rates of suicidal ideation cited in studies run as high as 70 per cent (Lesieur, 1998). Other studies have not found a significant link between problem gambling and suicidality (Cunningham-Williams et al., 1998), so the association is not entirely clear.

Certain characteristics appear to correlate with suicide risk. Frank et al. (1991) found that among people with gambling problems, those who were suicidal were significantly more likely than those without suicidality to have an early onset of problem gambling, severe "gambling addiction," serious relationship problems and a higher rate of problem substance use. A study by the Productivity Commission of Australia (1999) found that the rate of suicide attempts in problem gambling clients correlated with levels of debt, duration of gambling addiction and the amount of time spent in a diagnosed depression. The high rate of depression in people with gambling problems is probably enough to explain the high suicide risk.

Problem Gambling in Specific Populations

There is a growing body of work on the impact of gambling on specific populations, and the needs and characteristics of these groups. Only a few key issues are raised here; please consult the references for further reading.

WOMEN

Although there is considerable overlap between the experiences and needs of men and women with gambling problems, there are also some marked differences. As noted earlier, women tend to choose different games than men do. While men usually start gambling in their teens, women generally start later, in their thirties. Women often run into financial trouble far more quickly, probably because on average they have less money. Women with gambling problems have extremely high levels of past abuse and trauma, present life stressors and concurrent disorders (Boughton & Brewster, 2002). Women are more likely than men to use gambling as an escape from troubles, heavy responsibilities or stress.

One typical case is Patricia, a woman in her thirties who was under enormous stress, and had a great deal of responsibility at home and extremely high loads at work. She described her sojourns in front of the slot machines as *"her* time," when no one could reach her or demand anything of her. This staid and law-abiding woman embezzled $15,000 of her company's money a little at a time, always intending to pay it back. When the theft came to light she was devastated by her behaviour and its consequences.

OLDER ADULTS

Older adults are less likely than the general population to have a gambling problem. However, when they do gamble excessively the consequences may be more severe, because there is often no opportunity to make up the lost money. Seniors are valued customers for gambling venues: they have plenty of time, and can be bused in from seniors' centres and residences. For an older adult, a gambling venue can be very inviting; it provides a safe, often cheap outing among friendly people. However, seniors can be particularly vulnerable to developing a gambling problem, due to the loss of loved ones, loss of jobs and income, loss of health and resultant restriction in available activities.

Petry (2002) studied some differences between people with gambling problems in different age groups. One startling finding was the percentage of monthly income consumed by gambling. For older adults, this spending was far above their income, and older women spent on average two-and-a-half times their monthly income on gambling. Clearly the consequences of problem gambling for seniors can be very serious.

TABLE 30-1

Median Amount Gambled in Past Month As a Percentage of Monthly Income among Those Seeking Treatment for Problem Gambling

	AGE		
	18 – 35	36 – 55	56+
Men	94	67	187
Women	125	77	249

Source: From Petry (2002). Used by permission.

YOUTH

As mentioned earlier, youth typically have double or triple the level of problem gambling than does the adult population (AADAC, 2000; Shaffer et al., 1999). It is not clear whether the current youth cohort will continue to have higher rates of problem gambling in adulthood, perhaps due to the greater availability of legal gambling and its wide acceptance, or whether they will mature out of the problem.

Young people with gambling problems are predominantly male (Derevensky & Gupta, 1997), and the games of choice for underage bettors are card playing and sports betting. There is some evidence that youth with this problem also have difficulties in other areas (Gealt, 2002). Anecdotal evidence from adults with gambling problems suggests that the pattern often began their teens.

It is not easy to engage young people in treatment for problem gambling. Given the skills needed to work with youth, counsellors should probably be youth workers with additional skills in gambling counselling, rather than the reverse.

CULTURE

The relationship of problem gambling to culture is large and complex. Each ethnic or cultural group includes many subcultures, as well as generational differences, varying levels of acculturation, etc. In addition, each family has its own culture and beliefs, and its own preferences around seeking help. Thus it is not possible to make blanket statements about how to work on problem gambling with people from different communities. However, counsellors should explore cultural differences with clients, to understand the significance of these differences in relation to gambling. The importance of education on cultural competence for counsellors cannot be overemphasized (Gannam, 2001).

Gambling itself has different meanings and levels of acceptance in different cultures. For instance, some cultures and religions consider gambling to be a sin, while others use it in traditional and/or spiritual ways and still others regard certain levels of gambling as part of daily life. Cultures also differ as to, for example, who may gamble (for instance, according to age or gender), and what types of gambling and what gambling locations are considered acceptable. The family configuration—for example, whether it is nuclear or extended, close or distant from their community, and what gender roles and hierarchy apply—will also influence how a problem is identified and how it can be addressed.

For those from other countries, experiences both before and after immigration need to be explored. Refugees may be more vulnerable to gambling problems because of traumatic experiences and current stress. Immigrants in general may be at risk because they have lost status or income, they must struggle to achieve financial stability and support their families, they are isolated from potential supports, they experience discrimination, or they have problems with acculturation.

Gambling has a special place in some First Nations cultures. Traditionally, certain games have spiritual meanings for the group as a whole. Aboriginal people are more likely to say they gamble to spend time with friends and family. The losses sustained by Aboriginal communities through residential schools, dislocation, poverty, trauma and racism all increase people's vulnerability to addictive disorders. A study by the Ontario Federation of Indian Friendship Centres (2000) found very high levels of problem gambling in Aboriginal respondents. For First Nations cultures, the family is made up of the whole community. For this reason, it is preferable to deal with problem gambling on a community level, rather than in terms of the individual or the immediate family.

Cultures vary in the ways people feel comfortable seeking help (e.g., within or outside the cultural group; through a doctor, family member or religious leader). Language alone can create serious barriers in counselling; access to professional cultural interpreters is essential in a multicultural society. Partnerships with ethnically specific treatment providers are one approach to providing linguistically and culturally appropriate service.

TREATMENT

The interventions discussed in this chapter are largely cognitive-behavioural. This umbrella covers many therapeutic approaches, including:
• change-stage matching
• motivational interviewing
• brief solution-focused counselling
• identifying and increasing skills for coping with high-risk situations
• cognitive restructuring.

Formats include individual or group counselling, educational sessions, and family and marital therapy. The best choice depends on the client's needs and on what the agency can offer. Cognitive-behavioural techniques are widely used in Canada and elsewhere, and are increasingly accepted in the United States. Blaszczynski (1998), based in Australia, has published an excellent handbook on cognitive-behavioural approaches to problem gambling. Toneatto & Ladouceur (2003), in reviewing research on gambling treatment, found that cognitive-behavioural interventions appear to have the most empirical support. These techniques, with suitable adaptations, are useful for clients of all three pathways, but emotionally vulnerable clients (type two) and those with biologically based impulsivity (type three) may need additional interventions such as medication or psychotherapy.

Because cognitive-behavioural techniques are probably familiar to many readers, and are covered in detail elsewhere in this book (see index), the focus here will be on how elements of the technique are applied to problem gambling.

Assessment

When a client presents with a gambling problem, assessment focuses on largely the same areas that would be explored for substance use disorders:
• precipitating factors that brought the person into treatment
• current levels of functioning
• the person's relationships and work situation
• his or her legal situation
• physical and mental health history and any current problems
• past treatment
• crisis issues (including the potential for self-harm or harm to others)
• goals for treatment
• motivation levels.

Clients should be screened for substance use, both past and current. The specifics of the person's gambling history and behaviour should be explored in some detail, including the types of gambling he or she engages in; the location, frequency and amount of time spent; whether he or she gambles with companions; and typical patterns of play. Counsellors need to understand when gambling became a problem and why, and what the person's current triggers are. Financial issues should also be explored, including how much the person owes and to whom, and the level of arrears on bills and payments. In addition, a family history of mental health, substance use and problem gambling is often very revealing.

If there is any question as to whether a person has a gambling problem, one of the screens mentioned earlier should be used to help clarify the issues. Counsellors may choose to give each new client a comprehensive addiction and mental health screening. Note however that people with gambling problems often arrive in crisis, and many are impatient. There may be only a narrow window of opportunity to work with the client, and if response is not rapid this opportunity may be lost. An immediate supportive contact focused on the client's presenting problems will engage the client and raise the likelihood of his or her return. More comprehensive assessment can take place over subsequent sessions. It is helpful for agencies to have a counsellor available to screen and engage new clients as they call.

People in crisis due to gambling problems (along with their families) may need financial help including income support, as well as the help of credit counsellors, lawyers, psychiatrists, distress lines, food banks and shelters, among others. Case management at this stage includes setting short-term, manageable goals and giving concrete advice. Clients will be tempted to use any money that comes their way to gamble, in order to escape distress and give them the hope of an 11th-hour rescue. Even funds they obtain with great effort to help them out of a crisis—say, to avoid eviction—are at risk. Thus counsellors should advise clients to arrange for any such money to go through someone else's hands. It is often advisable to bring in the family at this stage, as they also need advice on how to handle the crisis in a way that will not lead to further trouble later. For instance, bailouts, co-signing loans or paying off creditors all tend to be counterproductive. More on the family's role will be found later in the chapter.

Stages of Change and Motivational Interviewing

The stages of change model (Prochaska & DiClemente, 1998) is as appropriate to problem gambling as it is to substance use (for a detailed description of the model, see Chapter 2). However, motivation to change often fluctuates even more in those with gambling problems, because of their experience of winning, or of seeing or hearing about wins. For instance, at one group session a new member described a $40,000 slot machine win, and his subsequent rapid loss of that money and $80,000 more that didn't belong to him. The story of the win brought on intense urges to gamble in the rest of the group; the story of the devastating losses and legal problems hardly had an impact.

Cognitive distortions will also affect motivation. For example, if people believe that although they lose on the horses, they are especially knowledgeable about football, they will tend to revert to the precontemplation stage during football season.

When clients are in the action stage, they may be so only in relation to a portion of the problem. For instance, credit counsellors are used to people with gambling problems identifying difficulties with money, rather than with gambling. Sometimes work, family, health or legal pressures are the prime motivators for a person to enter treatment. In this case, the client may still be in contemplation regarding the gambling itself, but may be willing to deal with the related issues; there may be some impact on the gambling in the process.

Motivational interviewing can provide a balanced viewpoint and a reality check (see Chapter 2 for a detailed discussion of motivational interviewing). The techniques for addressing cognitive distortions are valuable in this regard; they are touched on below. Just as it is important for people with substance use problems to identify how much they consume, it is vital for those with gambling problems to be clear about how much they spend. The counsellor should clarify and write down the figures as they go: income, amounts gambled, frequency of gambling, specific debts, etc. Clients are often vague on these points and may initially avoid such questions, but there is no better eye-opener than the realization that one is spending 90 per cent of one's income on gambling. Debts to family and friends are often barely mentioned or readily dismissed; if the people involved are not pressing for their money, the client may set aside these debts as unimportant or even non-existent. Bringing the impact of such debts back into focus can help motivate the person. The often extensive and debilitating effects of gambling on other parts of the person's life should also be explored. It goes without saying that the counsellor needs to remain non-judgmental in this work; his or her role is to clarify the facts and to let those facts speak for themselves.

Motivational interviewing is in some cases continued as needed during treatment: as the client's stage of change fluctuates, or as different issues emerge. People often need to remind themselves why they entered problem gambling treatment in the first place. For instance, clients who abstain from gambling and begin to accumulate money in the bank are likely to have urges to return to gambling.

One of the common presentations related to motivation arises with clients who acknowledge a problem but see no way out. They are already convinced that gambling has been extremely harmful, but are so mired in debt and other troubles that continuing to chase a win seems like their only hope. Some people who have been deceitful or dishonest can achieve real change only by making the terrifying choice to "come clean." By continuing to gamble, juggling their finances and so on, they have struggled to avoid the inevitable: loss of relationships, trust, status or employment. They may be subject to criminal prosecution. The more successful they have been at concealment, and/or the higher their original status in their family or community, the harder they find the choice to be honest. In such cases the client needs support, good information about the likely consequences of coming clean, and the assurance that people can and do get through such problems. The support of others with gambling problems is helpful in this regard. If the person has unrealistically pessimistic beliefs about the outcome of disclosing his or her difficulties, this should be addressed with cognitive therapy techniques. But complete reassurance is not possible. The person's spouse may indeed feel this is the last straw and leave. The employer may in fact prosecute. Counsellors can offer their belief in the client's ability to survive such eventualities, and can gently inform the person that if his or her gambling continues, such outcomes are inevitable in any case.

Goal Setting

People with gambling problems often hope to return to normal levels of gambling, rather than having to give it up altogether. Whether or not this is realistic depends on many factors (see Table 30-2).

TABLE 30-2

Criteria for Considering
Reduction vs. Abstinence Goals

	REDUCTION	ABSTINENCE
Stage of problem	early	later
Level of gambling problems as indicated by DSM-IV/SOGS	low	high
Concurrent disorders	no serious ones, especially before onset of problem gambling	significant ones (e.g., substance use, depression, impulsivity)
Goals	realistic (e.g., a small weekly budget for lottery tickets)	unrealistic (e.g., "I'll get my money back and then I'll quit.")
Reasons for gambling	appropriate (e.g., to socialize, to have fun)	inappropriate (e.g., to win, to avoid problems)
Supports and coping strategies	good	poor
Ability to tolerate some further losses	adequate	poor
Family able to accept further gambling	yes	no

Some gambling clients seem able to continue with a form of gambling that has never caused them trouble; usually this is their weekly lottery ticket. Others manage to restrict their gambling in other ways. A reduction goal may be a route to abstinence, or an end in itself. In either case, an initial period of abstinence is advisable in order to restore a healthier range of activities and to put gambling in perspective.

Brief solution-focused counselling techniques (e.g., Berg & Miller, 1992) can be used to develop reasonable goals, and to emphasize positives and a sense of progress, particularly when clients are feeling trapped and despondent. For instance, scaling questions can be used to ask the client what level he or she is at in terms of an identified problem, from one (worst) to 10 (best). The counsellor then asks what it would take to raise the client one point on the scale. This dialogue points to both long- and short-term goals. Brief solution-focused techniques tend to emphasize a client's strengths and abilities, and to focus on solutions rather than problems.

However, some gambling clients are overly optimistic; they focus on the short term and fail to plan realistically for anything beyond the immediate future. In this case an emphasis on positives is likely to feed into the client's prevailing overconfidence, which was part of the problem to begin with. The counsellor's role then is to provide realistic feedback, and to emphasize careful planning, the client's cheerful assurances notwithstanding. In all cases the counsellor needs to help the client achieve a balance: confidence based on a realistic assessment of skills, resources and supports. For a more detailed discussion of behaviour change and relapse prevention tools for problem gamblers, see Littman-Sharp (2001).

Identification of Triggers

Like people with substance use difficulties, those with gambling problems need to know what triggers their urges in order to learn how to cope. Gambling triggers may resemble those of other addictions, particularly when they relate to positive or negative emotions, relationships and social pressure. However, some triggers are unique to gambling. For instance, the vast majority of people with gambling problems are triggered by the availability of money or credit. Financial pressure is another common issue. Belief systems about gambling and the ability to win are also central. Also, gambling tends to lead to more gambling as the person wins and wants to win more, or loses and tries to win the money back.

A functional analysis of problem gambling reveals a wide variety of individual patterns. People gamble to have hope, to relieve pain, to cope with loss, to feel smart or accepted. Gambling provides entertainment, a predictable environment, a sense of freedom, the thrill of winning, stress relief. As with any addictive behaviour, the consequences tend to become causes as the gambling cycle repeats.

Personal triggers can be determined through interviews, self-monitoring or group brainstorms. It helps in such brainstorms to divide triggers into events, thoughts and feelings. Following a gambling incident, from the first decision to gamble through to the final consequence, provides a great deal of information on triggers. The Inventory of Gambling Situations (Littman-Sharp & Turner, 2001) is a 63-item questionnaire for identifying high-risk situations. It is based on the Inventory of Drinking Situations (Annis et al., 1982). Validation research on the inventory has identified 10 subscales of high-risk situations within four overall groupings (see Table 30-3).

TABLE 30-3

Inventory of Gambling Situations Subscales

1. Negative affect situations Negative emotions Conflict with others	3. Positive affect situations Pleasant emotions Social pressure Need for excitement
2. Temptation situations Urges and temptations Testing personal control	4. Gambling cycle situations Worry about debts Winning and chasing losses Confidence in skill

Clients commonly have multiple triggers, and the longer they have been gambling, the more likely this is to be true. Combinations of triggers are more likely to lead to relapse than are single triggers. For instance, someone trying to abstain may succumb if he or she simultaneously is depressed, gets unexpected money and hears about a supposed new winning system.

In identifying gambling triggers, we are seeking the antecedent of the *decision* to gamble, not of the gambling itself. Decisions are often made well before the first bet is placed, and once made are very hard to reverse.

While major triggers are obviously a key concern, less frequent triggers also need special attention, because they may take the person by surprise. For instance, resistance to gambling that is well established at home may dissolve on a work trip. The client may also need to be prepared for periodic triggers such as sports seasons or holidays.

Coping Strategies

Once specific triggers are identified, specific strategies must be developed to cope with them. As with triggers, it is helpful to divide these into behavioural, cognitive and affective strategies. Clients may tend to prefer only one or two of these types, for instance to focus on self-talk but to take no action, or to operate on impulse and action but to avoid thinking situations through. Again, the counsellor's role is to promote balance. The counsellor may need to focus on the client's faulty beliefs and misunderstandings about the odds of winning. Techniques for this are touched on below.

If the client is struggling with urges, detailed advance planning is very important. What route will the person take to avoid passing by the casino? Which bills will he or she pay first? What newspaper does not contain sports results? What will the person do on the weekend instead of playing bingo? The client will need to find ways to fill the large amounts of time that gambling has taken up, preferably in a way that meets at least some of the needs that gambling fulfilled. The person's plans should include small and frequent rewards for sticking to goals.

Most people with gambling problems need to avoid handling money, at least for a time. Counsellors should encourage clients to request their family's help in this regard; most families are relieved to take this on. The person's access to cash and credit should be reduced, but he or she should still be responsible for helping to manage bills, make financial plans and take on other family financial responsibilities. Relieving the person of all responsibilities would reinforce a childlike role rather than encouraging adult behaviour.

Another way to reduce access to gambling is self-exclusion. Most casinos allow this option, which involves a legal agreement to stay out of the casino for a specified period of time, with penalties if the person is found on the premises. In Ontario this involves a ban on entry to all casinos and slot facilities in the province. At present the person must go to a casino to arrange self-exclusion, and so he or she should be encouraged to take along a supportive friend or family member to ensure there is no relapse.

Self-exclusion is a very effective behavioural strategy for motivated and essentially law-abiding clients who are looking for reinforcement of their effort to avoid casinos. It is less effective for anyone inclined to evade the restriction. Canadian casinos are beginning to consider facial recognition and other technologies, but currently casinos are not able to prevent access by determined gamblers. Whether or how to enforce self-exclusion is an ongoing issue for the gambling industry, faced with media concern and a number of lawsuits. The provinces handle this issue in various ways. The contract used in Ontario states that self-exclusion is voluntary, and that the industry is not obligated to enforce it. There is no requirement prior to re-entry, once the contracted period is up. In contrast, Manitoba has introduced mandatory psychoeducational programs for self-excluders who wish to return to the casinos. These programs are a promising intervention for a vulnerable population.

Continued self-awareness and planning are necessary to avoid relapse. Clients need to catch warning signs early and deal with them promptly, before their habitual, over-learned patterns of behaviour take over. One of the tasks of counselling is to anticipate what events might lead to relapse and to prepare a list of more positive alternative responses.

Cognitive Restructuring

As mentioned earlier, faulty beliefs contribute to problem gambling. Toneatto (2001) describes cognitive therapy techniques that aim to correct beliefs based on such errors in thinking. The core belief of many people with gambling problems is that they can, through special knowledge or personal attributes, predict the outcome of games that are in fact not predictable. The person selectively recalls evidence that supports these beliefs, and discards contrary evidence. Instead of looking at results over time (i.e., heavy losses), he or she tends to take note of short-term wins that confirm existing beliefs.

People with gambling problems are not always aware of the beliefs and attitudes on which they base their decisions. To bring these underlying assumptions to the surface, the counsellor asks how the client makes betting decisions, and asks the client to explain his or her beliefs in some detail. For instance, the counsellor may ask, "If you win when you are watching the game on TV, how does that work? How is a game in another city affected by the fact that you are watching?" Just bringing these beliefs to a conscious level can raise doubts in the client's mind, and make it possible for the client to challenge his or her own thinking. Counsellors can educate clients about the games, their odds and what randomness means. Note, however, that it is not effective to argue about the characteristics of games that the client probably knows better than the counsellor. It is generally not productive to get caught up in the minutiae of why the person's "system" won't work, especially if the person is strongly invested in his or her belief system. What does work is asking how effective the person's strategy has been over time.

Related Issues

Counselling may uncover other issues that relate in various ways to the gambling. Some of these issues can be dealt with in the problem gambling treatment, while others may require referral.

Gambling clients generally struggle with serious relationship problems. The stress of juggling finances, keeping secrets and dealing with consequences often takes up so much of their time and energy that they have difficulty broadening their focus to include the impact on those around them. If possible, the family should be invited to join some or all of the counselling sessions. If anger and recriminations threaten to take over, it is sometimes better to give family members the chance to vent separately, before the family is seen together. More on family issues can be found below.

The client's finances need to be examined in detail and managed appropriately, to avoid the risk of relapse. If the counsellor has the relevant skills, he or she can give advice and help with budgeting; otherwise a referral to a credit counsellor is advisable. For this work to be effective, all debts and income must be revealed and the family must be involved in the process. Dealing with finances can be a very painful step for all concerned, and one that clients may take time to face.

Clients may be dealing with the legal consequences of criminal behaviour. Generally this is non-violent financial crime such as fraud, theft or embezzlement. Such clients may be referred by the legal system. Although mandated, it is not unusual for them to be highly motivated, particularly if this is their first experience of being charged; such clients are often shocked at the extremes to which their gambling has led them.

Those seeking treatment may also be involved in evictions, private suits, wrongful dismissal cases, negotiations with Revenue Canada, separation and divorce, and many other legal wrangles. Most legal issues should be referred to a lawyer. Clients who are destitute due to gambling may need to turn to Legal Aid or free legal clinics. Some lawyers will provide 30 minutes of free initial consultation. Such processes tend to move slowly, and these entanglements add greatly to clients' stress levels.

Any identified mental health problems may also require the help of experts. As mentioned earlier, some of the most common concurrent problems for people with gambling difficulties are depression, anxiety and impulsivity. A history should attempt to determine whether these symptoms predated the gambling problem. If not, it may resolve the issue to get the gambling and its results under control. Good psychiatric consultants with knowledge of problem gambling are invaluable when working with this population.

Self-Help

Gamblers Anonymous and Gam-Anon provide help and inspiration to many people with gambling problems (GA), and to their family members (Gam-Anon). It is helpful to hear from others who have been through the same experience and have found a way forward. Many clients benefit from a combination of professional counselling and self-help. These groups offer a great deal of wisdom, support and a program that addresses real issues facing those with gambling problems.

GA and Gam-Anon do not suit everyone, however. They adhere to a disease model and label, which act as a barrier to those unwilling to accept them; such people may not agree that they have a problem if that problem is represented as a disease. The two groups insist on total abstinence as the only viable goal, and do not distinguish between different levels of problems. They focus on spirituality, which does not fit well for many people. Historically, GA groups have been male-dominated and have not been as comfortable for women. Although there are attempts to alter this bias, research shows that women tend to do better in women-only groups. Another risk of self-help groups is that while messages from members may be wise and helpful, they may also reflect misunderstandings, bias or the individual's own troubled state.

Clients can be encouraged to try these groups and see how they respond to them. When self-helps groups work for a person, they provide support in many ways that professionals cannot, just as professionals provide services not available through self-help.

HELPING THE FAMILY

Counsellors should not underestimate the impact of problem gambling on the family, and the importance of family and community in treatment. Gambling treatment services should include family members as clients, whether or not the person with the gambling problem attends.

Family members are often more severely affected than the gambler by the financial stresses and resultant insecurity and loss. Spouses typically feel enraged, helpless, depressed and deeply fearful of the future. They may be desperately worried about meeting the needs of dependent children, humiliated by debts to other family members, harassed by creditors and a sense that all responsibilities are on their shoulders, and struggling with the loss of expectations for the future and with loss of the spousal relationship they thought they had. They are often isolated from supports because they feel they must keep "family business" within the family. Depending on the extent to which the gambling has been hidden, spouses may be coping with sudden and devastating losses of homes and security. The person who gambles, in his or her attempts to conceal the gambling, may over time have projected blame onto the spouse, damaging the relationship and the spouse's self-esteem. The effect of lying on trust in the relationship is insidious and extremely damaging.

In initial meetings, spouses need to have their feelings validated, and to be reassured that their reactions are a normal response to abnormal circumstances. They need to examine and process past hurts. Most need very much to have an honest conversation with their spouse, and to hear at least that the person regrets what he or she has done. They need to get onto firmer ground by learning all the facts, however upsetting. Any further concealment is very frightening, and will prevent real recovery in the relationship.

The person with the gambling problem, meanwhile, is struggling to overcome shame, loss of respect, and long habits of avoidance and concealment. A long process is sometimes needed before the person is ready to reveal everything. Some people, particularly characteristic optimists, prefer to think in the short term, and do not understand their spouse's need to process the past. If they have stopped gambling recently, they may see this as a sufficient answer to all the spouse's concerns. Such a person often needs some initial time and space to address immediate practical problems, increase his or her sense of self-efficacy, and reduce stress. The spouse's strong emotions are often more than the client can handle without becoming defensive and inflicting more pain.

Clearly the needs of the couple tend to clash. The counsellor's role is to validate both sets of needs and to help the couple reach agreements so that at least some needs of each person can be met. One useful technique is for the couple to process the past for a specified period each week, perhaps in the counsellor's office, and to agree that those issues will not be mentioned outside that time. The couple can also work to support each other's needs. For example, the person with a gambling problem can help ease the spouse's anxiety by being open about financial matters, while the spouse helps by joining his or her partner in relaxing leisure activities; or the client takes on more family responsibilities and the spouse offers positive feedback when these responsibilities are handled well.

A central issue in families is the distortion of roles: gamblers often act as and are treated as difficult adolescents, and spouses take on corresponding parental roles. The counsellor needs to address these imbalances and to help restore adult-to-adult communication between the couple. Communication skills training can be a helpful technique in this regard.

Other family members are also gravely affected by problem gambling. Elderly parents may lose their home in trying to rescue their children; young children may suffer stress, dislocation or neglect; and adults may worry about their parents' ability to remain independent, or may watch their siblings' lives and families deteriorate. All these people need help in meeting their unique needs. Adult family members need to decide what they can and cannot control, and what they can and cannot handle from the person with the gambling problem. They need to learn to respect their own needs and look after themselves and their children, rather than centring their lives on the gambling.

The issue of bailouts comes up frequently. A real concern is that bailing out the person may allow him or her to continue gambling. However, it is not always realistic for the family to withhold all financial aid; in some cultures it is close to impossible. Counsellors need to work with each family to find out what actions they can live with.

Some choose to help, but without letting the money go through the gambler's hands. Some insist the person gets treatment before they will help. Others offer help only to the person's spouse and children.

Sometimes reframing will help the family pull back and allow the person to face the consequences of his or her actions. For example, the counsellor may suggest that a good mother's job is not only to support her children, but also to let them learn from their mistakes so they will grow up strong and independent.

There are some good self-help manuals for family members of those with gambling problems, including *Behind the 8-Ball: A Guide for Families of Gamblers* (Berman & Siegel, 1992) and *Don't Leave It to Chance: A Guide for Families of Problem Gamblers* (Federman et al., 2000). As discussed earlier, some family members also benefit from the support of others like themselves at Gam-Anon meetings. Counselling services often hold groups for family members.

CONCLUSION

Reported prevalence rates for problem gambling suggest that between 640,000 and one million Canadians have multiple gambling problems (Azmier, 2001). The families of these people also suffer greatly. The number of people affected points to the need for treatment, prevention and research.

Working with people with gambling problems is both challenging and fascinating. The similarities to problem substance use mean that counsellors can use many of their existing skills, while the differences provide new and stimulating learning. At present, information and ideas about problem gambling are expanding exponentially. This is an emerging field, with new practices, new research and new approaches appearing constantly. This chapter touches only briefly on some of the knowledge and techniques available, and should be used as a starting point for learning, rather than a blueprint.

REFERENCES

Alberta Alcohol and Drug Abuse Commission. (2000). Proceedings of the Interprovincial Think Tank on Youth and Gambling. Edmonton, AB: author.

Alberta Alcohol and Drug Abuse Commission. (n.d.). AADAC Gambling Screen. Available: www.calgaryhealthregion.ca/familymedicine/tools/aadac_gambling_screen.pdf.

American Psychiatric Association. (2000). *Diagnostic and Statistical Manual of Mental Disorders* (4th ed., text rev.). Washington, DC: author.

Annis, H.M. (1982). *Inventory of Drinking Situations (IDS – 100)*. Toronto: Addiction Research Foundation.

Azmier, J.A. (2001). *Gambling in Canada 2001: An Overview*. Calgary, AB: Canada West Foundation.

Becona, E., Del Carmen Lorenzo, M. & Fuentes, M.J. (1996). Pathological gambling and depression. *Psychological Reports, 78*, 635–640.

Berg, I.K. & Miller, S.D. (1992). *Working with the Problem Drinker: A Solution-Focused Approach*. New York: W.W. Norton.

Berman, L. & Siegel, M.E. (1992). *Behind the 8-Ball: A Guide for Families of Gamblers*. Toronto: Simon and Schuster.

Blaszczynski, A. (1998). *Overcoming Compulsive Gambling: A Self-Help Guide Using Cognitive Behavioural Techniques*. London, England: Robinson.

Blaszczynski, A. (2000). Pathways to pathological gambling: Identifying typologies. *eGambling: Electronic Journal of Gambling Issues, 1*. Available: www.camh.net/egambling/issue1/feature/index.html.

Blaszczynski, A. & McConaghy, N. (1989). Anxiety and/or depression in the pathogenesis of addictive gambling. *The International Journal of the Addictions, 24*, 337–350.

Boughton, R. & Brewster, J. (2002). *Voices of Women Who Gamble in Ontario: A Survey of Women's Gambling—Barriers to Treatment and Treatment Service Needs*. Toronto: Ministry of Health and Long Term Care.

Canadian Centre on Substance Abuse (1997). Gambling: A multi-billion-dollar industry. In *Gambling in Canada—A Report by the National Council of Welfare* (chap. 1). Available: www.ccsa.ca/plweb-cgi/fastweb.exe?getdoc+view1+General+672+1++gambling%20in%20canada.

Carrasco, J.L., Saiz-Ruiz, J., Hollander, E., Cesar, J. & Lopez-Ibor, J.J. (1994). Low platelet monoamine oxidase activity in pathological gambling. *Acta Psychiatrica Scandanavica, 90*, 427–431.

Comings, D.E., Rosenthal, R.J., Lesieur, H.R. & Rugle, L. (1996). A study of the dopamine D2 receptor gene in pathological gambling. *Pharmacogenetics, 6*, 223–234.

Consumer Federation of America. (1999). *New Study: Typical American Household Has Net Financial Assets of $1,000*. Available: www.consumerfed.org/primerica2.pdf.

Cunningham-Williams, R.M., Cottler, L.B., Compton, W.M. III & Spitznagel, E.L. (1998). Taking chances: Problem gamblers and mental health disorders—Results from the St. Louis epidemiological catchment area study. *American Journal of Public Health, 88*(7), 1093–1096.

Darbyshire, P. (2001). The experience of pervasive loss: Children and young people living in a family where parental gambling is a problem. *Journal of Gambling Studies, 17*(1), 23–45.

Dement, W.C. & Vaughan, C. (1999). *The Promise of Sleep*. New York: Dell.

Derevensky, J.L. & Gupta, R. (1997, June). *Prevalence estimates of adolescent gambling: A comparison of the SOGS-RA, DSM-IV-J, and the GA 20 Questions*. Paper presented at the 10th International Conference on Gambling and Risk-Taking, Montreal.

Federman, E.J., Drebing, C.E. & Krebs, C. (2000). *Don't Leave It to Chance: A Guide for Families of Problem Gamblers*. Oakland, CA: New Harbinger.

Ferris, J. & Wynne, H. (2001). *The Canadian Problem Gambling Index: Final Report*. Available: www.ccsa.ca/docs/cpgi_final.htm#section3.

Frank, M.L., Lester, D. & Wexler, A. (1991). Suicidal behaviour among members of Gamblers Anonymous. *Journal of Gambling Studies, 7*(3), 249–254.

Gannam, V. (2001). Cultural background and problem gambling. In R.D. Murray (Ed.), *Helping the Problem Gambler*. Toronto: Centre for Addiction and Mental Health.

Gealt, R. (2002). *Does juvenile gambling predict delinquency: Act vs. attitude*. Paper presented at the 16th Annual National Conference on Problem Gambling, Dallas.

Grant, J.E., Kim, S.W. & Potenza, M.N. (2003). Advances in the pharmacological treatment of pathological gambling. *Journal of Gambling Studies, 19*(1), 85–109.

Grant, J.E., Kushner, M.G. & Kim, S.W. (2002). Pathological gambling and alcohol use disorder. *Alcohol Research and Health, 26*(2), 143–150.

Griffiths, M.D., Parke, J. & Wood, R.T.A. (2002). Excessive gambling and substance abuse: Is there a relationship? *Journal of Substance Abuse, 7*, 187–190.

Hollander, E. & Wong, C.M. (1995). Obsessive-compulsive spectrum disorders. *Journal of Clinical Psychiatry, 56*(suppl. 4), 3–6.

Korn, D.A. (2000). Expansion of gambling in Canada: Implications for health and social policy. *Canadian Medical Association Journal, 163*(1), 61–64.

Ladouceur, R. & Walker, M. (1998). The cognitive approach to understanding and treating pathological gambling. In A.S. Bellack & M. Hersen (Eds.), *Comprehensive Clinical Psychology*. New York: Pergamon.

Law, S. (2001). Special treatment issues: Concurrent disorders. In R.D. Murray (Ed.), *Helping the Problem Gambler*. Toronto: Centre for Addiction and Mental Health.

Lesieur, H. (January 1998). Testimony to the National Gambling Impact Study Commission, Atlantic City, New Jersey, 22 January 1998.

Lesieur, H.R. & Blume, S.B. (1987). The South Oaks Gambling Screen (SOGS): A new instrument for the identification of pathological gamblers. *American Journal of Psychiatry, 144*, 1184–1188.

Littman-Sharp, N. (2001). Teaching clients skills for change and relapse prevention. In R.D. Murray (Ed.), *Helping the Problem Gambler.* Toronto: Centre for Addiction and Mental Health.

Littman-Sharp, N. & Jain, U. (2000). Problem gambling and attention-deficit hyperactivity disorder. *eGambling: The Electronic Journal of Gambling Issues, 2.* Available: www.camh. net/egambling/issue2/clinic/.

Littman-Sharp, N. & Turner, N. (2001). *Inventory of gambling situations: Validation data on an instrument which identifies areas of risk for relapse.* Paper presented at the National Council on Problem Gambling Annual Conference, Seattle.

McCormick, R.A., Russo, A.M., Ramirez, L.F. & Taber, J.I. (1984). Affective disorders among pathological gamblers seeking treatment. *American Journal of Psychiatry, 141*(2), 215–218.

Meyer, G. & Stadler, M.A. (1999). Criminal behavior associated with pathological gambling. *Journal of Gambling Studies, 15,* 29–43.

Ontario Federation of Indian Friendship Centres (OFIFC). (2000). *Analysis Report on Friendship Centres Gambling Survey.*

Ontario Ministry of Finance Quarterly Update. (September 2002). Available: www.gov. on.ca/FIN/english/finances/2002/ofin022e.htm.

Ontario Problem Gambling Helpline statistics. (2003). Unpublished.

Peele, S. (1980). *The Addiction Experience.* Center City, MN: Hazelden. Modified from a two-part article that appeared in *Addictions* (Addiction Research Foundation), Summer 1977, 21–41; Fall 1977, 36–57. Available: www.peele.net/lib/addexp.html.

Petry, N.M. (2002). A comparison of young, middle-aged, and older adult treatment-seeking pathological gamblers. *The Gerontologist, 42*(1), 92–99.

Prochaska, J. & DiClemente, C. (1998). Toward a comprehensive, transtheoretical model of change: Stages of change and addictive behaviours. In W.R. Miller & N. Heather (eds.), *Treating Addictive Behaviors* (2nd ed.). New York, NY: Plenum Press.

Productivity Commission of Australia. (1999). The impacts of problem gambling. In *Australia's Gambling Industries: Inquiry Report* (chap. 7). Available: www.pc.gov.au/ inquiry/gambling/finalreport/chapter07.pdf.

Schwartz, B. (1984). *Psychology of Learning Behavior.* New York: W.W. Norton.

Schwarz, J. & Lindner, A. (1992). Inpatient treatment of male pathological gamblers in Germany. *Journal of Gambling Studies, 8*(1), 93–109.

Shaffer, H., Hall, M.N. & Vander Bilt, J. (1999). Estimating the prevalence of disordered gambling behavior in the United States and Canada: A research synthesis. *American Journal of Public Health, 89,* 1369–1376.

Shaffer, H., LaBrie, R., Scanlan, K.M. & Cummings, T.N. (1994). Pathological gambling among adolescents: Massachusetts Gambling Screen (MAGS). *Journal of Gambling Studies, 10*(4), 339–362.

Slutske, W.S., Eisen, S., True, W.R., Lyons, M.J., Goldberg, J. & Tsuang, M. (2000). Common genetic vulnerability for pathological gambling and alcohol dependence in men. *Archives of General Psychiatry, 57*, 666–673.

Specker, S.M., Carlson, G.A., Christenson, G.A. & Marcotte, M. (1995). Impulse control disorders and attention-deficit disorder in pathological gamblers. *Annals of Clinical Psychiatry, 7*(4), 175–179.

Sullivan, S. (1994). Why compulsive gamblers are at high suicide risk. *Community Mental Health in New Zealand, 8*, 40–47.

Taber, J.I. (1985). Pathological gambling: The initial screening interview. *Journal of Gambling Behavior, 1*(1), 23–34.

Toneatto, T. (2001). Cognitive therapy for problem gambling. In R.D. Murray (Ed.), *Helping the Problem Gambler.* Toronto: Centre for Addiction and Mental Health.

Toneatto, T. & Ladouceur, R. (2003). The treatment of pathological gambling: A critical review of the literature. *Psychology of Addictive Behaviors, 17*(4), 284–292.

Turner, N. & Horbay, R. (1998). Centre for Addiction and Mental Health (CAMH) Gambling Screen. Unpublished.

Turner, N., Littman-Sharp, N., Zangeneh, M. & Spence, W. (2003). Winners: Why do some develop gambling problems while others do not? Available: www.gambling research.org/download.sz/winners%20Turner.pdf?docid=1521.

Turner, N.E. & Liu, E. (1999). *The naive human concept of random events.* Paper presented at the 1999 Conference of the American Psychological Association, Boston.

Wiebe, J., Single, E. & Falkowski-Ham, A. (2001). *Measuring Gambling and Problem Gambling in Ontario.* Canadian Centre on Substance Abuse. Available: www. responsiblegambling.org/articles/CPGI_report-Dec4.pdf.

Winters, K.C., Stinchfield, R. & Fulkerson, J. (1993). Toward the development of an adolescent gambling problem severity scale. *Journal of Gambling Studies, 9*, 63–84.

Chapter 31

Tobacco Interventions for People with Alcohol and Other Drug Problems

PETER SELBY AND CHARL ELS

Everyone who works in substance use treatment knows that many, if not most, clients smoke. In fact, the prevalence of smoking in this population is as high as 85 to 90 per cent (Sullivan & Covey, 2002), or three times that of the general population. Although the benefits of smoking cessation are well-known, substance use treatment programs often overlook the opportunity to motivate and counsel clients to quit. Treatment providers often think that it is unrealistic to counsel clients to address tobacco use at the same time as dealing with a substance use problem. They know that quitting smoking can, for most clients, be even more difficult than giving up the substance for which they are seeking treatment (Kozlowski, Wilkinson et al., 1989). However, a significant number of clients in substance use treatment are willing to accept treatment for tobacco use (Saxon et al., 1997; Richter et al., 2001), and substance use counsellors are ideally situated to offer this treatment. Furthermore, addressing smoking may help to improve substance use treatment success (Bobo et al., 1987; Miller et al., 1983; Kohn et al., 2003).

In this chapter, we will examine the rationale and importance of addressing tobacco use in substance use clients. We will present and discuss the evidence for intervening with this population, and describe a humanistic framework to address tobacco use. Our goal is to help counsellors motivate and counsel their clients to quit smoking and engage in relapse prevention.

HEALTH EFFECTS OF TOBACCO USE

The health effects of tobacco use are astounding. Cigarettes are the only legal product that kills up to 50 per cent of the people who use them as intended by the manufacturer (Peto et al., 1996). Tobacco use kills 45,000 Canadians annually and accounts for more deaths than alcohol, illicit drugs, HIV, hepatitis C, suicide, murder and motor vehicle accidents combined (Jha, 1999; Makomaski Illing & Kaiserman, 1999). Worldwide, tobacco use kills 10,000 people daily and on average reduces lifespan by 22 years (Murray & Lopez, 1997). Unless we encourage and help people to quit, 500 million people alive today will die in the 21st century from tobacco use (Jha, 1999).

The costs of tobacco use are enormous. In 1992, Canadians spent 9.46 billion dollars in health and economic costs, which was more than was spent on all other substance use problems combined (Single et al., 1998).

The health effects of smoking and environmental tobacco smoke (ETS) exposure have been described for most of the last century (Bartecchi et al., 1995; Wald & Hackshaw, 1996) (see Table 31-2). However, many people who smoke are unaware of all the risks of using tobacco (Cummings et al., 2002). Smoke from cigarettes contains about 4,000 chemicals, of which at least 50 cause cancer. These include carbon monoxide, hydrogen cyanide, polyaromatic hydrocarbons such as benzene, pesticides and tobacco-specific nitrosamines. The increased health risks are seen in all people who smoke and in people who don't smoke, but are exposed to ETS. There is no safe level of cigarette smoking or exposure. There is, moreover, a consistent association between the dose of smoke exposure and the risk of mortality. Since cigarettes are the most frequently used tobacco product, cigarette smoke is the number one cause of tobacco-related mortality (Hoffmann et al., 1997). While smokeless tobacco use does not appear to have the same risk for lung cancer associated with smoking, the risks for oral diseases and cancers are significant (Critchley & Unal, 2003).

Although the most well-known health effects are lung cancer and emphysema, Table 31-1 presents a more comprehensive list of the adverse effects associated with tobacco use.

TABLE 31-1

Health Effects of Smoking and Environmental Tobacco Smoke Exposure

CANCER

- lung (85 per cent of lung cancers occur in smokers; one in 20 smokers will develop lung cancer)
- mouth, tongue, voice box, throat, stomach and bladder

CARDIOVASCULAR DISEASE

- heart attacks (smoking accounts for 40 to 45 per cent of heart attacks in people younger than 65)
- strokes

LUNG DISEASE

- chronic obstructive pulmonary disease (COPD) or emphysema (85 per cent of cases are due to smoking; one in seven smokers who smoke one pack per day for 20 years will develop COPD)
- higher risk for pneumonia
- worsening of asthma

DISEASES OF THE MOUTH

- gingivitis
- tooth loss
- bad breath

EFFECTS IN WOMEN

- osteoporosis
- breast cancer (controversial)
- adverse effects in pregnancy for mothers, fetuses and children

EFFECTS ON SKIN

- skin wrinkles (smoking ages skin by 15 to 20 years)

MISCELLANEOUS

- burns
- poor wound and fracture healing
- gastrointestinal problems
- gastro-esophageal reflux disease (GERD) or acid reflux
- peptic ulcers

Source: Bartecchi et al., 1994; Bartecchi et al., 1995; MacKenzie et al., 1994

Additive Health Effects of Combined Tobacco and Substance Use

The risk of cancer and cardiovascular disease is higher in people who use both tobacco and alcohol than it is in those who use either alone (Mitchell et al., 1999). In a landmark study of mortality in people who are alcohol dependent, it was found that 50 per cent died from tobacco-related causes and 34 per cent from alcohol-related causes (Hurt et al., 1996). Many of the health effects seen in substance-using populations may be due to the amount smoked and many people could benefit from quitting both drugs (Patkar, Lundy et al., 2002; Patkar, Sterling et al., 2002).

Cigarette Smoking Is Highly Addictive

In the past, it was argued that because nicotine does not cause intoxication and impairment, smoking was simply a bad habit and not a true addiction (Robinson & Pritchard, 1992). Now, the addictive nature of nicotine in tobacco is without question. Studies in both animals and humans have shown that nicotine releases dopamine in the same regions of the brain as do other drugs of abuse (Balfour, 2002). Inhaled smoke delivers nicotine to the brain within 10 to 15 seconds, making it highly addictive (Balfour, 2002) and comparable to opioids, alcohol and cocaine (Stolerman & Jarvis, 1995).

There is no diagnostic category in the *Diagnostic and Statistical Manual of Mental Disorders (DSM-IV)* for "nicotine abuse," as there is for "substance abuse." The only diagnostic category for tobacco use disorders is "nicotine dependence" (American Psychiatric Association, 1994). Although many people who smoke do not meet *DSM-IV* criteria for nicotine dependence, they are nevertheless physically dependent on nicotine, as evidenced by withdrawal and tolerance (Moolchan et al., 2002).

Seventy-seven per cent of Canadians who currently smoke have their first cigarette of the day within 60 minutes of waking (Canadian Tobacco Use Monitoring Survey, 2002). The only other substance so widely used upon waking is caffeine. For many people with substance use problems, tobacco was the first drug they started using and is often the last they give up. Most feel that it is harder to quit smoking than to quit the drug for which they are seeking treatment (Kozlowski, Wilkinson et al., 1989). This begs the question: Which drug is a client's true "drug of choice"?

TABLE 31-2

More Tobacco Facts

CIGARETTE DESIGN

Cigarettes consist of a tobacco column made from shredded tobacco leaf, reconstituted tobacco (other parts of the tobacco plant that have been crushed, made into sheets and shredded), and puff tobacco (loose-leaf tobacco that has been freeze-dried with ammonia and Freon to double its volume). Although Canadian cigarettes do not contain additives, they are no safer than American cigarettes.

The tobacco column is wrapped in cigarette paper that has been layered and impregnated with accelerants to ensure continued burning even when the smoker is not puffing. This poses a fire hazard.

The filter is made from acetate or cellulose and wrapped in special paper.

THE LIGHT AND MILD DECEPTION

So-called light or mild cigarettes are created by making ventilation holes in the filter either mechanically or by using lasers. Smokers compensate to get the nicotine they desire by using a combination of strategies: they increase the volume or number of puffs per cigarette or block the ventilation holes (National Cancer Institute, 2001). Regardless, since the late 1970s the nicotine content of Canadian cigarettes has been increasing steadily (Rickert, 2000). Readers who want to know more about the content of Canadian cigarettes may visit the B.C. Ministry of Health Web site at www.healthplanning.gov.bc.ca/tobacco.

TOBACCO USE IN FIRST NATIONS AND INUIT POPULATIONS

The prevalence of smoking in First Nations populations is about three to four times that of the general population. Sixty-two per cent of adults living on reserves and 70 per cent of Inuit between the ages of 20 and 29 smoke (Reading, 1996; Reading, 1997).

Although the tobacco plant is sacred among some First Nations, it is not revered by all groups or by the Inuit (von Gernet, 2000). The ceremonial use of tobacco typically involves burning it or using it in a smudge, but not inhaling the smoke (Bartecchi et al., 1995; Vidal, 1997).

IS TOBACCO A GATEWAY DRUG?

Although most people who smoke do not go on to develop other substance use problems, for those who do, smoking is often the first drug of abuse for most people who later develop alcohol or other drug problems. In a recent review of adolescent mental health and addiction problems, it was found that early onset of smoking before the age of 13 predicted later mental health and substance use disorders (Upadhyaya et al., 2002).

In a prospective study that followed 684 adolescents 14 to 18 years old up to age 24, lifetime history of smoking, especially in those who smoked daily, significantly increased the chances of future alcohol, cannabis or other illicit drug and polysubstance use in young adulthood (Lewinsohn et al., 1999). Quitting smoking for 12 months was associated with a lower risk of future alcohol use disorders.

Another study followed 4,327 Grade 7 students in the United States for five years. It found that early smokers were at least three times more likely by Grade 12 to use tobacco and marijuana regularly, use hard drugs, sell drugs, have multiple drug problems, drop out of school and experience early pregnancy and parenthood. They were also more likely to have low academic achievement and behavioural problems, and to exhibit delinquent behaviours, including stealing and violence (Ellickson et al., 2001). In susceptible individuals, it appears that smoking may be a gateway drug; efforts to discourage youth from smoking or to help them to quit could also help to prevent other addictions (Ellickson et al., 2001).

PREVALENCE OF SMOKING AND THE ASSOCIATION WITH SUBSTANCE USE

In Canada, the prevalence of smoking in the general population is 21 per cent (CTUMS, 2002). Here, and in other developed countries, smoking is more prevalent among people who have lower education, lower social class, blue-collar occupations, psychiatric illness and/or alcohol and other drug problems (Bergen & Caporaso, 1999; Kumra & Markoff, 2000). In substance use treatment populations, the prevalence of smoking may be as high as 85 to 90 per cent among clients (Sullivan & Covey, 2002) and is often also high among treatment providers. The following studies illustrate the incidence and the association of substance use and smoking.

Looking at alcohol use and smoking, a large United States general population study found that the incidence of smoking increases with the amount of alcohol consumed (Dawson, 2000). In the study, smoking was found in 22.5 per cent of lifetime alcohol abstainers, 27.6 per cent of non-abstainers, 53 per cent of heavy drinkers and 55.5 per cent of people with a diagnosis of either alcohol abuse or dependence in the past year.

Another United States population-based study found that 71 per cent of people who used illicit drugs also smoked. The study showed that the likelihood of smoking increased with the number of different drugs used. Those who reported using more than one drug were 2.4 times more likely to smoke than those who used only one drug (Richter et al., 2002). Also in the United States, a study of 452 injection drug users found that 91 per cent smoked (Clarke et al., 2001). The association between substance use and smoking has been similarly observed in an Australian study (Degenhardt & Hall, 2001).

The reasons for the association between substance use and smoking are complex. Research tells us that substance use increases the rate of smoking. In laboratory studies, the acute administration of opioids, alcohol, cocaine, caffeine or amphetamine increases the rate of smoking (Spiga, et al., 1998). Conversely, smoking can also increase cravings for substances. In cocaine users, exposure to nicotine in the presence of cocaine cues leads to more intense cravings for cocaine (Reid et al., 1998). For some people who smoke crack using cigarette ash, just watching a cigarette burn can trigger cocaine cravings.

Schoedel & Tyndale (2003) have demonstrated that when people drink they may be able to smoke many more cigarettes and vice versa. This is because alcohol and nicotine increase each other's breakdown.

This complex association between drinking and smoking makes it difficult for someone to quit smoking while actively drinking. As a rule of thumb, people should attempt to quit both together or to quit drinking before they attempt to quit smoking.

CLIENTS ARE READY TO ADDRESS SMOKING

Studies show that a substantial proportion of clients are ready to attempt smoking cessation while in substance use treatment. In a study of 207 clients admitted to an inpatient alcohol and other drug treatment program, 23.7 per cent were willing to attempt smoking cessation (Saxon et al., 1997). Ten per cent had abstained from smoking at the six-week follow-up. Clients attending methadone maintenance clinics have shown similar rates of willingness to attempt smoking cessation (Richter et al., 2001). About 13 per cent of clients undergoing alcohol and other drug treatment have quit smoking without formal help at 12-month follow-up (Kohn et al., 2003).

In a study of 1,007 young adults who smoke, those with an active alcohol problem in the preceding year were 60 per cent less likely to quit than those who did not have an alcohol problem. However, if the alcohol problem was not active, the participant was as likely to quit as someone without an alcohol problem (Breslau et al., 1996).

Even though only 25 per cent of clients may be willing to quit smoking while receiving treatment for other substance use, many are willing to explore the issue (Bernstein & Stoduto, 1999; Campbell et al., 1998).

If smoking is not addressed during treatment for substance use problems, there is a possibility the individual may either take up or relapse to smoking. In a study of a substance use treatment program where smoking was not addressed (Kohn et al., 2003), about 12 per cent of the clients either started to smoke or relapsed to smoking.

Client Attributes Associated with Quitting Smoking

A study of inpatient substance use treatment programs found that clients who believe that inpatient treatment is the best time to quit smoking are the most likely to accept smoking cessation treatment. Clients who accepted smoking cessation interventions tended to be younger, be more addicted to nicotine, have more smoking-related health problems, have a positive attitude about quitting smoking and believe smoking cessation would help them to address their substance use problem (Seidner et al., 1996).

A study of a methadone program found that clients who were older, used more nicotine patches and did not smoke in the first three weeks of quitting were more likely to be successful. Those who continued to use heroin were more likely to continue smoking (Frosch et al., 2002).

Client Characteristics That Make It Difficult to Quit

Although most "ever smokers" (those who have smoked at least one hundred cigarettes in their lives) have quit for more than six months, current smokers may represent a "hard-core group" who either smoke heavily or have comorbid conditions that make it difficult to quit (Thun & Heath, 1997).

For example, depression interferes with a person's ability to quit smoking (Kenford et al., 2002; Lerman et al., 2002; Patten et al., 2001). The risk of major depression can be seven times higher in those with a history of major depression who attempt to quit smoking (Glassman et al., 2001). In a Canadian study of 161 men and women in early recovery from alcohol problems, it was found that clients were more likely to use cigarettes to manage depression (Currie et al., 2001).

Effect on Prognosis

THE EFFECT OF QUITTING SMOKING ON RECOVERY FROM ALCOHOL AND OTHER DRUG PROBLEMS

Several studies show that quitting smoking during substance use treatment can increase rates of abstinence from alcohol and other drugs (Bobo et al., 1987). One study measured the effect of smoking on substance use treatment prognosis in terms of the number of days clients were abstinent. The longest duration of abstinence was found in those who quit smoking after beginning treatment (311 days) and in those who did not smoke when treatment began (295 days). The shortest duration of abstinence was found in those who continued to smoke (258 days) or who started or resumed smoking (247 days; Kohn et al., 2003). Quitting smoking during treatment for drugs other than alcohol has also been shown to reduce drug cravings (Campbell et al., 1995).

Clients in substance use treatment may be more motivated and confident about changing their substance use than their smoking, and seeking to address smoking may affect treatment retention. One study showed that clients who chose to change their alcohol use alone were more likely to stay in treatment than those who chose to change their smoking and drinking concurrently (Stotts et al., 2003). This study did not show, however, why those who chose to quit both drinking and smoking dropped out of treatment, or whether they had any ongoing need for treatment.

Other studies show that counselling clients to quit smoking during substance use treatment does not, at least, interfere with treatment success. For example, in a study of homeless veterans in residential treatment for substance dependence, most were able to address their smoking without jeopardizing their recovery from alcohol and other drug problems (Burling et al., 2001). A trial in 12 residential treatment programs found that low-intensity smoking cessation counselling was ineffective in getting clients to quit, but it did not affect alcohol recovery outcomes (Bobo et al., 1998).

The evidence shows that clients in substance use treatment who are ready to quit smoking should be provided with intensive smoking cessation treatment. Addressing smoking in clients with alcohol and drug problems is safe; one large study of people with a history of alcohol use problems or dependence found that only two to four per cent of relapses to alcohol use are directly attributable to quitting smoking (Martin et al., 1997). However, if a client does not appear to be tolerating the stress of quitting smoking, it is prudent for the counsellor to discuss delaying the quit attempt until the client feels more stable.

THE EFFECTS OF ALCOHOL AND OTHER DRUG USE ON QUITTING SMOKING

Drinking affects the ability to quit smoking and is also a risk factor for relapse to smoking. This may be due to the association of drinking with smoking, the loss of inhibition caused by alcohol, the environment in which both may be consumed or some other unknown factor.

In a study assessing the effects of substance use on smoking cessation, past substance use history did not affect the ability to quit or to remain abstinent from smoking (Humfleet et al., 1999). However, even low to moderate alcohol use at any time predicted relapse to smoking. Marijuana use did not predict relapse.

The ability to quit smoking appears to be related to the length of time the client abstained from alcohol. Those with long-term abstinence do not differ from the general population in their ability to quit smoking, which is between 20 to 30 per cent of those who quit in the action stage (Kalman et al., 2002).

Thus, it appears that abstinence from substances increases the chances of quitting smoking. Conversely, it also appears that quitting smoking can increase the chances of abstinence from substances.

METHADONE MAINTENANCE AND CESSATION

The prevalence of smoking in methadone-maintained patients can be as high as 92 per cent (Clemmey et al., 1997). Methadone dose increases are known to increase cravings for nicotine and the intensity of nicotine withdrawal (Story & Stark, 1991). Moreover, smoking may serve as a discriminative stimulus for methadone due to the long-term association between opioids and nicotine in these clients (Spiga et al., 1998). Another factor that can explain the high rates of smoking is the presence of concurrent depression among methadone clients (Meyer et al., 1996).

In an exploration of the relationship between smoking and methadone, 168 patients on methadone did not think smoking triggered drug use but that the converse was true (Stein & Anderson, 2003). They did not use cigarettes as a means to cope with urges and thought that quitting smoking at the same time as quitting drug use was appropriate. However, it was also observed that intensity of smoking can predict use of illicit opioids and cocaine during methadone treatment (Frosch et al., 2000).

Although people who use opioids perceive quitting smoking to be harder than quitting opioids (Frosch et al., 2000), in one clinic 61 per cent of methadone-maintained clients were ready to quit smoking in the next six months with a preference for on-site treatment and the use of nicotine replacement therapy (Clemmey et al., 1997). In another clinic, 58 per cent of methadone-maintained clients were somewhat or very interested in quitting smoking (Frosch et al., 1998). In a smoking cessation trial in this population, those clients who quit smoking were also more likely to provide drug-free urine samples during treatment (Frosch et al., 2002), again suggesting that addressing smoking may reduce other drug use as well.

GOALS OF TREATMENT

The overall goal of treatment is to engage clients in the process of smoking cessation to improve health and to engage in a life of recovery without tobacco. It is not recommended to demand smoking abstinence at treatment entry but rather to integrate a stage-based cessation program into the addiction treatment program (Bernstein & Stoduto, 1999; Campbell et al., 1998). This requires a systematic approach to consistently screen for smoking status, advise and assist clients to stop smoking completely and prevent relapse. This process of screening, advising on treatment goals and developing relapse prevention strategies with the client should sound familiar to addiction counsellors.

Addressing Smoking in Substance Use Treatment Facilities

In a survey of 223 treatment programs in Canada conducted in 2001, it was found that 54 per cent of all programs provide at least some assistance to their clients in quitting smoking (Currie et al., 2003). Outpatient programs (65 per cent) were more likely to offer services than residential programs (44 per cent). However, in most programs, smoking cessation services were offered on an individual ad hoc basis based on client request and only 10 per cent had formal smoking cessation services. Twelve per cent were contemplating the addition of formal cessation services. All programs offered smoking cessation as an optional part of treatment. Currently, the most common format is sequential treatment of alcohol or other drug use followed by nicotine dependence treatment. However, it should be noted that this study simply provided an environmental scan of the situation in Canada and not necessarily best practices for this client population. The dilemma is whether we should stand back and watch our clients succumb to the ill effects of smoking or explore their interest in addressing tobacco use as part of their treatment.

Barriers to Implementing Treatment

Treatment of nicotine dependence in clients with substance use problems has been neglected. The barriers can be perceived to be systemic, including lack of funding and poor policy development by funding and accreditation agencies. Provider and client attitudes and lack of knowledge about tobacco use also constitute barriers to treatment. Many counsellors find the very idea of addressing smoking during treatment abhorrent. The three most common myths are that people in substance use treatment are not motivated to quit smoking, that they will relapse to other drug use if they attempt to quit smoking, and that they are unable to quit smoking (Campbell et al., 1995). Many counsellors feel that people should not try to take on too much all at once or that requiring clients to quit smoking will prevent them from attending treatment (Bobo & Gilchrist, 1983). The smoking status of the counsellor is another barrier, although many clients do not think it affects their ability to be effective clinicians (Bernstein & Stoduto, 1999).

The contact between the addiction treatment system and the client may represent a missed opportunity to intervene and may in fact enable addictive behaviour. Many do not appreciate the similarity of dependence on tobacco and other substances. This could be because tobacco use does not visibly impair the user and its effects become evident only in the long term (Bartecchi et al., 1995). However, cases of people in nicotine withdrawal smoking cigarette butts (Aloot et al., 1993) or committing crimes to obtain cigarettes (Anonymous, 2002; DiFranza & Coleman, 2001) are evidence of the powerful effects of smoking. Some programs believe that the only intervention is to force all clients to quit smoking on admission. Programs that have done so have been met with resistance, underground smoking and premature discontinuation from the treatment program (Capretto, 1993; Goldsmith & Knapp, 1993; Karan, 1993; Kotz, 1993).

A more realistic approach is to help move clients through the stages of change and to allow clients to choose to address their tobacco use while they attend treatment (Bernstein & Stoduto, 1999). Addiction counsellors are uniquely situated to intervene effectively because they are knowledgeable about principles of recovery, are seen as credible sources for the treatment of addiction and often have long-term therapeutic relationships with their clients (Currie et al., 2003). For example, clients attending treatment in Toronto are increasingly amenable to treatment for smoking—from a low of 46 per cent at the Addiction Research Foundation in 1989 (Kozlowski, Skinner et al., 1989) to a high of 87 per cent in 1996 at the Donwood Institute. However, this increase could reflect the differences in the clientele served by the two facilities. It is likely that these clients are also susceptible to population-based tobacco control initiatives, such as taxation, cigarette package labelling and smoke-free bylaws in society, making smoking cessation more important.

FRAMEWORK FOR ADDRESSING SMOKING IN ALCOHOL AND OTHER DRUG TREATMENT PROGRAMS

The following steps are necessary to overcome some of the barriers outlined above and to address smoking in addiction treatment facilities. Broadly, these include policy changes in the facility, staff training and access to counselling and medical services to help both staff and clients stop smoking (Bernstein & Stoduto, 1999; Campbell et al., 1998).

Systemic and Programmatic Changes

Management support for smoke-free policies and options for clients (other than smoking during breaks) is necessary. Nutrition and exercise, if not part of the addiction program, are essential to prevent weight gain after smoking cessation. Exercise also has the additional benefit of improving mood. Management can also help arrange treatment for staff interested in quitting smoking either with on-site programs or through employee assistance programs (Moher et al., 2003). Currently, many jurisdictions have free telephone quit lines and/or Web-based resources to help people quit. Managers can also ensure they budget for smoking cessation medications, since many clients may not be able to afford them on their own income. Integration of smoking cessation into the values and mission of the treatment agency is also important. In addition, facilities should develop policies that ban the acceptance of sponsorship from tobacco companies.

Smoke-Free Policies

Smoke-free policies and indoor spaces help people to quit smoking (Stephens et al., 2001). Fortunately, policies and bylaws that protect people from environmental tobacco smoke (ETS) are more commonplace now than in the past, and many buildings are smoke-free. Many addiction treatment facilities do not permit smoking indoors but clients are free to smoke outside. Some have designated ventilation rooms; other, more progressive facilities do not permit smoking anywhere on the property and require clients who smoke to participate in a smoking cessation program. One study showed that clients in a mandatory smoking cessation program were more likely to be engaged in the process, to seek information and to follow their treatment plan (Joseph et al., 1993). However, other studies found high drop-out rates when outright bans were introduced without adequate planning and treatment (Kotz, 1993). Treatment facility tobacco-use policies should address where smoking is permitted on the property, and the level of intervention with all clients. They should also include interventions to address smoking by staff, and should establish appropriate boundaries with regard to smoking with clients and during sessions.

Staff Training

There is evidence that counsellor training on smoking cessation coupled with client education significantly changes clients' attitudes and readiness to quit smoking as part of their treatment plan (Perine & Schare, 1999). Staff attitudes are likely to change with a comprehensive approach of policy change and education of staff about the importance of the issue (Campbell et al., 1998).

Components of a Clinical Intervention

The components of an evidence-based clinical intervention are collectively known as the "five A" model: Ask, Advise, Assess, Assist and Arrange (Fiore, 2000).

ASK

All clients of substance use treatment should be screened for tobacco use and their interest in quitting (Fiore, 2000). Counsellors should record the type(s) of tobacco product(s) used, along with the quantity and frequency of use. The level of nicotine dependence can be measured using the Fagerstrom Test for Nicotine Dependence (Heatherton et al., 1991) or the Cigarette Dependence Scale (Etter et al., 2003). These tests guide the use of nicotine replacement therapy. For people who smoke less than 10 cigarettes per day or who smoke occasionally, behavioural treatment and advice may be sufficient. For people who are heavily dependent, the use of intensive counselling and medications may be necessary. Those who have quit should be congratulated and supported in maintaining their cessation while in treatment and during after-care. They should also be advised to avoid ETS.

Explore Relevant Aspects of the Client's History

A careful psychiatric history should be obtained whenever possible with special atten-tion to depression, anxiety, eating disorders, psychotic disorders and bipolar disorders. These conditions are associated with higher prevalence of smoking as well as difficulty quitting (El-Guehaly et al., 2002). A patient taking psychiatric medications should not stop smoking abruptly without first consulting with a doctor or pharmacist to make sure that no adjustment to the dose is required. An exploration of past quit attempts helps counsellors understand the level of dependence, the psychological and social strengths of the client, successful behaviours and strategies used to quit, as well as trig-gers for relapse. Since it often takes four to 11 attempts to stop smoking completely, educating clients about smoking cessation as a process rather than an event helps build hope in those who have tried, but not yet succeeded in quitting, and who may experience a sense of failure.

Clients with a history of major depression should be evaluated with the Beck Depression Inventory (Beck, 1987). If a client is currently depressed, it is important to treat the depression while or before the client attempts to quit smoking. For a client who is not currently depressed, it is important to monitor depressive symptoms while the person is attempting to quit smoking.

Ask also about medical symptoms. People who smoke are more likely to report respiratory, cardiovascular, gastrointestinal and nose and throat problems.

ADVISE

All clients should be advised to quit smoking due to its detrimental health effects (Fiore, 2000). Some clients may resent being advised to quit when they are seeking treatment for substance use problems. Therefore, sensitivity to the client's readiness is important.

ASSESS

Assessment of the client's readiness to quit as measured by a composite scale of importance and confidence could help tailor treatment. A stage-matched intervention may have some benefit and should be employed. For the purposes of smoking cessation, the stages of change are defined as follows:
• precontemplation: Not ready to quit smoking in six months
• contemplation: Ready to quit in the next six months but not the next month
• preparation: Ready to quit within the next month
• action: Has quit smoking but for less than six months
• maintenance: Has quit smoking for more than six months
• relapse/treatment failure: Smoking at least one cigarette per day for seven consecutive days or smoking one or more cigarettes on one or more days in a two-week period (Hughes, Keely et al., 2003) is considered a relapse or failure of the intervention. Smoking less than either of those amounts should be considered a lapse or slip.

Clients who resume smoking should be reassessed for their willingness to try again since many are still interested in addressing their tobacco use. Remember that change typically follows a non-linear pattern. People are susceptible to both intra-therapeutic and extra-therapeutic factors that can move them in either direction along the continuum of change.

ASSIST

There is a strong relationship between the intensity of counselling and smoking cessation. Treatment may be delivered in groups or individually. Each session should be longer than 10 minutes (ideally 30 to 60 minutes). At least four sessions with an after-care component are recommended. Treatment should involve problem solving, intra-treatment and extra-treatment social support.

The addition of cognitive behaviour therapy to address depression in clients with a history of alcohol dependence has been shown to increase treatment attendance and short-term success in quitting smoking (Patten, et al., 2002).

All clients should be encouraged to use pharmacotherapy unless there is a medical contraindication. Counsellors can encourage the client to discuss the issue with his or her family doctor or pharmacist.

Motivational techniques, such as exploring the pros and cons of changing, should be used with all clients. In the preparation phase (i.e., if the client is ready to quit in the next 30 days), clients should be encouraged to set a target quit date. It is also important in this phase to discuss strategies clients can use to cope with withdrawal, cravings and cues; extra-therapeutic social support is recommended. To increase the odds of quitting, living space and vehicle should be smoke-free (Fiore, 2000; Stephens et al., 2001). Harm reduction strategies include smoking outdoors and gradually reducing the number of cigarettes smoked per day, but not switching to light or ultra-light cigarettes since people tend to compensate for the lower level of nicotine by taking more puffs or inhaling more deeply (Kozlowski et al., 1998).

For those unwilling to quit, motivational interviewing techniques to explore and resolve their ambivalence and resistance are recommended.

Use of Pharmacotherapy

In all the clinical trials conducted to date, pharmacotherapy approximately doubles the chances of quitting and sustaining the quit (Fiore, 2000; Hughes, Stead et al., 2003; Silagy et al., 2002). Nicotine replacement (nicotine patch, gum or inhaler), bupropion SR (Zyban®) and nortriptyline all produce similar long-term abstinence rates.

The choice of medication depends on individual differences and contraindications. For example, bupropion SR may be the best choice for clients with a history of depression due to its antidepressant effects and its ability to be combined safely with other common antidepressants (DeBattista et al., 2003; Kennedy et al., 2002). However, bupropion SR cannot be given to anyone with an allergy to the medication, seizure disorder, eating disorder or uncontrolled bipolar disorder. Patients with past (not currently active) alcohol problems respond favourably to bupropion SR (Tonstad, 2002). However those actively drinking or in early withdrawal from alcohol or other drugs should not take it due to the risk of seizures.

Nicotine replacement can be used by anyone who smokes more than 10 cigarettes per day and is available in several forms over the counter. One study found that clients with past alcohol problems were likely to respond favourably to nicotine replacement therapy, continuing with a sustained quit at the six month follow-up (Hughes, Novy et al., 2003).The recommended duration of treatment varies from seven to 52 weeks of medication and should be tailored to each client. Some clients may find it difficult to stop nicotine gum, but it is safer than smoking (Hurt et al., 1995) and clients can be helped to stop use without risking relapse to smoking.

Alternative Therapies

Currently, it is uncertain whether hypnosis, acupuncture and/or laser therapy are efficacious for smoking cessation (Fiore et al., 2000; Lancaster et al., 2000). However, there are many anecdotal reports of sustained response to these methods.

ARRANGE

Periodic follow-up is recommended for clients who are not ready to quit. For those who have quit, follow-up sessions are advised during the first week of quitting to explore slips, negative mood and other predictors of relapse. Thereafter, the frequency and duration of follow-ups can be decided based on individual preferences and staff availability.

MEASURES OF SUCCESS

Success can be measured in several ways: Standard measures look at biochemically verified self-report of continuous abstinence (not even a single puff of a cigarette) six months after the quit date, while other studies also look at quit rates at one year. Since clients enter treatment for alcohol and or other drug problems at different stages of change with respect to quitting smoking, it is more realistic to monitor changes in readiness than only smoking cessation rates. Therefore, an effective tobacco intervention program moves clients in a precontemplation stage into contemplation and so on.

CONCLUSION

Tobacco is a potential gateway drug that kills 50 per cent of the people who use it. Ten thousand people worldwide are killed daily from an addiction that, until recently, our field has ignored. Given the serious health problems that tobacco use causes in clients with alcohol and other drug problems, every counsellor needs to intervene. Although many clients have difficulty quitting smoking, with appropriate interventions, they can be helped to address their tobacco use. The "five A" model for smoking cessation provides an approach that focuses on the client, matching treatment to his or her individual stage of change.

Those who wish to address their smoking can do so without jeopardizing their recovery from substance use problems. Smoking cessation may even help them in their recovery from other substance use problems, and protect against relapse (Sullivan & Covey, 2002).

REFERENCES

Aloot, C.B., Vredevoe, D.L. & Brecht, M.L. (1993). Evaluation of high-risk smoking practices used by the homeless. *Cancer Nursing, 16*(2), 123–130.

American Psychiatric Association. (1994). *Diagnostic and Statistical Manual of Mental Disorders.* (4th ed.). Washington, DC: author.

Anonymous. (2002). Usual sources of cigarettes for middle and high school students—Texas, 1998–1999. *Morbidity and Mortality Weekly Report, 51*(40), 900–901.

Balfour, D.J.K. (2002). The neurobiology of tobacco dependence: A commentary. *Respiration, 69*(1), 7–11.

Bartecchi, C.E., MacKenzie, T.D. & Schrier, R.W. (1994). The human costs of tobacco use (1). *New England Journal of Medicine, 330*(13), 907–912.

Bartecchi, C.E., MacKenzie, T.D. & Schrier, R.W. (1995). The global tobacco epidemic. *Scientific American, 272*(5), 44–51.

Beck, A. & Steer, R.A. (1987). *Manual for the Revised Beck Depression Inventory.* San Antonio, TX: Psychological Corp.

Bergen, A.W. & Caporaso, N. (1999). Cigarette smoking. *Journal of the National Cancer Institute, 91*(16), 1365–1375.

Bernstein, S.M. & Stoduto, G. (1999). Adding a choice-based program for tobacco smoking to an abstinence-based addiction treatment program. *Journal of Substance Abuse Treatment, 17*(1–2), 167–173.

Bobo, J.K. & Gilchrist, L.D. (1983). Urging the alcoholic client to quit smoking cigarettes. *Addictive Behaviors, 8*(3), 297–305.

Bobo, J.K., Gilchrist, L.D., Schilling, R.F.D., Noach, B. & Schinke, S.P. (1987). Cigarette smoking cessation attempts by recovering alcoholics. *Addictive Behaviors, 12*(3), 209–215.

Bobo, J.K., McIlvain, H.E., Lando, H.A., Walker, R.D. & Leed-Kelly, A. (1998). Effect of smoking cessation counseling on recovery from alcoholism: Findings from a randomized community intervention trial. *Addiction, 93*(6), 877–887.

Breslau, N., Peterson, E., Schultz, L., Andreski, P. & Chilcoat, H. (1996). Are smokers with alcohol disorders less likely to quit? *American Journal of Public Health, 86*(7), 985–990.

Burling, T.A., Burling, A.S. & Latini, D. (2001). A controlled smoking cessation trial for substance-dependent inpatients. *Journal of Consulting and Clinical Psychology, 69*(2), 295–304.

Campbell, B.K., Krumenacker, J. & Stark, M.J. (1998). Smoking cessation for clients in chemical dependence treatment. A demonstration project. *Journal of Substance Abuse Treatment, 15*(4), 313–318.

Campbell, B.K., Wander, N., Stark, M.J. & Holbert, T. (1995). Treating cigarette smoking in drug-abusing clients. *Journal of Substance Abuse Treatment, 12*(2), 89–94.

Capretto, N.A. (1993). Confronting nicotine dependency at the Gateway Rehabilitation Center. *Journal of Substance Abuse Treatment, 1*(2), 113–116.

Clarke, J.G., Stein, M.D., McGarry, K.A. & Gogineni, A. (2001). Interest in smoking cessation among injection drug users. *American Journal of Addiction, 10*(2), 159–166.

Clemmey, P., Brooner, R., Chutuape, M.A., Kidorf, M. & Stitzer, M. (1997). Smoking habits and attitudes in a methadone maintenance treatment population. *Drug and Alcohol Dependence, 44*(2–3), 123–132.

Critchley, J.A. & Unal, B. (2003). Health effects associated with smokeless tobacco: A systematic review. *Thorax, 58*(5), 435–443.

CTUMS 2002: *Summary of Results for 2002 (February to December).* Health Canada Tobacco Control Programme. Available: www.hc-sc.gc.ca/hecs-sesc/tobacco/research/ctums/2002/annual_summary.html.

Cummings, K.M., Morley, C.P. & Hyland, A. (2002). Failed promises of the cigarette industry and its effect on consumer misperceptions about the health risks of smoking. *Tobacco Control, 11*(Suppl 1), I110–I117.

Currie, S.R., Hodgins, D.C., el-Guebaly, N. & Campbell, W. (2001). Influence of depression and gender on smoking expectancies and temptations in alcoholics in early recovery. *Journal of Substance Abuse, 13*(4), 443–458.

Currie, S.R., Nesbitt, K., Wood, C. & Lawson, A. (2003). Survey of smoking cessation services in Canadian addiction programs. *Journal of Substance Abuse Treatment, 24*(1), 59–65.

Dawson, D.A. (2000). Drinking as a risk factor for sustained smoking. *Drug and Alcohol Dependence, 59*(3), 235–249.

DeBattista, C., Solvason, H.B., Poirier, J., Kendrick, E. & Schatzberg, A.F. (2003). A prospective trial of bupropion SR augmentation of partial and non-responders to serotonergic antidepressants. *Journal of Clinical Psychopharmacology, 23*(1), 27–30.

Degenhardt, L. & Hall, W. (2001). The relationship between tobacco use, substance-use disorders and mental health: Results from the National Survey of Mental Health and Well-being. *Nicotine and Tobacco Research, 3*(3), 225–234.

DiFranza, J.R. & Coleman, M. (2001). Sources of tobacco for youths in communities with strong enforcement of youth access laws. *Tobacco Control, 10*(4), 323–328.

El-Guehaly, N., Cathcart, J., Currie, S., Brown, D. & Gloster, S. (2002). Smoking cessation approaches for persons with mental illness or addictive disorders. *Psychiatric Services, 53*(9), 1166–1170.

Ellickson, P.L., Tucker, J.S. & Klein, D.J. (2001). High-risk behaviors associated with early smoking: Results from a 5-year follow-up. *Journal of Adolescent Health, 28*(6), 465–473.

Etter, J.F., Le Houezec, J. & Perneger, T.V. (2003). A self-administered questionnaire to measure dependence on cigarettes: The cigarette dependence scale. *Neuropsychopharmacology, 28*(2), 359–370.

Ferrence, R., Lothian, S. & Cape, D. (2000). Contemporary patterns of nicotine use in Canada and the United States. In R.G. Ferrence, J. Slade, R. Room & M. Pope (Eds.), *Nicotine and Public Health* (pp. 287–309). Washington, DC: American Public Health Association.

Fiore, M., Bailey W.C., Cohen S.J. et al. (2000a). *Treating Tobacco Use and Dependence: Clinical Practice Guideline*. Rockville, MD: US Department of Health and Human Services. Public Health Services.

Fiore, M., Bailey, W.C., Cohen, S.J., Dorfman, S.F., Fox, B.J., Goldstein, M.G. et al. (2000b). A clinical practice guideline for treating tobacco use and dependence: A US Public Health Service report. *Journal of the American Medical Association, 283*(24), 3244–3254.

Frosch, D.L., Nahom, D. & Shoptaw, S. (2002). Optimizing smoking cessation outcomes among the methadone maintained. *Journal of Substance Abuse Treatment, 23*(4), 425–430.

Frosch, D.L., Shoptaw, S., Jarvik, M.E., Rawson, R.A. & Ling, W. (1998). Interest in smoking cessation among methadone maintained outpatients. *Journal of Addictive Disorders, 17*(2), 9–19.

Frosch, D.L., Shoptaw, S., Nahom, D. & Jarvik, M.E. (2000). Associations between tobacco smoking and illicit drug use among methadone-maintained opiate-dependent individuals. *Experimental and Clinical Psychopharmacology, 8*(1), 97–103.

Glassman, A.H., Covey, L.S., Stetner, F. & Rivelli, S. (2001). Smoking cessation and the course of major depression: A follow-up study. *Lancet, 357*(9272), 1929–1932.

Goldsmith, R.J. & Knapp, J. (1993). Towards a broader view of recovery. *Journal of Substance Abuse Treatment, 10*(2), 107–111.

Heatherton, T.F., Kozlowski, L.T., Frecker, R.C. & Fagerstrom, K.O. (1991). The Fagerstrom Test for Nicotine Dependence: A revision of the Fagerstrom Tolerance Questionnaire. *British Journal of Addiction, 86*(9), 1119–1127.

Hoffmann, D., Djordjevic, M.V. & Hoffmann, I. (1997). The changing cigarette. *Preventive Medicine, 26*(4), 427–434.

Hughes, J.R., Keely, J.P., Niaura, R.S., Ossip-Klein, D.J., Richmond, R.L. & Swan, G.E. (2003). Measures of abstinence in clinical trials: Issues and recommendations. *Nicotine and Tobacco Research, 5*(1), 13–25.

Hughes, J.R., Novy, P., Hatsukami, D.K., Jensen, J. & Callas, P.W. (2003). Efficacy of nicotine patch in smokers with a history of alcoholism. *Alcohol Clinical and Experimental Research, 27*(6), 946–954.

Hughes, J.R., Stead, L.F. & Lancaster, T. (2000). Antidepressants for smoking cessation. *The Cochrane Library, Issue 4, 2000*. Chichester, U.K.: John Wiley.

Humfleet, G., Munoz, R., Sees, K., Reus, V. & Hall, S. (1999). History of alcohol or drug problems, current use of alcohol or marijuana, and success in quitting smoking. *Addictive Behaviors, 24*(1), 149–154.

Hurt, R.D., Offord, K.P., Croghan, I.T., Gomez-Dahl, L., Kottke, T.E., Morse, R.M. et al. (1996). Mortality following inpatient addictions treatment: Role of tobacco use in a community-based cohort [see comments] [published erratum appears in *Journal of the American Medical Association 276*(10), 784] *Journal of the American Medical Association, 275*(14), 1097–1103.

Hurt, R.D., Offord, K.P., Lauger, G.G., Marusic, Z., Fagerstrom, K.O., Enright, P.L. et al. (1995). Cessation of long-term nicotine gum use—a prospective, randomized trial [see comments]. *Addiction, 90*(3), 407–413.

Jha, P., Chaloupka, F. (1999). *Curbing the Epidemic: Governments and the Economics of Tobacco Control.* Washington, DC: World Bank.

Joseph, A.M., Nichol, K.L. & Anderson, H. (1993). Effect of treatment for nicotine dependence on alcohol and drug treatment outcomes. *Addictive Behaviors, 18*(6), 635–644.

Kalman, D., Tirch, D., Penk, W. & Denison, H. (2002). An investigation of predictors of nicotine abstinence in a smoking cessation treatment study of smokers with a past history of alcohol dependence. *Psychology of Addictive Behaviors, 16*(4), 346–349.

Karan, L.D. (1993). Initial encounters with tobacco cessation on the Inpatient Substance Abuse Unit of the Medical College of Virginia. *Journal of Substance Abuse Treatment, 10*(2), 117–123.

Kenford, S.L., Smith, S.S., Wetter, D.W., Jorenby, D.E., Fiore, M.C. & Baker, T.B. (2002). Predicting relapse back to smoking: Contrasting affective and physical models of dependence. *Journal of Consulting and Clinical Psychology, 70*(1), 216–227.

Kennedy, S.H., McCann, S.M., Masellis, M., McIntyre, R.S., Raskin, J., McKay, G. et al. (2002). Combining bupropion SR with venlafaxine, paroxetine, or fluoxetine: A preliminary report on pharmacokinetic, therapeutic, and sexual dysfunction effects. *Journal of Clinical Psychiatry, 63*(3), 181–186.

Kohn, C.S., Tsoh, J.Y. & Weisner, C.M. (2003). Changes in smoking status among substance abusers: Baseline characteristics and abstinence from alcohol and drugs at 12-month follow-up. *Drug and Alcohol Dependence, 69*(1), 61–71.

Kotz, M.M. (1993). A smoke-free chemical dependency unit: The Cleveland Clinic experience. *Journal of Substance Abuse Treatment, 10*(2), 125–131.

Kozlowski, L.T., Goldberg, M.E., Yost, B.A., White, E.L., Sweeney, C.T. & Pillitteri, J.L. (1998). Smokers' misperceptions of light and ultra-light cigarettes may keep them smoking. *American Journal of Preventive Medicine, 15*(1), 9–16.

Kozlowski, L.T., Skinner, W., Kent, C. & Pope, M.A. (1989). Prospects for smoking treatment in individuals seeking treatment for alcohol and other drug problems. *Addictive Behaviors, 14*(3), 273–278.

Kozlowski, L.T., Wilkinson, D.A., Skinner, W., Kent, C., Franklin, T. & Pope, M. (1989). Comparing tobacco cigarette dependence with other drug dependencies: Greater or equal 'difficulty quitting' and 'urges to use,' but less 'pleasure' from cigarettes. *Journal of the American Medical Association, 261*(6), 898–901.

Kumra, V. & Markoff, B.A. (2000). Who's smoking now? The epidemiology of tobacco use in the United States and abroad. *Clinics in Chest Medicine, 21*(1), 1–9, vii.

Lancaster, T., Stead, L., Silagy, C. & Sowden, A. (2000). Effectiveness of interventions to help people stop smoking: Findings from the Cochrane Library. *British Medical Journal, 321*(7257), 355–358.

Lerman, C., Roth, D., Kaufmann, V., Audrain, J., Hawk, L., Liu, A. et al. (2002). Mediating mechanisms for the impact of bupropion in smoking cessation treatment. *Drug and Alcohol Dependence, 67*(2), 219–223.

Lewinsohn, P.M., Rohde, P. & Brown, R.A. (1999). Level of current and past adolescent cigarette smoking as predictors of future substance use disorders in young adulthood. *Addiction, 94*(6), 913–921.

MacKenzie, T.D., Bartecchi, C.E. & Schrier, R.W. (1994). The human costs of tobacco use (2). *New England Journal of Medicine, 330*(14), 975–980.

Makomaski Illing, E.M. & Kaiserman, M.J. (1999). Mortality attributable to tobacco use in Canada and its regions, 1994 and 1996. *Chronic Diseases in Canada, 20*(3), 111–117.

Martin, J.E., Calfas, K.J., Patten, C.A., Polarek, M., Hofstetter, C.R., Noto, J. et al. (1997). Prospective evaluation of three smoking interventions in 205 recovering alcoholics: One-year results of Project SCRAP-Tobacco. *Journal of Consulting and Clinical Psychology, 65*(1), 190–194.

Meyer, T.J., Lin, M.M. & Brown, L.S., Jr. (1996). Nicotine dependence and depression among methadone maintenance patients. *Journal of the National Medical Association, 88*(12), 800–804.

Mitchell, B.E., Sobel, H.L. & Alexander, M.H. (1999). The adverse health effects of tobacco and tobacco-related products. *Primary Care, 26*(3), 463–498.

Moher, M., Hey, K. & Lancaster, T. (2004) Workplace interventions for smoking cessation. *The Cochrane Library, Issue 1, 2004.* Chichester, U.K.: John Wiley.

Moolchan, E.T., Radzius, A., Epstein, D.H., Uhl, G., Gorelick, D.A., Cadet, J.L. et al. (2002). The Fagerstrom Test for Nicotine Dependence and the Diagnostic Interview Schedule: Do they diagnose the same smokers? *Addictive Behaviors, 27*(1), 101–113.

Murray, C.J. & Lopez, A.D. (1997). Global mortality, disability, and the contribution of risk factors: Global Burden of Disease Study. *Lancet, 349*(9063), 1436–1442.

National Cancer Institute. *Risks Associated with Smoking Cigarettes with Low Machine-Measured Yields of Tar and Nicotine.* (2001). Bethesda, MD: author.

Patkar, A.A., Lundy, A., Leone, F.T., Weinstein, S.P., Gottheil, E. & Steinberg, M. (2002).

Tobacco and alcohol use and medical symptoms among cocaine dependent patients. *Substance Abuse, 23*(2), 105–114.

Patkar, A.A., Sterling, R.C., Leone, F.T., Lundy, A. & Weinstein, S.P. (2002). Relationship between tobacco smoking and medical symptoms among cocaine-, alcohol-, and opiate-dependent patients. *American Journal of Addiction, 11*(3), 209–218.

Patten, C.A., Gillin, J.C., Golshan, S., Wolter, T.D., Rapaport, M. & Kelsoe, J. (2001). Relationship of mood disturbance to cigarette smoking status among 252 patients with a current mood disorder. *Journal of Clinical Psychiatry, 62*(5), 319–324.

Perine, J.L. & Schare, M.L. (1999). Effect of counselor and client education in nicotine addiction on smoking in substance abusers. *Addictive Behaviors, 24*(3), 443–447.

Peto, R., Lopez, A.D., Boreham, J., Thun, M., Heath, C., Jr. & Doll, R. (1996). Mortality from smoking worldwide. *British Medical Bulletin, 52*(1), 12–21.

Reading, J. (1996). *Eating Smoke: A Review of Non-traditional Use of Tobacco among Aboriginal People*. Ottawa: Medical Services Branch, Health Canada. Minister of Supply and Services Canada.

Reading, J. (1997). *The Tobacco Report: First Nations and Inuit Regional Health Survey* (pp. 89–135). Ottawa: First Nations and Inuit Regional Health Survey National Steering Committee.

Reid, M.S., Mickalian, J.D., Delucchi, K.L., Hall, S.M. & Berger, S.P. (1998). An acute dose of nicotine enhances cue-induced cocaine craving. *Drug and Alcohol Dependence, 49*(2), 95–104.

Richter, K.P., Ahluwalia, H.K., Mosier, M.C., Nazir, N. & Ahluwalia, J.S. (2002). A population-based study of cigarette smoking among illicit drug users in the United States. *Addiction, 97*(7), 861–869.

Richter, K.P., Gibson, C.A., Ahluwalia, J.S. & Schmelzle, K.H. (2001). Tobacco use and quit attempts among methadone maintenance clients. *American Journal of Public Health, 91*(2), 296–299.

Rickert, W. (2000). Today's cigarettes: Steps toward reducing the health impact. In R.G. Ferrence, J. Slade, R. Room & M. Pope (Eds.), *Nicotine and Public Health* (pp. 135–158). Washington, DC: American Public Health Association.

Robinson, J.H. & Pritchard, W.S. (1992). The role of nicotine in tobacco use. *Psychopharmacology (Berl), 108*(4), 397–407.

Saxon, A.J., McGuffin, R. & Walker, R.D. (1997). An open trial of transdermal nicotine replacement therapy for smoking cessation among alcohol- and drug-dependent inpatients. *Journal of Substance Abuse Treatment, 14*(4), 333–337.

Seidner, A.L., Burling, T.A., Gaither, D.E. & Thomas, R.G. (1996). Substance-dependent inpatients who accept smoking treatment. *Journal of Substance Abuse Treatment, 8*(1), 33–44.

Silagy, C., Lancaster, T., Stead, L., Mant, D. & Fowler, G. (2002). Nicotine replacement therapy for smoking cessation. *The Cochrane Library, Issue 1, 2004.* Chichester, U.K.: John Wiley.

Single, E., Robson, L., Xie, X. & Rehm, J. (1998). The economic costs of alcohol, tobacco and illicit drugs in Canada, 1992. *Addiction, 93*(7), 991–1006.

Spiga, R., Schmitz, J. & Day, J., 2nd. (1998). Effects of nicotine on methadone self-administration in humans. *Drug and Alcohol Dependence, 50*(2), 157–165.

Stein, M.D. & Anderson, B.J. (2003). Nicotine and drug interaction expectancies among methadone maintained cigarette smokers. *Journal of Substance Abuse Treatment, 24*(4), 357–361.

Stephens, T., Pederson, L.L., Koval, J.J. & Macnab, J. (2001). Comprehensive tobacco control policies and the smoking behaviour of Canadian adults. *Tobacco Control, 10*(4), 317–322.

Stolerman, I.P. & Jarvis, M.J. (1995). The scientific case that nicotine is addictive. *Psychopharmacology (Berl), 117*(1), 2–10; discussion 14–20.

Story, J. & Stark, M.J. (1991). Treating cigarette smoking in methadone maintenance clients. *Journal of Psychoactive Drugs, 23*(2), 203–215.

Stotts, A.L., Schmitz, J.M. & Grabowski, J. (2003). Concurrent treatment for alcohol and tobacco dependence: Are patients ready to quit both? *Drug and Alcohol Dependence, 69*(1), 1–7.

Sullivan, M.A. & Covey, L.S. (2002). Current perspectives on smoking cessation among substance abusers. *Current Psychiatry Reports, 4*(5), 388–396.

Thun, M.J. & Heath, C.W., Jr. (1997). Changes in mortality from smoking in two American Cancer Society prospective studies since 1959. *Preventive Medicine, 26*(4), 422–426.

Tonstad, S. (2002). Use of sustained-release bupropion in specific patient populations for smoking cessation. *Drugs, 62*(Suppl 2), 37–43.

Upadhyaya, H.P., Deas, D., Brady, K.T. & Kruesi, M. (2002). Cigarette smoking and psychiatric comorbidity in children and adolescents. *Journal of the American Academy of Child and Adolescent Psychiatry, 41*(11), 1294–1305.

Vidal, C. (1997). Tobacco reduction. *In Touch, 6*(2). Available: www.niichro.com/library. html#anchor324876.

von Gernet, A. (2000). Origins of nicotine use and the global diffusion of tobacco. In R.G. Ferrence, J. Slade John, R. Room & M. Pope (Eds.), *Nicotine and Public Health* (pp. 3–15). Washington, DC: American Public Health Association.

Wald, N.J. & Hackshaw, A.K. (1996). Cigarette smoking: An epidemiological overview. *British Medical Bulletin, 52*(1), 3–11.

About the Authors

JANE BARON, RN, MSc, is a past manager for the Lifestyle Enrichment for Senior Adults program (LESA) in Ottawa, a treatment program for people over age 55 with social and/or health problems related to their use of alcohol or other psychoactive drugs. From the program's inception in 1981, Jane was an advocate for a holistic approach to the treatment of seniors' substance use problems. Along with her program responsibilities, she developed materials and provided training on how to identify and intervene with an older person with substance use problems.

JENNIFER BARR, BA, is an education and publishing consultant for the Central East Region with the Centre for Addiction and Mental Health. Before moving to the Ottawa area in 2002, she worked for 13 years in Peterborough, Ontario, as a trainer, educator and community developer in the prevention and treatment of substance use problems. She has led several provincial projects, including the development of a handbook for professionals working with older adults, called *Choosing to Change*, and an Internet resource for youth about alcohol, called "Virtual Party."

CHRISTINE BOIS holds an MASc (University of Waterloo) in psychopharmacology and clinical psychology. She has worked in both addiction and mental health programs in the areas of treatment, research and education. She is currently manager of the Concurrent Disorders priority area at the Centre for Addiction and Mental Health. Previously, she was manager of an addiction assessment referral agency operated by the former Addiction Research Foundation. She has experience as a consultant in the areas of health promotion, system planning and treatment development. Other areas of work include substance use and older adults, and alcohol and violence.

FRED J. BOLAND, PhD, is a retired faculty member and former chair of clinical training in the Psychology Department at Queen's University, Kingston, Ontario. His major research interests included theoretical, treatment and relapse prevention aspects of substance use and eating disorders.

RICHARD J. BOUDREAU received his undergraduate degree from Boston College. While completing graduate work in Washington, DC, he did specialized studies in clinical behavioural sciences at Georgetown University and the National Institutes of Health. He also completed a diploma program in the Department of Psychiatry at McMaster University, Hamilton, with specialization in family therapy, as well as an MEd at the University of Toronto. His long career at the Addiction Research Foundation, a founding partner of the Centre for Addiction and Mental Health, focused primarily on clinical services and clinical education, especially as they apply to couples and family treatment of addiction.

KIM CALDERWOOD, PhD, RSW, is an assistant professor in the School of Social Work at the University of Windsor. She is a registered social worker with both clinical and community development experience. She has specialized in the area of concurrent disorders since 1994 and most recently has conducted research on interagency co-ordination across addiction and mental health services in non-metropolitan regions.

VIRGINIA CARVER, PhD, has worked in the addiction field since the early 1970s. For most of that time she worked as a program consultant with the Addiction Research Foundation (now part of the Centre for Addiction and Mental Health) and subsequently with Health Canada. She is currently continuing to do addiction-related work as a private contractor. Her main areas of interest are substance use treatment and services for women and older adults.

GLORIA CHAIM, MSW, RSW, is currently serving as project manager for the Pathways to Healthy Families Program at the Jean Tweed Centre, on a secondment from the Centre for Addiction and Mental Health, where she was clinical director, Assessment and General Treatment Program and Addiction Treatment Program for Special Populations. Gloria has worked in the substance use treatment field for over 20 years and has prior experience in community mental health settings. She has focused on clinical work and research, as well as training and education, as they relate to her areas of special interest—primarily youth, families and couples. She is particularly interested in integrating research, training and education to facilitate program development that will meet the needs of special population groups that are frequently underserved.

JULIANNE CONRY, PhD, is assistant professor emeritus at the University of British Columbia. Since 1984, she has been active in research on fetal alcohol syndrome (FAS) and the clinical assessment of children with FAS, and is now the psychologist with the multidisciplinary FAS team at the Asante Centre in Maple Ridge, British Columbia. She has appeared as an expert witness on FAS in the Provincial and Supreme Courts of British Columbia. She is co-author of the book *Fetal Alcohol Syndrome and the Criminal Justice System.* She was the principal writer and researcher for the B.C. Ministry of Education document *Teaching Students with Fetal Alcohol Syndrome/Effects: A Resource Guide for Teachers.* She is co-chair of Health Canada's National Advisory Committee on fetal alcohol spectrum disorders, and a member of the sub-committee on diagnosis, screening and surveillance.

GERRY COOPER, EdD, has worked in a variety of roles within the mental health and addiction field since 1976. Currently, he is the North Region unit manager for the Centre for Addiction and Mental Health. Gerry has produced or co-produced many educational resources, including course curricula, videotapes, CD-ROMs and Web pages. He has participated in the planning and delivery of many training programs for adult learners, written extensively on various mental health- and addiction-related topics, and taught at several post-secondary institutions. His doctoral thesis from the Ontario Institute for Studies in Education/University of Toronto won the 2001 Dissertation Award of the U.S. National Council on Problem Gambling.

CHRISTINE M.A. COURBASSON is the head of the Eating Disorders and Addiction Clinic at the Centre for Addiction and Mental Health (CAMH). She received her PhD in clinical psychology from York University. Subsequently, she received a post-doctoral fellowship at CAMH, investigating the psychological determinants of resiliency and treatment success in people with substance use problems, conducting assessments, and providing treatment to people with concurrent disorders. She holds a status appointment with the Department of Psychiatry at the University of Toronto and is also an adjunct faculty member at the Adler School of Professional Psychology in Toronto. She is involved in training clinicians in the application of dialectical behavioural therapy for eating disorders and addiction. Her clinical and research interests include the treatment of concurrent substance use, eating disorders, depression, anxiety and personality disorders; coping with stress; mindfulness; resiliency; expectancies and the role of the self in eating disorders. She has received many awards, is the author of a number of scientific articles and book chapters, and has lectured on a variety of topics related to her clinical and research interests.

FARZANA DOCTOR, MSW, RSW, has worked with the LGBTTTIQ community since 1993. She is currently the service manager for Rainbow Services at CAMH, a program for LGBTTTIQ people with alcohol and other drug concerns.

JULIA DRAKE is a communications specialist whose background includes positions with the Addiction Research Foundation (now part of the Centre for Addiction and Mental Health) and the Canadian Diabetes Association. While running her own business, Drake Communications, Julia included among her clients the University of Toronto's Centre for Health Promotion, the Alcohol Policy Network and the Canadian Cancer Society. She has served as a communications adviser to an Ontario cabinet minister and has several years of experience as a newspaper reporter and magazine editor. She currently manages communications for Upper Canada College in Toronto. A graduate of Queen's University, Kingston, Ontario (BA, English), she also studied print journalism at Ryerson University, Toronto.

CHARL ELS was born and raised in South Africa. He completed medical school and the residency program in psychiatry at the University of the Free State. He is a Fellow of the College of Medicine of South Africa, and practised psychiatry for a number of years before immigrating to Canada in 1999. He served as clinical director of the Alberta Mental Health

Board's Dual Diagnosis Service at Alberta Hospital Ponoka for three years, after which he completed a clinical fellowship in addiction medicine at the University of Toronto and the Centre for Addiction and Mental Health (CAMH). He subsequently completed a second clinical fellowship in schizophrenia and nicotine dependence at CAMH. He is certified as an addiction specialist by the American Society of Addiction Medicine (ASAM). He currently works as an addiction psychiatrist in the Department of Psychiatry, University of Alberta Hospital, and at Alberta Hospital Edmonton's Assertive Community Treatment (ACT) program. He has been appointed as clinical assistant professor in the departments of Psychiatry at both the University of Calgary and the University of Alberta. He recently joined the Advisory Committee on Tobacco Research for the Alberta Alcohol and Drug Abuse Commission (AADAC). His main interest is the study of nicotine dependence in people with mental illness, and he is currently enrolled in an open studies course related to this topic at the University of Alberta.

MARGARET FLOWER, RN, SSW, began her career at the Addiction Research Foundation in 1983 as executive director of the Community Older Person's Alcohol (COPA) program, where she worked for seven years. During this time, Margaret was involved in the research she later used to develop and implement the OPUS 55 (Older Persons Unique Solutions) program at the Centre for Addiction and Mental Health. As program manager at OPUS 55 since it began in 1999, Margaret provides education and consultation across Ontario.

PETER M. FORD, MB, FRCP(C), is a faculty member in the Department of Medicine, Queen's University, Kingston, Ontario. He is director of the regional AIDS clinic that operates out of Kingston General Hospital and serves a wide area of both urban and rural eastern Ontario, as well as providing services for the local penitentiaries. He has a research interest in the epidemiology of HIV infection within the penitentiary system.

MICHAEL GITBERG is a psychotherapist who became interested in psychological trauma while working at Concurrent Disorders Program, Centre for Addiction and Mental Health. In the past five years he has specialized in working with women and men with addictions who have survived severe childhood sexual and physical abuse and neglect. His practice is informed by psychodynamic and relational perspectives and by his knowledge of interpersonal group psychotherapy. His most recent training is in sensorimotor psychotherapy, which aims to heal somatic manifestations of trauma. He currently works with a unique multidisciplinary team at the Trauma Therapy Program of Sunnybrook and Women's College Health Sciences Centre, and has a private practice.

TIM GODDEN, BSc, BAA(J), MSW, RSW, has been a therapist at the Centre for Addiction and Mental Health since 1999, conducting individual and group treatment and psychoeducational interventions in four different outpatient programs, including Guided Self-Change, Structured Relapse Prevention, Evening Health Service, and Back on Track (the impaired driving remedial program). He also teaches motivational interviewing workshops for staff at CAMH, through the Education and Health Promotion department and the Concurrent

Disorders Service. In the decade before coming to CAMH, he worked as a community mental health counsellor.

SUSAN HARRISON, BA (Hon.), BEd, MSW, was a teacher for several years before pursuing a degree in social work, graduating in 1979. Her career since then has included experience in the fields of child welfare and school social work, but has been primarily in addiction. Prior to her current position as Central East regional director, Centre for Addiction and Mental Health, Susan was the director of a women's addiction treatment centre. She has given many workshops and presentations on addiction-related topics, her special interest and expertise being women and addictions. She also led the project team to develop Ontario's remedial program for convicted impaired drivers.

MARILYN A. HERIE, PhD, RSW, has been a therapist and project leader at the Centre for Addiction and Mental Health (CAMH) since 1992, and is an adjunct professor at the Faculty of Social Work, University of Toronto. Her focus at CAMH has been on the development and dissemination of research-based practice protocols, including Structured Relapse Prevention (1996), Guided Self-Change for EAPs (1996), the Back on Track program for convicted impaired drivers (2000), and the development and evaluation of on-line courses. In addition, Marilyn is a clinical trainer and therapist specializing in the group and individual treatment of adults with substance use problems. Marilyn has facilitated hundreds of workshops and presented at academic conferences throughout Canada and in other countries. She has co-authored books, book chapters and articles in scholarly journals on brief treatment, alcohol dependence, relapse prevention, dissemination research and on-line learning. Marilyn also teaches an on-line course on addiction treatment in the Faculty of Social Work, University of Toronto. She received her doctorate in social work at the University of Toronto, where she conducted research on Web-based continuing education for therapists and health care practitioners.

KEITH HUMPHREYS, PhD, associate professor of psychiatry at Stanford University School of Medicine, received his doctorate in clinical/community psychology from the University of Illinois at Urbana, and his practice licence from the State of California Board of Psychology. He currently directs a US Department of Veterans Affairs program evaluation research centre that studies treatments and self-help programs for substance abuse and psychiatric disorders. Professor Humphreys has published more than a hundred scientific articles, has received national and international awards for his work and has been a consultant to many organizations, including the White House Office on National Drug Control Policy and the Center for Mental Health Services. He has also served as a consultant on mental health-related issues to agencies internationally.

EVA INGBER, MSW, RSW, works as an advanced practice clinician at the Centre for Addiction and Mental Health (CAMH). In this role, she works with a number of teams to provide clinical consultation and work on program development in various addiction services, including the women's program. She has specialized in the area of women and addiction for over 12 years.

She has worked as both a clinician and a manager in the women's addiction programs at CAMH and at the former Addiction Research Foundation. Eva received training and worked as part of CAMH's dialectical behaviour therapy team for one year. In the last year, she has been working with a team that has written a women's substance abuse treatment program for Corrections Canada. This program is currently being piloted across Canada in the women's federal prisons.

MELDON KAHAN, MD, CCFP, FRCPC, is medical director of the Addiction Medicine Service at St. Joseph's Health Centre, Toronto, a staff physician at the Centre for Addiction and Mental Health, and associate professor in the Department of Family and Community Medicine at the University of Toronto. He has a particular interest in the education of family physicians.

HANNAH KAUFMAN, MSS, is a clinical social worker at the Kingston Regional Cancer Centre, Ontario. She has experience in the field of HIV/AIDS in hospital, community, prison and professional settings, providing counselling, education and prevention services. Her community activism includes board and committee work with HIV/AIDS Regional Services. She received her MSS at Bryn Mawr College, Pennsylvania.

JOHN KELLY, PhD, is a consulting assistant professor of psychiatry and behavioral sciences at Stanford University School of Medicine. He received his doctorate in clinical psychology from the joint doctoral program at the University of California, San Diego/San Diego State University. Dr. Kelly is also a licensed chemical dependency counsellor. He currently works as a research scientist in the US Department of Veterans Affairs, where he studies treatments for substance use disorders, along with patient involvement in, and effects from, mutual aid programs. He also serves on the executive committee of, and as a translation co-ordinator for, the VA Quality Enhancement Research Initiative (QUERI), SUD Module, whose aim is to translate and transfer scientific evidence into improvements in clinical care for people with addiction problems.

SHEILA LACROIX, BSc, MLS, is library co-ordinator at the Centre for Addiction and Mental Health (CAMH) library. Ms. Lacroix has been providing reference and research service to CAMH staff and other professionals since 1991. Her work includes disseminating addiction and mental health information through the development of information products such as bibliographies and resource guides. She is a regular contributor to CAMH's journal *crosscurrents* and to *SALIS News*, the newsletter of SALIS (Substance Abuse Librarians and Information Specialists).

NINA LITTMAN-SHARP, MSW, CGC, is manager of the Problem Gambling Service at the Centre for Addiction and Mental Health. She has worked with people who gamble since 1995. Nina presents and writes on several clinical and research topics, including relapse prevention, couple and family work, ADHD and problem gambling, and gambling and fatigue. Nina is one of the authors of the Inventory of Gambling Situations, an instrument that assesses areas of risk for relapse. She moderates a 400-member international listserv for problem gambling professionals.

JACKIE LLOYD-RAI, CCW, RSW, has worked in the field of addiction for 24 years. Her experience has included all aspects of the continuum of care. Jackie has worked in outpatient, residential and institutional settings. Her early training and professional development was with the Canadian Armed Forces at the Addiction Rehabilitation Centre, Kingston, Ontario. She has worked in both the federal and provincial prison systems in addiction and cultural program delivery. Over her career, she has provided direct services in individual and family counselling, and group and individual counselling for men, women and adolescents. Jackie has experience in program development and clinical supervision, and she helped launch (and was an instructor in) the Addictions Program at Career Canada College. She is currently the executive director of Vesta Recovery Program for Women, Ottawa.

DENNIS LONG, MSW, is executive director of Breakaway Youth and Family Services, Toronto. Previously, he was the Metro Toronto Treatment Services consultant for the Addiction Research Foundation (ARF), and has also been a trainer for the ARF's School for Addiction Studies, a psychiatric social worker at Humber Memorial Hospital, and a child and youth worker. In addition, he is currently president of the board of the Alcohol and Drug Recovery Association of Ontario. He has spoken on the subject of harm reduction at the International Conference on the Reduction of Drug Related Harm in Florence, Italy, and at symposia in Toronto. He has also provided training in harm reduction and youth treatment throughout Ontario.

DAVID MARSH, MD, CCSAM, graduated in medicine from Memorial University of Newfoundland following prior training in neuroscience and pharmacology. From 1995 to 2003 he worked at the Centre for Addiction and Mental Health, most recently as clinical director, Addiction Medicine, and held an academic appointment at the University of Toronto. He is currently physician leader, Addiction Medicine, for Vancouver Coastal Health and Providence Health Care. In this role he provides clinical leadership for publicly funded addiction treatment in both community and acute care settings across the region surrounding Vancouver. Dr. Marsh is also clinical associate professor in the Department of Health Care and Epidemiology, Faculty of Medicine, University of British Columbia. His research interests include the integration of pharmacotherapy and psychotherapy in the treatment of substance use disorders, and focus primarily on novel interventions for opioid dependence. He is presently a co-investigator on several peer-reviewed research grants, including the North American Opiate Medication Initiative (NAOMI) study of heroin prescription for treatment-refractory opioid dependence.

PETER MENZIES, MSW, RSW, PhD candidate, has more than 20 years' experience working with individuals and families in the areas of poverty, child welfare, homelessness, addiction and mental health. In his role as Manager, Aboriginal Services, at the Centre for Addiction and Mental Health (CAMH), Peter has developed partnerships between CAMH and both

Aboriginal and non-Aboriginal organizations across Ontario and Canada. A sessional lecturer at several post-secondary institutions, as well as at the Toronto Hostel Training Centre, Peter offers students both theoretical and practical perspectives on working with disadvantaged populations. As an Aboriginal person, Peter brings a distinct world view to social work practice. Peter has published articles relating to social work practice and Aboriginal issues.

MICHAEL NAYMARK, MA, has worked in the substance dependence field for over 20 years, both as a front-line therapist and as a manager. He is currently the manager of the Cocaine Service, and of the treatment component for the Toronto Drug Treatment Court program, at the Centre for Addiction and Mental Health.

ALAN C. OGBORNE was formerly a senior scientist at the Centre for Addiction and Mental Health, and is now in private practice. He holds a bachelor's degree in psychology from the University of Exeter, England, and a PhD in social psychology from the London School of Economics. His main professional interest has been in the evaluation of addiction treatment services and systems.

CATHERINE OLIVER, MSW, RSW, began her social work career working with people with developmental disabilities, including dual diagnoses. In 2000, she joined the multidisciplinary team at the Clinical Immunology Outpatient Clinic at Kingston General Hospital, Ontario, where she provides social work interventions with people infected or affected by HIV/AIDS.

JANE PATERSON, MSW, RSW, is deputy chief of professional services and social worker in chief at the Centre for Addiction and Mental Health (CAMH). She has been a clinical social worker for 20 years, working primarily with people who are seriously mentally ill. Her clinical work has included working with people with co-occurring substance use problems. She also has extensive experience in family treatment. In her current role, she is involved in establishing the professional practice structure at CAMH. She has also been involved in many education and training initiatives at CAMH and in the community.

JAMES O. PROCHASKA is director of the Cancer Prevention Research Center and professor of clinical and health psychology, both at the University of Rhode Island. He is the author of over 200 publications, including three books, *Changing for Good*, *Systems of Psychotherapy* and *The Transtheoretical Approach*. He is internationally recognized for his work as a developer of the stage model of behaviour change. He is the principal investigator on over $60 million in research grants for the prevention of cancer and other chronic diseases. In addition, he has served as a consultant to the American Cancer Society, Centers for Disease Control, Health Maintenance Organizations, the British National Health Service, major corporations, and numerous universities and research centres. Dr. Prochaska has won numerous awards, including the Top Five Most Cited Authors in Psychology from the American Psychology Society and an Innovator's Award from the Robert Wood Johnson Foundation, and is the first psychologist to win a Medal of Honor for Clinical Research from the American Cancer Society.

LORNA SAGORSKY originally trained in physical therapy in South Africa, graduating in 1962. Lorna joined the Addiction Research Foundation (now part of the Centre for Addiction and Mental Health) as a senior therapist in 1980, specializing in stress management for both inpatients and outpatients. In 1990, Lorna transferred to the brief treatment division of general addiction services, which she has managed since 1997. In 1998, Lorna received training in teaching motivational interviewing, an integral part of brief treatment. She has conducted numerous workshops for a wide variety of audiences. She is also Toronto manager/clinician for the Back on Track program (Ontario's remedial measures program for impaired drivers), and has revised the manuals used in the program.

MARTHA SANCHEZ-CRAIG earned a PhD in counselling psychology at the University of Toronto in 1972. In 1973, she joined the Addiction Research Foundation (now part of the Centre for Addiction and Mental Health), and was a senior scientist when she recently retired. In a 20-year program of research with numerous colleagues, she developed a cognitive-behavioural approach for early intervention with alcohol and other drug use problems, which has been tested in Canada, South America and Europe. The methods are described in numerous publications, including a therapist's manual for secondary prevention of alcohol problems and a self-help book, both published by the Addiction Research Foundation.

PETER SELBY, MBBS, CCFP, MHSc, ASAM, is clinical director, Addictions Program, and head of the Nicotine Dependence Clinic at the Centre for Addiction and Mental Health (CAMH). He is an assistant professor in the departments of Family and Community Medicine, Public Health Sciences, and Psychiatry, within the Faculty of Medicine, University of Toronto. Dr. Selby has been an invited speaker at more than 100 national, international and local symposia, workshops and seminars on addiction, health behaviour change and pregnancy. His areas of research interest include the use of Zyban® in the retreatment of relapsed smokers, Web-based smoking interventions, and the treatment of substance use, including smoking, in pregnancy.

JOANNE SHENFELD received her MSW from the University of Toronto in 1986. She has been with the former Addiction Research Foundation and the Centre for Addiction and Mental Health (CAMH) for over 12 years. Joanne has extensive clinical experience in the addiction field with individuals, couples, families and groups, through her work in Youth and Family Services at CAMH. She has been involved in research and program development, along with training and education. Currently, Joanne is service manager for the Family Service, and provides clinical supervision in the day and residential addiction program at CAMH's Donwood site. Her most recent clinical research project involves a study on multiple couples therapy, which resulted in a published treatment manual.

RANIA SHUGGI, BSc, is manager of Back on Track, Ontario's remedial measures program for impaired drivers, at the Centre for Addiction and Mental Health (CAMH). She graduated from the University of Toronto with a specialty in psychology, and joined CAMH in 1997. She was initially involved with client satisfaction research, before joining the Back on Track program in 1999. She worked on developing the program and training the staff involved in service delivery. She is currently working on raising awareness about impaired driving and its consequences in Ontario, while pursuing her MBA.

WAYNE SKINNER, MSW, RSW, is deputy clinical director, Addictions Program, at the Centre for Addiction and Mental Health, with responsibility for concurrent disorders and for problem gambling. He is assistant professor in the Department of Psychiatry and adjunct senior lecturer in the Faculty of Social Work at the University of Toronto. He directs the Addiction Studies certificate program in Continuing Education at U of T's St Michael's College. He also teaches an on-line course, "Addictions in Contemporary Society," at York University, Toronto. He has worked in the addiction field for over 25 years, playing a leading role in concurrent disorders since 1996. His clinical and research interests in treatment and recovery extend from brief interventions for people with mild to moderate addictive behaviours to mutual aid pathways for people with severe addictions, and harm reduction approaches for people who do not seek or benefit from conventional therapies. Concerned about the current tendency to understand addictions as essentially biopsychological processes, he emphasizes the need for more comprehensive approaches that include the role of inter-personal and sociostructural factors in shaping addictive behaviours. He is editing a book on the treatment of concurrent disorders, to be published by CAMH.

PATRICK D. SMITH is vice president, Clinical Programs, at the Centre for Addiction and Mental Health and head, Addiction Psychiatry Program, at the University of Toronto. He received a PhD in clinical psychology at the University of Nebraska, with specialty training in substance abuse. He was awarded a Fulbright Research Scholarship to the University of Canterbury in Christchurch, New Zealand, where he studied cross-cultural aspects of problem drinking. Dr. Smith completed his predoctoral internship at the Yale University School of Medicine, with his primary placement at the Substance Abuse Treatment Unit. He was awarded a U.S. National Institute on Drug Abuse (NIDA) post-doctoral fellowship, which he completed at Yale's Department of Psychiatry, within the School of Medicine. Dr. Smith has received various awards and has had many senior clinical and administrative positions. He has clinical experience in providing individual, group and family therapy in the areas of substance use and mental health. His clinical research interests are in the area of substance use, specifically alcohol and other drug expectancies, adolescent substance abuse and mental health, eating disorders, smoking cessation, and cross-cultural factors in substance use and mental health.

SHIRLEY SMITH holds an MSW from Columbia University and has worked in the field of addiction and mental health for the past 20 years, in both Canada and the United States. She was the director of Women and Specialty Programs at the Donwood Institute, a founding partner of the Centre for Addiction and Mental Health (CAMH). She also served as manager of the Metro Addiction Assessment and Referral Service (MAARS) for the Greater Toronto area. In 2002, she implemented CAMH's Psychological Trauma Program, and is presently managing the program. Shirley has taught social work and addiction at Atkinson College, York University, for the past decade and, together with a core team of instructors, designed and taught the first Concurrent Disorders Certificate Program for Special Populations.

ROBERT M. SOLOMON, LLB, LLM, is a professor in the Faculty of Law at the University of Western Ontario. He has published widely in the last 30 years on various aspects of alcohol and other drug law and policy. He has travelled extensively across Canada as a consultant and public speaker. In recent years, he has designed several professional development programs for addiction counsellors.

CATE SUTHERLAND is executive director of the Addictions Centre (Hastings/Prince Edward Counties) Inc., Ontario, which provides residential and outpatient treatment. Areas of interest in Cate's 25-year career in the addiction field include service provision to correctional clients and innovative program development.

JEREMY TOMLINSON, MEd, works as a psychotherapist in private practice in Toronto. His practice specializes in sexuality issues/sex therapy, issues for gay, lesbian, bisexual and two-spirited people, and recovery from substance use problems. He also teaches part-time in the Human Services Counsellor program at George Brown College, Toronto. He has worked with the issues of sexuality and substance use at several community-based agencies, including Planned Parenthood of Toronto, Youthlink Inner City and Kids Help Phone. He has also worked as a therapist doing individual, couple and family therapy at Family Service Agencies in Burlington, Brampton and Mississauga, Ontario. He is a graduate of the Ontario Institute for Studies in Education / University of Toronto.

TONY TONEATTO is a research scientist in the Clinical Research Department at the Centre for Addiction and Mental Health. He received his doctorate in clinical psychology from McGill University, Montreal, in 1987, and is a registered psychologist. He is an assistant professor in the departments of Public Health Sciences and Psychiatry at the University of Toronto. His research interests include concurrent alcohol use and psychiatric disorders, treatment of problem gambling, and natural recovery from substance dependence.

BERYL TSANG holds an MA in Asian Studies from York University, Toronto, and has worked in the fields of international development, cultural diversity and anti-racism for the last 10 years. She was formerly a cultural interpreter with the Canadian International Development Agency's China Project, a senior program consultant with the Addiction Research Foundation's Training and Education Department, a special consultant with the Ontario Management Board Secretariat's Employment Equity Implementation Project, and the executive director of the Regent Park Focus Community Coalition against Substance Abuse. Beryl is currently a trainer/materials developer with Education Wife Assault, an internationally recognized violence-prevention and education organization. She is the author of numerous articles, books and education materials on gender and identity.

ELSBETH TUPKER, MSW, is a clinical services consultant at the Centre for Addiction and Mental Health. Her 25 years of experience in the addiction field is primarily with youth, and includes treatment, program development, research and professional training. She has co-authored a number of publications: *Youth and Drugs: An Educational Package for*

Professionals; Let 'Em Go: How to Support Youth in Creating Their Own Solutions; and First Contact: A Brief Treatment for Young Substance Users.

SYDNEY J. USPRICH is a professor in the Faculty of Law at the University of Western Ontario. Specializing in criminal law and evidence, he combines over 30 years of teaching and research in those areas, with several years of practical experience as a part-time Crown attorney. In addition to numerous articles on criminal law and on alcohol and drug law and policy, he is co-author of *Evidence and Procedure in Canadian Labour Arbitration.*

LUCY VAN WYK, MSW, RSW, is clinical director of the Jean Tweed Centre, Toronto. Lucy's clinical experience has been in the areas of treatment for abused women and children and the treatment of women with substance use problems. She provides supervision for the Centre's clinical staff and development of the Centre's programs and services. Lucy developed and implemented a specialized treatment program for women with concurrent histories of trauma and substance use.

KEITH WALKER, PhD, is a staff psychologist with the Lyndhurst Centre of the Toronto Rehabilitation Institute. He has worked in the addiction field since 1972 and in the field of spinal cord rehabilitation since 1991. He served on the Addiction Research Foundation's Disability Issues Advisory Committee, which advocated for the development of accessible addiction services in Ontario. He has developed patient education materials about alcohol use following spinal cord injury. His current interests include the development of patient-centred strategies for the promotion of healthy lifestyles among patients in spinal cord rehabilitation programs.

LYN WATKIN-MEREK, RN, has worked at the former Addiction Research Foundation and the Centre for Addiction and Mental Health (CAMH) for 23 years as a nurse, discharge planner, assessment worker, therapist, senior therapist and—for the past 10 years—in management. She was the manager of the Structured Relapse Prevention programs and the Youth Program. She is currently a manager in the Law and Mental Health Program where, beside her management duties, she facilitates relapse prevention programs for clients with severe mental illness who are also involved in the criminal justice system. Lyn has co-authored the book *Structured Relapse Prevention: An Outpatient Counselling Approach* (1996) and manuals for the Back on Track remedial measures program for impaired drivers (2000). Lyn recently returned to school to complete her post-graduate nursing degree.

D. ADRIAN WILKINSON obtained his doctorate in psychology at Oxford University. After postdoctoral studies at York University, Toronto, he joined the Addiction Research Foundation (ARF), where he worked for 18 years. His principal research interests were treatment of substance use problems in youth and young adults, and the neuropsychological consequences of chronic heavy use of alcohol and other drugs. In 1988, he left the ARF and established a practice as a research consultant. He is currently director of research at Mensana Corporation in Toronto.

WENDY WOBESER is an assistant professor in the Department of Medicine at Queen's University, Kingston, Ontario. Dr. Wobeser works in the Clinical Immunology Clinic, where she cares for people with HIV, who are often co-infected with HCV. The clinic emphasizes the provision of optimal care to all populations, including people with addiction problems and those who are incarcerated.

HELEN YOUNGSON, MEd, retired from the Addiction Research Foundation in 1994 after 16 years of helping develop new services and programs in the Ottawa-Carleton community. Early in her career, she became a friend of Alcoholics Anonymous (AA), and helped recovering community members establish an AA group for gays, a Families Anonymous group, a Women for Sobriety group, the first attempt at a local Narcotics Anonymous group, and an AA open speakers meeting in a women's treatment centre. Her previous experience in community development—with the YWCA, the City of Toronto (Urban Renewal) and the Hamilton and District Community Information Centre—directed her interest and energy to mutual aid approaches to solving the health, social, economic and political problems of individuals and neighbourhoods.

Index

A

Aboriginal people
  Children's Aid Society and, 466
  child welfare policies and, 464–466
  concurrent disorders and, 456
  Constitution Act (1982) and, 462
  cultural values and healing, 469–471
  depression and, 456
  disability rates, 307
  Elders, role of, 460, 461, 470, 471
  European colonization, impact of, 460–461, 466
  family life and residential schools, 463–464, 467–469
  federal jurisdiction over, 461–466
  gambling and, 692
  Indian Act (1876), 457, 461–462, 476
  intergenerational trauma and, 467–469
  Inuit people, 457, 458
  legacy of dependency, 466–467
  legal definition of, 456–457
  mainstream *vs.* traditional cultural values (Table 20-4), 473–475
  medicine wheel and, 471, 475–476
  Metis people, 457, 458
  migration from reserves, 459–460
  morbidity and substance use, 455–456, 467
  pre-European contact social roles, 460
  provincial jurisdiction over, 462, 464–466
  relapse prevention and, 161
  residential schools, impact of, 462–469
  self-identification of, 458–459, 470
  suicide and, 455
  tobacco use and, 713
  traditional healing, 402, 469–472
  traditional languages of, 459, 463
  urban demographics of, 459–460, 476–477
Abstinence
  AA and, 172–173, 174
  as alcohol treatment goal, 128, 129–130, 134–137
  client's fears of, 131
  cocaine and, 670
  cognitive deficits and, 525, 526

concurrent disorders and, 591, 595
from gambling, 696, 698–699
vs. moderation, 127–128
NA and, 177, 178
opioid dependence and, 657
relapses and, 144
SMART Recovery and, 180
from smoking and substance use, 716–717
SOS and, 181
trauma assessment and, 423
twelve-step facilitation treatment and, 183, 184
youth and, 135, 386
Abstinence violation effects, 11
Abuse. *See also* child abuse; physical abuse; sexual abuse; trauma
  definition, 418
  eating disorders and, 562–563
  exploring trauma and, 425
Acamprosate, 201, 209
Acquired brain injury (ABI), 398
Acquired immune deficiency syndrome. *See* HIV/AIDS
Adaptive behaviour, fetal alcohol syndrome and, 505
Addiction. *See also* dependence; substance use
  definition, 75, 143
  as disability, 310
Addictive voice recognition techniques (AVRT), 188
ADHD. *See* attention-deficit/hyperactivity disorder
Adolescents. *See also* youth
  alcohol use and, 202
  assessment focus areas for, 388, 390–394
  binge-eating and, 573
  cannabis and, 219
  concurrent disorders case study (Jesse), 403–405
  consent to treatment, 96–98
  developmental tasks of life and, 389
  drug testing and, 70
  drug use and, 385
  early onset of smoking, 713–714
  eating disorders and, 571
  family therapy and, 402–403
  intoxication and, 7, 135
  mutual aid groups and, 186, 188

Amnesia, alcohol-related (Korsakoff's syndrome), 205, 520, 521, 524
Amphetamines, 222
Amsterdam, harm reduction strategies in, 230
Amyl nitrate (poppers), 354, 366, 368, 540
Anabolic steroids, 220–221, 233
Annis, Helen, 148
Anorexia nervosa. *See also* eating disorders
    diagnostic criteria of, 556
    men and, 572
    mortality rate for, 556
    physical signs of, 565
    starvation and, 556, 564
    treatment, 566, 567
Antagonist drug therapy, 201
Anti-anxiety medication. *See individual drug names*
Anti-craving therapy, 201
Antidepressants. *See also individual drug names*
    eating disorders and, 567
    for gambling, 688
    MDMA use and, 222
    older adults and, 332
    for tapering, 215
    women and, 254
Anxiety. *See also* post-traumatic stress disorder
    LGBTTTIQ communities and, 355
    withdrawal symptoms and, 206, 207
    women and medication for, 254
Art therapy, 432
Ascites, 203
Asexual people, 364, 373
Assertiveness, women and, 260–261
Assessment. *See also* screening
    benefits of, 54–55
    case management of, 45, 49–55
    client sensitivities and, 54
    concurrent disorders and women, 257
    consent, voluntary, and, 93
    drug testing and, 70
    family members and, 54, 485–486
    individualized, 47
    initial *vs.* ongoing, 53
    interventions and, 55, 57
    older adults and, 338–340
    processes for, 52–54
    resistance to, 54–55
    Structured Relapse Prevention counselling and, 149–150
    standardized instruments for, 51–52
    trauma and substance use, 423–427
    women and, 258–259
    youth, 388–390
Assessor/case manager
    as advocate, 59
    required skills, 48, 59–61
Ativan. *See* lorazepam
Attention-deficit/hyperactivity disorder (ADHD), 395–396

bipolar disorder and, 397
and children of alcoholic mothers, 498
conduct disorders and, 396, 397
fetal alcohol syndrome and, 498, 503, 505
gambling and, 683, 684
learning disabilities and, 399
Autism, 503
Autosexual people, 373
Aversive therapy, 201

B

Back on Track Remedial Measures Program, 642, 647
Bagot Commission (1842), 462, 463
Bandura, Albert, 143, 153
Bangkok, drug use in, 612
BASIS 32 (assessment questionnaire), 390
Battery, definition, 92–93
BBCM Foundation (Canada), 372
BDSM. *See* bondage/discipline, dominance/submission, sadism/masochism
Beck Depression Inventory, 339, 721
Benton Visual Retention Test, 521
Benzodiazepines, 213–215. *See also individual drug names*
    for alcoholic withdrawal symptoms, 206, 213
    effects of, 213–214
    intoxication and, 213
    memory problems and, 503, 522
    older adults and, 333, 337
    tapering, 214
    withdrawal symptoms, 214
Bereavement. *See* grief and loss
Binge-eating disorder. *See also* eating disorders
    diagnostic criteria for, 557–558
    dialectical behavioural therapy and, 569–570
    physical signs of, 565
    as tension release, 564
    treatment for, 566
Biphobia, 356, 363, 373
Bipolar disorder (manic depression), 396, 397
    attention-deficit/hyperactivity disorder and, 397
Birth to 3 Program, 510
Bisexual people, 373. *See also* LGBTTTIQ communities
    body image and, 364
    substance use and HIV/AIDS, 366, 367
Blackouts
    alcohol dependence and, 507
    alcohol-induced, 206
    among Back on Track clients, 642
    driving and, 106
Blaszczynski, A., 683
Blood-borne diseases. *See also* injection drug use; hepatitis B virus; hepatitis C virus; HIV/AIDS
    alcohol use and, 607, 616
    effects of, 607

G

H